HUMAN EVOLUTION
Processes and Adaptations

FIRST EDITION

Edited by Steven J. C. Gaulin

University of California — Santa Barbara

First published in the United States of America in 2010 by University Readers, Inc.

Back cover photo by Gordon Bear.

15 14 13 12 11 1 2 3 4 5

Printed in the United States of America

ISBN: 978-1-609279-71-4

www.cognella.com 800.200.3908

CONTENTS

Section 2: Speciation

Section 3: Classification

Section 4: The Comparative Method

Section 5: Kin Selection

Section 6: Reciprocity

Section 7: Sexual Selection

PART II
Adaptations

Section 8: Ancestral Humans

Section 9: Bipedalism

Section 10: Costly Brains

Section 11: Ecology and Diet

Section 12: Tools

Section 13: Origin and Spread of *Homo sapiens*

Section 14: Mating

Section 15: Language

Section 16: Menopause

Section 17: Homosexuality

Section 18: Domestication

Acknowledgments

This book grew out of my efforts to unwrap some of the scientific mysteries of human evolution for several generations of students. Still, despite my intoxication with the subject, this book would never have come about without the encouragement, insights, and experience of my editor, Marissa Waggoner. The production team at University Readers is a class act: Jessica Knott, Jennifer Bowen, and Brent Hannify were prompt with key information, efficient with project management, and supremely knowledgeable about every aspect of production. The permissions group led by Kristine Maglunob made all the chapters fall into place with apparent ease, and I greatly enjoyed collaborating with Monica Hui Hekman and especially Stephen Milano on cover design. Tayler James acted as my editorial assistant throughout. She helped me finalize the chapter selections and insightfully critiqued all of the chapter introductions for content, level, and style. To the extent that you find the introductions useful preparation for reading the chapters, you have Tayler to thank. I join you in thanking her and all of the wonderful folks mentioned above.

Preface

This book is about you. It is about your friends, your parents, your brothers and sisters; it is about everybody you know or might ever know because it is about humankind. It is about how—and why—humans have come to be the way we are. The answers to such vast questions might seem forever beyond our grasp. But if we take a scientific approach we can make genuine progress. The many tendrils of science are constantly reaching into new nooks and crannies of inquiry; in the process they are finding new wedges and levers of understanding, new handholds and angles of attack. They are, collectively, colonizing zones of knowledge that used to be entirely empty. As they do so, answers to these age-old questions are emerging from the shadows.

I have had the privilege of teaching a university course of this general type for more than 30 years. Over those three decades, the front of scientific knowledge about humankind has made huge advances. We now have more and better-substantiated facts, and we have theories that are much more solid to explain them. It has been an exciting time to be an anthropologist, and I have organized this book in a way that I hope will convey some of this excitement of discovery.

While there is much that anthropologists can say with confidence, no one should claim we now have all the answers. This book has many themes and subthemes, but one of the more important ones is that scientific knowledge is always provisional. Newton developed theories that coherently explained all of the then-known facts about motion. In fact, Newtonian theory still works well today for designing everything from kitchen blenders to Mars-bound spacecraft, but its provisional character was made plain in the early 20th century. Newton's primitive instruments prevented him from discovering that his theories do not work in the realm of the very small or the very fast. Newton was not wrong, but his ideas were incomplete and needed the updating provided by Einstein and his contemporaries.

This thumbnail history of physics makes a more general point: science is a public endeavor and anyone can play. The basic rules are simple: Take as many facts (observations) as you can and explain them with the simplest theory—the theory with the fewest assumptions. Judging by these rules, scientists hold on to the most successful theories until

something better comes along. True, this means that all scientific understanding is subject to revision. Although this provisional character might shake your confidence in science, it really should do the opposite. When observations and theories are constantly being checked and challenged, discrepancies will be discovered and better theories will come forward to replace the weaker ones. This competition among ideas is precisely why science advances. No one would debate that the chemistry of today is better than the alchemy of 400 years ago—better in the sense that it works; we can do things with it. The same is true when we compare the biology of today to the biology of the past.

The theories that anchor this book, evolutionary theory and genetic theory, are the core theories that unite all of the biological sciences. Playing by the rules of science—explaining as much as possible with the fewest assumptions—Darwinian evolutionary theory and Mendelian genetic theory have stood up to the questioning assaults of a century-and-a-half of aspiring competitors. For this reason, and this reason alone, scientists continue to use these theories to generate and test predictions about the nature of living things, and they continue to teach them to each generation of new students.

Darwin explained how living things adapt to their circumstances and Mendel explained the genetic accounting system that all but ensures this outcome. Most college-aged Americans have heard of these two great biologists and can give some summary of their ideas. Like so many other things, this is both good and bad. It is good because the theories are so central to understanding both ourselves and all the plants and animals with which we share our planet. But it is bad because neither theory is as simple as it first appears. Many hundreds of books and tens of thousands of articles have been written exploring the complexities and subtleties of each. Not surprisingly, most non-scientists have a faulty and fragmentary picture of these theories. The overarching goal of the book is to remedy those faults and to equip you to effectively use the powerful analytical tools of modern biology. Looking through the lenses of Darwinian and Mendelian theory, many surprising insights about humankind pop into clear focus. To understand why something is the way it is, you need to understand the processes that built it.

Following this logic, this book has two sections: *Processes* and *Adaptations*. The first of these is devoted to building your understanding of how evolution happens, of what genes are and how they work, and of the so-called modern synthesis that joined Darwinian and Mendelian frameworks into a single super-theory about the nature of all living things. A "nuts-and-bolts" chapter leads off this section by introducing and integrating all the basic concepts of both Darwinian and Mendelian theory. Other chapters in this section have two purposes: to concretely illustrate these processes at work and to draw out in clear terms further implications or refinements of the theories. The ideas they contain—such as kin selection—are parallel to Einstein's refinements of Newtonian theory. When you master this section, you will not only understand how evolution happens, but also be able to use the conceptual tool kit of the modern evolutionist to frame and test hypotheses about human nature and its origins.

The *Adaptations* section offers a suite of examples illustrating precisely how this testing and framing of hypotheses is done. It begins by summarizing what the fossil record reveals about our ancestors. After that, a series of chapters explores the various ways in which humans are relatively unique, as well as some of the ways in which we are not. The goal of each chapter is to focus on a single human trait—our ability to walk on our hind legs, our huge brains, our language abilities, our parental care patterns, female menopause—and to ask how and why it evolved in our lineage. The readings illustrate how working anthropologists, archaeologists, linguists, and geneticists have been able to use the analytical tools of evolutionary science. Together, this collection of readings begins to sketch the essence of human nature and the suite of evolutionary pressures that have sculpted it.

You will find that the chapters in this reader are quite diverse in style. Some, like the first, are very much like standard textbook chapters. At the opposite extreme you will find articles from the professional scientific literature: examples of scientists communicating new findings to other scientists. In between these two poles there are chapters excerpted from popular books designed for interested non-specialists, as well as review papers intended to help working scientists keep up with developments in fields where they may be less-than-expert. To guide you through this mix of ideas and styles, every chapter is preceded by an introduction. The introduction will relate the reading to what you have already learned and anticipate how it prepares the way for material that follows so that you can understand its place in the overall conceptual framework of the course. Each introduction will also briefly summarize the main message of the chapter and define any terms that will be new to you. In this way, each introduction serves as your "travel guide" to the new territory. In writing each introduction, I, in turn, have been guided by the explicit comments and questions of the students who came before you; they have been *my* best teachers over the years. It will probably be helpful to read each introduction twice, once before and once after reading its associated chapter.

In addition to—perhaps I should say in spite of—his major contributions to physics, Isaac Newton is remembered for his modesty. He wrote, "If I have seen further than others, it is by standing upon the shoulders of giants." I now invite you to expand your worldview by standing on the shoulders of two towering giants—Charles Darwin, who is buried right beside Newton in Westminster Abbey, and Gregor Mendel, who died in obscurity. Regardless of their very different final resting places, their combined views shed enormous light on who we are. Let's begin to share their vision.

Part I
PROCESSES

SECTION 1

NATURAL SELECTION, GENETICS, AND ADAPTATION

Introduction to Chapter 1

(and to the Book as a Whole)

In this initial chapter, we will develop the explanatory framework of both the book and the course.

The fundamental premise of twenty-first century biology is that life as we know it is a product of evolution. This premise has many implications. For example, the array of living things we see today is not static. Just the opposite: it has been changing for more than a billion years, and it continues to change right before our eyes. (You will meet a clear example of evolution in our lifetimes in Chapter 2.)

Darwin is often misremembered as having "proved" evolution. He did not do that, nor could he have. But putting philosophical issues of proof and disproof aside, Darwin's actual contribution was to offer a plausible *mechanism* that could cause evolution to happen. The mechanism he proposed is natural selection, which is fully detailed in Chapter 1. Please give it full attention because understanding how natural selection operates is the key to nearly everything else in this book.

As natural selection causes evolution, it has several observable effects. Even though these various effects are caused by the same process, different branches of evolutionary science have grown up to study them. First, because natural selection causes change, the creatures that are alive today will inevitably be somewhat different from those that lived in the past. Thus, one obvious effect of natural selection is that it produces a residue of older, now-extinct life forms. Paleontologists and paleoanthropologists are evolutionary specialists who study extinct life forms. (We will see some of their work in Chapters 9 and 10.) Second, any new life forms that emerge from older ones do so gradually, and they can thus be arranged in ancestor–descendant relationships and lineages. Taxonomists specialize in figuring out these ancestor–descendant relationships. (We will examine their methods in detail in Chapter 5, and we will be relying on their methods throughout the book.)

The last and most important effect is that natural selection hones the fit between the organism and its environment; it causes organisms to be well *adapted* to their environments. It is fair to say that this is the effect studied by most modern biologists, whether they focus on humans, other animals, plants, fungi, bacteria, viruses, or algae. Chapter 1 explains how and why natural selection produces adaptation. (Chapters 2, 3, and 11–21 all explore specific suites of adaptations.)

As already noted, the theory of natural selection requires that there be direct links between the generations: something is passed or transmitted from parent to offspring. Mendel was the first person to clearly see what was passed, and in describing that process he founded the entire field of genetics. It is important to understand the relationship between Darwin's theory of evolution by natural selection and Mendel's theory of genetic transmission. Selection causes evolution; genes do not. Genetics is related to evolution the way dollars are related to economics. Dollars are the tokens we use to do economic accounting and to keep track of what is happening economically. Likewise, genes are the way we do evolutionary accounting and keep track of what is happening evolutionarily. Joining Darwinian and Mendelian theory allows us to explain how the good or poor adaptation of parents can influence what the next generation is like. In parallel, this conjoined theory allows us to keep track of the progress and pace of evolution.

Genes are real physical entities and, since Mendel, we have learned a great deal about what they are made of and how they affect the traits of organisms. These topics open up the subfield of molecular genetics. As you will see, natural selection acts on gene products, not on the genes themselves. Thus, understanding the nature of gene products allows more precise applications of evolutionary thinking.

The final sections of Chapter 1 continue to unpack the modern theory that has grown out of the union of Darwinism and Mendelism. On the basis of these theories, how well adapted should we expect organisms to be? What is the role of the current, as opposed to the historical, environment in shaping the adaptations we see? Can selection work on the mind as well as the body? And finally, when we say that selection refines adaptation, what entity (the gene, the individual, the social group, or the species) is adapting? By the time these questions have been settled in your mind, you will be ready to start thinking about the living world—including yourself—in evolutionary terms.

CHAPTER 1
Adaptation and Natural Selection (2009)

Steven J. C. Gaulin and David A. Puts

DARWIN'S REVOLUTIONARY IDEA

Almost anywhere you look, living things seem well suited to the conditions of their lives. Among the vertebrates, for example, fish have featherlike gills specialized for extracting vital oxygen molecules dissolved in water, whereas land vertebrates have lungs whose multitudes of tiny pockets provide a vast, wet surface across which oxygen can diffuse from the air. It is not a coincidence that aquatic vertebrates have specializations for harvesting oxygen from water and terrestrial vertebrates have specializations for collecting oxygen from air. In 1859, Charles Darwin proposed a mechanism that could explain how such adaptation to the environment occurs.

Darwin called the mechanism *natural selection* to emphasize his idea that nature chooses the designs that work best in any given environment, thus shaping organisms to meet the challenges they face. How could the inanimate force of nature accomplish this creative act? This was Darwin's great discovery. First, he recognized that within any given type of organism there is considerable variation. The members of a species are not identical; for example, they vary slightly in size, shape, coloration, and the size of their various body parts. As these different individuals attempt to live out their lives, some will inevitably be more successful than others, because they are better at escaping predators, better at fending of disease, better at finding food, better at attracting mates, or better at providing for their progeny. In these (and other) ways, some of the naturally occurring variation among individuals turns out to be useful in what Darwin called "the struggle for existence." Individuals who happen to have traits better suited to survival and reproduction under the prevailing conditions end up leaving more offspring. Darwin combined this idea with a fundamental concept of heredity, the fact that offspring tend to resemble their parents.

Now, if some types of individuals survive and reproduce more than others, and if individuals replicate their traits when they reproduce, then traits that contribute to survival and reproduction accumulate in the population over time. And by the same logic, traits that disadvantage individuals in the struggle for existence get passed to relatively few offspring and, over the generations, are eventually eliminated. The favorable traits that accumulate over time because of their contribution to reproduction Darwin called *adaptations*. The spread of many such adaptations over many generations continually refines the fit between organisms and their environment.

Darwin named this process *natural selection* on analogy with the kind of selection that had been practiced by animal and plant breeders for several thousand years. Simply by choosing to breed those individuals with the most desirable characteristics, people had produced cattle with high milk yields, docile sheep that gave large quantities of soft wool, and obedient dogs to herd them both. We call this selective breeding process *artificial selection*. Darwin suggested that, just as a breeder selects which cows to breed by their milk yields, so too could nature "choose" individuals to breed according to their traits. For instance, an arctic environment could metaphorically choose mammals with dense fur coats or thick layers of subcutaneous fat because those without these traits would freeze to death before reproducing. Over time, *natural* selection could lead to significant change in a species, just as *artificial* selection has changed a wolf ancestor into many breeds of domesticated dogs.

Humans have bred pigeons that tumble as they fly, dogs with pathetically short legs, trees that give seedless fruit, and tulips so outrageously fancy that the 17th century Dutch were willing to pay the equivalent of $50,000 for a single bulb! Such traits would be quite disadvantageous except under the doting care of humans. For example, direct flight is better for escaping falcons; wild tulips are just big and bright enough to attract their pollinators. The process of natural selection does not change species capriciously. It shapes them for a single ultimate purpose, reproduction. This is true simply because only those that reproduce pass on their traits to the next generation and those that don't reproduce don't pass on anything. Adaptations can thus be thought of as designs for reproduction. Designs for reproduction are transmitted to offspring, and other kinds of designs are not transmitted and therefore disappear. Adaptations are thus preserved by natural selection because they aid reproduction in some way. This idea is central to modern evolutionary theory and deserves further examination.

Natural Selection Builds Adaptations

The reproductive organs are clearly designed for reproduction, but the list of adaptations does not end there. All living things consist of a large set of complicated, integrated functional traits that would impress any engineer. Migratory birds can apparently sense small deviations in the earth's magnetic field and hear the roar of the surf on beaches many miles away. Some frogs can hibernate at the bottom of dried up ponds for a decade, only to reemerge and breed when rains finally come. Bats can "see" by processing the echoes of their voices well enough to intercept an evasive insect in mid-air. Each of these traits was designed by natural selection because it solved some immediate environmental problem such as obtaining food or avoiding danger. This is entirely consistent with our theory. Natural selection can design traits like echolocation, hibernation, and a magnetic sense if—and only if—they contribute to reproduction. For example, if better nourished individuals produce more offspring, then natural selection can shape a wide array of traits that help organisms locate, capture, and digest food, because individuals who lack these traits would leave fewer offspring.

Naturally occurring variations among individuals are always being tested against the environment. Any variation that aids reproduction, whether it happens to be in the heart, the kidneys, or the brain, will be passed to the next generation. For example, an improvement in the brain that aids reproduction is just as much a design for reproduction as an improvement in the gonads. Both are adaptations. Adaptations exist because they improve the fit between the organism and the environment and thereby enhance the chances of reproduction.

Of course, some of the features of organisms are not adaptations. Such nonadaptive features could arise simply by chance, or they could be incidental side effects of other traits that are adaptations. For example, your nose should not be regarded as an adaptation for holding up your sunglasses because it was not designed by natural selection for that purpose. How, then, do we recognize adaptations? Adaptations are often structurally complex, made up of several integrated parts. And they show evidence of design for a particular function, in that the parts work together to efficiently accomplish that function. Let's return to the example of the human nose. Most of its features are much more consistent with the idea that it was designed to filter, humidify, warm, and conduct air to and from the lungs, than with the idea that it was designed to support glasses. If it were merely a sunglasses holder it would lack many of the internal structural features it does have, and it might be expected to have certain external features—a more pronounced ridge perhaps—that it lacks. A few traits may be controversial, but with adequate information it is usually not too difficult to decide whether or not a particular trait is an adaptation.

For example, all the features of the vertebrate eye work together in a way that convinces us it is an adaptation for seeing. Any other idea, such as the suggestion that its parts might have fallen into their present arrangement by chance or that it is really designed for something other than seeing, is inconsistent with what we know about its structure and workings.

Adaptations Are Specialized

Jack-of-all-trades is a master of none. This old saying crystallizes the insight that being competent at many tasks usually compromises the ability to do any one task especially well. This is true for individual humans, tools, or machines and will likewise be true for individual adaptations. Notice that the heart pumps blood, the lungs aerate it, and the liver detoxifies it. We don't have a general "blood-handling" adaptation. Instead, even in the relatively narrow domain of blood handling, each of several organs is specialized for a specific function. To understand why, think about a carpenter's toolbox. It contains drills, saws, planes, hammers, files, clamps—a wide array of specialized implements, each finely tuned for particular tasks. You could cut a board in half by drilling a series of closely spaced holes across the middle. But given the choice, you'd probably use the saw instead; that would be much more efficient and produce a much nicer cut. Present-day toolboxes have drills and saws because round holes and straight cuts are two different kinds of useful outcomes, and each is best produced by a different kind of tool.

Remember that selection is constantly refining adaptations to achieve better and more efficient results. So this general principle that tools are specialized for specific functions applies to adaptations as well as to human-designed tools. Each adaptation tends to be specialized for solving a narrow class of problems simply because less specialized designs didn't work so well and selection tended to weed them out. For example, the vertebrate eye discussed previously shows a marvelous degree of specialization for resolving images from reflected light. It's stunningly good at that task. And it's downright miserable at most others; imagine trying to hear (i.e., detect sound waves) with your eyes! Detecting sound waves is possible—ears are specialized for that task—but it's impossible for eyes because they're designed for, specialized for, a different task.

Darwin's Theory Must Rest on a Theory of Heredity

Part of the elegance of Darwin's theory of adaptation by natural selection is its generality. The most successful variants will spread in any group of reproducers where offspring resemble their parents. The logic of Darwin's idea is inescapable. But Darwin had a difficult time convincing his contemporaries about natural selection because he—and virtually everyone else alive at that time—didn't understand *why* offspring resemble their parents. Thus, the theory of genetics and the theory of evolution by natural selection have inevitably been joined over the last eighty years. Only if we have a coherent theory of heredity can we explain how the advantaged members of one generation manage to pass on their advantages to the next generation.

Genetics

Mendelian Genetics

Although Darwin did not know it, his contemporary, an Austrian monk named Gregor Mendel, had been conducting breeding experiments on garden pea plants that would lead to a better understanding of heredity and a vindication of Darwin's theory. Mendel deduced from his experiments that the units of heredity, which we now call *genes,* pass undiluted from, parent to offspring via sex cells called *gametes.* (In humans and other animals, gametes consist of sperm and eggs.) Mendel was able to deduce several other features of the hereditary system. For example, he recognized that normal adults carry two copies of each gene, a condition we call *diploidy.* To maintain this diploid condition over the generations, adults pass only one or the other of these gene copies, not both, to each of their offspring via *haploid* (=half) sex cells. When each of the two parents passes one gene copy, the offspring ends up with the normal double (that is, diploid) dose for each gene.

It is now known that living things carry a huge amount of genetic information. Normal humans, for example, have about 60,000 (30,000 diploid pairs) of genes. These 30,000 pairs constitute the human *genome.* With few exceptions, all the cells in your body contain the entire 30,000-pair genome. These genes are not scattered randomly in the cells. First of all, they are clustered in the cell nucleus. Second, within the nucleus the genes are grouped together into long sequences, called *chromosomes;* the human genome is grouped into 23 of these sequences. Remembering that humans and most other organisms are diploid, you won't be surprised to learn that we each carry 23 chromosomes received from our mother and a matching set of 23 from our father.

The notion of "matching set" requires a bit of clarification. In some ways the match is very precise, and in other ways the deviation from a perfect match is very important. The precise matches are spatial: The arrangement of genes on the paternal and maternal chromosomes is generally identical. To follow this example we suggest you visit the Web site *http://www.ornl.gov/hgmis/poster/chromosome/chromo01.html* where you can view a map of human chromosome 1. About three-fourths of the way along the chromosome is a gene called "glaucoma." Nearby you'll see a gene that affects susceptibility to atherosclerosis and, a bit farther away, a gene that affects susceptibility to measles. The point is that all normal copies of human chromosome 1, regardless of whether they came from a man or a woman, will have this same identical sequence of these genes. Likewise, all copies of chromosome 2 have a fixed arrangement of the particular genes they contain, as do chromosomes 3, 4, and on down the line. Because these arrangements are fixed, we can build maps—as the Human Genome Project researchers did—and we can talk about the place, or *locus,* where a gene associated with a certain trait occurs. For example, we could talk about the glaucoma locus.

Because the paternal and maternal chromosomes have the same arrangement of *loci* (the plural of locus), we say they are *homologous.*

You probably know that glaucoma is a disease that, if untreated, will eventually cause blindness. Why do you have a gene that causes blindness? Fortunately, you probably don't. Here's an explanation for why so many of the genes on the chromosome maps are named for diseases. To figure out what genes do, scientists have to find a defective version of the gene. In other words, they can only tell what job a gene does when it doesn't do its job. You know, "What happens if I unplug this cord?" "Oops!" Thus, scientists have tended to name genes for the problems they cause when they are defective. The notion of a defective gene gives us a window into ways in which the paternal and maternal chromosomes may not match.

The "glaucoma gene" on chromosome 1 is presumably a gene that affects intraocular pressure (glaucoma results when this pressure is too high). If we are lucky, we carry the normal version of the gene, which produces a normal level of pressure, and we never develop glaucoma. At least one alternative at this locus is a slightly modified version of this normal gene, an *allele.* Alleles are just alternative versions of a gene that can occur at the same locus. Understanding all this, it might make more sense to talk about the "intraocular pressure locus" and to recognize that there are (at least) two alleles that could occur at this locus. One of these alleles causes normal pressure and one causes above-normal pressure, making its carrier susceptible to glaucoma.

Thus, one way in which maternal and paternal chromosomes might not match perfectly is that they can carry different alleles. It turns out that well over half of the 30,000 loci in the human genome are *monomorphic,* having only a single gene with no alternative alleles. (This is presumably because selection has eliminated all but the best allele at these loci.) But the remaining 30 to 40 percent of the loci have multiple alleles. For example, you probably know that the blood-type locus on chromosome 9 has three alleles: A, B, and O. Of course this doesn't mean that you have three alleles at your blood-type locus. Remember, you are diploid, so you will have two genes for each locus, one that came from your mother and one from your father. These might simply be two identical copies of the same allele (for example, BB) or they might be two different alleles (such as AO). When a person's two alleles match at a particular locus, we say they are *homozygous* at that locus. When they carry different versions of the gene, different alleles, we say they are *heterozygous.* These terms are easy to remember because *homo* means "the same" and *hetero* means "different."

The ABO system also provides a clear example of another important genetic concept, *dominance.* Dominance refers to a relationship between the effects of alleles. The effects of dominant alleles can be seen if one copy is present. The effects of recessive alleles are noticeable only when two copies are present, that is, in the homozygous state. In heterozygous individuals with either AO or BO genotypes, the O is not expressed. That means that O is recessive to both A and B. It would be equally correct to say that A and B are both dominant to O. Since dominance and recessiveness are relational properties, A's and B's dominance over O tells us nothing about their relation to each other. In fact, in AB heterozygotes, the effects of both alleles are apparent in the phenotype.

Some alternative versions of genes are clearly defective. On the other hand, as the ABO system suggests, there can be multiple alleles at a locus without any of them being "bad." Here's a simple example to show one way this might work. There is a locus on human chromosome 11 that encodes the formula for hemoglobin. Hemoglobin is the protein in red blood cells that allows them to transport oxygen and carbon dioxide. This locus is not monomorphic: There are multiple alleles. One version, the so-called *s* allele, causes sickle-cell anemia in homozygous individuals, that is, in people who received an *s* allele from both parents. Sickle-cell anemia certainly is bad, but what happens when a person has only one copy of the *s* allele and one copy of the normal hemoglobin allele? It turns out that these heterozygous individuals are more resistant to malaria than individuals who are homozygous for the normal allele. Do you see how evolution proceeds in this case? In areas where malarial parasites are common, individuals who have two copies of the normal hemoglobin allele often die of malaria, and those who have two copies of the *s* allele die of anemia. This means that those most likely to survive and reproduce are the heterozygous individuals. Because these individuals carry one copy of each allele, their reproductive success tends to maintain both alleles in the population—thereby keeping the locus polymorphic. If you wanted to test this explanation, you would look to see where the *s* allele is most common. As predicted, it reaches its highest frequency in west-central Africa, where malarial parasites are most abundant.

In this case, two alleles at a locus work together or interact to produce a favorable result. Genes often interact not only with other alleles at the same locus but also with genes at other loci, and with the environment, in building the organism. Here's a practice test. In the ABO system there are six possible diploid genotypes: AA, AO, BB, BO, OO, and AB. Remembering the dominance relationships detailed previously, how many phenotypes are there? The answer is four.

We need to emphasize one more important way in which paternal and maternal genetic contributions might differ. Earlier we mentioned that a normal human genotype consists of 23 pairs of chromosomes. Chromosomes 1 through 22 are always paired, with the qualification that, as you now know, some loci may be heterozygous. "Chromosome 23" is paired in females but unmatched in males. We put "Chromosome 23" in quotes because this is not its normal name: In actuality this final pair is referred to as the sex chromosomes, X and Y. Females have two X chromosomes, whereas males have one X and one Y chromosome. Most of the loci on the X and the Y do not match. Thus females can be heterozygous or homozygous for genes on the X. Males, on the other hand, generally can't be either because there is no possibility of a match between genes on their X and genes on their Y. The technical term for this is *autozygous:* Males are autozygous for most genes on their X and Y chromosomes.

All of this emphasis on matching of the paternal and maternal chromosomes might seem unnecessary, but it turns out to be essential to one of the basic processes of sex. That process is called *meiosis,* but to make its intricacies clear, we'll begin by describing a simpler nonsexual process called *mitosis.* Remember that all your cells, from bone cells to liver cells to skin cells, have the same genotype—in fact, the very genotype that was first created by the union of your father's haploid sperm and your mother's haploid egg. How has this genotype been conserved and replicated throughout your body? The answer is by mitosis. Mitosis is cell reproduction via cell division. In mitosis the cell grows by accumulating nutrients, but just before it divides, it copies all of its genetic material. The 23 maternal chromosomes copy themselves, and the 23 paternal chromosomes copy themselves. Then, the copies sort themselves out so that, as a new cell membrane divides the cell in half, one complete diploid set of maternal and paternal genes gets distributed to each of the two "daughter" cells. Thus, mitosis is the process that maintains genetic identity throughout the body.

Meiosis, in contrast, is all about diversity. Mitosis occurs almost everywhere in the body, but meiosis occurs only in the gonads, the testes and ovaries, in humans. Beyond their general versus restricted distribution, there are also important differences between the mechanics of mitosis and meiosis. Mitosis conserves the diploid state. Meiosis produces haploid cells from diploid cells by a complicated process of gene shuffling (Fig. 1). In meiosis, the set of chromosomes inherited from the father aligns along the equator of the dividing cell with the set of chromosomes inherited from the mother. The maternal chromosome 1 pairs with its homologue, paternal chromosome 1. Maternal chromosome 2 pairs with its homologue from the father, and so forth, so that all homologous chromosomes are paired on the cell's equator. For most paired chromosomes (all but the X and Y in males), a process called *crossing-over* or *recombination* then occurs, in which the two homologous chromosomes swap some of their genes in a precise locus-by-locus fashion. Crossing-over thus has the effect of shuffling the maternally derived and paternally derived chromosomal material. Further variation is generated when the cell divides, as each new haploid cell receives whichever set of chromosomes (a mixture of maternally and paternally derived genes) happened to line up on that side of the dividing cell. Thus, the precise ratio of maternally derived to paternally derived chromosomes that go into a gamete is usually close to 50/50. Because the shuffling is random, a little more of one type of chromosome than the other is likely. Recombination is like shuffling a giant 30,000-card deck, and it

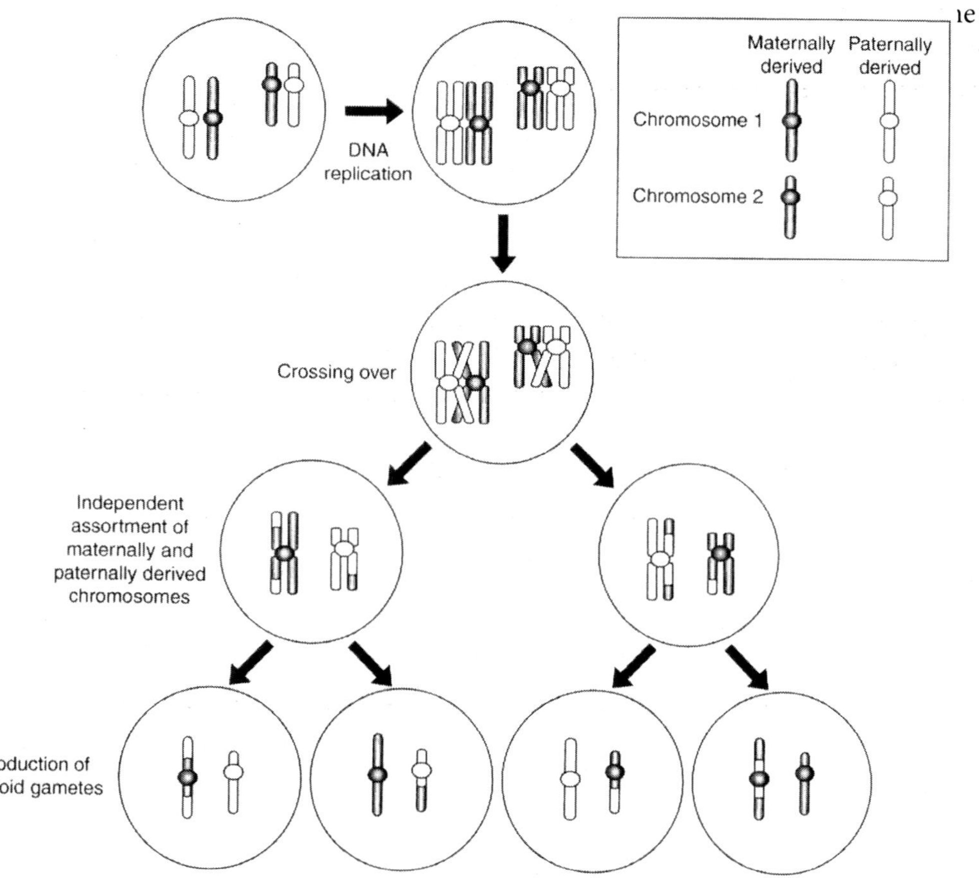

Figure 1. Meiosis shuffles maternally and paternally derived genes in the production of haploid gametes.

Molecular Genetics

The preceding section explained the mechanics of heredity and gene transmission, but exactly what are genes, and how do they do what they do? Genes are long strands of a molecule called deoxyribonucleic acid (DNA). Since genes are strung one after another to form chromosomes, chromosomes are just very long strands of DNA. DNA consists of a long sequence of four smaller molecules called bases, which include adenine, cytosine, guanine, and thymine (A, C, G, and T in the language of genetics). A gene is a message written in this four-letter code. The alleles of a gene differ from each other slightly in terms of the sequence of these bases.

In the *cytoplasm* of each cell, outside of its nucleus, the genetic message encoded in the DNA is read and translated. The role of this message is disarmingly simple. DNA directs the synthesis of protein molecules, for example, the hemoglobin molecule discussed previously. The tens of thousands of different genes possessed by oak trees and salamanders and yeast and monkeys code for an equal diversity of proteins. From this perspective, alleles are slightly different versions of a gene's DNA sequence that code for slightly different proteins. Proteins serve many separate functions in organizing, building, and maintaining the phenotypes of organisms. Among animals, proteins function in supporting the body, movement, transporting materials within the body, defense against parasites and pathogens, and as chemical messengers and receptors of chemical messages. But perhaps the most important proteins are *enzymes,* which regulate the chemical reactions of the body.

The properties of organisms, like the properties of all matter, are determined by chemical composition and structure. When enzymes regulate chemical reactions, they are contributing to the properties of the organism in which they reside. Enzymes act as catalysts. They lower the amount of energy required for a chemical reaction to take place within a cell, thus regulating the rate at which various metabolic processes occur. The building up or breaking down of chemical compounds in the body involves *metabolic pathways* (see Fig. 1.6).

A metabolic pathway represents the steps through which one chemical compound must go in order to be transformed into another. At any step, a chemical compound may be transformed into several other compounds. The reaction required for each transformation is catalyzed by a particular enzyme. For example, the purple flower color in Mendel's pea plants is caused by a purple pigment called *anthocyanin,* which is produced from a colorless intermediate compound. The conversion of the colorless compound into anthocyanin is catalyzed by an enzyme encoded by the *P* allele. Having even one copy of the *P* allele allows the plant to transform enough of the colorless intermediate to attain a typical purple coloration. However, having no copies of the *P* allele means that no anthocyanin will be produced, and the plant's flowers will appear white rather than purple.

Thus, to answer the question at the beginning of this section, genes affect the phenotype by coding for proteins, which have important roles in the construction and maintenance of the body. And as you saw, proteins interact with other proteins. For instance, the effects of one enzyme on the phenotype depend on other enzymes acting before it and after it in metabolic pathways. And because proteins are encoded by genes, this means that one gene can influence the expression of other genes. In fact, the expression of genes is affected not only by the interaction of their associated proteins but also by environmental signals that switch genes on or off. Such signals typically originate from outside of the cells in which genes reside and even depend on circumstances outside of the body. For example, the food you eat and the stimulation of your endocrine system through your senses both affect chemical signals in your body that regulate the expression of genes.

This is fundamentally important, both to the organism and to our understanding of genetics. If an organism had the right combination of genes, it could adjust various biological processes to the environment in an appropriate way. For example, it could adjust its production of a digestive enzyme to the supply of foods that could be processed by that enzyme. This "smart" response would allow the organism to save resources, producing an enzyme only when it is useful. Such patterns of response might seem miraculous, but they are in fact the norm: We are walking collections of thousands of these smart response patterns. The detailed genetic mechanism underlying this sort of digestive response earned its discoverers, François Jacob, André Lwoff, and Jacques Monod, the 1965 Nobel Prize in medicine and physiology.

This realization blows the lid off an old and treasured myth: Genes are destiny; if you have the gene, you have the trait. True, a gene sometimes has a fairly constant effect on a particular aspect of the phenotype. For example, if you have the sickle-cell allele, you will have some red blood cells that are sickle-shaped (see Section 3.3.3). But the phenotypic effects of many genes depend much more heavily on their interactions with other genes and the environment.

The "genes-are-destiny" myth is wrong for another reason. Genes help build traits that track environmental variation and adjust the phenotype in response. For example, your eyes track variation in ambient light and adjust the diameter of your pupils accordingly. These traits are said to be *facultative.* We will discuss facultative traits in greater detail in Section 3.4.2. For now, it is important to note that the existence of both facultative traits and environment-dependent gene expression dispels the myth that genes are destiny. With a little thought, you will also realize that these facts utterly destroy the usefulness of the nature/nurture dichotomy.

The Synthesis of Natural Selection Theory and Modern Genetics

Equipped with a basic understanding of modern genetics we are now able to resolve the difficulties of Darwin's theory that resulted from his misunderstanding of the hereditary system.

Mutation: The Ultimate Source of Genetic Variation and Fuel for Natural Selection

Although Darwin could not explain how new hereditary variation was introduced into populations, we now understand its source. While there are many mechanisms within cells that "proofread" newly copied strands of DNA, undetected errors occasionally occur during DNA replication. If such a gene-copying error, or *mutation,* occurs prior to meiosis, a gamete may contain the mutation. And if this gamete is involved in fertilization, the new mutation will be passed on to every cell of the developing offspring. Offspring carrying the mutation that mature and reproduce will pass it on to half of their offspring (on average), and so on.

When a gene mutates by copying itself incorrectly, a new allele, a slightly modified DNA sequence, is created. This new allele will typically specify a slightly different protein, and selection will evaluate the fitness of the phenotypes built by that new protein. Genetic mutations are thus the ultimate source of hereditary variation in populations and the fodder for natural selection. Ordinarily, copying errors interfere with gene function. The phenotype produced by a new mutant allele typically is less fit than the phenotype produced by the ancestral allele from which it derived. Selection quickly eliminates these harmful new alleles. But every once in a while, by chance, a new mutant allele produces a phenotype that is actually fitter than the one produced by the ancestral allele. This is the stuff of new adaptations. Such beneficial new alleles spread because of the higher reproductive success of the phenotypes they produce. Of course, it can take many generations for the new allele to replace the ancestral one. Thus, sometimes when we see a locus with two alleles, we are just witnessing evolution in progress. A favorable new mutant is in the process of spreading, but it has not yet completely replaced its alternative allele.

Selection cannot create new variants but only chooses among existing alternatives. The alternatives among which selection chooses are the phenotypes produced by alternative alleles. We know that alternative alleles arise by mutation. In other words, the raw material for natural selection originally comes from random errors in the genetic process. This is why selection cannot create variation. Variation comes into existence through genetic, not selective, processes. Selection evaluates these alternatives once they exist, eliminating the harmful ones and spreading the beneficial ones.

Darwinian Selection in a Mendelian World

Darwin wrote in *The Origin of Species* that selection would cause favorable traits to become more common. He said this because he knew that individuals with favorable traits would leave more offspring. And he knew what was obvious to anyone: Parents pass on their characteristics to their offspring. The argument is logical, but a critical detail is missing: Darwin could not say exactly how traits were transmitted to offspring. We now know that, when selection favors a reproductively advantageous trait, selection is *indirectly* favoring the genes associated with the trait. The genes for the advantageous trait get passed on at a higher rate than their alternative alleles, so the trait and the genes associated with it spread in the population. This is an important idea, so let's dissect it a bit more.

Selection cannot evaluate genes directly; it "sees" only the phenotypes they produce. On the other hand, successful phenotypes are not directly passed on to the next generation; only the genes that built the phenotypes are. One analogy would be to say that, in each generation, genes audition for the future by building phenotypes. The phenotypes that perform well get to pass on some (remember, sex cells are haploid) of the genes that directed their performance. In this way, the genes that build the best performers become more common. Thus, the differential reproductive success of phenotypes changes the frequency of the underlying genes.

Let's take a specific example. Remember that in Mendel's peas the *P* allele produces an enzyme that converts a colorless compound into the pigment anthocyanin that shows up in the phenotype by making the flowers purple. When Mendel chose to breed only plants with purple flowers, he was indirectly choosing the *P* allele and selecting out the alternative allele. The offspring's phenotypes resembled their parents' phenotypes because they inherited their parents' genes. This association between genotype and phenotype is absolutely crucial to evolution by natural selection. Selection is only able to spread a favorable trait through the population when phenotypes—flower color in this example—are reliably associated with genotypes.

Selection and Heritability

The association between genotype and flower color in Mendel's pea plants was very strong, so his selective breeding brought about substantial change in the composition of his garden. Nonetheless, there was some variation in flower color that was not caused by variation in genotype. Environmental differences between plants in exposure to sunlight, nutrients in the soil, and water almost certainly contributed to some variation in the shade of purple in the flowers.

The strength of the association between phenotype and genotype is measured by *heritability*. To understand heritability precisely, we need three concepts. First, we need the notion of phenotypic variation. This is just a measure of how much variation there is in the population for the trait of interest. For example, we could estimate the phenotypic variation for height just by measuring the height of some reasonable sample of people. We would find considerable variation; people vary widely in height. This phenotypic variation is the result of two other kinds of variation: genetic and environmental. The people in our sample presumably differ from one another in height because of the alleles they carry.

Likewise, the people in our sample probably have had different experiences affecting their height; for example, they may have differed in their nutritional regimes while they were growing up. Heritability, then, is a ratio of two of these measures. It asks "How much of the total phenotypic variation in the trait of interest is due to the fact that people have different genes affecting the trait?"

Hypothetically, heritability can range from 1 to 0. A value of 1 means that all of the phenotypic variation is due to the fact that people carry different alleles; environment makes no contribution to the differences between individuals. A value of 0 means the reverse: Environment explains all of the phenotypic variation; none of the differences between individuals are caused by genetic differences. You can imagine traits at both ends of this continuum. For example, whether you have sickle-cell anemia or not depends entirely on your genotype. Those with the *ss* genotype have the disease, and those with any other genotype do not. Thus, sickle-cell anemia has a very high heritability, approaching 1. Conversely, speaking English has a very low heritability, near 0. This is because the language you speak depends on the language you happened to hear while you were an infant, on your early experience. Chinese, Russian, or Vietnamese infants adopted by American parents grow up speaking perfect idiomatic English. Genetic differences are more or less irrelevant in shaping what language we speak.

These two examples have no special status other than to make the point that we can easily imagine traits with very high or very low heritability. Most traits, however, have moderate heritabilities, in the range of 0.4 to 0.6. For example, many personality traits such as extroversion, agreeableness, and conscientiousness fall in this range.

All this may get you wondering how heritability is actually measured. The answer is complex and largely beyond the scope of this book (for a full presentation, see Mealey 2000), but you probably already have an informal familiarity with one of the key methods: twin studies. Monozygotic (identical) twins share all their genes and, typically, their environments. Dizygotic (fraternal) twins share only half their genes, and again, their environments. Comparison of the level of similarity between these two classes of twins allows an estimate of genetic contributions to the trait of interest. Likewise, comparing twins reared together versus those reared apart gives useful estimates of environmental contributions.

All of this emphasis on heritability is quite appropriate since heritability is critical to selection. The higher a trait's heritability, the more effectively selection can work on it. Here's why: In Section 3.2.2 you learned that selection spreads genes by allowing some phenotypes to reproduce at higher rates than others. When phenotypes differ because of the genes they carry (high-heritability traits), selection spreads the genes that assemble the better phenotypes. On the other hand, when phenotypes differ principally because of their

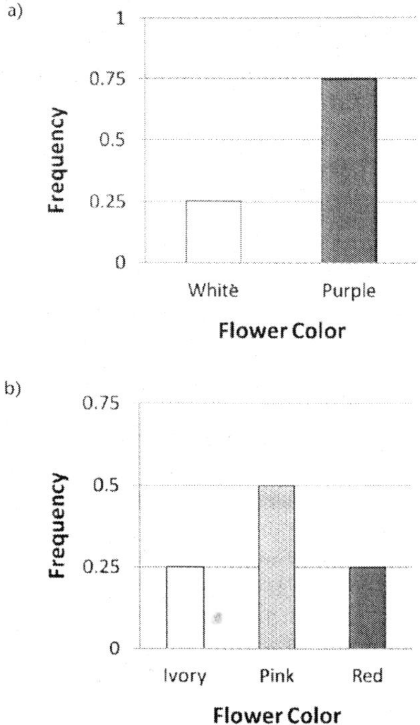

Figure 2. Frequency distribution of flower color in (a) garden peas and (b) snapdragons.

environments, not because of the genes they carry (low-heritability traits), reproductive advantages have little impact on what genes get passed to the next generation.

With this new understanding of the hereditary system, we can refine our understanding of natural selection. We can now say that the requirements are (1) heritable variation and (2) reproductive differences associated with the variation.

Beyond One-Gene/One-Trait Genetics

Brilliant as he was, Mendel was also quite lucky to have studied the traits he did. All of the traits Mendel examined showed the same inheritance pattern as flower color: Variation among plants in only one gene with two alleles explained almost all of the phenotypic variation among the plants. One allele was always dominant to the other, and environmental differences between plants contributed to only a small amount of the phenotypic variation. We now know that this simple inheritance pattern does not characterize most traits of organisms.

In many cases, the phenotype of a heterozygote does not match the phenotype of either homozygote. Instead, heterozygotes are often intermediate between the two homozygotes.

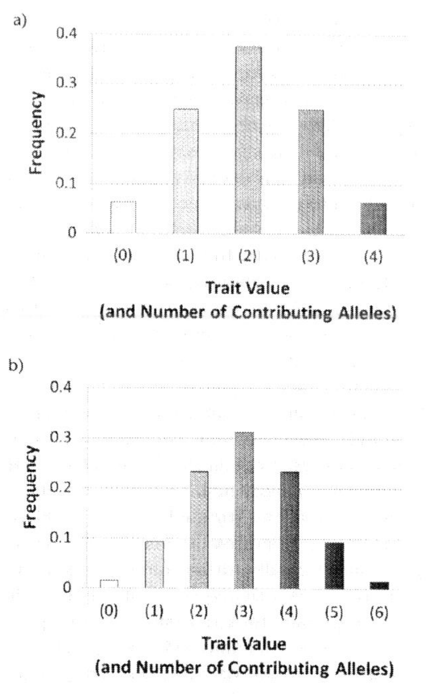

Figure 3. Phenotypic variation caused by differences among individuals in (a) two genes having two alleles each, and (b) three genes having two alleles each.

In other words, most traits do not show complete dominance. For example, in snapdragon plants, flower color is determined by alleles at the *I* locus. Snapdragons that have genotype *II* have red flowers, and those that have genotype *ii* have ivory-colored flowers. Unlike garden pea heterozygotes, however, snapdragon heterozygotes (*Ii*) do not resemble either homozygote; instead they have pink flowers, intermediate between the phenotypes of the two homozygotes. Thus, for snapdragon flower color, there are not just two trait values but three. Whereas crosses between heterozygotes for flower color in garden pea plants lead to a phenotypic ratio of 3:1 (due to compete dominance), similar crosses in snapdragons lead to a phenotypic ratio of 1:2:1 (see Fig. 2).

This situation accords well with what we see in many traits: a bell-shaped, or *normal,* distribution around the average. But even the snapdragon example is an oversimplification of the typical phenotypic character; for most characters, variation at more than one genetic locus is responsible for phenotypic variation. When variation at multiple genetic loci causes variation in a trait, we say the trait is *polygenic.* Figure 3 shows how the frequency distribution of flower color would look if it were a polygenic trait with differences at either two or

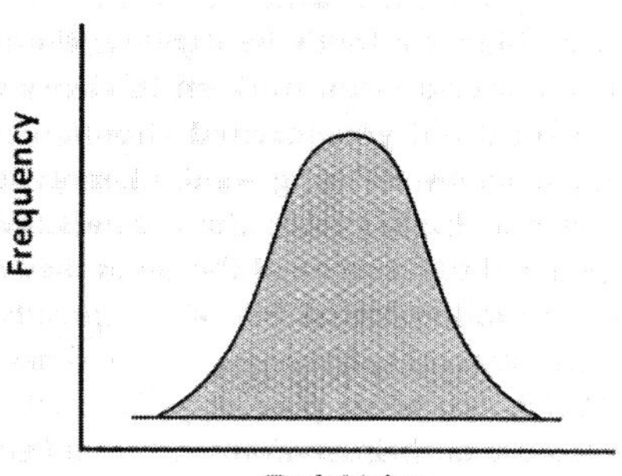

Figure 4. Frequency distribution of a continuous (polygenic) trait.

three genetic loci (with two alleles per locus) contributing to variation among phenotypes. Finally, we must include the contribution of environmental differences among individuals to phenotypic variation. Thus, both genetic differences and environmental differences can cause phenotypic differences among individuals. The result is a phenotypic character with a continuous, normal frequency distribution (see Fig. 4).

Remember, our primary interest concerns the workings of selection. Thus, as our picture of genetics becomes more sophisticated, we need to continually reconnect it to our picture of evolution. Let's now consider how selection might operate on a polygenic trait with moderately high heritability. Height in humans would be a reasonable example. What would happen if selection favored an increase in human height?

Each individual carries genes at several loci that, in interaction with environmental factors, affect height. On average, tall individuals have more genes for tallness than short individuals do. More precisely, this means that, at the loci affecting height, they have more alleles promoting tallness than do shorter individuals. It follows that if taller individuals are experiencing higher reproductive success, then alleles for tallness are passed on at a higher rate than alleles for shortness are at all of the height-influencing loci.

Alleles for tallness thus increase in frequency, and alleles for shortness decrease in frequency, with three results. First, the average height of the population increases, because the average individual will have more alleles for tallness than was the case before selection. Second, the whole distribution shifts to the right: The shortest types will completely disappear from the population and the tallest individual will be taller than any seen before. This too is a result of the changing mix of genes for tallness and shortness in the population. As genes for shortness decrease in frequency, the combinations of many "short" alleles that produce the shortest individuals become very unlikely. In parallel, as genes for tallness increase in frequency, the combinations that would produce very tall individuals become more likely. In this way, selection on polygenic traits tends to move the entire bell-shaped curve until it becomes centered on the current optimum value. Finally, the *variance,* or spread, of the distribution decreases. This is because some short alleles—and thus some sources of phenotypic variation—have been removed from the population. With fewer different alleles affecting height in the population, there is less variation in height among individuals, and this is reflected in the frequency distribution.

The Precision of Adaptation

Constraints on Perfection

The Constraint of Cost

A common misconception surrounding natural selection is that some traits are universally valuable and thus will always be favored by natural selection. For example, some people might view intelligence as an advantageous trait under any conditions. If so, evolution could be perceived as a progression toward greater intelligence, since greater intelligence would be favored in all species, in all habitats, and at all moments in time. Here's where this line of thinking fails. Building and maintaining a large brain is extremely costly. Your brain represents about 2.5 percent of your total body mass, but it consumes roughly 25 percent of total energy. This is why the brain dies first in cases of oxygen deprivation; it is an energy hog. For such a costly brain to be favored by selection, it must confer substantial fitness benefits. In fact, this is a general idea: Any trait must pay for itself in increased reproductive success; otherwise selection will get rid of it. Bacteria and mosquitoes, for example, produce many offspring very rapidly and have not required a large brain to do so. Eyes would seem to be another advantageous trait, yet hundreds of cave-dwelling and deep sea insect and fish species have lost their eyes over evolutionary time because, in the absence of light, eyes were not worth their production costs. Thus, there is never some universally optimum trait or trait value. The contribution of a trait to reproductive success can be evaluated only in terms of its fitness costs and benefits to particular organisms living under a specified set of environmental conditions.

The Constraint of Variation

Even for a particular species, living under a specified set of circumstances, many adaptations are imperfect. One reason for this is constraints on raw materials. Remember that selection is not like a human engineer. Selection cannot automatically churn out a new design every time it encounters a new environmental challenge. If you've been impressed with the logic of Darwin's argument, you may well ask "Why not?" The answer is that selection only chooses variants; it does not create them. Mutations—blind, random gene-copying errors—are the raw material out of which selection builds adaptations. But selection has no way of *causing* a particular mutation, no matter how useful a trait it might build.

The Constraint of Time

In addition to constraints of costs and materials, there are also temporal constraints. Traits are passed to the present generations because they conferred a reproductive advantage on their possessors in *previous* generations. Traits that harmed the fitness of potential ancestors failed to get themselves into offspring and thus hit evolutionary dead ends. So we expect today's organisms to be adapted to their *ancestors'* environment. If the environment has remained relatively constant, organisms are likely to be adapted to their own environment as well. However, if the environment has changed dramatically, organisms are less likely to have genotypes that are adaptive under the current conditions. This concept is especially important for understanding human adaptation. The environments in which humans find themselves have been changing rapidly for the past ten thousand years or so. For most of our evolution, people probably lived in small, nomadic groups and obtained their subsistence through foraging for animals and plants. This set of environmental conditions is often called the *environment of evolutionary adaptedness,* or *EEA* (Tooby and DeVore 1987). The rapid rate of cultural change since the advent of agriculture has resulted in a set of environmental conditions to which modern humans are in many ways less adapted than they are to the conditions of the EEA. For example, the widespread fears of snakes and spiders are probably better suited to ancestral conditions than to modern society in which such dangers are relatively minimal. On the other hand, few people fear automobiles. Yet in modern Western society automobiles result in hundreds of times more deaths annually than do snakes and spiders combined.

Adaptations That Track Environmental Change

The preceding section argued that environmental change reduces the precision of adaptation. This conclusion is correct for changes at medium time scales, but not so true for slow changes or for rapidly fluctuating conditions. Very slow change doesn't disrupt adaptation because selection can keep pace, making the necessary allele substitutions as environmental conditions shift. Rapid fluctuations within the lifespan of individuals represent an even more interesting case. If we assume, as we have, that different conditions favor different adaptations, how can selection cope with rapidly fluctuating conditions? You have met the answer already: Facultative adaptations track the environment and adjust the phenotype appropriately.

Consider your pupils. At a proximate level, the diameter of the pupil is determined by the constriction or relaxation of the muscles of the iris. Pupil size, in turn, determines

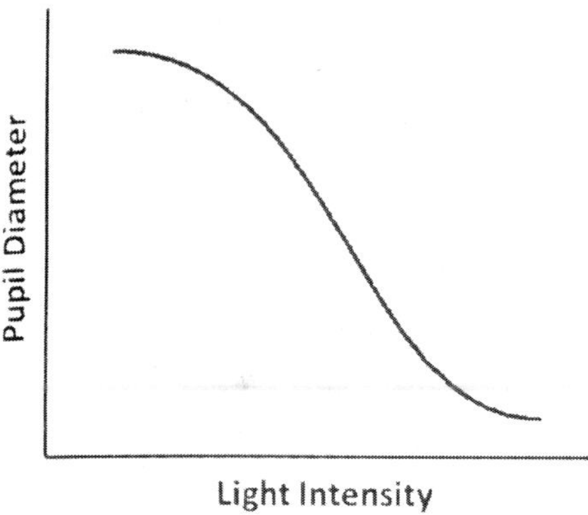

Figure 5. Reaction norm of pupil diameter to ambient light intensity. Pupil diameter is a facultative trait.

how much light reaches the photoreceptive cells of the retina on the back of the eye, thus regulating how much light is available for constructing an image of the world. Too little light results in an image that is dark and poorly defined. On the other hand, too much light results in an image that is too light, appears washed out, and is also poorly defined. A constant amount of light facilitates an optimal pupil diameter that allows as much light as possible to strike the retina but not so much that the image is "overexposed" and washed out. The point is, however, that the amount of light in the environment is *not* constant: It changes markedly over the course of the day, ranging from very low light on a moonless night to extremely bright light in an open field at midday. Because this environmental variable fluctuates so radically (there are about 10 trillion times as many photons in the sunny field as on the moonless night), natural selection has favored not a single value for pupil diameter in humans but rather a particular pattern of response, called a *reaction norm,* that tracks environmental variation in an adaptive way. Your pupils have a reaction norm to light intensity. They become very wide at night when light intensity is low, letting in as much light as possible, and very small during the day when light intensity is high, keeping too much light from hitting the retina (see Fig. 5).

Evolutionarily speaking, why is pupil size variable? Individuals who were not able to adjust their pupil size to the range of normal light conditions were at a disadvantage. They saw well only at one light level and less well under brighter or darker conditions. As a consequence they probably would have produced relatively few offspring. Adjusting pupil size to prevailing light conditions is a good idea. Any mutant genes that contributed to the assembly of mechanisms for making such adjustments had a reproductive advantage. In general, whenever an important environmental feature varies during the ordinary lifetimes of individuals, selection will tend to construct facultative adaptations that track it. *Obligate* adaptations, adaptations that resist environmental interference, will be favored in cases where the relevant environmental feature changes little, or where the costs of adjusting the phenotype would be too great.

One final caution is appropriate. Some phenotypic changes are not the result of facultative adaptations. Sweating is a facultative response to high environmental temperatures. Bursting into flames is not. Both are phenotypic changes, but only the former is adaptive. For a less dramatic example, sun tanning is a facultative response to high levels of solar radiation, but sun burning is not. Both sun burning and bursting into flames are the result of failures to respond—they are *susceptibilities.* Susceptibilities occur when the facultative responses of the organism are overwhelmed. Remember that, like all adaptations, facultative traits are the result of sculpting by natural selection in real environments. We can respond adequately to cold and heat over a particular temperature range because our ancestors' genes were tested for their ability to cope with that range. Thus, facultative responses occur within the range of historically normal environments and have the effect of keeping fitness prospects high. Failures to respond tend to occur outside the range of normal environments and damage fitness prospects. Now, armed with these insights, try to explain why sun burning occurs in modern humans.

In sum, traits are likely to be obligate when relevant environmental variables are fairly stable or when the trait would be too costly to change. On the other hand, traits are expected to be facultative when relevant environmental variables fluctuate and when the trait is not too costly to modify. In other words, facultative traits are favored by selection when the benefits of flexibility are high and the associated costs are low. Because these conditions generally apply to behavioral traits (energetically inexpensive change can occur rapidly), behaviors are among the quintessential facultative adaptations. Behavioral adaptations are discussed next.

Are Facultative Traits Heritable?

Remember that natural selection is ineffective at shaping low-heritability traits. This may seem to present a problem for facultative traits. After all, by definition facultative traits respond to aspects of the environment. For facultative traits, individuals are likely to differ from one another largely due to environmental differences rather than genetic differences. In other words, the heritability of facultative traits is generally low. For example, the diameter of your pupils is more likely to resemble someone who is genetically unrelated but in the same room than it is to resemble your parents' pupil diameters if they are currently lying on a beach in Jamaica. This apparent paradox is easily resolved: Natural selection shapes facultative adaptations not by favoring single trait values (which have low heritability) but by favoring reaction norms (which can be highly heritable).

Scott Carroll (Carroll 1993, Carroll and Corneli 1995) elegantly demonstrated how natural selection could favor a heritable reaction norm for a facultative behavioral trait. Carroll studied soapberry bugs (also called red-shouldered bugs), insects found in the southeastern United States. Female soapberry bugs may copulate with several males and thus lay eggs fertilized by multiple males. Consequently, males often remain clasped to the female well after copulation to increase the number of eggs they fertilize by preventing other males from copulating with her before she lays. However, such *mate guarding,* as it is called, decreases the number of females with whom a male can mate because it takes time away from locating and courting other females. Thus there are two opposing selection pressures on mate guarding: Too little mate guarding will seriously decrease the number of a female's eggs that are fertilized by the male, whereas too much mate guarding will seriously decrease his number of mates.

You might think that there is an optimal balance between these two opposing forces, one that favors some intermediate level of mate guarding. This idea is generally correct, but the right level depends on both the numbers of competing males (who could fertilize the current mate if the male left her) and the numbers of available females (whose eggs are the reward for leaving the current mate). Thus, Carroll noted that the relative fitness returns from mate guarding depend on the local sex ratio, that is, on the ratio of males to females. If there are many males and few females, the benefits of mate guarding should be high (eliminate lots of competing sperm) and the costs should be low (few additional females are available anyway). On the other hand, if there are few males and many females, mate guarding should be a less useful reproductive tactic.

From our present perspective, an added benefit of Carroll's work is the prediction that in environments where the sex ratio fluctuates markedly, a male's frequency of mate guarding would be facultatively dependent on the sex ratio. When Carroll took soapberry bugs back to the laboratory, this is precisely what he found. Under conditions of a high sex ratio (many males, few females), males were very likely to mate guard. As the sex ratio declined, so did the males' tendency to mate guard.

Carroll carefully plotted each individual male's probability of mate guarding at each experimental sex ratio to determine a reaction norm for each male. He found that there was variation among males in their reaction norms. Some males' probability of mate guarding increased steeply with an increase in the sex ratio, while other males' probability of mate guarding showed a more gradual increase. Carroll also found that these reaction norms were heritable: Sons' reaction norms resembled their fathers' reaction norms. Because he had demonstrated heritable variation in reaction norms, and because there were almost certainly reproductive differences associated with this variation, Carroll concluded that natural selection was working to shape male soapberry bugs' patterns of response to the availability of females.

The Mind Is a Collection of Facultative Adaptations

Let's dissect the behavior of soapberry bugs a bit more. We have said that their mate guarding behavior is facultatively dependent on the sex ratio, and it is. But male soapberry bugs don't just clamp down on thin air whenever the local sex ratio is female-biased. A male must have just copulated with a female to produce this behavior. Thus, mate guarding depends on two environmental variables: the presence of a female with whom a male has just copulated and a female-biased local sex ratio. In addition, male soapberry bugs do not always mate guard even when they have just copulated and the sex ratio is heavily male-biased, so additional variables must affect mate guarding. Perhaps the presence of predators causes a male to seek shelter rather than mate guard, for example. This is certainly a complex behavioral system for such a "dumb" little bug. How do such systems work?

Every facultative relationship is a link between an environmental variable and some flexible response in the phenotype. And each link requires some sort of mechanism that performs the "translation"—that is, that converts the change in the environment to a change in the phenotype. When a response is linked to several features of the environment, as is mate guarding in the present example, several such translation mechanisms are required, with perhaps additional modulators to make sure that the different translators don't interfere with each other and work together in the right way. In the case of behavioral traits, these translators and modulators fall into the broad category of psychological mechanisms. The label *psychological* is appropriate whether we are talking about insects or people.

The point is that complex behavior is made from multiple psychological mechanisms, multiple facultative adaptations, each of which adjusts the behavior in response to a particular feature of the environment. The more complex a behavioral pattern is, the more facultative adaptations must underlie that behavior. Mate guarding in soapberry bugs must depend on at least three facultative adaptations.

Evolutionary psychologists call these mechanisms *mental modules*. The mind is thus said to be *modular*, meaning it is composed of a large set of psychological mechanisms, each helping to adjust some specific sort of behavior in relation to a particular feature of the environment. This modularity does not necessarily imply that mental mechanisms are discretely represented in the neurochemistry or neuro-circuitry of soapberry bugs, bee-eaters, or humans. Mental modules may be distributed widely across the many connections of the nervous systems of organisms. Rather, the term *modular* implies that natural selection has favored specific patterns of response to fitness-related environmental variation; however, these patterns may be wired into the nervous system. Organisms are thus expected to have mental modules that represent adaptive solutions to the survival and reproductive challenges recurring over the evolutionary history of their species. Throughout this book, we will discuss various mental modules (sometimes implicitly, sometimes explicitly) that evolved in humans to solve such problems as locating suitable mates, competing for mates, caring for offspring, and forming alliances with group members. Because human behavior is so varied and so complex, we can be certain that it is guided by a large number of mental modules.

Levels of Selection

The Unit of Selection

Recall that the theory of natural selection is extremely general. Anything that satisfies its preconditions will evolve via natural selection. In fact, these preconditions are satisfied by at least three major levels in the hierarchy of biological organization—populations (and other groups), individuals, and genes. Consequently, natural selection must operate at all of these levels. For example, populations with successful characteristics can increase in size and fission off into new populations with similar characteristics at a higher rate than can other populations. This selective advantage of some populations over others could lead to an increase in the frequency of certain types of populations or even entire groups of species. Similarly, individuals with advantageous characteristics are more likely to produce many offspring, who also bear these characteristics. As a result, traits that are advantageous to individual survival and reproduction spread in populations. Finally, a gene tends to increase in frequency if its phenotypic effects on organisms get the gene copied at a higher rate than its alleles.

Much of the time, there may be no conflict between the selective processes operating at these different levels of organization. By producing traits that increase their own reproduction, alleles increase the reproduction of their bearers and may confer an advantage to the entire group. However, what if things are not so harmonious? What if, for example, a trait that increases its bearers' reproductive success decreases the success of its neighbors in the local group?

The evolutionary biologist John Maynard Smith (1976) analyzed such a scenario to derive the conditions under which group-level or individual-level selection would win out in the case of a conflict between these levels of selection. Maynard Smith considered three kinds of groups: groups composed only of *altruists,* groups composed of only *selfish* individuals, and mixed groups composed of some altruists and some selfish individuals. Altruists are defined as individuals whose traits benefit other members of the group at a cost to the altruists' own fitness. Selfish individuals possess traits that benefit only their own reproduction at the expense of the group. Maynard Smith hypothesized that pure groups of altruists would reproduce more groups by division and migration than would selfish groups because altruist groups would be less likely to go extinct. Mixed groups, on the other hand, would soon become pure selfish groups. This follows from the fact that, by their definition, altruists decrease their own fitness to increase the fitness of other members of the group. Meanwhile, selfish individuals reap the benefits bestowed on them by altruists and act only to increase their own fitness. Consequently, selfish individuals enjoy higher reproductive success than do altruists. Selfishness thus spreads, turning mixed groups into selfish ones.

Maynard Smith saw that, in order for selection at the level of groups to foster altruism, altruist groups would have to produce new altruist groups faster than they could be "infected" by selfish individuals. *Infection* refers to the migration of selfish individuals from selfish or mixed groups into pure altruist groups. This kind of infection could easily occur in species in which new groups are produced by migration of individuals from existing groups. Every infection puts a formerly altruistic group on a trajectory to being first a mixed group and eventually a pure selfish group. This infection can thus only be cancelled by the eventual extinction of the resulting selfish group. If infections are more common than extinctions—a very likely case in nature—selection at the level of groups will never keep pace with selection at the level of individuals, and group-selected altruism will be eliminated.

Another way to predict the outcome of conflicting selection at different levels is an examination of the degree to which phenomena at each level satisfy the prerequisites for natural selection. Selection should be stronger where its preconditions are more fully satisfied. In this regard, note that the prerequisite of heritable variation is satisfied most completely at the level of the gene. For this criterion to be fully satisfied at the level of the population, populations would have to copy themselves exactly. This is essentially impossible: A new population is very unlikely to be composed of individuals possessing exactly the same characteristics, in exactly the same proportions, as the parent population. Similarly, complete heritability is unrealistic at the level of the individual. Your offspring carry only half your genes. Even in asexual organisms, environmental differences will always contribute to some measurable phenotypic variation between parent and offspring.

Genes, however, do make exact copies of themselves, except in the very rare event of genetic mutation. Dawkins (1989) proposed that the gene is the largest reproducing "unit" that exactly satisfies all of the preconditions for natural selection. There is variation among genes (alleles) that is transmissible from one generation to the next, and genes affect their own replication by coding for proteins that build phenotypes and thus determine the

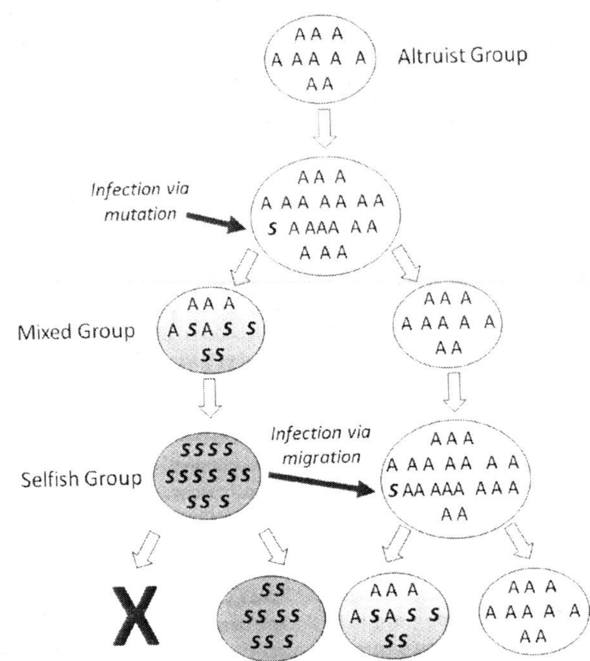

Figure 6. Group selection favors traits that benefit the group, whereas individual selection favors traits that increase individual fitness. Group selection sometimes opposes individual selection, as in favoring indiscriminate altruism (designated "A") toward group members. The outcome of conflict between selection at multiple levels is determined by the rate at which pure altruist groups "reproduce" (grow and fission into more groups), relative to the rate at which altruist groups are "infected" by selfish individuals (designated "S") through mutation or migration. Selfishness spreads in altruist groups, turning them into selfish groups, which are more likely to go extinct. Group selection can win out only if the reproductive advantage of altruist groups is large relative to the rate of infection by selfish individuals, an unlikely event in nature.

gene's chances of being transmitted to the next generation. The gene is therefore the basic unit of selection.

Kin Selection and Inclusive Fitness Theory

Because the gene fits the preconditions for natural selection so well, we can expect selection to have had a major effect at this level of biological organization and to have been somewhat less influential at other levels. As social scientists, however, we are interested not so much in which genes have been successful at propagating themselves as we are in what sorts of traits organisms can be expected to possess. On the other hand, the core of Darwin's legacy is that the answers to these two questions are tightly intertwined. The characteristics of higher levels of biological organization are expected to have benefited the genes that shape these characteristics. As a result, individual organisms are predicted to possess traits that have reliably increased the reproduction of the genes that underlie them.

We can predict what sorts of traits will exist at the individual level by answering a related question: *What phenotypic effects might cause selection to favor a gene over its alleles?* This is a slightly tricky question because a typical gene may be found in many different environments, interacting with many different genes at the same and other loci. For this reason, there are probably very few alleles that *always* increase reproductive success—that is, that increase reproductive success in every body that carries them. On the other hand, a gene doesn't have to do that well to be favored by selection. A gene could be favored by selection by jumping a much lower hurdle: increasing reproduction in some bodies, decreasing reproduction in others, but averaging an increase in reproduction relative to the effects of alternative alleles. For example, a gene that is slightly detrimental to reproductive success in males may be favored over its alleles if it significantly increases the reproductive success of females. Here, we are not assuming that male possessors of a gene actively affect the reproductive success of female possessors of the gene or vice versa—only that a gene's positive effects in some bodies more than compensate for its negative effects in others. This is sufficient to spread and maintain a gene in natural populations.

In teaching about evolution, we call this strategy "the front door to the next generation." A gene that increases the fitness of its average carrier will inevitably spread. This is an important idea, and we should pause to give it proper attention. On the other hand, one of the most exciting evolutionary discoveries of the 20th century was that there is also a "back door to the next generation." At first blush, the idea sounds like science fiction—like a hidden passage to another dimension or time travel. But literally thousands of studies have tested its detailed predictions since the late W. D. Hamilton unveiled his theory of *kin selection* (Hamilton 1964a, b), and it now stands as close to fact as we ever get in science. In a nutshell, Hamilton suggested that a gene could spread if it caused its bearers to *decrease* their own fitness in order to increase the reproduction of *other bearers of the same gene.* In fact, this provides an explanation for altruism, an explanation that the failed theory of group selection could not provide.

Let's dissect the argument supporting kin selection theory. If a gene is to be favored by selection, it must, in total, confer more fitness benefit than cost on its bearers. Of course, it could confer costs on some bearers and benefits on others, as long as the benefits outweighed the costs. When a gene causes one individual to behave altruistically toward another individual, the cost to the gene is simply the reproductive cost to the altruist (let's call this cost *c*). However, the benefit to the gene is slightly more complicated. The *expected* benefit to the "altruist gene" is not merely the reproductive benefit (let's call it *b*) conferred on the recipient of the altruism, because the recipient may not possess the altruist gene. Rather, the expected benefit to the altruist gene is equal to the reproductive benefit (b) bestowed on the recipient of the altruism, multiplied by the probability (r) that the recipient also possesses the altruist gene. Because such an altruist gene is favored by selection only if the expected benefits to the gene exceed the expected costs, the following relationship obtains:

$$rb > c$$

That is, the benefit to the recipient, multiplied by the probability that the recipient and the altruist share the altruist gene, must be greater than the cost to the altruist. This relationship is known as *Hamilton's rule.* Such altruistic behavior is thus more likely to occur when (1) the cost to the altruist is small, (2) the benefit to the recipient is large, and (3) there is a high probability that the recipient and the altruist share a particular gene.

When is the probability high that the altruist and the recipient share a gene? When the altruist and the recipient are close genetic relatives. In fact, the variable *r* is called the *coefficient of relatedness.* Individuals can share genes by chance, of course, but the only factor that systematically elevates the likelihood of gene sharing above the chance level is kinship. For example, the coefficient of relatedness between full siblings is 0.5; likewise, parents and their offspring are linked by an *r* of 0.5 (because of meiosis). Grandparents and grandchildren have an *r* of 0.25, which is the same as the coefficient of relatedness between aunts and uncles and their nieces and nephews. For first cousins, $r = 0.125$. We can now make a prediction about the sorts of traits we can expect organisms to possess given the strength of gene-level selection: Organisms are expected to possess traits (both morphological and behavioral) that tend to increase their own reproductive success or the reproductive success of their close genetic relatives. The sum of (1) an organism's reproductive success and (2) the organism's effects on the reproduction of its relatives (multiplied by their coefficients of relatedness) is the organism's *inclusive fitness.* We thus expect that organisms will tend to possess traits that, in the evolutionary past, increased inclusive fitness. When organisms use altruism to increase their inclusive fitness, we expect their behavior to be facultatively dependent on the relationship among *r, b,* and *c.* A vast literature, spanning creatures from ants through monkeys and apes to people, suggests that these predictions match the behavior of real organisms. Kin selection is the topic of Chapter 6.

Summary

Natural selection is the engine of adaptive evolution. It is fueled by the trickle of new alleles produced randomly by genetic mutation. Selection differentially preserves any alleles that augment reproduction in the prevailing environment. Phenotypic traits of high heritability—ones where much of the phenotypic variation is due directly to genetic variation—are most subject to natural selection. The outcomes of natural selection are adaptations, designs for reproduction that address recurring environmental challenges. These adaptations may be either obligate or facultative, depending on the temporal patterning of environmental variation and on the costs of mounting a flexible response.

Genes are units of heredity; they are composed of DNA and reside in the nucleus of all our cells. Most cells are diploid, produced by mitosis, and have the full double dose of genes (i.e., homologous paternal and maternal chromosomes). Haploid gametes (e.g., eggs and sperm) are produced by meiosis and contain a single dose of hereditary material that, due to recombination, is a mix of paternal and maternal genes. Genes shape the phenotype by directing the assembly of proteins that interact with each other and with the environment. Variation in a given phenotypic trait may be affected primarily by genes at one locus or, more commonly, by genes at several loci acting in concert.

While natural selection is a powerful force, having designed all the adaptations of all living things, it is constrained by three factors: Some potentially useful adaptations may be too costly, sometimes the necessary variation may be lacking, and in some cases selection will not have had sufficient time to build the needed trait.

Behavioral traits are subject to evolution and, like all other aspects of the phenotype, are shaped by gene-gene and gene-environment interactions. Most behavioral adaptations have significant facultative components; the array of facultative behavioral mechanisms (mental modules) is thought to be quite large.

Selection works most effectively at the lowest levels in the hierarchy of life (i.e., the gene) because its prerequisites are best satisfied there. Selection at the level of the gene can nevertheless explain phenomena at higher levels such as altruism.

References

Carroll, S. P. 1993. Divergence in male mating tactics between two populations of the soapberry bug. 1. Guarding vs. nonguarding. *Behavioral Ecology* 4(2):156–64.

Carroll, S. P. and P. S. Corneli. 1995. Divergence in male mating tactics between two populations of the soapberry bug. 2. Genetic change and the evolution of a plastic reaction norm in a variable social-environment. *Behavioral Ecology* 6(1):46–56.

Dawkins, R. 1989. *The selfish gene* (new ed.). Oxford, England: Oxford University Press.

Hamilton, W. D. 1964a. The genetical evolution of social behaviour I. *Journal of Theoretical Biology* 7:1–16.

Hamilton, W. D. 1964b. The genetical evolution of social behaviour I. *Journal of Theoretical Biology* 7:17–52.

Maynard Smith, J. 1976. Group selection. *Quarterly Review of Biology* 51:277–83.

Mealey, L. 2000. *Sex differences: Development and evolutionary strategies.* San Diego: Academic Press.

Tooby, J., and L. DeVore 1987. The reconstruction of hominid behavioral evolution through strategic modeling. In *Primate models for the origin of human behavior,* ed. W. Kinzey. New York: SUNY Press.

Introduction to Chapter 2

Evolution is not something that happened in the dry, dusty past and is now finished; this chapter documents how the shift to a new food source has caused recent and rapid evolutionary change in the feeding-related anatomy of a Mediterranean lizard species.

Chapter 2 is one of four primary research studies in this book. Like the other primary studies, it is a relatively brief communication among scientific professionals. This introduction will explain the chapter's central message and give you the supporting concepts you need to read and understand it. As in most of the chapters, my introduction ends with a short glossary of terms that may be new to you.

Anthony Herrel and his coauthors provide a report about a field experiment that was used to study rates of evolutionary change. Their basic question was this: How quickly can natural selection create new adaptations? To begin the experiment, 5 male and 5 female lizards, all belonging to the same species, were removed from one island where they occur naturally and then released on a small nearby island where they previously did not occur. In other words, one island was "seeded" with a lizard species from elsewhere to see what would happen. At the time the report was published, the experiment had been running for about 30 lizard generations. Was that enough time to see any adaptive changes in transplanted population? As you will soon see, the answer is yes. But first, let's meet the cast of characters.

The scientific name of the study species is *Podarcis sicula.* Because this species is not found in English-speaking countries, its English common name is not stable; it is variously called "Italian wall lizard" or "Istanbul lizard." The great virtue of scientific names is that they are the same in every language. Regardless of whether you speak Mandarin or Malay, you will know what animal I am talking about when I say "*Podarcis sicula.*" Similar to your name, scientific names have two parts. The first part is the genus name. It is the more inclusive part of the name in the sense that there may be more than one species in a genus—just as there may be more than one Bach in the Bach family. The second part is the species name. By convention, the genus name is always capitalized and the species name never is, even when it is based on a person's name, such as *Rhea darwinii*, a large flightless South American bird. Both parts of a scientific name should be italicized as they are here (or underlined if you cannot italicize). Just as a genus may include several species, higher levels can include several genera (the plural of genus). The next level up from genus is family. The genus *Podarcis* is in the family Lacertidae, which includes all the species of wall lizards. An abbreviated picture of the array of reptiles mentioned in Chapter 2 is shown in Figure A below. The lizards in this experiment were taken from Pod Kopište, the "original island," and they were released on Pod Mrčaru, the "colony island." Are you wondering yet what Herrel and his team found?

Observations showed that the lizards were eating very different diets on the two islands. Figure 2 in the chapter shows these differences for two seasons: spring and summer. On each island the diets do change somewhat with the season, but that is not the most dramatic difference you see in the graphs. On the original island, Pod Kopište, where the lizards have presumably lived for many generations, they eat mainly arthropods (insects, spiders, etc.). But on Pod Mrčaru, the colony island, they eat a lot of plant material, especially in the summer. Let's talk numbers. On Pod Kopište, plant material makes up between 4% and 7% of the diet. But on Pod Mrčaru, the colony population eats between 36% and 61% plant material, roughly 10 times as much as on the original island! This is a big change in diet; presumably the lizards had to make this change because there are fewer insects on the colony island. The point of the article, however, is not why they changed their diet, but what happened when they did.

Plant foods contain a lot of cellulose, a tough material that makes up the walls of plant cells. The leafy parts of plants—which the colony population was eating a lot of (see Figure 3)—are especially high in cellulose. Eating cellulose is problematic in two ways. First, it is tough and fibrous. This toughness makes it difficult to bite off and chew mouthfuls of plant leaves. Second, cellulose is indigestible by all vertebrates (you and lizards are both vertebrates). No lizard can break it down and release the food energy it contains. The only way for a vertebrate to get food energy out of cellulose is to recruit the help of commensal invertebrates to live in their guts and do the digestion for them. Usually, as has happened in cattle and leaf monkeys, the digestive system of the plant eaters evolves into multiple subcompartments. These modifications slow the passage of food through the gut and create special environments, giving the invertebrate helpers both extra time and special places to do their digestive work.

Let's review the facts. The colonists came from a population where the lizards were eating very little leaf material. But recently—within the last 30 generations—the colonists began eating a lot more of it. This leaf material is hard to bite and can only be digested with commensal assistance. Knowing these facts, we can make some predictions about the kinds of adaptive changes we should expect in our colony population:

1. There will be changes in the head anatomy that increase bite strength.
2. There will be changes in the gut anatomy that give time and space for cellulose digestion.

These adaptive changes are precisely what Herrel and his team found.

A few facts about guts will be helpful. The cecum is part of the digestive system. When comparing many species, it is clear that the cecum is large and complex in species that eat a lot of plant material, but small and simple in species that eat mainly animals. The cecal valves of the colonists create fermenting chambers, which slow down the rate of food passage through the gut. Further supporting this interpretation, the colonists have cellulose-digesting nematodes (small worms) in their cecal chambers.

This study by Herrel and his colleagues also illustrates ways of thinking that will be useful to you. First and foremost is the idea of planned comparisons. The most obvious comparison is the one between the original population and the colonists. This comparison lets us ask whether a change in diet produced adaptive changes in the lizards' feeding and digestive anatomy. Because we know the colonists are recently derived from the original population, this comparison is a direct way of assessing how much evolution has occurred.

The second comparison is the one between the study species and other species of lizards (and snakes). Here is the logic the authors are using. We know that the colonists' closest relatives—the original population of *Podarcis sicula*—lack cecal valves. But just how great an innovation is it for the colony population to evolve this feature of the gut? A good way to explore this question is to see how many of *Podarcis sicula*'s more distant relatives have cecal valves. That is why the authors mention various other lizards. For example, they note that another species of *Podarcis* (*Podarcis melisellensis*) lacks cecal valves. They also stress that less than one percent of all scaled reptile species have cecal valves. And the few that do have them—in their own family, Lacertidae, and in the more distantly related families, Igaunidae and Agamidae—are all plant eaters. In other words, the pattern of evolution among lizards seems to suggest that cecal valves are adaptive only for plant eaters. This kind of comparative evidence for adaptation will be pursued more explicitly in Chapter 3.

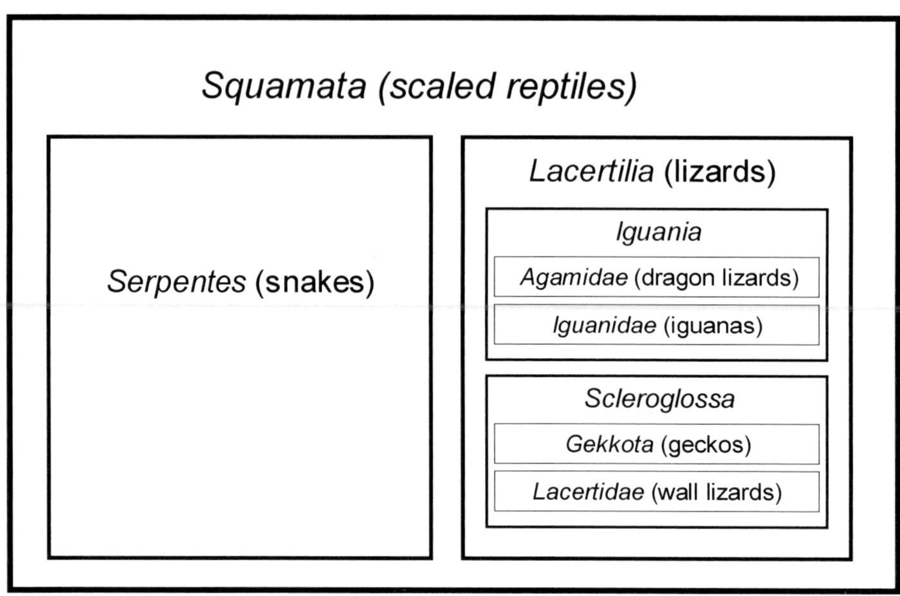

Figure A. An abbreviated picture of relationships among the species referenced in Chapter 2. The study species, *Podarcis sicula*, is in the family Lacertidae (wall lizards). Wall lizards and geckos are included along with several other kinds of lizards (not shown) in Scleroglossa. Likewise, all Scleroglossa lizards are grouped together with all Iguania lizards (and several others not shown) to form the most inclusive group of lizards, Lacertilia. This, in turn, is grouped with Serpentes to form the Squamata, scaled reptiles. (What other reptiles are there besides the scaled ones? After you master Chapter 5, you will be ready to understand that there are also feathered reptiles, commonly called birds.)

A few more comments will make your reading easier. "Haldanes" and "Darwins" are two units for measuring the speed of evolution. To help you understand these units, here's an analogy from the realm of physical speed. You could measure how fast your car is going in miles per hour, or you could measure it in miles per year. There are approximately 8,760 hours in a year, so 50 miles per hour is equal to 438,000 miles per year. Darwins and Haldanes also measure the rate at which something happens per unit time and, as in our analogy, their time units differ. The time unit for a Darwin is a million years; the time unit for a Haldane is a generation. That is why the numbers in columns 1 and 2 of Table 1 look so different.

Finally, also on the topic of numbers, let me mention statistics. The three paragraphs that begin, "Morphometric data describing head size and shape show that both males and females of the two populations differ significantly ..." discuss a lot of statistical analysis. This kind of statistics, called inferential statistics, is a branch of science/math unto itself. If you have not been indoctrinated into its language and methods, inferential statistics will not be comprehensible to you. However, only the *language* of inferential statistics is complicated. The questions it asks are pretty simple: Are the differences we see real (significant), or are they just a matter of chance? (Differences associated with small *P*-values are more likely to be real.) Here is what you should do: read these three paragraphs for the ordinary English words and phrases; those sentences describe what the authors found. You can ignore all the Greek-looking material in brackets and parentheses—all the MANOVAs, ANCOVAs, Wilkses, and *F*-statistics. The article reverts to ordinary English after the three statistical paragraphs!

One other question that might occur to you concerns sex differences. It seems that the female colonists' heads changed more than the male colonists' heads. Although the authors do not explain why this happened, I can suggest a plausible idea. Most phenotypic traits probably represent compromises between different selection pressures. For example, consider the fact that melanin lowers the risk of skin cancer but increases the risk of vitamin D deficiency. Therefore, your rate of melanin synthesis will represent a compromise of these two opposing selection pressures. Likewise, head shape in lizards involves compromises, and the compromises are probably different for males and females. This is likely to be true because male lizards often compete aggressively for mates, and that competition tends to take the form of wrestling and clamping the jaws on the opponent. On the other hand, females generally do not fight over mating opportunities. Thus, well before the lizards increased their plant eating, selection for bigger, more powerful jaws already existed in males—but not in females. When the dietary change came, the already bigger male jaws enlarged less than the previously small jaws of females. In Chapter 8 you will learn why mating competition influenced male evolution more than female evolution and how to predict when it will also (or instead) shape females.

In conclusion, this research article shows that adaptive evolutionary change can occur in a relatively small number of generations. In this study we have a very good estimate of how long these changes took because we know exactly when the lizards were introduced to the new island and when their diet changed. This dietary shift to plant eating changed which head features and gut features were advantageous. The lizards that had any genetic tendency to develop these advantageous traits were more likely to survive and reproduce on Pod Mrčaru. Consequently, their advantageous genes spread through the population in a mere 36 years.

Chapter 2 Glossary

cecal valves: Valves that divide the cecum, a part of the intestine, into a series of smaller compartments.

cellulose: A carbohydrate that is the principal component of plant (but not animal) cell walls. It is tough, fibrous, and indigestible by any animal with a backbone, but it can be digested by some invertebrates.

commensal: Literally means sharing food. In this chapter we are interested in commensal invertebrates that live in the digestive system of plant-eating vertebrates and do the cellulose-digesting work for their vertebrate hosts.

Darwins, Haldanes: units for measuring the rate of evolution; see above. The time unit for a Darwin is a million years, and the time unit for a Haldane is a generation.

herbivore: A plant eater.

lacertid lizard, scleroglossan lizard, agamid lizard, iguanid lizard: Various kinds of lizards more and less closely related to the study species; see Figure A in this introduction.

mitochondrial DNA: Genetic information passed only from mothers to daughters and used to confirm that the original population and the colony population really are the same species.

morphology: Anatomy, structure.

morphometrics: Measurements of anatomical traits, e.g., how wide is the lizard's head?

Podarcis sicula: Genus and species name (like *Homo sapiens*) of the lizard whose evolution is being studied; see above.

SVL: An abbreviation for snout-vent length, the standard way of measuring how big a lizard is. The snout is the tip of the nose, and the vent is the combined excretory and reproductive opening (did you really want to know?). SVL thus intentionally neglects tail length because tails can be artificially shortened by all kinds of accidents (including biologists' scissors).

squamates: Members of the Squamata, including all scaled reptiles.

CHAPTER 2
Rapid Large-Scale Evolutionary Divergence in Morphology and Performance Associated with Exploitation of a Different Dietary Resource (2008)

Anthony Herrel[*†‡], *Katleen Huyghe*[†], *Bieke Vanhooydonck*[†], *Thierry Backeljau*[†§], *Karin Breugelmans*[§], *Irena Grbac*[¶], *Raoul Van Damme*[†], *and Duncan J. Irschick*[I]

Although rapid adaptive changes in morphology on ecological time scales are now well documented in natural populations, the effects of such changes on whole-organism performance capacity and the consequences on ecological dynamics at the population level are often unclear. Here we show how lizards have rapidly evolved differences in head morphology, bite strength, and digestive tract structure after experimental

* Department of Organismic and Evolutionary Biology, Harvard University, 26 Oxford Street, Cambridge, MA 02138;

† Department of Biology, University of Antwerp, Universiteitsplein 1, B-2610 Antwerpen, Belgium;

§ Royal Belgian Institute of Natural Sciences, Vautierstraat 29, B-1000 Brussels, Belgium;

¶ Department of Zoology, Croatian Natural History Museum, Demetrova 1, HR-1000, Zagreb, Croatia;

I Department of Biology and Organismic Evolutionary Program, University of Massachusetts at Amherst, 221 Morrill Science Center, Amherst, MA 01003

‡ To whom correspondence should be addressed. E-mail: anthony.herrel@ua.ac.be.

Anthony Herrel, Katleen Huyghe, Bieke Vanhooydonck, Thierry Backeljau, Karin Breugelmans, Irena Grbac, Raoul Van Damme, and Duncan J. Irschick, "Rapid Large-Scale Evolutionary Divergence in Morphology and Performance Associated with Exploitation of a Different Dietary Resource," from *Proceedings of the National Academy of Sciences*, Vol. 105 No. 12; March 25, 2008, pp. 4792–4795.

introduction into a novel environment. Despite the short time scale (≈36 years) since this introduction, these changes in morphology and performance parallel those typically documented among species and even families of lizards in both the type and extent of their specialization. Moreover, these changes have occurred side-by-side with dramatic changes in population density and social structure, providing a compelling example of how the invasion of a novel habitat can evolutionarily drive multiple aspects of the phenotype.

Recent reviews have illustrated how rapid adaptive evolution is common and may be considered the rule rather than the exception in some cases (1, 2). Experimental introductions of populations in novel environments have provided some of the strongest evidence for natural selection and adaptive divergence on ecological time scales (3–6). However, little is known about the degree to which the observed changes in morphology may affect the population structure and behavioral ecology of organisms through the mediating effects of whole-organism performance (7, 8). Consequently, our understanding of how rapid phenotypic changes affect ecological processes at the population level is limited (2, 9). Moreover, despite the fact that microevolutionary responses to environmental changes have been well documented, the unpredictability and reversibility of changes of morphological traits in fluctuating environments (10, 11) have raised questions regarding how these microscale changes can lead to the emergence of novel structures as seen on macroevolutionary scales (2).

Here we address these issues by examining the outcome of a remarkable 36-year experimental introduction with the lizard *Podarcis sicula*. In 1971 five adult pairs of this species were moved from the small islet of Pod Kopište (0.09 km2) to the nearby Pod Mrčaru (0.03 km2) by Nevo and coworkers (12). Both islets lie in the middle of the South Adriatic Sea near the larger island of Lastovo and belong to Croatia. Although the islet of Pod Mrčaru was originally inhabited by another lacertid lizard species (*Podarcis melisellensis*), repeated visits (twice yearly over the past three years, beginning in 2004) show that this species has become extinct on Pod Mrčaru. Genetic mitochondrial DNA analyses indicate that the lizards currently on Pod Mrčaru are indeed *P. sicula* and are genetically indistinguishable from lizards from the source population [supporting information (SI) Fig. 5].

Morphometric data describing head size and shape show that both males and females of the two populations differ significantly in head morphology [MANOVA; males: Wilks's $\lambda = 0.463$, $F_{9,115} = 14.81$, $P < 0.001$; females: Wilks's $\lambda = 0.425$, $F_{9,123} = 18.45$, $P < 0.001$ (Table 1 and Fig. 1)] with lizards on Pod Mrčaru having longer, wider, and taller heads than lizards on Pod Kopište (Table 1 and Fig. 1). Differences between populations are not merely the result of differences in overall size but represent distinct changes in head shape [MANCOVA with SVL as covariate; males: slopes, Wilks's $\lambda = 0.918$, $F_{6,131} = 1.96$, $P = 0.08$; intercepts, Wilks's $\lambda = 0.387$, $F_{6,132} = 34.88$, $P < 0.001$; females: slopes, Wilks's $\lambda = 0.983$, $F_{8,122} = 0.25$, $P = 0.98$;

intercepts, Wilks's $\lambda = 0.754$, $F_{8,123} = 5.02$, $P < 0.001$; juveniles: slopes, Wilks's $\lambda = 0.969$, $F_{6,39} = 0.21$, $P = 0.97$; intercepts, Wilks's $\lambda = 0.498$, $F_{6,40} = 6.72$, $P < 0.001$ (Table 1 and Fig. 1)].

Differences in head size and shape also translate into significant differences in bite force between populations (males: $F_{1,44} = 4.93$, $P = 0.03$; females: $F_{1,38} = 16.94$, $P < 0.01$). Whereas the difference in bite force is the result of overall head size differences in females (ANCOVA; slopes, $F_{1,36} = 0.02$, $P = 0.91$; intercepts, $F_{1,37} = 1.55$, $P = 0.22$), in males size variation does not explain the difference in bite force (ANCOVA; slopes, $F_{1,42} = 0.25$, $P = 0.62$; intercepts, $F_{1,43} = 18.42$, $P < 0.01$).

Our data show that *P. sicula* lizards consume more plant material on Pod Mrčaru compared with the ancestral population on Pod Kopište. Analysis of stomach contents shows marked differences in diet between populations in both spring ($F_{1,204} = 22.9$, $P < 0.01$) and summer ($F_{1,74} = 103.13$, $P < 0.01$) but no differences in diet between sexes in either population ($F_{1,202} = 1.36$, $P = 0.24$). Seasonal differences in diet were significant in lizards from the introduced population (Pod Mrčaru, $F_{1,184} = 30.31$, $P < 0.01$) with plants composing between 34% (spring) and 61% (summer) of the total volume of the food eaten (Fig. 2). In contrast, plant consumption was low (7% to 4%) and did not differ seasonally for lizards from the source population (Pod Kopište, $F_{1,94} = 0.33$, $P = 0.57$). Moreover, ≈50% of the plant matter eaten year round by lizards from Pod Mrčaru consists of items with high cellulose content, such as leaves and stems (Fig. 3).

Table 1. Phenotypic, performance, and ecological divergence for two populations of *P. sicula* 36 years after the introduction of 10 individuals in a new environment

			Pod Kopište		Pod Mrčaru	
	Haldanes, mf	Darwins, m/f	Male	Female	Male	Female
SVL, mm	0.044/0.045	2,713/3,350	63.06 ± 4.68	56.80 ± 5.30	69.54 ± 2.86	64.08 ± 2.93
Mass, g	0.028/0.034	6,384/9,441	5.07 ± 1.37	3.36 ± 1.16	6.38 ± 1.42	4.72 ± 1.24
Head length, mm	0.045/0.049	2,978/3,209	14.67 ± 1.08	12.25 ± 0.84	16.33 ± 0.77	13.75 ± 0.64
Head width, mm	0.046/0.051	3,359/3,799	8.09 ± 0.67	6.55 ± 0.46	9.13 ± 0.42	7.51 ± 0.38
Head height, mm	0.048/0.048	4,326/4,228	6.29 ± 0.59	5.12 ± 0.46	7.35 ± 0.43	5.95 ± 0.38
Lower jaw length, mm	0.045/0.048	2,936/3,349	15.70 ± 1.23	12.80 ± 0.94	17.45 ± 0.72	14.44 ± 0.71
Jaw outlever, mm	0.045/0.049	2,972/3,463	14.17 ± 1.10	11.60 ± 0.87	15.77 ± 0.65	13.14 ± 0.62
Snout length, mm	0.045/0.049	2,841/3,339	10.40 ± 0.78	8.77 ± 0.64	11.52 ± 0.47	9.89 ± 0.45
Open inlever, mm	0.016/0.011	2,417/2,223	1.54 ± 0.31	1.20 ± 0.16	1.68 ± 0.28	1.30 ± 0.27
Close inlever, mm	0.039/0.039	3,403/3,844	3.76 ± 0.39	2.83 ± 0.29	4.25 ± 0.31	3.25 ± 0.30
Bite force, N	0.007/0.018	3,690/8,170	9.85 ± 2.29	4.99 ± 1.61	11.25 ± 2.42	6.70 ± 1.90
% of plants			9 ± 7	4 ± 5	60 ± 34	48 ± 23

Lizards were transplanted from Pod Kopište to Pod Mrčaru. Table entries are means ± standard deviations. Divergence rates are indicated for males (m) and females (f) separately. SVL, snout-vent length.

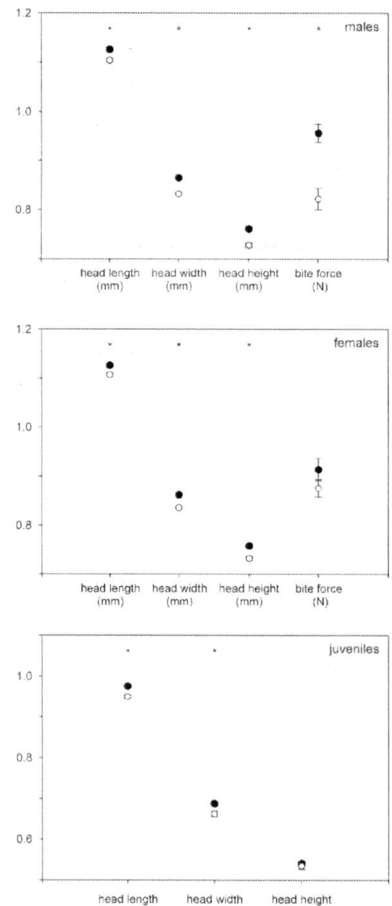

Figure 1. Graphs illustrating differences in aspects of head morphology and bite force for male (*Top*), female (*Middle*), and juvenile (*Bottom*) lizards from two populations (filled symbols, Pod Mrcaru; open symbols, Pod Kopište) having diverged for 36 years. On the graphs, the size-adjusted means are represented, thus illustrating body-size-independent variation in morphology and bite force. Population differences are highly significant and show how lizards on Pod Mrcaru generally have bigger heads and greater bite forces. The *y* axis gives the log10-transformed size-adjusted head dimensions and bite force. Error bars depict 1 standard deviation. Asterisks depict significant differences between populations.

This shift to a predominantly plant-based diet has resulted in the dramatic evolution of intestinal morphology. Morphological analysis of preserved specimens shows the presence of cecal valves (Fig. 4) in all individuals, including a hatchling (26.4-mm snout-vent length, umbilical scar present) and a very young juvenile (33.11-mm snout-vent length) examined from Pod Mrčaru. These valves are similar in overall appearance and structure to those found in herbivorous lacertid, agamid, and iguanid lizards (13, 14) and are not found in other populations of *P. sicula* (13) or in *P. melisellensis*. Cecal valves slow down food passage and provide for fermenting chambers, allowing commensal microorganisms to convert cellulose to volatile fatty acids (15, 16). Indeed, in the lizards from Pod Mrčaru, nematodes were common in the hindgut but absent from individuals from Pod Kopište. The fact that <1% of all currently known species of squamates have cecal valves (13, 14) illustrates the unusual nature of these structures in this population. The evolution of these structures has likely gone hand in hand with a novel association between *P. sicula* on Pod Mrčaru and a set of microorganisms assuring the digestion of cellulose as is suggested by the presence of nematodes in the hindgut of individuals from Pod Mrčaru.

Our data show that in only 36 years (≈30 generations) the experimental introduction of a small propagule of lizards (five males and five females) into a novel environment has resulted in large differences in external morphology with high phenotypic divergence rates (17) up to 8,593 darwins or 0.049 haldanes [Table 1; note, however, that these are synchronic rates (1) and assume no additional colonization of the island by *P. sicula*]. Moreover, the invasion of a novel environment has resulted in the evolution of a novel phenotypic character that is rarely observed in lizards and that cannot be quantified by such metrics. More importantly, the observed morphological changes appear adaptive because they result in an increase in bite performance in both sexes. Because plants are tough, fibrous materials, high bite forces may allow lizards to crop smaller pieces from larger plants (13, 18) and thus may help the breakdown of the indigestible cell walls (19, 20). Previous data show that lizards that include plant matter into their diet do indeed have higher bite forces (13, 18). Interestingly, phenotypic divergence rates are higher for females (the sex with the smallest heads and lowest bite forces) than males, suggesting that selection for high bite forces is directly related to the inclusion of tough and fibrous items into the diet. Additionally, functional components of the jaw system related to jaw opening (e.g., the inlever for jaw opening) show much lower divergence rates, again suggesting that morphological changes are specifically associated with the ability to bite hard and the increased consumption of plant matter (Table 1).

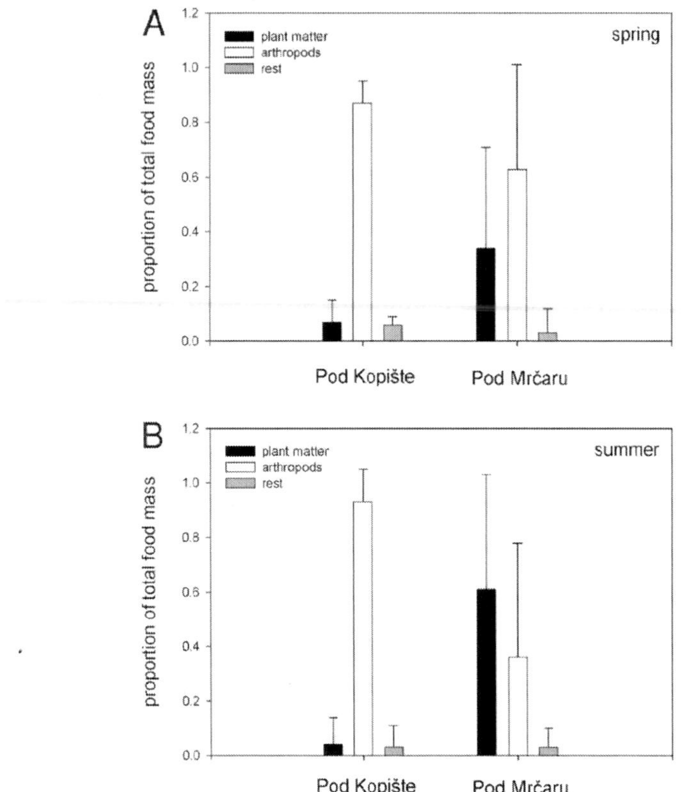

Figure 2. Graphs illustrating differences in diet between populations in spring (*A*) and summer (*B*). Differences in the proportions of plants (black bars), invertebrate prey (white), and rest fraction (gray) are highly significant between populations. Seasonal differences in diet were highly significant on Pod Mrčaru but not on Pod Kopište. Error bars depict 1 standard deviation.

The relatively large fraction of leaves included into the diet of lizards in the introduced population of Pod Mrčaru has apparently also resulted in the evolution of cecal valves, a structure previously unreported for this species and rare in this family and scleroglossan lizards in general (13, 14, 18). Our data also add to the growing number of studies suggesting that the inclusion of plant matter into the diet of small temperate lizards may be more common than previously thought (21, 22). Moreover, our data show not only rapid, directional changes in quantitative phenotypic traits related to the inclusion of plant matter into the diet, but also the evolution of novel morphological structures on extremely short time scales. Although the presence of cecal valves and large heads in hatchlings and

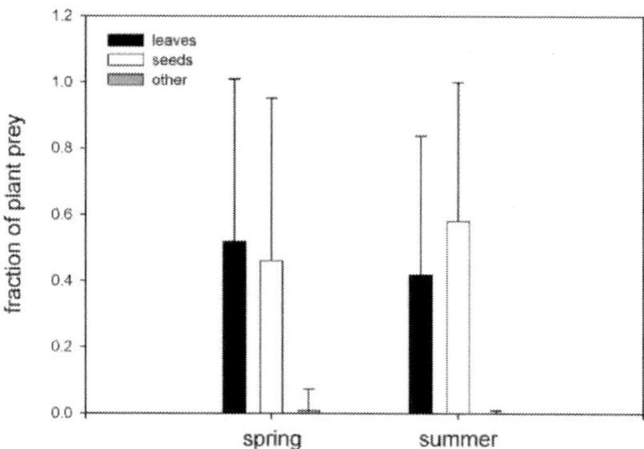

Figure 3. Bar graph illustrating the fraction of plant prey in the diet of lizards from Pod Mrčaru consisting of leaves (black), seeds (white), and other plant material (gray). Fibrous, indigestible materials such as leaves compose a large fraction of the diet in both spring and summer. Error bars depict 1 standard deviation.

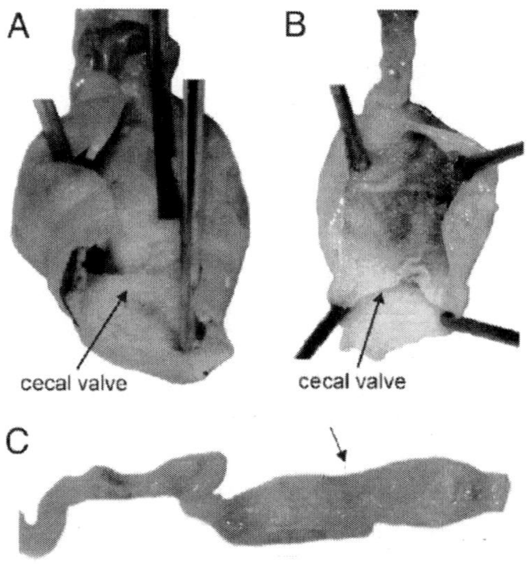

Figure 4. Photographs illustrating the cecal valves in a male (*A*), a female (*B*), and a hatchling (*C*) *P. sicula* from Pod Mrčaru. Note the thick cecal wall and pronounced ridges. The arrow in *C* indicates the position of the cecal valve in a hatchling as seen from the outside.

juveniles suggests a genetic basis for these differences, further studies investigating the potential role of phenotypic plasticity and/or maternal effects in the divergence between populations are needed.

The inclusion of plant matter into diet may have had profound effects on the population structure as well. Because of the larger food base available and the increase in the predictability of the food source, lizard densities on Pod Mrčaru are much greater (0.01 versus 0.05 lizards per trap per hour, caught in unbaited traps, on Pod Kopište and Pod Mrčaru, respectively). This, in turn, likely affected the social structure, and lizards on Pod Mrčaru do no longer appear to defend territories. Moreover, changes in foraging style (browsing versus active pursuit of mobile prey) and social structure may also have resulted in the dramatic changes in limb proportions and maximal sprint speed previously documented for this population (23). Thus, our data show how rapid phenotypic changes may affect population structure and dynamics through their effect on behavioral ecology and life history of animals. They also show that rapid evolution can result in changes in both qualitative and quantitative characters.

Methods

Samples and Phylogenetic Analysis.

Islands were visited in spring and summer of 2004, 2005, and 2006. Lizards were caught by noose and transported to the field laboratory or measured *in situ*. Small tail clips (±4 mm) were taken from all individuals and stored in 100% ethanol for genetic analysis. To corroborate morphological identifications, a subset of specimens from both islands (Pod Kopište, $n = 8$; Pod Mrčaru, $n = 7$) and a set of reference specimens of *P. melisellensis* from Lastovo Island ($n = 7$) were subjected to DNA sequence analysis. Total genomic DNA was extracted by using the QIAamp DNA Mini Kit (Qiagen). Two mitochondria l DNA fragments (12S rDNA and 16S rDNA) were amplified by PCR by using the primer pairs 12SaL (5'-AAACTGGGATTAGATACCCCACTAT-3') and 12SaH (5'-GAGGGTGACGGGCGGTGTGT-3') for the 12S fragment (modified from ref. 24) and 16Sar (5'-CCGGTCTGAACTCAGAT-CACGT-3') and 16Sbr (5'-CGCCTGTTTAACAAAAACAT-3') for the 16S fragment (25). PCRs were performed in a total volume of 25 µl, containing 200 µM of each dNTP, 0.2 µM of each primer, 2.5 µl of TaqPCR buffer (10x), 1.25 units of *Taq* polymerase (Qiagen *Taq* for 12S and Sigma REDTaq for 16S), and DNA template (1 µl for 12S and 3 µl for 16S). The PCR protocols started with an initial DNA denaturation at 95°C (5 min) and ended with a final extension step of 5 min at 72°C. Amplification was done in 35 cycles of 95°C (1 min), 50°C (1 min), and 72°C (2 min) for 12S and 95°C (45 s), 46°C (45 s), and 72°C (90 s) for 16S. PCR products were purified with the GFX PCR DNA and Gel Band Purification Kit of Amersham Biosciences and sequenced by using the Big Dye Terminator v1.1 Cycle Sequencing Kit (Applied Biosystems) on an AB 3130 XL Genetic Analyzer. Sequences were edited and aligned with BioEdit software (26). The MEGAv4 (27) was used to calculate pairwise Jukes-Cantor distances and to construct a neighbor-joining tree based on a concatenated alignment of both gene fragments, including all published data of specimens for which both gene fragments were available in the GenBank database (28, 29) and with *Podarcis muralis* as outgroup (SI Fig. 5). Branch support was obtained by 1,000 bootstrap replicates.

Morphology and Performance.

Snout-vent length, head dimensions, and body mass were measured for 258 adult lizards in the spring of 2004 and 2006 (Pod Kopište, $n = 100$; Pod Mrčaru, $n = 158$). Snout-vent length and head dimensions were measured by using digital calipers, and body mass was measured by using a digital scale. Variables measured included head length, head width, head height, and lower jaw length as overall head size indicators. Additionally, biomechanically relevant measurements including the jaw outlever, the inlever for jaw opening and jaw closing, and snout length were measured as described elsewhere (30). Bite forces were measured in 100 lizards (Pod Kopište, $n = 42$; Pod Mrčaru, $n = 58$) during the spring of 2004 using a Kistler force transducer set in a custom-built holder and connected to a Kistler charge amplifier (30, 31). Lizards were induced to bite the transducer five times, and the maximal value was retained for analysis. All morphological and performance data were log10-transformed before analysis. Divergence rates for morphology and performance were calculated in darwins and haldanes as suggested previously (17).

Diet Analysis.

A total of 330 lizards (Pod Kopište, $n = 119$; Pod Mrčaru, $n = 211$) were stomach-flushed by using previously described methods (30), and stomach contents were stored in 70% ethanol. The stomach contents were analyzed down to order for invertebrate. Plant matter was divided in leaves, seeds, and a rest fraction. All invertebrate prey were measured (±0.01 mm) and weighed (±0.01 mg). Plant fractions were weighed separately, and seeds were both measured and weighed. Unidentifiable items were weighed together as a single group. The relative proportion of plant, arthropod, and the remainder were calculated per individual and arcsine-transformed before analysis.

Lizard Abundance.

To get a relative assessment of lizard abundance, an array of 20 plastic cups was randomly placed across the island and left overnight. The next day lizards were retrieved from the traps, counted, measured, and released.

Acknowledgments

We are indebted to Hendrik Van De Voorde (Royal Belgian Institute of Natural Sciences) for help with DNA sequencing. B.V. is a postdoctoral fellow of the Fund for Scientific Research, Flanders. This work was supported by a research program of the Fund for Scientific Research, Flanders (G.0111.06) and National Science Foundation Grant IOB 0421917 (to D.J.I.).

Edited by Gordon H. Orians, University of Washington, Seattle, WA, and approved January 31, 2008 (received for review December 19, 2007).

Author contributions: A.H., K.H., B.V., T.B., R.V.D., and D.J.I. designed research; A.H., K.H., B.V., I.G., R.V.D., and D.J.I. performed research; A.H., K.H., B.V., T.B., and K.B. analyzed data; and A.H., K.H., B.V., and T.B. wrote the paper.

The authors declare no conflict of interest.

This article is a PNAS Direct Submission.

Data deposition: The sequences reported in this paper have been deposited in the GenBank database [accession nos. EU362067-EU362088 (the 16S rDNA fragment) and EU362089- EU362110 (the 12S rDNA fragment).

This article contains supporting information online at www.pnas.org/cgi/content/full/ 0711998105/DC1.

References

1. Hendry AP, Kinnison MT (1999) The pace of modern life: Measuring rates of contemporary microevolution. *Evolution (Lawrence, Kans)* 53:1637–1653.
2. Carroll SP, Hendry AP, Reznick DN, Fox CW (2007) Evolution on ecological time scales. *Funct Ecol* 21:387–393.
3. Losos JB, Warheit KI, Schoener TW (1997) Adaptive differentiation following experimental island colonization in *Anolis* lizards. *Nature* 387:70–73.
4. Phillips BL, Brown GP, Webb JK, Shine R (2006) Invasion and the evolution of speed in toads. *Nature* 439:803.
5. Reznick DN, Bryga H, Endler JA (1990) Experimentally induced life-history evolution in a natural population. *Nature* 346:357–359.
6. Losos JB, Schoener TW, Spiller DA (2004) Predator-induced behaviour shifts and natural selection in field-experimental lizard populations. *Nature* 432:505–508.
7. Arnold SJ (1983) Morphology, performance and fitness. *Am Zool* 23:347–361.
8. Huey RB, Stevenson RD (1979) Integrating thermal physiology and ecology of ectotherms—discussion of approaches. *Am Zool* 19:357–366.
9. Yoshida T, Jones LE, Ellner SP, Fussman GF, Hairston NG, Jr (2003) Rapid evolution drives ecological dynamics in a predator-prey system. *Nature* 424:303–306.
10. Grant PR, Grant BR (2002) Unpredictable evolution in a 30-year study of Darwin's finches. *Science* 296:707–711.
11. Grant PR, Grant BR (2006) Evolution of character displacement in Darwin's finches. *Science* 313:224–226.
12. Nevo E, *et al.* (1972) Competitive exclusion between insular *Lacerta* species (Sauria, Lacertidae). *Oecologia* 10:183–190.
13. Herrel A, Vanhooydonck B, Van Damme R (2004) Omnivory in lacertid lizards: Adaptive evolution or constraint? *J Evol Biol* 17:974–984.
14. Iverson JB (1980) Colic modifications in iguanine lizards. *J Morphol* 163:79–93.
15. McBee RH (1971) Significance of the intestinal microflora in herbivory. *Annu Rev Ecol Syst* 1:65–176.
16. Troyer K (1984) Diet selection and digestion in *Iguana iguana*: The importance of age and nutrient requirements. *Oecologia* 61:201–207.
17. Kinnison MT, Hendry AP (2001) The pace of modern life II: From rates of contemporary microevolution to pattern and process. *Genetica* 112–113:145–164.
18. Herrel A (2007) in *Foraging Behavior in Lizards,* eds Reilly SM, McBrayer LD, Miles DB (Cambridge Univ Press, Cambridge, UK), pp 209–236.

19. Bjorndal KA, Bolten AB (1992) Body size and digestive efficiency in a herbivorous freshwater turtle: Advantages of a small bite size. *Physiol Zool* 65:1028–1039.
20. Bjorndal KA, Bolten AB, Moore JE (1990) Digestive fermentation in herbivores: Effect of food particle size. *Physiol Zool* 63:710–721.
21. Espinoza RE, Wiens JJ, Tracy CR (2004) Recurrent evolution of herbivory in small cold-climate lizards: Breaking the ecophysiological rules of reptilian herbivory. *Proc Natl Acad Sci USA* 101:16819–16824.
22. Cooper WE, Jr, Vitt LJ (2002) Distribution, extent, and evolution of plant consumption by lizards. *J Zool London* 257:487–517.
23. Vervust B, Grbac I, Van Damme R (2007) Differences in morphology, performance and behaviour between recently diverged populations of *Podarcis sicula* mirror differences in predation pressure. *Oikos* 116:1343–1352.
24. Kocher TD, *et al.* (1989) Dynamics of mitochondrial DNA evolution in animals: Amplification and sequencing with conserved primers. *Proc Natl Acad Sci USA* 86:6196 -6200.
25. Simon C, *et al.* (1994) Evolution, weighting, and phylogenetic utility of mitochondrial gene sequences and a compilation of conserved polymerase chain reaction primers. *Ann Entomol Soc Am* 87:651–701.
26. Hall TA (1999) BioEdit: A user-friendly biological sequence alignment editor and analysis program for Windows 95/98/NT. *Nucleic Acids Symp Ser* 41:95–98.
27. Tamura K, Dudley J, Nei M, Kumar S (2007) MEGA4: Molecular Evolutionary Genetic Analysis (MEGA) software version 4.0. *Mol Biol Evol* 24:1596–1599.
28. Podnar M, Mayer W, Tvrtkovic N (2005) Phylogeography of the Italian wall lizard, *Podarcis sicula*, as revealed by mitochondrial DNA sequences. *Mol Ecol* 14:575–588.
29. Podnar M, Mayer W, Tvrtkovic N (2004) Mitochondrial phylogeography of the Dalmatian wall lizard, *Podarcis melisellensis* (Lacertidae). *Org Div Evol* 4:307–317.
30. Herrel A, Joachim R, Vanhooydonck B, Irschick DJ (2006) Ecological consequences of ontogenetic changes in head shape and bite performance in the Jamaican lizard *Anolis lineatopus*. *Biol J Linn Soc* 89:443–454.
31. Herrel A, Spithoven L, Van Damme R, De Vree F (1999) Sexual dimorphism of head size in *Gallotia galloti*; testing the niche divergence hypothesis by functional analyses. *Funct Ecol* 13:289–297.

SECTION 2

SPECIATION

Introduction to Chapter 3

Evolution might produce relatively rapid change, or it might prevent change for rather long periods of time, but any changes that natural selection favors are likely to be small, incremental changes.

When I listen to a lecture given by another professor, the first thing I ask myself is, "Who (or what position) is the lecturer arguing with?" This is a sensible mindset because the lecturer *is* often arguing against some position that he or she thinks is wrong. In academia we are always trying to show how our ideas are new, different, and better, and this often involves showing how the older ideas are flawed. Einstein showed that Newton's ideas were in some ways inadequate. Students should keep this "argumentative" style of presentation in mind because many of their better professors will lecture this way.

Chapter 3 is this kind presentation. As you can tell by the title, the position that Professor Dawkins argues against is called "punctuationism." Dawkins' argument is actually subtle. He is not arguing that punctuationism is completely wrong. Instead, Dawkins will explain that the label punctuationism has been confusingly and uncritically expanded to include two different ideas. One of these two, "saltationism," he persuasively argues must be wrong. The other is the idea that evolution sometimes happens quickly and sometimes happens very slowly. On this issue, Dawkins thinks the punctuationists are correct, but he chides them for confusing the history of evolutionary thought by pretending that their idea is new.

Throughout this chapter, Dawkins reveals his two finest talents. First, he is an important evolutionary biologist, justly famous for his ground-breaking books such as *The Selfish Gene*. But he also holds an endowed professorship at Oxford University in "the public understanding of science." In other words, his second great talent is that he is a world-class explainer of complex ideas. For this reason, my introduction to this chapter can be brief.

Still, a few comments will be helpful. The argument laid out in this chapter is an argument between punctuationists, such as Stephen Jay Gould and Niles Eldridge, and more mainstream or conventional evolutionists, like Dawkins, Stebbins, Mayr, and especially Darwin himself. (I have to say that I feel odd writing the word "conventional" in association with evolution, one of the most radical scientific ideas of all time!) The argument between these camps is about two related topics: (1) where new species come from, and (2) how we should think about gaps in the fossil record. Gould was a paleontologist, a person who studies fossils. Paleontologists are principally interested in the *history* of life on Earth. Dawkins, Stebbins, and Mayr are not paleontologists. They study the *process* of evolution as it can be observed and measured in our time and the consequences of that process in terms of the adaptive traits of organisms. Darwin himself dug up quite a few fossils and considered them to be important evidence for his theory, but in his writings he was also more of a "process person" than a "history person."

Let's take these two topics—the origin of new species and the gaps in the fossil record—separately. All evolutionists, including the punctuationists, think that new species come from older species by branching. A single ancestral species splits into two descendant species. The question is, how? "Gradualists" believe that surviving offspring were always very much like their parents. In other words, there never were any very big phenotypic changes from one generation to the next—or if there were, these offspring died young! "Saltationists" believe there often were big phenotypic leaps from parent to offspring; or at least they believe that new species often arose as a consequence of such big leaps. A key point of this chapter is that despite their headline-grabbing rhetoric, punctuationists are *not* saltationists; they are gradualists. Saltationism is dead; long dead, for all the logical reasons explained in this chapter.

Turning to the second topic, puntuationists do have something to say about the gaps in the fossil record. But, as Dawkins explains, what they have to say accords very well with the conventional view. That issue is a tempest in a teapot. In other words, in this chapter Dawkins is cleaning up some conceptual and theoretical confusion. As he does so, he paints a very clear picture of a key issue in evolution—the origin of species.

Chapter 3 Glossary

gradualism: The idea that surviving offspring are always very much like their parents and that new species do not emerge as a result of large-scale mutations.

punctuationism: The focus of the chapter; as argued by its creators, an idea that mistakenly confounds saltationism with arguments about rates of evolutionary change and explanations for gaps in the fossil record.

saltationism: The opposite of gradualism; the ideas that new species are founded by offspring that are very different from their parents, and these new species emerge as a result of large-scale mutations.

stasis: Periods, possibly long, during which little evolutionary change is occurring.

Chapter 3
Puncturing Punctuationism

Richard Dawkins

The children of Israel, according to the Exodus story, took 40 years to migrate across the Sinai desert to the promised land. That is a distance of some 200 miles. Their average speed was, therefore, approximately 24 yards per day, or 1 yard per hour; say 3 yards per hour if we allow for night stops. However we do the calculation, we are dealing with an absurdly slow average speed, much slower than the proverbially slow snail's pace (an incredible 55 yards per hour is the speed of the world record snail according to the *Guinness Book of Records*). But of course nobody really believes that the average speed was continuously and uniformly maintained. Obviously the Israelites travelled in fits and starts, perhaps camping for long periods in one spot before moving on. Probably many of them had no very clear idea that they were *travelling* in any particularly consistent direction, and they meandered round and round from oasis to oasis as nomadic desert herdsmen are wont to do. Nobody, I repeat, really believes that the average speed was continuously and uniformly maintained.

But now suppose that two eloquent young historians burst upon the scene. Biblical history so far, they tell us, has been dominated by the 'gradualistic' school of thought. 'Gradualist' historians, we are told, literally believe that the Israelites travelled 24 yards per day; they folded their tents every morning, crawled 24 yards in an east-northeasterly direction, and then pitched camp again. The only alternative to 'gradualism', we are told, is the dynamic new 'punctuationist' school of history. According to the radical young punctuationists, the Israelites spent most of their time in 'stasis', not moving at all but camped, often for years at a time, in one place. Then they would move on, rather fast, to a new encampment, where they again stayed for several years. Their progress towards the promised land, instead of being gradual and continuous, was jerky: long periods of stasis

Richard Dawkins, "Chapter 9: Puncturing Punctuationism," from *The Blind Watchmaker*, pp. 223–252.

punctuated by brief periods of rapid movement. Moreover, their bursts of movement were not always in the direction of the promised land, but were in almost random directions. It is only when we look, with hindsight, at the large scale *macromigrational* pattern, that we can see a trend in the direction of the promised land.

Such is the eloquence of the punctuationist biblical historians that they become a media sensation. Their portraits adorn the front covers of mass circulation news magazines. No television documentary about biblical history is complete without an interview with at least one leading punctuationist. People who know nothing else of biblical scholarship remember just the one fact: that in the dark days before the punctuationists burst upon the scene, everybody else got it wrong. Note that the publicity value of the punctuationists has nothing to do with the fact that they may be right. It has everything to do with the allegation that earlier authorities were 'gradualist' and wrong. It is because the punctuationists sell themselves as revolutionaries that they are listened to, not because they are right.

My story about the punctuationist biblical historians is, of course, not really true. It is a parable about an analogous alleged controversy among students of biological evolution. In some respects it is an unfair parable, but it is not totally unfair and it has enough truth in it to justify its telling at the beginning of this chapter. There is a highly advertised school of thought among evolutionary biologists whose proponents call themselves punctuationists, and they did invent the term 'gradualist' for their most influential predecessors. They have enjoyed enormous publicity, among a public that knows almost nothing else about evolution, and this is largely because their position has been represented, by secondary reporters more than by themselves, as radically different from the positions of previous evolutionists, especially Charles Darwin. So far, my biblical analogy is a fair one.

The respect in which the analogy is unfair is that in the story of the biblical historians 'the gradualists' were *obviously* nonexistent straw men, fabricated by the punctuationists. In the case of the evolutionary 'gradualists', the fact that they are non-existent straw men is not quite so obvious. It needs to be demonstrated. It is possible to interpret the words of Darwin and many other evolutionists as gradualist in intent, but it then becomes important to realize that the word gradualist can be interpreted in different ways to mean different things. Indeed, I shall develop an interpretation of the word 'gradualist' according to which just about everybody is a gradualist. In the evolutionary case, unlike in the parable of the Israelites, there is genuine controversy lurking, but that genuine controversy is about little details which are nowhere near important enough to justify all the media hype.

Among evolutionists, the 'punctuationists' were originally drawn from the ranks of palaeontology. Palaeontology is the study of fossils. It is a very important branch of biology, because evolutionary ancestors all died long ago and fossils provide us with our only direct evidence of the animals and plants of the distant past. If we want to know what our evolutionary ancestors looked like, fossils are our main hope. As soon as people realized what fossils really were—previous schools of thought had held that they were creations of the devil, or that they were the bones of poor sinners drowned in the flood—it became clear that any theory of evolution must have certain expectations about the fossil record. But there has been some discussion of exactly what those expectations are, and this is partly what the punctuationism argument is about.

We are lucky to have fossils at all. It is a remarkably fortunate fact of geology that bones, shells and other hard parts of animals, before they decay, can occasionally leave an imprint which later acts as a mould, which shapes hardening rock into a permanent memory of the animal. We don't know what proportion of animals are fossilized after their death—I personally would consider it an honour to be fossilized—but it is certainly very small indeed. Nevertheless, however small the proportion fossilized, there are certain things about the fossil record that any evolutionist should expect to be true. We should be very surprised, for example, to find fossil humans appearing in the record before mammals are supposed to have evolved! If a single, well-verified mammal skull were to turn up in 500 million year-old rocks, our whole modern theory of evolution would be utterly destroyed. Incidentally, this is a sufficient answer to the canard, put about by creationists and their journalistic fellow travellers, that the whole theory of evolution is an 'unfalsifiable' tautology. Ironically, it is also the reason why creationists are so keen on the fake human footprints, which were carved during the depression to fool tourists, in the dinosaur beds of Texas.

Anyway, if we arrange our genuine fossils in order, from oldest to youngest, the theory of evolution expects to see some sort of orderly sequence rather than a higgledy-piggledy jumble. More to the point in this chapter, different versions of the theory of evolution, for instance 'gradualism' and 'punctuationism', might expect to see different kinds of pattern. Such expectations can be tested only if we have some means of *dating* fossils, or at least of knowing the order in which they were laid down. The problems of dating fossils, and the solutions of these problems, require a brief digression, the first of several for which the reader's indulgence is asked. They are necessary for the explanation of the main theme of the chapter.

We have long known how to arrange fossils in the order in which they were laid down. The method is inherent in the very phrase 'laid down'. More recent fossils are obviously laid down on top of older fossils rather than underneath them, and they therefore lie above them in rock sediments. Occasionally volcanic upheavals can turn a chunk of rock right over and then, of course, the order in which we find fossils as we dig downwards will be exactly reversed; but this is rare enough to be obvious when it occurs. Even though we seldom find a complete historical record as we dig down through the rocks of any one area, a good record can be pieced together from overlapping portions in different areas (actually, although I use the image of 'digging down', palaeontologists seldom literally dig downwards through strata; they are more likely to find fossils exposed by erosion at various depths). Long before they knew how to date fossils in actual millions of years, palaeontologists had worked out a reliable scheme of geological eras, and they knew in great detail which era came before which. Certain kinds of shells are such reliable indicators of the ages of rocks that they are among the main indicators used by oil prospectors in the field. By themselves, however, they can tell us only about the relative ages of rock strata, never their absolute ages.

More recently, advances in physics have given us methods to put absolute dates, in millions of years, on rocks and the fossils that they contain. These methods depend upon the fact that particular radioactive elements decay at precisely known rates. It is as though precision-made miniature stopwatches had been conveniently buried in the rocks. Each stopwatch was started at the moment that it was laid down. All that the palaeontologist has to do is dig it up and read off the time on the dial. Different kinds of radioactive decay-based geological stopwatches run at different rates. The radiocarbon stopwatch buzzes round at a great rate, so fast that, after some thousands of years, its spring is almost wound down and the watch is no longer reliable. It is useful for dating organic material on the archaeological/ historical timescale where we are dealing in hundreds or a few thousands of years, but it is no good for the evolutionary timescale where we are dealing in millions of years.

For the evolutionary timescale other kinds of watch, such as the potassium-argon watch, are suitable. The potassium-argon watch is so slow that it would be unsuitable for the archaeological/ historical timescale. That would be like trying to use the hour hand on an ordinary watch to time an athlete sprinting a hundred yards. For timing the megamarathon that is evolution, on the other hand, something like the potassium-argon watch is just what is needed. Other radioactive 'stopwatches', each with its own characteristic rate of slowing down, are the rubidium-strontium, and the uranium-thorium-lead watches. So, this digression has told us that if a palaeontologist is presented with a fossil, he can usually know when the animal lived, on an absolute timescale of millions of years. We got into this discussion of dating and timing in the first place, you will remember, because we were interested in the expectations about the fossil record that various kinds of evolutionary theory—'punctuationist', 'gradualist', etc.—should have. It is now time to discuss what those various expectations are.

Suppose, first, that nature had been extraordinarily kind to palaeontologists (or perhaps unkind, when you think of the extra work involved), and given them a fossil of every animal that ever lived. If we could indeed look at such a complete fossil record, carefully arranged in chronological order, what should we, as evolutionists, expect to see? Well, if we are 'gradualists', in the sense caricatured in the parable of the Israelites, we should expect something like the following. Chronological sequences of fossils will always exhibit smooth evolutionary trends with fixed rates of change. In other words, if we have three fossils, A, B and C, A being ancestral to B, which is ancestral to C, we should expect B to be proportionately intermediate in form between A and C. For instance, if A had a leg length of 20 inches and C had a leg length of 40 inches, B's legs should be intermediate, their exact length being proportional to the time that elapsed between A's existence and B's.

If we carry the caricature of gradualism to its logical conclusion, just as we calculated the average speed of the Israelites as 24 yards per day, so we can calculate the average rate of lengthening of the legs in the evolutionary line of descent from A to C. If, say, A lived 20 million years earlier than C (to fit this vaguely into reality, the earliest known member of the horse family, *Hyracotherium,* lived about 50 million years ago, and was the size of a terrier), we have an evolutionary growth rate of 20 leg-inches per 20 million years, or one-millionth of an inch per year. Now the caricature of a gradualist is supposed to believe that the legs steadily grew, over the generations, at this very slow rate: say four-millionths of an inch per generation, if we assume a horse-like generation-time of about 4 years. The gradualist is supposed to believe that, through all those millions of generations, individuals with legs four-millionths of an inch longer than the average had an advantage over individuals with legs of average length. To believe this is like believing that the Israelites travelled 24 yards every day across the desert.

The same is true even of one of the fastest known evolutionary changes, the swelling of the human skull from an *Australopithecus*-like ancestor, with a brain volume of about 500 cubic centimetres (cc), to the modern *Homo sapiens*'s average brain volume of about 1,400 cc. This increase of about 900 cc, nearly a tripling in brain volume, has been accomplished in no more than three million years. By evolutionary standards this is a rapid rate of change: the brain seems to swell like a balloon and indeed, seen from some angles, the modern human skull does rather resemble a bulbous, spherical balloon in comparison to the flatter, sloping-browed skull of *Australopithecus.* But if we count up the number of generations in three million years (say about four per century), the average rate of evolution is less than a hundredth of a cubic centimetre per generation. The caricature of a gradualist is supposed to believe that there was a slow and inexorable change, generation by generation, such that in all generations sons were slightly brainier than their fathers, brainier by 0.01 cc. Presumably the extra hundredth of a cubic centimetre is supposed to provide each succeeding generation with a significant survival advantage compared with the previous generation.

But a hundredth of a cubic centimetre is a tiny quantity in comparison to the range of brain sizes that we find among modern humans. It is an often-quoted fact, for instance, that the writer Anatole France—no fool, and a Nobel prizewinner—had a brain size of less than

1,000 cc, while at the other end of the range, brains of 2,000 cc are not unknown: Oliver Cromwell is frequently cited as an example, though I do not know with what authenticity. The average per-generation increment of 0.01 cc, then, which is supposed by the caricature of a gradualist to give a significant survival advantage, is a mere hundred-thousandth part of the *difference* between the brains of Anatole France and Oliver Cromwell! It is fortunate that the caricature of a gradualist does not really exist.

Well, if this kind of gradualist is a non-existent caricature—a windmill for punctuationist lances—is there some other kind of gradualist who really exists and who holds tenable beliefs? I shall show that the answer is yes, and that the ranks of gradualists, in this second sense, include all sensible evolutionists, among them, when you look carefully at their beliefs, those that call themselves punctuationists. But we have to understand why the punctuationists *thought* that their views were revolutionary and exciting. The starting point for discussing these matters is the apparent existence of 'gaps' in the fossil record, and it is to these gaps that we now turn.

From Darwin onwards evolutionists have realized that, if we arrange all our available fossils in chronological order, they do *not* form a smooth sequence of scarcely perceptible change. We can, to be sure, discern long-term trends of change—legs get progressively longer, skulls get progressively more bulbous, and so on—but the trends as seen in the fossil record are usually jerky, not smooth. Darwin, and most others following him, have assumed that this is mainly because the fossil record is imperfect. Darwin's view was that a complete fossil record, if only we had one, *would* show gentle rather than jerky change. But since fossilization is such a chancy business, and finding such fossils as there are is scarcely less chancy, it is as though we had a cine film with most of the frames missing. We can, to be sure, see movement of a kind when we project our film of fossils, but it is more jerky than Charlie Chaplin, for even the oldest and scratchiest Charlie Chaplin film hasn't completely lost nine-tenths of its frames.

The American palaeontologists Niles Eldredge and Stephen Jay Gould, when they first proposed their theory of punctuated equilibria in 1972, made what has since been represented as a very different suggestion. They suggested that, actually, the fossil record may not be as imperfect as we thought. Maybe the 'gaps' are a true reflection of what really happened, rather than being the annoying but inevitable consequences of an imperfect fossil record. Maybe, they suggested, evolution really did in some sense go in sudden bursts, punctuating long periods of 'stasis', when no evolutionary change took place in a given lineage.

Before we come to the sort of sudden bursts that they had in mind, there are some conceivable meanings of 'sudden bursts' that they most definitely did not have in mind. These must be cleared out of the way because they have been the subject of serious misunderstandings. Eldredge and Gould certainly would agree that some very important gaps really are due to imperfections in the fossil record. Very big gaps, too. For example the Cambrian strata of rocks, vintage about 600 million years, are the oldest ones in which we find most of the major invertebrate groups. And we find many of them already in an advanced state of evolution, the very first time they appear. It is as though they were just planted there, without any evolutionary history. Needless to say, this appearance of sudden planting has delighted creationists. Evolutionists of all stripes believe, however, that this really does represent a very large gap in the fossil record, a gap that is simply due to the fact that, for some reason, very few fossils have lasted from periods before about 600 million years ago. One good reason might be that many of these animals had only soft parts to their bodies: no shells or bones to fossilize. If you are a creationist you may think that this is special pleading. My point here is that, when we are talking about gaps of this magnitude, there is no difference whatever in the interpretations of 'punctuationists' and 'gradualists'. Both schools of thought despise so-called scientific creationists equally, and both agree that the *major* gaps are real, that they are true imperfections in the fossil record. Both schools of thought agree that the only alternative explanation of the sudden appearance of so many complex animal types in the Cambrian era is divine creation, and both would reject this alternative.

There is another conceivable sense in which evolution might be said to go in sudden jerks, but which is also not the sense being proposed by Eldredge and Gould, at least in most of their writings. It is conceivable that some of the apparent 'gaps' in the fossil record really do reflect sudden change in a single generation. It is conceivable that there really never were any intermediates; conceivable that large evolutionary changes took place in a single generation. A son might be born so different from his father that he properly belongs in a different species from his father. He would be a mutant individual, and the mutation would be such a large one that we should refer to it as a macromutation. Theories of evolution that depend upon macromutation are called 'saltation' theories, from *saltus*, the Latin for 'jump'. Since the theory of punctuated equilibria frequently is confused with true saltation, it is important here to discuss saltation, and show why it cannot be a significant factor in evolution.

Macromutations—mutations of large effect—undoubtedly occur. What is at issue is not whether they occur but whether they play a role in evolution; whether, in other words, they are incorporated into the gene pool of a species, or whether, on the contrary, they are always eliminated by natural selection. A famous example of a macromutation is 'antennapaedia' in fruitflies. In a normal insect the antennae have something in common with the legs, and they develop in the embryo in a similar way. But the differences are striking as well, and the two sorts of limb are used for very different purposes: the legs for walking; the antennae for feeling, smelling and otherwise sensing things. Antennapaedic flies are freaks in which the antennae develop just like legs. Or, another way of putting it, they are flies that have no antennae but an extra pair of legs, growing out of the sockets where the antennae ought to be. This is a true mutation in that it results from an error in the copying of DNA. And it breeds true if antennapaedic flies are cosseted in the laboratory so that they survive long enough to breed at all. They would not survive long in the wild, as their movements are clumsy and their vital senses are impaired.

So, macromutations do happen. But do they play a role in evolution? People called saltationists believe that macromutations are a means by which major jumps in evolution could take place in a single generation. If saltationism were true, apparent 'gaps' in the fossil record needn't be gaps at all. For example, a saltationist might believe that the transition from sloping-browed *Australopithecus* to dome-browed *Homo sapiens* took place in a single macromutational step, in a single generation. The difference in form between the two species is probably less than the difference between a normal and an antennapaedic fruitfly, and it is theoretically conceivable that the first *Homo sapiens* was a freak child—probably an ostracized and persecuted one—of two normal *Australopithecus* parents.

There are very good reasons for rejecting all such saltationist theories of evolution. One rather boring reason is that if a new species really did arise in a single mutational step, members of the new species might have a hard time finding mates. But I find this reason less telling and interesting than two others which have already been foreshadowed in our discussion of why major jumps across Biomorph Land are to be ruled out. The first of these points was put by the great statistician and biologist R. A. Fisher. Fisher was a stalwart opponent of all forms of saltationism, at a time when saltationism was much more fashionable than it is today, and he used the following analogy. Think, he said, of a microscope which is almost, but not quite perfectly, in focus and otherwise well adjusted for distinct vision. What are the odds that, if we make some random change to the state of the microscope (corresponding to a mutation), we shall improve the focus and general quality of the image? Fisher said:

> It is sufficiently obvious that any large derangement will have a very small probability of improving the adjustment, while in the case of alterations much less than the smallest of those intentionally effected by the maker or the operator, the chance of improvement should be almost exactly one half.

I have already remarked that what Fisher found 'easy to see' could place formidable demands on the mental powers of ordinary scientists, and the same is true of what Fisher thought was 'sufficiently obvious'. Nevertheless, further cogitation almost always shows him to have been right, and in this case we can prove it to our own satisfaction without too much difficulty. Remember that we are assuming the microscope to be almost in correct focus before we start. Suppose that the lens is slightly lower than it ought to be for perfect focus, say a tenth of an inch too close to the slide. Now if we move it a small amount, say a hundredth of an inch, in a random direction, what are the odds that the focus will improve? Well, if we happen to move it *down* a hundredth of an inch, the focus will get worse. If we happen to move it *up* a hundredth of an inch, the focus will get better. Since we are moving it in a random direction, the chance of each of these two eventualities is one half. The smaller the movement of adjustment, in relation to the initial error, the closer will the chance of improvement approach one half. That completes the justification of the second part of Fisher's statement.

But now, suppose we move the microscope tube a large distance—equivalent to a macromutation—also in a random direction; suppose we move it a full inch. Now it doesn't matter which direction we move it in, up or down, we shall still make the focus worse than it was before. If we chance to move it down, it will now be one and one-tenth inches away from its ideal position (and will probably have crunched through the slide). If we chance to move it up, it will now be nine-tenths of an inch away from its ideal position. Before the move, it was only one-tenth of an inch away from its ideal position so, either way, our 'macromutational' big move has been a bad thing. We have done the calculation for a very big move ('macromutation') and a very small move ('micromutation'). We can obviously do the same calculation for a range of intermediate sizes of move, but there is no point in doing so. I think it really will now be sufficiently obvious that the smaller we make the move, the closer we shall approach the extreme case in which the odds of an improvement are one-half; and the larger we make the move, the closer we shall approach the extreme case in which the odds of an improvement are zero.

The reader will have noticed that this argument depends upon the initial assumption that the microscope was already pretty close to being in focus before we even started making random adjustments. If the microscope starts 2 inches out of focus, then a random change of 1 inch has a 50 percent chance of being an improvement, just as a random change of one-hundredth of an inch has. In this case the 'macromutation' appears to have the advantage that it moves the microscope into focus more quickly. Fisher's argument will, of course, apply here to 'megamutations' of, say, 6 inches movement in a random direction.

Why, then, was Fisher allowed to make his initial assumption that the microscope was nearly in focus at the start? The assumption flows from the role of the microscope in the analogy. The microscope after its random adjustment stands for a mutant animal. The microscope before its random adjustment stands for the normal, unmutated parent of the supposed mutant animal. Since it is a parent, it must have survived long enough to reproduce, and therefore it cannot be all that far from being well-adjusted. By the same token, the microscope before the random jolt cannot be all that far from being in focus, or the animal that it stands for in the analogy couldn't have survived at all. It is only an analogy, and there is no point in arguing over whether 'all that far' means an inch or a tenth of an inch or a thousandth of an inch. The important point is that if we consider mutations of ever-increasing magnitude, there will come a point when, the larger the mutation is, the less likely it is to be beneficial; while if we consider mutations of ever-decreasing magnitude, there will come a point when the chance of a mutation's being beneficial is 50 per cent.

The argument over whether macromutations such as antennapaedia could ever be beneficial (or at least could avoid being harmful), and therefore whether they could give rise to evolutionary change, therefore turns on *how* 'macro' the mutation is that we are considering. The more 'macro' it is, the more likely it is to be deleterious, and the less likely it is to be incorporated in the evolution of a species. As a matter of fact, virtually all the mutations studied in genetics laboratories—which are pretty macro because otherwise geneticists wouldn't notice them—are deleterious to the animals possessing them (ironically I've met people who think that this is an argument *against* Darwinism!). Fisher's microscope argument, then, provides one reason for scepticism about 'saltation' theories of evolution, at least in their extreme form.

The other general reason for not believing in true saltation is also a statistical one, and its force also depends quantitatively on *how* macro is the macromutation we are postulating. In this case it is concerned with the complexity of evolutionary changes. Many, though not all, of the evolutionary changes we are interested in are advances in complexity of design. The extreme example of the eye, discussed in earlier chapters, makes the point clear. Animals with eyes like ours evolved from ancestors with no eyes at all. An extreme saltationist might postulate that the evolution took place in a single mutational step. A parent had no eye at all, just bare skin where the eye might be. He had a freak offspring with a fully developed eye, complete with variable focus lens, iris diaphragm for 'stopping down', retina with millions of three-colour photocells, all with nerves correctly connected up in the brain to provide him with correct, binocular, stereoscopic colour vision.

In the biomorph model we assumed that this kind of multidimensional improvement could not occur. To recapitulate on why that was a reasonable assumption, to make an eye from nothing you need not just one improvement but a large number of improvements. Any one of these improvements is pretty improbable by itself, but not so improbable as to be impossible. The greater the number of simultaneous improvements we consider, the more improbable is their simultaneous occurrence. The coincidence of their simultaneous occurrence is equivalent to leaping a large distance across Biomorph Land, and happening to land on one particular, predesignated spot. If we choose to consider a sufficiently large number of improvements, their joint occurrence becomes so improbable as to be, to all intents and purposes, impossible. The argument has already been sufficiently made, but it may be helpful to draw a distinction between two kinds of hypothetical macromutation, both of which *appear* to be ruled out by the complexity argument but only one of which, in fact, is ruled out by the complexity argument. I label them, for reasons that will become clear, Boeing 747 macromutations and Stretched DC8 macromutations.

Boeing 747 macromutations are the ones that really are ruled out by the complexity argument just given. They get their name from the astronomer Sir Fred Hoyle's memorable misunderstanding of the theory of natural selection. He compared natural selection, in its alleged improbability, to a hurricane blowing through a junkyard and chancing to assemble a Boeing 747. This is an entirely false analogy to apply to natural selection, but it is a very good analogy for the idea of certain kinds of macromutation giving rise to evolutionary change. Indeed, Hoyle's fundamental error was that he, in effect, thought (without realizing it) that the theory of natural selection *did* depend upon macromutation. The idea of a single macromutation's giving rise to a fully functioning eye with the properties listed above, where there was only bare skin before, is, indeed, just about as improbable as a hurricane assembling a Boeing 747. This is why I refer to this kind of hypothetical macromutation as a Boeing 747 macromutation.

Stretched DC8 macromutations are mutations that, although they may be large in the magnitude of their effects, turn out not to be large in terms of their complexity. The Stretched DC8 is an airliner that was made by modifying an earlier airliner, the DC8. It is like a DC8, but with an elongated fuselage. It was an improvement at least from one point of view, in that it could carry more passengers than the original DC8. The stretching is a large increase in length, and in that sense is analogous to a macromutation. More interestingly, the increase in length is, at first sight, a complex one. To elongate the fuselage of an airliner, it is not enough just to insert an extra length of cabin tube. You also have to elongate countless ducts, cables, air tubes and electric wires. You have to put in lots more seats, ashtrays, reading lights, 12-channel music selectors and fresh-air nozzles. At first sight there seems to be much more complexity in a Stretched DC8 than there is in an ordinary DC8, but is there really? The answer is no, at least to the extent that the 'new' things in the stretched plane are just 'more of the same'.

What has this to do with mutations in real animals? The answer is that some real mutations cause large changes that are very like the change from DC8 to Stretched DC8, and some of these, although in a sense 'macro' mutations, have definitely been incorporated in evolution. Snakes, for instance, all have many more vertebrae than their ancestors. We could be sure of this even if we didn't have any fossils, because snakes have many more vertebrae than their surviving relatives. Moreover, different species of snakes have different numbers of vertebrae, which means that vertebral number must have changed in evolution since their common ancestor, and quite often at that.

Now, to change the number of vertebrae in an animal, you need to do more than just shove in an extra bone. Each vertebra has, associated with it, a set of nerves, a set of blood vessels, a set of muscles etc., just as each row of seats in an airliner has a set of cushions, a set of head rests, a set of headphone sockets, a set of reading-lights with their associated cables etc. The middle part of the body of a snake, like the middle part of the body of an airliner, is composed of a number of *segments*, many of which are exactly like each other, however complex they all individually may be. Therefore, in order to add new segments, all that has to be done is a simple process of duplication. Since there already exists genetic machinery for making one snake segment—genetic machinery of great complexity, which took many generations of step-by-step, gradual evolution to build up—new identical segments may easily be added by a single mutational step. If we think of genes as 'instructions to a developing embryo', a gene for inserting extra segments may read, simply, 'more of the same here'. I imagine that the instructions for building the first Stretched DC8 were somewhat similar.

We can be sure that, in the evolution of snakes, numbers of vertebrae changed in whole numbers rather than in fractions. We cannot imagine a snake with 26.3 vertebrae. It either had 26 or 27, and it is obvious that there must have been cases when an offspring snake had at least one whole vertebra more than its parents did. This means that it had a whole extra set of nerves, blood vessels, muscle blocks, etc. In a sense, then, this snake was a *macro*-mutant, but only in the weak 'Stretched DC8' sense. It is easy to believe that individual snakes with half a dozen more vertebrae than their parents could have arisen in a single mutational step. The 'complexity argument' against saltatory evolution does not apply to Stretched DC8 macromutations because, if we look in detail at the nature of the change involved, they are in a real sense not true macromutations at all. They are only macromutations if we look, naïvely, at the finished product, the adult. If we look at the *processes* of embryonic development they turn out to be micromutations, in the sense that only a small change in the embryonic *instructions* had a large apparent effect in the adult. The same goes for antennapaedia in fruitflies and the many other so-called 'homeotic mutations'.

This concludes my digression on macromutation and saltatory evolution. It was necessary, because the theory of punctuated equilibria is frequently confused with saltatory evolution. But it *was* a digression, because the theory of punctuated equilibria is the main topic of this chapter, and that theory in truth has no connection with macromutation and true saltation.

The 'gaps' that Eldredge and Gould and the other 'punctuationists' are talking about, then, have nothing to do with true saltation, and they are much much smaller gaps than the ones that excite creationists. Moreover, Eldredge and Gould originally introduced their theory, *not* as radically and revolutionarily antipathetic to ordinary, 'conventional' Darwinism—which is how it later came to be sold—but as something that *followed* from long-accepted conventional Darwinism, properly understood. To gain this proper understanding, I'm afraid we need another digression, this time into the question of how new species originate, the process known as 'speciation'.

Darwin's answer to the question of the origin of species was, in a general sense, that species were descended from other species. Moreover, the family tree of life is a branching one, which means that more than one modern species can be traced back to one ancestral one. For instance, lions and tigers are now members of different species, but they have both sprung from a single ancestral species, probably not very long ago. This ancestral species may have been the same as one of the two modern species; or it may have been a third modern species; or maybe it is now extinct. Similarly, humans and chimps now clearly belong to different species, but their ancestors of a few million years ago belonged to one single species. Speciation is the process by which a single species becomes two species, one of which may be the same as the original single one.

The reason speciation is thought to be a difficult problem is this. All the members of the single would-be ancestral species are capable of interbreeding with one another: indeed, to many people, this is what is *meant* by the phrase 'single species'. Therefore, every time a new daughter species begins to be 'budded off', the budding off is in danger of being frustrated by interbreeding. We can imagine the would-be ancestors of the lions and the would-be ancestors of the tigers failing to split apart because they keep interbreeding with one another and therefore staying similar to one another. Don't, incidentally, read too much into my use of words like 'frustrated', as though the ancestral lions and tigers, in some sense, 'wanted' to separate from each other. It is simply that, as a matter of fact, species obviously *have* diverged from one another in evolution, and at first sight the fact of interbreeding makes it hard for us to see how this divergence came about.

It seems almost certain that the principal correct answer to this problem is the obvious one. There will be no problem of interbreeding if the ancestral lions and the ancestral tigers happen to be in different parts of the world, where they can't interbreed with each other.

Of course, they didn't go to different continents in order to allow themselves to diverge from one another: they didn't think of themselves as ancestral lions or ancestral tigers! But, given that the single ancestral species spread to different continents anyway, say Africa and Asia, the ones that happened to be in Africa could no longer interbreed with the ones that happened to be in Asia because they never met them. If there was any tendency for the animals on the two continents to evolve in different directions, either under the influence of natural selection or under the influence of chance, interbreeding no longer constituted a barrier to their diverging and eventually becoming two distinct species.

I have spoken of different continents to make it clear, but the principle of geographical separation as a barrier to interbreeding can apply to animals on different sides of a desert, a mountain range, a river, or even a motorway. It can also apply to animals separated by no barrier other than sheer distance. Shrews in Spain cannot interbreed with shrews in Mongolia, and they can diverge, evolutionarily speaking, from shrews in Mongolia, even if there is an unbroken chain of interbreeding shrews connecting Spain to Mongolia. Nevertheless the idea of geographical separation as the key to speciation is clearer if we think in terms of an actual physical barrier, such as the sea or a mountain range. Chains of islands, indeed, are probably fertile nurseries for new species.

Here, then, is our orthodox neo-Darwinian picture of how a typical species is 'born', by divergence from an ancestral species. We start with the ancestral species, a large population of rather uniform, mutually interbreeding animals, spread over a large land mass. They could be any sort of animal, but let's carry on thinking of shrews. The landmass is cut in two by a mountain range. This is hostile country and the shrews are unlikely to cross it, but it is not quite impossible and very occasionally one or two do end up in the lowlands on the other side. Here they can flourish, and they give rise to an outlying population of the species, effectively cut off from the main population. Now the two populations breed and breed separately, mixing their genes on each side of the mountains but not across the mountains. As time goes by, any changes in the genetic composition of one population are spread by breeding throughout that population but *not* across to the other population. Some of these changes may be brought about by natural selection, which may be different on the two sides of the mountain range: we should hardly expect weather conditions, and predators and parasites, to be exactly the same on the two sides. Some of the changes may be due to chance alone. Whatever the genetic changes are due to, breeding tends to spread them *within* each of the two populations, but not *between* the two populations. So the two populations diverge genetically: they become progressively more unlike each other.

They become so unlike each other that, after a while, naturalists would see them as belonging to different 'races'. After a longer time, they will have diverged so far that we should classify them as different species. Now imagine that the climate warms up so that travel through the mountain passes becomes easier and some of the new species start trickling back to their ancestral homelands. When they meet the descendants of their long-lost cousins, it turns out that they have diverged so far in their genetic makeup that they can no longer successfully interbreed with them. If they do hybridize with them the resulting offspring are sickly, or sterile like mules. So natural selection penalizes any predilection, on the part of individuals on either side, towards hybridizing with the other species or even race. Natural selection thereby finishes off the process of 'reproductive isolation' that began with the chance intervention of a mountain range. 'Speciation' is complete. We now have two species where previously there was one, and the two species can coexist in the same area without interbreeding with one another.

Actually, the likelihood is that the two species would not coexist for very long. This is not because they would interbreed but because they would compete. It is a widely accepted principle of ecology that two species with the same way of life will not coexist for long in one place, because they will compete and one or other will be driven extinct. Of course our two populations of shrews might no longer have the same way of life; for instance, the new species, during its period of evolution on the other side of the mountains, might have come to specialize on a different kind of insect prey. But if there is significant competition between the two species, most ecologists would expect one or other species to go extinct in the area of overlap. If it happened to be the original, ancestral species that was driven extinct, we should say that it had been replaced by the new, immigrant species.

The theory of speciation resulting from initial geographical separation has long been a cornerstone of mainstream, orthodox neo-Darwinism, and it is still accepted on all sides as the main process by which new species come into existence (some people think there are others as well). Its incorporation into modern Darwinism was largely due to the influence of the distinguished zoologist Ernst Mayr. What the 'punctuationists' did, when they first proposed their theory, was to ask themselves: Given that, like most neo-Darwinians, we accept the orthodox theory that speciation starts with geographical isolation, what should we expect to see in the fossil record?

Recall the hypothetical population of shrews, with a new species diverging on the far side of a mountain range, then eventually returning to the ancestral homelands and, quite possibly, driving the ancestral species extinct. Suppose that these shrews had left fossils; suppose even that the fossil record was *perfect,* with no gaps due to the unfortunate omission of key stages. What should we expect these fossils to show us? A smooth transition from ancestral species to daughter species? Certainly not, at least if we are digging in the main landmass where the original ancestral shrews lived, and to which the new species returned. Think of the history of what actually happened in the main landmass. There were the ancestral shrews, living and breeding happily away, with no particular reason to change.

Admittedly their cousins the other side of the mountains were busy evolving, but their fossils are all on the other side of the mountain so we don't find them in the main landmass where we are digging. Then, suddenly (suddenly by geological standards, that is), the new species returns, competes with the main species and, perhaps, replaces the main species. Suddenly the fossils that we find as we move up through the strata of the main landmass change. Previously they were all of the ancestral species. Now, abruptly and without visible transitions, fossils of the new species appear, and fossils of the old species disappear.

The 'gaps', far from being annoying imperfections or awkward embarrassments, turn out to be exactly what we should positively *expect,* if we take seriously our orthodox neo-Darwinian theory of speciation. The reason the 'transition' from ancestral species to descendant species appears to be abrupt and jerky is simply that, when we look at a series of fossils from any one place, we are probably not looking at an *evolutionary* event at all: we are looking at a *migrational* event, the arrival of a new species from another geographical area. Certainly there were evolutionary events, and one species really did evolve, probably gradually, from another. But in order to see the evolutionary transition documented in the fossils we should have to dig elsewhere—in this case on the other side of the mountains.

The point that Eldredge and Gould were making, then, could have been modestly presented as a helpful rescuing of Darwin and his successors from what had seemed to them an awkward difficulty. Indeed that is, at least in part, how it *was* presented—initially. Darwinians had always been bothered by the apparent gappiness of the fossil record, and had seemed forced to resort to special pleading about imperfect evidence. Darwin himself had written:

> The geological record is extremely imperfect and this fact will to a large extent explain why we do not find interminable varieties, connecting together all the extinct and existing forms of life by the finest graduated steps. He who rejects these views on the nature of the geological record, will rightly reject my whole theory.

Eldredge and Gould could have made this their main message: Don't worry Darwin, even if the fossil record *were* perfect you shouldn't expect to see a finely graduated progression if you only dig in one place, for the simple reason that most of the evolutionary change took place somewhere else! They could have gone further and said:

> Darwin, when you said that the fossil record was imperfect, you were understating it. Not only is it imperfect, there are good reasons for expecting it to be *particularly* imperfect just when it gets interesting, just when evolutionary change is taking place; this is partly because evolution usually occurred in a different place from where we find most of our fossils; and it is partly because, even if we are fortunate enough to dig in one of the small

> outlying areas where most evolutionary change went on, that evolutionary change (though still gradual) occupies such a short time that we should need an extra *rich* fossil record in order to track it!

But no, instead they chose, especially in their later writings in which they were eagerly followed by journalists, to sell their ideas as being radically *opposed* to Darwin's and opposed to the neo-Darwinian synthesis. They did this by emphasizing the 'gradualism' of the Darwinian view of evolution as opposed to the sudden, jerky, sporadic 'punctuationism' of their own. They even, especially Gould, saw analogies between themselves and the old schools of 'catastrophism and 'saltationism'. Saltationism we have already discussed. Catastrophism was an eighteenth- and nineteenth-century attempt to reconcile some form of creationism with the uncomfortable facts of the fossil record. Catastrophists believed that the apparent progression of the fossil record really reflected a series of discrete creations, each one terminated by a catastrophic mass extinction. The latest of these catastrophes was Noah's flood.

Comparisons between modern punctuationism on the one hand, and catastrophism or saltationism on the other, have a purely poetic force. They are, if I may coin a paradox, deeply superficial. They sound impressive in an artsy, literary way, but they do nothing to aid serious understanding, and they can give spurious aid and comfort to modern creationists in their disturbingly successful fight to subvert American education and textbook publishing. The fact is that, in the fullest and most serious sense, Eldredge and Gould are really just as gradualist as Darwin or any of his followers. It is just that they would compress all the gradual change into brief bursts, rather than having it go on all the time; and they emphasize that most of the gradual change goes on in geographical areas away from the areas where most fossils are dug up.

So, it is not really the *gradualism* of Darwin that the punctuationists oppose: gradualism means that each generation is only slightly different from the previous generation; you would have to be a saltationist to oppose that, and Eldredge and Gould are not saltationists. Rather, it turns out to be Darwin's alleged belief in the constancy of rates of evolution that they and the other punctuationists object to. They object to it because they think that evolution (still undeniably gradualistic evolution) occurs rapidly during relatively brief bursts of activity (speciation events, which provide a kind of crisis atmosphere in which the alleged normal resistance to evolutionary change is broken); and that evolution occurs very slowly or not at all during long intervening periods of stasis. When we say 'relatively' brief we mean, of course, brief relative to the geological timescale in general. Even the evolutionary jerks of the punctuationists, though they may be instantaneous, by geological standards, still have a duration that is measured in tens or hundreds of thousands of years.

A thought of the famous American evolutionist G. Ledyard Stebbins is illuminating at this point. He isn't specifically concerned with jerky evolution, but is just seeking to dramatize the speed with which evolutionary change can happen, when seen against the timescale of available geological time. He imagines a species of animal, of about the size of a mouse. He then supposes that natural selection starts to favour an increase in body size, but only very very slightly. Perhaps larger males enjoy a slight advantage in the competition for females. At any time, males of average size are slightly less successful than males that are a tiny bit bigger than average. Stebbins put an exact figure on the mathematical advantage enjoyed by larger individuals in his hypothetical example. He set it at a value so very very tiny that it wouldn't be measurable by human observers. And the rate of evolutionary change that it brings about is consequently so slow that it wouldn't be noticed during an ordinary human lifetime. As far as the scientist studying evolution on the ground is concerned, then, these animals are not evolving at all. Nevertheless they are evolving, very slowly at a rate given by Stebbins's mathematical assumption, and, even at this slow rate, they would eventually reach the size of elephants. How long would this take? Obviously a long time by human standards, but human standards aren't relevant. We are talking about geological time. Stebbins calculates that at his assumed very slow rate of evolution, it would take about 12,000 generations for the animals to evolve from an average weight of 40 grams (mouse size) to an average weight of over 6,000,000 grams (elephant size). Assuming a generation-time of 5 years, which is longer than that of a mouse but shorter than that of an elephant, 12,000 generations would occupy about 60,000 years. 60,000 years is too *short* to be measured by ordinary geological methods of dating the fossil record. As Stebbins says, 'The origin of a new kind of animal in 100,000 years or less is regarded by paleontologists as "sudden" or "instantaneous".'

The punctuationists aren't talking about jumps in evolution, they are talking about episodes of relatively rapid evolution. And even these episodes don't have to be rapid by human standards, in order to appear instantaneous by geological standards. Whatever we may think of the theory of punctuated equilibria itself, it is all too easy to confuse gradualism (the belief, held by modern punctuationists as well as Darwin, that there are no sudden leaps between one generation and the next) with 'constant evolutionary speedism' (opposed by punctuationists and allegedly, though not actually, held by Darwin). They are not the same thing at all. The proper way to characterize the beliefs of punctuationists is: 'gradualistic, but with long periods of "stasis" (evolutionary stagnation) punctuating brief episodes of rapid gradual change'. The emphasis is then thrown onto the long periods of *stasis* as being the previously overlooked phenomenon that really needs explaining. It is the emphasis on stasis that is the punctuationists' real contribution, not their claimed opposition to gradualism, for they are truly as gradualist as anybody else.

Even the emphasis on stasis can be found, in less-exaggerated form, in Mayr's theory of speciation. He believed that, of the two geographically separated races, the original large ancestral population is less likely to change than the new, 'daughter' population (on the other side of the mountains in the case of our shrew example). This is not just because the daughter population is the one that has moved to new pastures, where conditions are likely to be different and natural selection pressures changed. It is also because there are some theoretical reasons (which Mayr emphasized but whose importance can be disputed) for thinking that large breeding populations have an inherent tendency to *resist* evolutionary change. A suitable analogy is the inertia of a large heavy object; it is hard to shift. Small, outlying populations, by virtue of being small, are inherently more likely, so the theory goes, to change, to evolve. Therefore, although I spoke of the two populations or races of shrews as diverging from each other, Mayr would prefer to see the original, ancestral population as relatively static, and the new population as diverging from it. The branch of the evolutionary tree does not fork into two equal twigs: rather, there is a main stem with a side twig sprouting from it.

The proponents of punctuated equilibrium took this suggestion of Mayr, and exaggerated it into a strong belief that 'stasis', or lack of evolutionary change, is the norm for a species. They believe that there are genetic forces in large populations that actively *resist* evolutionary change. Evolutionary change, for them, is a rare event, coinciding with speciation. It coincides with speciation in the sense that, in their view, the conditions under which new species are formed—geographical separation of small, isolated subpopulations—are the very conditions under which the forces that normally resist evolutionary change are relaxed or overthrown. Speciation is a time of upheaval, or revolution. And it is during these times of upheaval that evolutionary change is concentrated. For most of the history of a lineage it stagnates.

It isn't true that Darwin believed that evolution proceeded at a constant rate. He certainly didn't believe it in the ludicrously extreme sense that I satirized in my parable of the children of Israel, and I don't think he really believed it in any important sense. Quotation of the following well-known passage from the fourth edition (and later editions) of *The Origin of Species* annoys Gould because he thinks it is unrepresentative of Darwin's general thought:

> Many species once formed never undergo any further change ... ; and the periods, during which species have undergone modification, though long as measured by years, have probably been short in comparison with the periods during which they retain the same form.

Gould wants to shrug off this sentence and others like it, saying:

> You cannot do history by selective quotation and search for qualifying footnotes. General tenor and historical impact are the proper criteria. Did his contemporaries or descendants ever read Darwin as a saltationist?

Gould is right, of course, about general tenor and historical impact, but the final sentence of this quotation from him is a highly revealing *faux pas. Of course,* nobody has ever read Darwin as a saltationist and, of course, Darwin was consistently hostile to saltationism, but the whole point is that saltationism is not the issue when we are discussing punctuated equilibrium. As I have stressed, the theory of punctuated equilibrium, by Eldredge and Gould's own account, is not a saltationist theory. The jumps that it postulates are not real, single-generation jumps. They are spread out over large numbers of generations over periods of, by Gould's own estimation, perhaps tens of thousands of years. The theory of punctuated equilibrium is a gradualist theory, albeit it emphasizes long periods of stasis intervening between *relatively* short bursts of gradualistic evolution. Gould has misled himself by his own rhetorical emphasis on the purely poetic or literary resemblance between punctuationism, on the one hand, and true saltationism on the other.

I think it would clarify matters if, at this point, I summarized a range of possible points of view about rates of evolution. Out on a limb we have true saltationism, which I have already discussed sufficiently. True saltationists don't exist among modern biologists. Everyone that is not a saltationist is a gradualist, and this includes Eldredge and Gould, however they may choose to describe themselves. Within gradualism, we may distinguish various beliefs about rates of (gradual) evolution. Some of these beliefs, as we have seen, bear a purely superficial ('literary' or 'poetic') resemblance to true, anti-gradualist saltationism, which is why they are sometimes confused with it.

At another extreme we have the sort of 'constant speedism' that I caricatured in the Exodus parable with which I began this chapter. An extreme constant speedist believes that evolution is plodding along steadily and inexorably all the time, whether or not there is any branching or speciation going on. He believes that quantity of evolutionary change is strictly proportional to time elapsed. Ironically, a form of constant speedism has recently become highly favoured among modern molecular geneticists. A good case can be made for believing that evolutionary change at the level of protein molecules really does plod along at a constant rate exactly like the hypothetical children of Israel; and this *even if* externally visible characteristics like arms and legs are evolving in a highly punctuated manner. But as far as adaptive evolution of large-scale structures and behaviour patterns are concerned, just about all evolutionists would reject constant speedism, and Darwin certainly would have rejected it. Everyone that is not a constant speedist is a variable speedist.

Within variable speedism we may distinguish two kinds of belief, labelled, 'discrete variable speedism' and 'continuously variable speedism'. An extreme 'discretist' not only believes that evolution varies in speed. He thinks that the speed flips abruptly from one discrete level to another, like a car's gearbox. He might believe, for instance, that evolution has only two speeds: very fast and stop (I cannot help being reminded here of the humiliation of my first school report, written by the Matron about my performance as a seven-year-old in folding clothes, taking cold baths, and other daily routines of boarding-school life: 'Dawkins has only three speeds: slow, very slow, and stop'). 'Stopped' evolution is the 'stasis' that is thought by punctuationists to characterize large populations. Top-gear evolution is the evolution that goes on during speciation, in small isolated populations round the edge of large, evolutionarily static populations. According to this view, evolution is always in one or other of the two gears, never in between. Eldredge and Gould tend in the direction of discretism, and in this respect they are genuinely radical. They may be called 'discrete variable speedists'. Incidentally, there is no *particular* reason why a discrete variable speedist should necessarily emphasize speciation as the time of high-gear evolution. In practice, however, most of them do.

'Continuously variable speedists', on the other hand, believe that evolutionary rates fluctuate continuously from very fast to very slow and stop, with all intermediates. They see no particular reason to emphasize certain speeds more than others. In particular, stasis, to them, is just an extreme case of ultra-slow evolution. To a punctuationist, there is something very special about stasis. Stasis, to him, is not just evolution that is so slow as to have a rate of zero: stasis is not just passive lack of evolution because there is no driving force in favour of change. Rather, stasis represents a positive *resistance* to evolutionary change. It is almost as though species are thought to take active steps *not* to evolve, *in spite of* driving forces in favour of evolution.

More biologists agree that stasis is a real phenomenon than agree about its causes. Take, as an extreme example, the coelacanth *Latimeria*. The coelacanths were a large group of 'fish' (actually, although they are called fish they are more closely related to us than they are to trout and herrings) that flourished more than 250 million years ago and apparently died out at about the same time as the dinosaurs. I say 'apparently' died out because in 1938, much to the zoological world's astonishment, a weird fish, a yard and a half long and with unusual leg-like fins, appeared in the catch of a deep-sea fishing boat off the South African coast. Though almost destroyed before its priceless worth was recognized, its decaying remains were fortunately brought to the attention of a qualified South African zoologist just in time. Scarcely able to believe his eyes, he identified it as a living coelacanth, and named it *Latimeria*. Since then, a few other specimens have been fished up in the same area, and the species has now been properly studied and described. It is a 'living fossil', in the sense that it has changed hardly at all since the time of its fossil ancestors, hundreds of millions of years ago.

So, we have stasis. What are we to make of it? How do we explain it? Some of us would say that the lineage leading to *Latimeria* stood still because natural selection did not move it. In a sense it had no 'need' to evolve because these animals had found a successful way of life deep in the sea where conditions did not change much. Perhaps they never participated in any arms races. Their cousins that emerged onto the land did evolve because natural selection, under a variety of hostile conditions including arms races, forced them to. Other biologists, including some of those that call themselves punctuationists, might say that the lineage leading to modern *Latimeria* actively resisted change, *in spite of* what natural selection pressures there might have been. Who is right? In the particular case of *Latimeria* it is hard to know, but there is one way in which, in principle, we might go about finding out.

Let us, to be fair, stop thinking in terms of *Latimeria* in particular. It is a striking example but a very extreme one, and it is not one on which the punctuationists particularly want to rely. Their belief is that less extreme, and shorter-term, examples of stasis are commonplace; are, indeed, the norm, because species have genetic mechanisms that actively resist change, even if there are forces of natural selection urging change. Now here is the very simple experiment which, in principle at least, we can do to test this hypothesis. We can take wild populations and impose our own forces of selection upon them. According to the hypothesis that species actively resist change, we should find that, if we try to breed for some quality, the species should dig in its heels, so to speak, and refuse to budge, at least for a while. If we take cattle and attempt to breed selectively for high milk yield, for instance, we should fail. The genetic mechanisms of the species should mobilize their anti-evolution forces and fight off the pressure to change. If we try to make chickens evolve higher egg-laying rates we should fail. If bullfighters, in pursuit of their contemptible 'sport', try to increase the courage of their bulls by selective breeding, they should fail. These failures should only be temporary, of course. Eventually, like a dam bursting under pressure, the alleged anti-evolution forces will be overcome, and the lineage can then move rapidly to a new equilibrium. But we should experience at least some resistance when we first initiate a new program of selective breeding.

The fact is, of course, that we do not fail when we try to shape evolution by selectively breeding animals and plants in captivity, nor do we experience a period of initial difficulty. Animal and plant species are usually immediately amenable to selective breeding, and breeders detect no evidence of any intrinsic, anti-evolution forces. If anything, selective breeders experience difficulty *after* a number of generations of successful selective breeding.

This is because after some generations of selective breeding the available genetic variation runs out, and we have to wait for new mutations. It is conceivable that coelacanths stopped evolving because they stopped mutating—perhaps because they were protected from cosmic rays at the bottom of the sea!—but nobody, as far as I know, has seriously suggested this, and in any case this is not what punctuationists mean when they talk of species having built-in resistance to evolutionary change.

They mean something more like 'cooperating' genes: the idea that groups of genes are so well adapted to each other that they resist invasion by new mutant genes which are not members of the club. This is quite a sophisticated idea, and it can be made to sound plausible. Indeed, it was one of the theoretical props of Mayr's inertia idea, already referred to. Nevertheless, the fact that, whenever we try selective breeding, we encounter no initial resistance to it, suggests to me that, if lineages go for many generations in the wild without changing, this is not because they resist change but because there is no natural selection pressure in favour of changing. They don't change because individuals that stay the same survive better than individuals that change.

Punctuationists, then, are really just as gradualist as Darwin or any other Darwinian; they just insert long periods of stasis between spurts of gradual evolution. As I said, the one respect in which punctuationists do differ from other schools of Darwinism is in their strong emphasis on stasis as something positive: as an active resistance to evolutionary change rather than as, simply, absence of evolutionary change. And this is the one respect in which they are quite probably wrong. It remains for me to clear up the mystery of why they *thought* they were so far from Darwin and neo-Darwinism.

The answer lies in a confusion of two meanings of the word 'gradual', coupled with the confusion, which I have been at pains to dispel here but which lies at the back of many peoples' minds, between punctuationism and saltationism. Darwin was a passionate anti-saltationist, and this led him to stress, over and over again, the extreme gradualness of the evolutionary changes that he was proposing. The reason is that saltation, to him, meant what I have called Boeing 747 macromutation. It meant the sudden calling into existence, like Pallas Athene from the head of Zeus, of brand-new complex organs at a single stroke of the genetic wand. It meant fully formed, complex working eyes springing up from bare skin, in a single generation. The reason it meant these things to Darwin is that that is exactly what it meant to some of his most influential opponents, and they really believed in it as a major factor in evolution.

The Duke of Argyll, for instance, accepted the evidence that evolution had happened, but he wanted to smuggle divine creation in by the back door. He wasn't alone. Instead of a single, once and for all creation in the Garden of Eden, many Victorians thought that the deity had intervened repeatedly, at crucial points in evolution. Complex organs like eyes, instead of evolving from simpler ones by slow degrees as Darwin had it, were thought to have sprung into existence in a single instant. Such people rightly perceived that such instant 'evolution', if it occurred, would imply supernatural intervention: that is what they believed in. The reasons are the statistical ones I have discussed in connection with hurricanes and Boeing 747s. 747 saltationism is, indeed, just a watered-down form of creationism. Putting it the other way around, divine creation is the ultimate in saltation. It is the ultimate leap from inanimate clay to fully formed man. Darwin perceived this too. He wrote in a letter to Sir Charles Lyell, the leading geologist of his day:

> If I were convinced that I required such additions to the theory of natural selection, I would reject it as rubbish … I would give nothing for the theory of Natural selection, if it requires miraculous additions at any one stage of descent.

This is no petty matter. In Darwin's view, the whole *point* of the theory of evolution by natural selection was that it provided a *non*-miraculous account of the existence of complex adaptations. For what it is worth, it is also the whole point of this book. For Darwin, any evolution that had to be helped over the jumps by God was not evolution at all. It made a nonsense of the central point of evolution. In the light of this, it is easy to see why Darwin constantly reiterated the *gradualness* of evolution. It is easy to see why he wrote that:

> If it could be demonstrated that any complex organ existed, which could not possibly have been formed by numerous, successive, slight modifications, my theory would absolutely break down.

There is another way of looking at the fundamental importance of gradualness for Darwin. His contemporaries, like many people still today, had a hard time believing that the human body and other such complex entities could conceivably have come into being through evolutionary means. If you think of the single-celled *Amoeba* as our remote ancestor—as, until quite recently, it was fashionable to do—many people found it hard in their minds to bridge the gap between *Amoeba* and man. They found it inconceivable that from such simple beginnings something so complex could emerge. Darwin appealed to the idea of a gradual series of small steps as a means of overcoming this kind of incredulity. You may find it hard to imagine an *Amoeba* turning into a man, the argument runs; but you do not find it hard to imagine an *Amoeba* turning into a slightly different kind of *Amoeba*. From this it is not hard to imagine it turning into a slightly different kind of slightly different kind of …, and so on. This argument overcomes our incredulity only if we stress that there was an extremely large number of steps along the way, and only if each step is very tiny. Darwin was constantly battling against this source of incredulity, and he constantly made use of the same weapon: the emphasis on gradual, almost imperceptible change, spread out over countless generations.

Incidentally, it is worth quoting J. B. S. Haldane's characteristic piece of lateral thinking in combating the same source of incredulity. Something like the transition from *Amoeba* to man, he pointed out, goes on in every mother's womb in a mere nine months. Development is admittedly a very different process from evolution but, nevertheless, anyone sceptical of the very *possibility* of a transition from single cell to man has only to contemplate his own foetal beginnings to have his doubts allayed. I hope I shall not be thought a pedant if I stress, by the way, that the choice of *Amoeba* for the title of honorary ancestor is simply following a whimsical tradition. A bacterium would be a better choice, but even bacteria, as we know them, are modern organisms.

To resume the argument, Darwin laid great stress on the gradualness of evolution because of what he was arguing *against*: the misconceptions about evolution that were prevalent in the nineteenth century. The *meaning* of 'gradual', in the context of those times, was 'opposite of saltation'. Eldredge and Gould, in the context of the late twentieth century, use 'gradual' in a very different sense. They in effect, though not explicitly, use it to mean 'at a constant speed', and they oppose to it their own notion of 'punctuation'. They criticize gradualism in this sense of 'constant speedism'. No doubt they are right to do so: in its extreme form it is as absurd as my Exodus parable.

But to couple this justifiable criticism with a criticism of Darwin is simply to confuse two quite separate meanings of the word 'gradual'. In the sense in which Eldredge and Gould are opposed to gradualism, there is no particular reason to doubt that Darwin would have agreed with them. In the sense of the word in which Darwin was a passionate gradualist, Eldredge and Gould are also gradualists. The theory of punctuated equilibrium is a minor gloss on Darwinism, one which Darwin himself might well have approved if the issue had been discussed in his time. As a minor gloss, it does not deserve a particularly large measure of publicity. The reason it has in fact received such publicity, and why I have felt obliged to devote a whole chapter of this book to it, is simply that the theory has been sold—oversold by some journalists—as if it were radically opposed to the views of Darwin and his successors. Why has this happened?

There are people in the world who desperately want not to have to believe in Darwinism. They seem to fall into three main classes. First, there are those who, for religious reasons, want evolution itself to be untrue. Second, there are those who have no reason to deny that evolution has happened but who, often for political or ideological reasons, find Darwin's theory of its *mechanism* distasteful. Of these, some find the idea of natural selection unacceptably harsh and ruthless; others confuse natural selection with randomness, and hence 'meaninglessness', which offends their dignity; yet others confuse Darwinism with Social Darwinism, which has racist and other disagreeable overtones. Third, there are people, including many working in what they call (often as a singular noun) 'the media', who just like seeing applecarts upset, perhaps because it makes good journalistic copy; and Darwinism has become sufficiently established and respectable to be a tempting applecart.

Whatever the motive, the consequence is that if a reputable scholar breathes so much as a hint of criticism of some detail of current Darwinian theory, the fact is eagerly seized on and blown up out of all proportion. So strong is this eagerness, it is as though there were a powerful amplifier, with a finely tuned microphone selectively listening out for anything that sounds the tiniest bit like opposition to Darwinism. This is most unfortunate, for serious argument and criticism is a vitally important part of any science, and it would be tragic if scholars felt the need to muzzle themselves because of the microphones. Needless to say the amplifier, though powerful, is not hi-fi: there is plenty of distortion! A scientist who cautiously whispers some slight misgiving about a current nuance of Darwinism is liable to hear his distorted and barely recognizable words booming and echoing out through the eagerly waiting loudspeakers.

Eldredge and Gould don't whisper. They speak out, with eloquence and power! What they say is often pretty subtle, but the message that gets across is that something is wrong with Darwinism. Hallelujah, 'the scientists' said it themselves! The editor of *Biblical Creation* has written:

> it is undeniable that the credibility of our religious and scientific position has been greatly strengthened by the recent lapse in neo-Darwinian morale. And this is something we must exploit to the full.

Eldredge and Gould have both been doughty champions in the fight against redneck creationism. They have shouted their complaints at the misuse of their own words, only to find that, for *this* part of their message, the microphones suddenly went dead on them. I can sympathize, for I have had a similar experience with a different set of microphones, in this case politically rather than religiously tuned.

What needs to be said now, loud and clear, is the truth: that the theory of punctuated equilibrium lies firmly within the neo-Darwinian synthesis. It always did. It will take time to undo the damage wrought by the overblown rhetoric, but it will be undone. The theory of punctuated equilibrium will come to be seen in proportion, as an interesting but minor wrinkle on the surface of neo-Darwinian theory. It certainly provides no basis for any 'lapse in neo-Darwinian morale', and no basis whatever for Gould to claim that the synthetic theory (another name for neo-Darwinism) 'is effectively dead'. It is as if the discovery that the Earth is not a perfect sphere but a slightly flattened spheroid were given banner treatment under the headline:

COPERNICUS WRONG. FLAT EARTH THEORY VINDICATED.

But, to be fair, Gould's remark was aimed not so much at the alleged 'gradualism' of the Darwinian synthesis as at another of its claims. This is the claim, which Eldredge and Gould dispute, that all evolution, even on the grandest geological timescale, is an extrapolation of events that take place within populations or species. ~~They believe that there is a higher form of selection which they call 'species selection'.~~

SECTION 3

CLASSIFICATION

Introduction to Chapter 4

Because there are so many kinds of creatures, it is helpful to be able to organize them into groups. Their evolutionary ancestry provides an objective way to do this.

People have been classifying organisms since at least the time of Aristotle, long before Darwin proposed his evolutionary views. In fact, the strong human tendency to think in categorical terms has been extensively studied by modern psychologists, so it is not surprising that it seems natural to us to group plants and animals together into more and less similar types.

We have already glimpsed a simplified biological classification for reptiles in Chapter 2. The time has now come to ask whether some kinds of classification schemes are inherently more defensible than others. Does it make more sense to group together animals that have mammary glands than to group together animals that have spots? Are both grouping schemes equally appropriate? Do we have any guidance besides our preferences and intuitions? Suppose I really like spots; why shouldn't I use the presence/absence of spots as my classification principle?

In Chapter 4, Mark Ridley suggests that we *do* have an objective principle to go on. He argues that our classification schemes should reflect what happened during evolution. All organisms are linked together over the history of life on Earth in a massive, branching tree. This tree defines their *phylogeny*, their pattern of ancestor–descendant relationships. It is important to begin our discussion by recognizing that all living organisms are related. Why else would they all use the same molecules (DNA, RNA, etc.) to encode and interpret their hereditary material? Humans and salamanders and oak trees and algae are all descended from the original DNA-based life form. But how does relatedness help with classification? Do we just put all DNA-based life forms (all the life we know of) in one group and stop there? Actually, we can do much better. Because the tree of life is constantly branching, we can ask how old or new any given branch is; did it emerge early in the history of life, or did it appear just recently?

To think about this more concretely, let's consider the simplified example in Figure B (below). This figure is arranged with form (morphology) arrayed horizontally and with time running vertically. Species that are close together on the horizontal axis, for example K and L, look similar. Species that are close together on the vertical axis existed close in evolutionary time. For example, J, K, L, and M are all contemporary species, alive now. P and Q are both extinct but they lived at the same time in the past. R lived even longer ago.

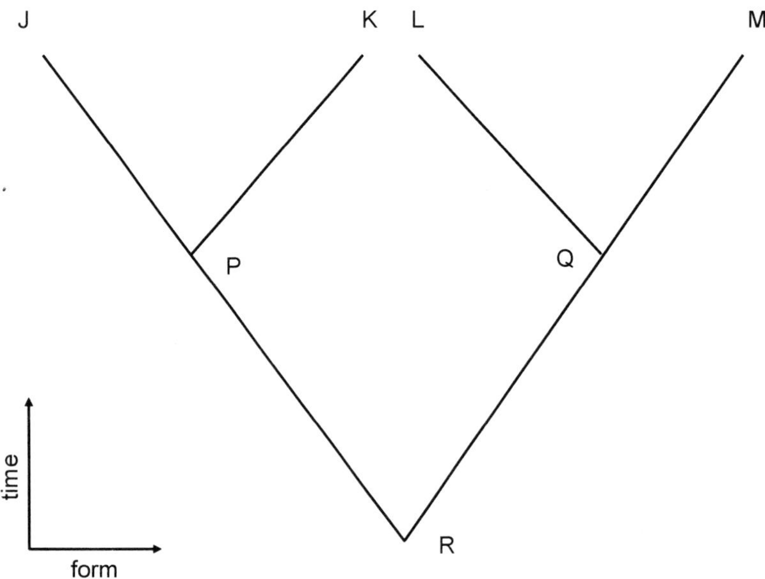

Figure B. Hypothetical phylogenetic tree of 7 species. The vertical axis is time and the horizontal axis is form (morphology).

What this diagram shows is the order of branching that connects this set of species; it shows the phylogenetic tree for this group. R split into two lineages that eventually gave rise to P and Q, and then each of those split into two lineages. Thus R is the ancestor of all the other species. Likewise, P is the ancestor of J and K, and Q is the ancestor of L and M. The classification method advocated by Ridley, phylogenetic classification, simply reflects the pattern of branching. Thus J and K are put in one group because of their shared common ancestor, P; and L and M are put in a different group because of their different common ancestor, Q.

Classifications based on the order of branching are inevitably hierarchical. Hierarchical simply means that smaller, more exclusive groups are nested within larger, more inclusive groups. Just as J and K form one group and L and M form another group at the same classificatory level, a larger group can be formed from all four because they all share a more ancient common ancestor, R. What we have done in forming these ever-more-inclusive groups is simply to trace our way back to progressively more ancient common ancestors, ancestors who necessarily link up more and more species.

Because the concepts are clear in Figure B, now is a good time to arm you with another pair of ideas that all evolutionists need: "divergence" and "convergence." In Chapter 3 we learned how a single species can split to form two new ones, two new branches on the tree of life. And the current chapter will show you how to use those branching events to classify organisms. But what happens after the branches separate? Often they continue to grow apart. "Apart" simply means that each lineage continues to accumulate its own unique set of adaptations. This is called divergence, and it is very common as each new species evolves in adjustment to its particular circumstances. In Figure B, species J and M had a common ancestor in the relatively distant past, but they have been diverging ever since. More recently, species J and K diverged from each other, and likewise, species L and M diverged. But as species K diverged from J and as species L diverged from M, species K and L came to resemble each other in certain respects. This happens because similar environments cause even distantly related species to evolve similar traits. This is called convergence. In terms of their overall body plan, whales and dolphins have converged on bony and cartilaginous fishes. As you will see in Chapter 5, in terms of their sense of smell, howler monkeys have converged on some of our closest relatives.

Ridley does not begin by advocating phylogenetic methods of classification. Instead, he gets there by a process of elimination. Along the way, you meet an alternative method (and a minimally discussed hybrid between the two). The phylogenetic approach (discussed above) is based on recency of common ancestry. Those biologists who base their classifications on the principle of phylogeny use a technique called "cladistics" and are hence sometimes called "cladists." In other words, cladistics is a set of tools for creating phylogenetic classifications. The other method is called the "phenetic" method, and it simply tries to measure overall similarity without any regard to ancestor–descendant relationships. Those biologists who base their classifications on the principle of overall similarity use a technique called "numerical taxonomy" and are hence sometimes called "numerical taxonomists." In other words, numerical taxonomy is a set of tools for creating phenetic classifications.

Lastly there is the hybrid method that combines elements of the phylogenetic and phenetic approach. Ridley calls the hybrid method—and this is unfortunate, from my point of view—"evolutionary." This method is not very important to understand, because it has no clear rules for how to mix phenetic and phylogenetic techniques. What *is* critical to understand are the differences between the phenetic and phylogenetic approaches.

Both phenetic and phylogenetic methods could produce hierarchical (nested) schemes. We have already seen how the phylogenetic method does this. The phenetic method could achieve nesting as well. It could group the most similar animals together, then group these with other animals that are slightly less similar, and continue on in this manner, making more inclusive groups by progressively relaxing its similarity criteria. Indeed, Figure 2 in Chapter 4 shows the way pheneticists try to build nested classification schemes. Notice the word "try." Figure 2 is essential to our understanding because it shows that pheneticists do *not* have an objective (principle-based) method for deciding what is "next most similar." This is one key reason why Ridley rejects phenetics.

In contrast, Ridley recommends phylogenetic classifications, primarily because they reflect what actually happened as the tree of life pushed out new shoots and the shoots grew into branches and pushed out more shoots. The only trouble with the phylogenetic method of classification is this: all that branching happened in the past and we were not there to see it! So, *if we knew the order of branching*, it would be an ideal basis for our classification; but how can we know it? That is what cladistic methods are for, to deduce the order of branching from similarities in the traits of living species.

Now this goal might seem similar to what phenetics is trying to do. Both cladists and pheneticists have to measure the traits of organisms and look for similarities. But there is a key difference. Pheneticists try to measure lots of traits, as many as they can. Cladists intentionally ignore some traits! You might well wonder how throwing away some of the data could produce a more acceptable result. The cladists' logic hinges on the distinction between "primitive" similarities and "derived" similarities. Cladists believe that primitive similarities reveal nothing about common ancestry—which is what they are striving to learn about—but derived similarities do. Well then, we had better learn the difference.

A primitive similarity is one that was present in the common ancestor of the entire group whose members you are trying to classify. A derived similarity is one that has evolved since the common ancestor of that group. Ridley gives several examples, but to help you grasp this important distinction, I will add one as well. Let's say we are trying to deduce the relationships among mammals (animals that produce milk to feed their young); in other words, we want to discover the natural kinds of mammals. For the purpose of my example, I am going to stipulate that having four legs is a primitive similarity for mammals. This means that the common ancestor of all living mammals had four legs. What then would be a derived "leg state" for mammals? It would be having anything *but* four legs: how about flippers and a tail fin? As you know, there are some mammals that fit this description: whales and dolphins. Cladists would say that because whales and dolphins share the derived state of having flippers and a tail fin instead of four legs, whales and dolphins are more closely related to each other than to the rest of mammals.

Remember, sharing the primitive state of four-leggedness tells us *nothing* about the relationships among the rest of mammals. The fact that weasels and antelope and pangolins (look them up!) all have four legs does not mean they are especially closely related; the common ancestor of all mammals had four legs, so the animals just mentioned, like most mammals, have simply retained that primitive state.

For my example, I stipulated that four-leggedness was the primitive state for mammals. Did you question my assumption? If so, you are right to recognize that we cannot just accept such assertions; we need reliable methods for determining which of two (or more) states is primitive and which is derived. As Chapter 4 unveils, cladists have methods (three, in fact) for doing just that.

Chapter 4 Glossary

cladistics: A set of methodological tools used to classify organisms phylogenetically.

convergence: Phenotypic similarity that results when somewhat distantly related species experience similar selection pressures.

divergence: Phenotypic differences that result when somewhat closely related species experience different selection pressures.

numerical taxonomy: A set of methodological tools used to classify organisms phenetically.

phenetic: Pertaining to overall similarity among species. An approach to classifying organisms based on those ancestor–descendant relationships.

phylogenetic: Pertaining to the ancestor–descendant relationships among species. An approach to classifying organisms based on those ancestor–descendant relationships.

Chapter 4
Principles of Classification (1985)

Mark Ridley

What is the proper relation of the theory of evolution and the classification of living things? The strongest possible relation would be one of practical necessity, if classification were practically impossible without the theory of evolution. The facts of history alone show that this relation does not hold. People had successfully classified animals and plants for two millennia before evolution was ever accepted. The simplest act of classification, indeed, requires no theory at all, let alone the theory of evolution; it merely requires that groups be recognized, defined, and named. A group, in this simple sense, is a collection of organisms that share a particular defining trait; the group Chordata for instance contains all animals that possess a notochord, a hollow dorsal nerve chord, and segmented muscles. Classification, as the definition and naming of groups, is in principle easy, but it is also important. It is even essential. Biologists could not communicate or check their discoveries if their specimens had not been classified into publicly recognized groups.

If communication were the only purpose of classification it would not matter what groups were defined, provided that the definitions were agreed upon. Chordata happens to be a group that is generally recognized, but by the same method we could define other groups that are not normally recognized. We might, for instance, define the Ocellata as the group of all living things that possess eyes. It would contain most vertebrates, many insects and crustaceans, some molluscs and worms, and some other odd invertebrates. The Ocellata has not, so far as I know, ever been considered as a taxonomic group; but, if classification is only a matter of defining and naming groups, we might ask why it is not.

That question brings us to the fundamental problem of classification. Different traits define different groups. We could just accept some groups and not others. We could agree that Ocellata is intrinsically as good a group as Chordata, but declare that it just so happens that we have decided to recognize Chordata but not Ocellata. Classification would then be subjective. And if that satisfied us, evolution would not only be practically unnecessary but completely unnecessary, for there would be no more to classification than its practice.

Most biologists, however, are not so easily satisfied. They would prefer the choice of groups to be principled rather than subjective. Then, if we do recognize Chordata but not Ocellata, it must be because some principle shows that the Chordata are an acceptable group, but the Ocellata are not. A perfect principle would unambiguously show whether any group was acceptable, and admit no conflict between acceptable groups. No groups would then be chosen subjectively: they would all be chosen by reference to the principle. Even in the absence of a perfect principle, a principle might still be useful if it narrowed down the number of groups that were acceptable. Once the need for a principle of the choice of traits is recognized, a third relation of the theory of evolution and classification is opened up between practical necessity and complete dispensability. If evolution supplied the only valid principle of choosing traits it would be philosophically necessary for classification, or if merely one among several principles, philosphically desirable. We have seen that evolution is practically unnecessary: from now on we shall be concerned with whether it is philosophically necessary, philosophically desirable, or completely unnecessary.

We can assume that the classification of life will at all events be hierarchical. A hierarchical classification is one whose groups are contained completely within more inclusive groups, with no overlap: humans (for example) are contained within the genus *Homo*, which is contained within the order of primates, which is contained within the class Mammalia, which is contained within the sub-phylum Vertebrata, which is within the phylum Chordata, which is within the kingdom Animalia. In principle biological classifications might not be hierarchical, but in practice they nearly all are. We are not ignoring a contentious practical issue.

What, then, could supply a principle for the hierarchical classification of life? Two kinds of answers have been offered: a *phenetic* hierarchy, or a *phylogenetic* one. A phenetic hierarchy is one of the similarity of form of the groups being classified; it is defined by any traits, such as leg length, skin colour, number of spines on back, or some collection of them. A phylogenetic hierarchy is one of the pattern of evolutionary descent; groups are formed according to recency of common ancestry.

The phenetic and phylogenetic principles may agree or disagree, according to the species considered. Figure 1 shows the phenetic and phylogenetic relations of three sets of three species. The phenetic and phylogenetic classifications are the same if the rate of evolution is approximately constant and its direction is divergent, as is probably true of a human, a chimp, and a rabbit (Figure 1a): the human and the chimp share a more recent common ancestor and resemble each other more closely than does either with the rabbit. The two principles disagree when there is convergence or differential rates of divergent evolution. A barnacle, a limpet, and a lobster illustrate the case of convergence (Figure 1b): the barnacle and limpet are phonetically closer, but the barnacle has a more recent common ancestor with the lobster. The barnacle has converged, during evolution, on to the molluscan form. The salmon, lungfish, and cow illustrate the other source of disagreement (Figure 1c): a lungfish is phenetically more like a salmon than a cow; but it shares a more recent common ancestor with a cow than with a salmon. The evolutionary line leading from lungfish to cows has changed so rapidly that cows now look utterly different from their piscine ancestors. Lungfish indeed have hardly changed at all in 400 million years; they are often called living fossils.

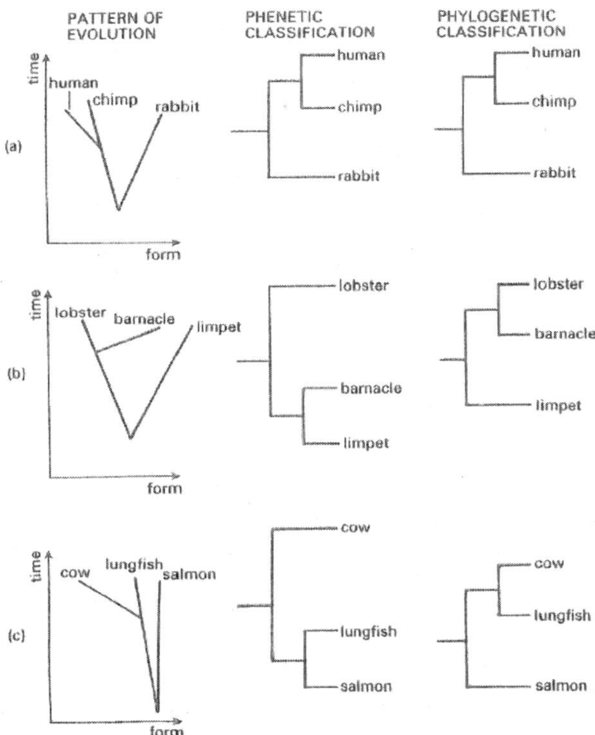

Figure 1. Phenetic and phylogenetic classification.

The pattern of evolution (left), phenetic classification (centre), and phylogenetic classification (right) for three cases. Phenetic and phlyogenetic classification agree in the case of (a) human, chimp, and rabbit; but disagree when there is convergence, as in the case of (b) barnacle, limpet, and lobster, or when there is differential divergence, as in the case of (c) salmon, lungfish, and cow.

Clearly, evolution is a necessary assumption of phylogenetic classification: if organisms did not have evolutionary relations, we could not classify according to them. But evolution is not an assumption of the phenetic system: we could classify organisms by their similarity of appearance whether they shared a common ancestor or had been separately created. In the phenetic system, classification is by similarity of appearance, not evolution. If the phylogenetic principle is invalid, evolution will be completely unnecessary in classification; if both principles are valid, evolution will be philosophically desirable; if only the phylogenetic principle is valid, evolution will be philosophically necessary. If neither principle is valid, we shall have to fall back on the kind of subjectivity that we aimed to escape from. Such is the significance of the question of whether the two principles are valid.

Phenetic and phylogenetic classification have each grown into a whole school, complete with its own philosophical self-justifications, techniques, and advocates. Phenetic classification is advocated by the school of numerical taxonomy; phylogenetic by the school called cladism. There is another important school of classification as well. It is a school often called evolutionary taxonomy, whose practitioners are more numerous than either numerical or cladistic taxonomy. But despite its importance, we need not concern ourselves with it here. Its hierarchical classifications mix phenetic and phylogenetic components; the 'evolutionary' classification of the barnacle, limpet, and lobster is phylogenetic, but of lungfish, salmon, and cow is phenetic. In covering the pure extremes, we shall cover the arguments of the mixed school too. What we want to know are the justifications of numerical taxonomy, which should justify phenetic classification, and of cladism, which should justify phylogenetic classification. Let us take phenetic classification first.

We have already met the difficulty of classification by an arbitrarily chosen trait. It is that some traits define some groups, other traits other groups; eyes defined the (customarily unrecognized) Ocellata, notochords the (customarily recognized) Chordata. If our only principle is to pick traits and define groups by them, we are left with a subjective choice among conflicting groups like Ocellata and Chordata. The numerical taxonomic school, which flourished from the late fifties into the sixties, believed that it had an answer to this problem. It would classify not by single traits, but by as many traits as possible. It would study dozens, even hundreds, of traits, which it would then average in order to define its groups. It came with a repertory of statistical procedures designed to realize that end. The general kind of statistic is what is called a multivariate cluster statistic. Given many measurements of many traits in the units to be classified, the cluster statistic averages all the measurements, to form groups (or 'clusters') of units according to their similarity in all the traits. The groups in the classification are said to be defined by their 'overall morphological similarity'. It was believed that if many traits were used, the groups discerned by the

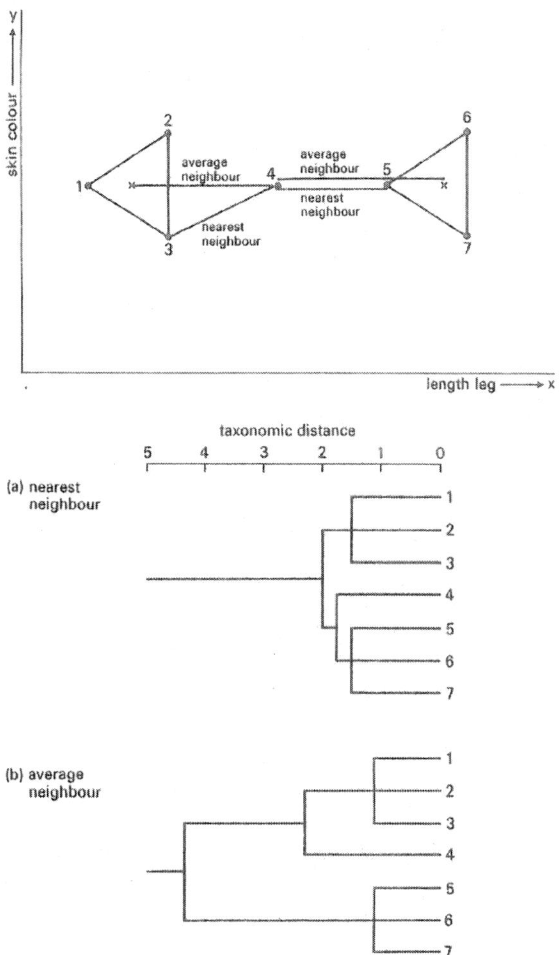

Figure 2. Two cluster statistics in disagreement.

Seven species (nos. 1–7) have been measured for two traits, leg length and skin colour, and plotted in a two-dimensional space, with their leg length on the x-axis and their skin colour on the y-axis. Two cluster statistics, a nearest neighbour statistic and an average neighbour statistic, have been used to classify the seven species. The resulting classifications are shown below: (a) by nearest neighbour (b) by average neighbour. Both statistics first recognize the two groups, one of species 1, 2, 3, and the other of species 5, 6, 7. They disagree about the classification of species 4. The nearest neighbour statistic joins it to the group with the nearest *nearest* neighbour: it compares the two distances labelled nearest neighbour: the one to species 5 is shorter: species 4 is classified with species 5, 6, and 7 (classification (a)). The average neighbour statistic joins it to the group with the nearest *average* neighbour. The two points marked x are the average distances from species 4 to each group. The average neighbour statistic compares the two distances labelled average neighbour: the distance to the group of species 1, 2, and 3 is shorter, and species 4 is therefore classified with them (classification (b)).

---

cluster statistic would be less arbitrary. Whereas groups defined by a few different traits may contain very different members, as did Chordata and Ocellata, groups defined by a large number of traits (it was thought) would have more consistent memberships.

We must consider a cluster statistic in more detail. The clusters are formed according to what is called the 'distance' between the units being classified. A distance in this sense is not the distance from one place to another, such as five miles, but is the difference between the values of a trait in two groups. Suppose that we are classifying two species. If the legs of one species are on average six inches long and those of the other four inches, the distance between the two species with respect to leg length is two inches. Numerical taxonomy, however, does not operate with only one trait. It uses dozens. The distance between the groups is therefore measured as the average for all the traits. If we had also measured skin colour in the two species and the distance between the colours had been 0.3 units, then the average distance for the leg length and skin colour combined is $(2 + 0.3)/2 = 1.15$ units. This figure is called the 'mean trait distance'; it would also be possible to use the Euclidean distance, which is measured, in two dimensions, by Pythagoras's theorem. The method can be applied for an indefinitely large number of traits and species (or whatever unit). The cluster statistic can then set to work.

The cluster statistic forms groups (or 'clusters') by successively aggregating the units with the shortest distances to each other. It forms a hierarchy of clusters as more and more distant units are added in. The numerical taxonomy, or phenetic classification, of the species will then be exactly defined. The classification *is* the hierarchic output of the statistic.

The advantages which numerical taxonomy claims for itself are its objectivity and repeatability. Any taxonomist could take the same group of animals or plants, measure many traits quantitatively, feed the measurements into the cluster statistic, and the same classification would always emerge. Numerical taxonomists claimed that by contrast the methods used to reconstruct phylogenetic trees were hopelessly vague and woolly. We have not yet come to those techniques; but we can look now at how well the method of numerical taxonomy stands up by its own criterion. Is numerical taxonomy, and its resulting phenetic classification, really objective and repeatable?

The answer is that it is not. The reason is abstract, but too important to ignore. It was pointed out most powerfully by an Australian entomologist, L. A. S. Johnson, in 1968. When I wrote above that the cluster statistic simply forms a hierarchy by adding in turn the next least distant group, I ignored a problem. There is more than one cluster statistic, because there is more than one way of recognizing the 'nearest' group. As we shall see, these different cluster statistics define different groups. If numerical taxonomy is truly objective, its own principle must dictate which cluster statistic should be used and which classificatory groups recognized. If it does not its own claim to repeatability will be exploded. It will be hoist on its own petard.

We can illustrate the point by two different statistics, called a nearest neighbour statistic and an average neighbour statistic. These are just two among many, which makes the real problem even worse than what follows; but we can use only two statistics to illustrate the nature, if not the extent, of the problem. Nearest neighbour statistics form successively more inclusive groups by combining the subgroups with the nearest neighbour to each other. We can see it in Figure 2, along with the average neighbour statistic, which forms more inclusive groups not from those subgroups with the nearest *nearest* neighbour, but from those with the nearest *average* neighbour.

In Figure 2, the nearest neighbour and average neighbour cluster statistics produce different hierarchies. In many cases the two statistics will produce hierarchies of the same shape, even if they do differ quantitatively. But sometimes they will not. The two statistics then give different classifications. (The Figure only has two dimensions, which might be, say, leg length and skin colour; as we have seen, numerical taxonomists rely on many more than two traits. But that simplification is only to fit the printed page; it does not matter for the general point. Indeed the problem grows worse as more dimensions are introduced).

The principle of numerical taxonomy provides no guidance among the different cluster statistics. It implies no criterion by which to choose among the different hierarchies produced by different statistics. The principle of numerical taxonomy is to classify according to 'overall morphological similarity', but overall morphological similarity can only be measured by a cluster statistic. There is no higher measure of overall morphological similarity against which the different cluster statistics can be compared. When different statistics conflict, the practical numerical taxonomist has to decide which one he prefers. He can make a choice, of course; but it will have to be subjective.

The principle of phenetic classification, therefore, is a failure. Numerical taxonomy successfully removed subjectivity from the choice of traits, but only to see it pop up again (in a less obvious but equally destructive form) in the choice of cluster statistic. If phenetic relations cannot provide a valid principle for the hierarchical classification of living things, what about phylogeny?

Here there is more hope. Unlike the hierarchy of phenetic resemblance (or overall morphological similarity), the phylogenetic hierarchy does exist independently of our techniques to measure it. The phylogenetic tree is a unique hierarchy. It really is true, of any two species, that they either do or do not share a more recent common ancestor with each other than with another species. In phylogenetic classification, there is no problem of subjective choice among different possible hierarchies. There is only one correct phylogeny. If the evidence suggests that one classification is more like it than another, that is the classification to choose. The Chordata are allowed, but the Ocellata are not, because the group of chordates share a common ancestor but the group of species that possess eyes do not. Sometimes there will not be enough evidence to say whether one classification is more phylogenetic than another: then we should either have to make a provisional subjective choice, or refuse to choose until more evidence becomes available. The advantage of the phylogenetic principle is that it does possess a higher criterion to compare the evidence with: the phylogenetic hierarchy. This advantage had been vaguely understood by many evolutionary taxonomists, but it was first thoroughly thought through by the German entomologist Hennig. Cladism is sometimes called Hennigian classification.

Now that we have solved the philosophical problem we are left with the practical one. How can phylogenetic relations be discovered? Evolution took place in the past. Unlike phenetic relations, phylogenetic relations cannot be directly observed. They have to be inferred. But how?

For each species, we need to know which other species it shares its most recent common ancestor with, for that is the species with which it should be classified. How can we discover it? The method proposed by Hennig (and previously applied by many others) is to look for traits that are evolutionary innovations. During evolution, traits change from time to time. According to whether a particular trait is an earlier or a later evolutionary stage, it can be called a primitive or a derived trait. Most traits pass through several stages in evolution, and whether a particular stage is primitive or derived depends on which other stage it is being compared with: it is primitive with respect to later stages, but derived with respect to earlier ones. Consider as an example the evolution of the vertebrate limb. The most primitive stage is its absence; then, in fish, it appears as a fin; in amphibians the fin evolves into the tetrapodan pentadactyl (five-digit) limb; it has stayed like that in most vertebrates, but in some lizards and independently in some ungulates the number of digits on the limb has been reduced from five to four, three, two, or even (in horses) one. If we compare amphibians with fish, the pentadactyl limb is the derived state and fins the primitive state of this trait; but if we compare an amphibian with a horse, the five-toed state becomes primitive and the one-toed state in the horse is now the derived. Similarly if we compare the hand of a human with the front foot of a horse, the pentadactyl human hand is in the primitive state relative to the single-toed equine foot.

Such is the meaning of primitive and derived states. The distinction is necessary, in Hennig's system, in order that the derived traits can be selected for use in classification. The derived traits are selected because shared derived traits indicate common ancestry, whereas shared primitive traits do not. Let us stay with the same example. Suppose that we wish to classify a five-toed lizard, a horse, and an ape in relation to each other. The ape and the lizard share the trait 'five-toed', but this does not indicate that they share a more recent common ancestor than either does with the horse: the trait is primitive and does not indicate common ancestry within the group of horse, ape, lizard. Whenever there is an evolutionary innovation, it is retained (until the next evolutionary change) by the species descended from the innovatory species: shared derived traits do indicate common ancestry. That is why they are used to discover phylogenetic relations.

We can now move a further step in the search for a method. The problem has now become to distinguish primitive from derived traits. In the case of the vertebrate limb we assumed that the course of evolution was known. But how could it be discovered to begin with? There are several techniques. We need not consider them all. Let us look at one in detail to demonstrate that the distinction can be made. Let us consider outgroup comparison. The simplest case has one trait, with two states, in two species; lactation and its absence, for instance, in a horse and a toad. The problem is whether lactation in horses is derived with respect to its absence in toads, or its absence in toads is derived with respect to its presence in horses. The solution, by outgroup comparison, is obtained by examining the state of some related species, called the outgroup. The outgroup should be a species which is not more closely related to one of the two species than the other, that is why it is an *out*group: it is separated from the species under consideration. In this case any fish or invertebrate would do but a cow would not, because it is more closely related to the horse than it is to the toad. By the method of outgroup comparison, that trait is taken to be primitive which is found in the outgroup. Whether we took a species of fish or an invertebrate, the answer would be the same. The outgroup lacks lactation: lactation is the derived state.

The result of outgroup comparison is uncertain. It will be wrong whenever there is unrecognized convergence. Thus if we compared the trait 'body shape' in dolphins and dogs with some such outgroup as a fish we should determine that the dog had the derived shape. Actually the dolphin does. No one would be mistaken in the case of dolphins and fish; but other more subtle cases of convergence surely exist which are not as easy to recognize, and in them outgroup comparison will be misleading. But although it can go wrong, it is probably better than nothing. Shared traits are probably more often due to common ancestry than to convergence: but only more often, not always.

Advocates of phenetic classification often remark that phylogenetic classification is impossible because its techniques are circular. In the case of outgroup comparison, for instance, in order to apply the technique we needed to know that the outgroup (the fish) was less related to the toad and the horse than either to each other. It appears that we need to know the classification before we can apply the techniques; which would be quite a problem since the technique is supposed to be used to discover the classification. The problem, however, is not as destructive as it appears.

The argument of outgroup comparison is not circular. It works by what is often called successive approximation. It is the method by which theories are developed in all sciences. As new facts are collected and considered, they are examined in the light of the present theory. If they fit it, confidence in the theory is increased. If they do not, they may suggest a new theory, which can be used in considering yet further evidence. There is a continual reexamination of the theory in the light of new evidence, and when the theory is changed, our interpretation of all previous evidence should change too. This is not circular reasoning: it is testing a theory. In outgroup comparison, we can start with some crude idea of which species is an outgroup; if further evidence fits the crude idea, the hypothesis is (tentatively) confirmed, and it can then be used in interpreting further facts. Let us consider a hypothetical example.

Let us suppose that we have six species, and we suspect that one of them is less closely related than the other five. That one can be used as an outgroup. Comparison with it can be used to classify the other five, whose relations are not yet known. We first examine a trait in all six species. We take the state in the outgroup to be primitive for the group of five. Figure 3 shows the procedure. There are two points to notice. One is that the procedure can start from a very vague starting point; we do not need a firm classification to apply outgroup comparison. The other is that, if further evidence demands it, we can modify our initial ideas. If one trait after another suggests that species 6 is *not* separate from 1–5 then we can modify the classification, and put 6 in its appropriate place. All the previous steps would then have to be reconsidered. As the analysis proceeds any error at the beginning has a decreasing effect; the initial errors are gradually discovered, and their damaging consequences removed. Such is the method of successive approximation. It is the common method of scientific theory-building: only sciences that completely lack theories can do without the feedback between the interpretation of facts and the testing of theories.

Outgroup comparison is not the only cladistic method. Another method supposes that, as the organism develops, the evolutionarily derived stages appear after the primitive stages. The backbone of vertebrates is a derived state relative to its absence in invertebrates; and the backbone develops after its absence in a vertebrate embryo. Like outgroup comparison, the embryological criterion is imperfect but better than nothing. Another method is to look at the order in which the traits appear in the fossil record. The most powerful technique is to take all these methods together, and use all the evidence available. I do not wish to give the impression that the techniques of reconstructing phylogeny are perfect. They are far from that. Many problems remain, especially that of how to reconcile conflicting information from different traits. But although the system has difficulties, it is probably not altogether impractical. The cladistic evidence suggests that humans share a more recent common ancestor with chimps than with butterflies, and few biologists would deny that the evidence is correct in this case.

Derived traits, therefore, can be distinguished from primitive ones. Groups can be defined by shared derived traits. The cladistic system of phylogenetic classification is workable. But although cladistic groups can be recognized and defined, and although the classification (so far as it is phylogenetic) will be philosophically sound, it will only be valid for any one time. Evolution is continually going on; the traits of lineages continually change. What will define a group at one time may not define it at another. The traits defining groups are temporarally contingent, not essential. Biological groups do not have Aristotelian 'essences'. The phylogenetic group Vertebrata may happen to be defined, at present, by the

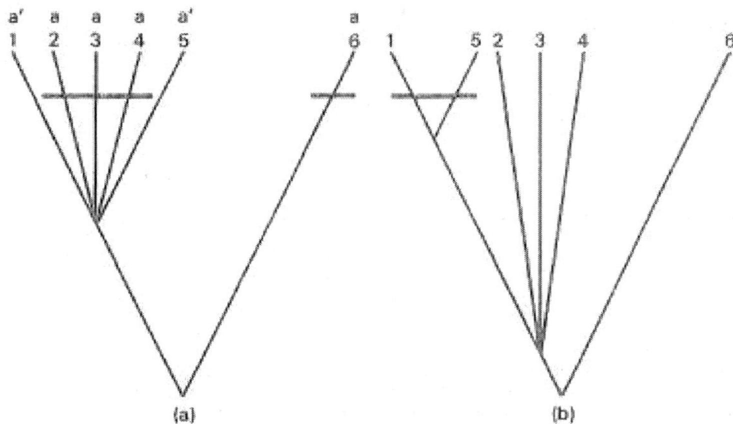

Figure 3. Outgroup comparison by successive approximation.

(a) Five species (nos. 1–5) are to be classified, and it is thought that another species (6) is less related to them than any of the five to each other. Trait *A* is compared in all six species: species 2, 3, and 4 have it in state *a*, as does species 6, but species 1 and 5 have another state *a*'; by outgroup comparison *a*' is reasoned to be a derived state. (b) Species 1 and 5 are classified together, for they share a derived trait. The relations of species 2, 3, and 4 remain unknown; but the procedure can be repeated when evidence for new traits becomes available.

possession of bones (or cartilage), but that may no longer be true in a million years' time. A descendant of a vertebrate species may lack bones, and the trait will cease to define the evolutionary group. The traits that define groups are not eternal and inevitable: they just happen to be useful sometimes.

For the same reason, difficulties arise when species from different times (particularly fossils and present-day species) are put in the same classification. It can be done, but it is often awkward. Because traits are continually changing, groups with members from more than one geological period cannot be defined by constant traits. Furthermore, because species may vary in space, the traits used in a classification strictly only apply to one place. But spatial variation, being more limited than temporal variation, is less of a practical problem. Spatial and temporal changes in traits are both only difficulties in the practice, not in the philosophy, of phylogenetic classification. The phylogenetic relations of a species remain real. The difficulty is in their discovery; phylogenetic relations have to be inferred from shared derived traits. But because traits do not remain constant in time and space, they are not perfectly reliable guides to the true phylogenetic relations of a species.

Because phylogenetic classifications are defined by shared traits, it is tempting to think that phylogenetic classification is really a form of phenetic classification. There is a measure of truth in this idea. Phylogenetic classification is defined by shared traits, and to that extent is phenetic. But it could not be otherwise. All classifications are phenetic in this sense. The proper description of a classificatory system as phylogenetic or phenetic should not be according to the techniques that it uses, but the hierarchy that it seeks to represent. There is an utterly different philosophy behind the two systems. One tries to represent the branching pattern of evolution; the other tries to represent the pattern of morphological similarity.

Moreover, different *kinds* of traits define phylogenetic and phenetic classifications. Phylogenetic classification supposes that some traits—shared derived traits in particular—are better indicators of phylogeny than are others. Phylogenetic classification, at least of the cladistic variety, uses only shared derived traits. Phenetic classification, by contrast, indiscriminately uses both primitive and derived traits. Both for reasons of philosophy and technique therefore it is misleading to call phylogenetic classification a form of phenetic classification.

Phylogenetic classification is philosophically preferable to its only competitor, phenetic classification. It is also a practical possibility. Its main problems are in its techniques, which are (as yet) far from perfect. But the techniques of cladism have been improved, even within their short history, and further work, particularly on molecules, should improve them further. The difficulty in phenetic classification is more fundamental. Its claim to preference, which is its objectivity, is a false claim. It is left with little to recommend itself by. Phenetic classification should, I think, be avoided whenever possible. Classifications, if they are to be objective, must represent phylogeny.

If this conclusion is correct, evolution and classification are closely related. The relation is one of philosophical necessity. Evolution is required to justify the kind of classification that is practised. Evolution is not merely desirable, but necessary, because phylogeny is the only known principle of classification. If we were content with merely subjective classification, evolution would be unnecessary. But if we are not—if we seek a principled classification—evolution becomes essential. It underwrites the entire philosophy of phylogenetic classification. Without evolution, phylogenetic classification, and its method of searching for derived traits, would be as subjective as any other technique. Only because we can assume that evolution is true, can we even begin to think about phylogenetic classification. Then we need techniques to detect phylogeny. The source of those techniques is our understanding of how traits change in evolution. The theory of evolution, therefore, not only guarantees the philosophy of classification: it is also the breeding ground of taxonomic techniques.

SECTION 4

THE COMPARATIVE METHOD

Introduction to Chapter 5

Natural selection does not construct every conceivable adaptation in every species; because adaptations have costs, selection sometimes also deletes adaptations. A significant clue to the function of adaptations is their distribution across species.

Chapter 5 is another primary research study. It looks at two sensory systems: the sense of smell (olfaction) and the sense of vision. The fundamental question of the research study is, has selection produced a trade-off between these two systems? In particular, do species with more complex visual systems have less complex olfactory systems, and vice versa? To test this proposition, the study explicitly looks for convergence, as discussed near the end of the introduction to Chapter 4.

The reason the authors ask this question is that *all adaptations are costly*—costly to build, to maintain and to run. If circumstances change and a particular adaptation is no longer providing sufficient returns (in terms of reproductive success), selection will delete it. As an example which we will discuss in class, selection has deleted eyes, time and time again, in species that have colonized deep underground caves (where there is no light). In this article, the authors ask whether selection has simplified, and thus reduced the costs of the olfactory system, in species with highly sophisticated visual systems.

The authors need a way to measure the complexity of each sensory system. Their measure of complexity for vision is a simple presence/absence measure: presence or absence of full trichromatic vision. Some primates (the group of mammals that includes humans, apes, monkeys and lemurs) have full trichromatic vision, and some do not; thus, in terms of this article, some primates have complex visual systems and some do not.

In everyday terms, full trichromatic vision refers to the kind of rich color vision that you have. We have, in our retinas, cells that are sensitive to light. Different colors of light have different physical wavelengths. Color vision works because in our retinal cells there are pigments that are sensitive to these different wavelengths. Each pigment is a protein whose recipe is encoded by a different gene (see Chapter 1 to remind yourself how genes specify protein recipes). To have "full" trichromatic vision you need three different genes: one for a pigment sensitive to short wavelengths, one for a pigment sensitive to medium wavelengths and one for pigment sensitive to long wavelengths.

These pigment genes are not all on the same chromosome. The short-wavelength pigment gene is on an autosome. An autosome is a non-sex chromosome; the X-chromosome and the Y-chromosome are *not* autosomes but all the rest are. Humans have 22 pairs of autosomes (remember, we're diploid); in addition to these autosomes, females have two X-chromosomes, but males have one X and one Y. Where are the other two pigment genes? In the primates with full trichromatic vision, the other two pigment genes are at two different loci on the X-chromosome. The middle-wavelength pigment gene is at one X-chromosome locus, and the long-wavelength pigment gene is at another X-chromosome locus. This means that females will have two copies of the middle-wavelength gene and two copies of the long wavelength gene, whereas males will have only one copy of each. But one copy is enough to make sufficient pigment of each, so both sexes will be able to see in all three wavelengths, that is, both sexes will see in full color.

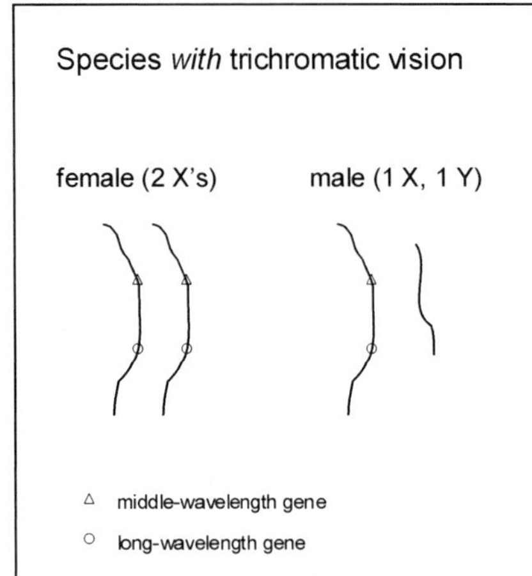

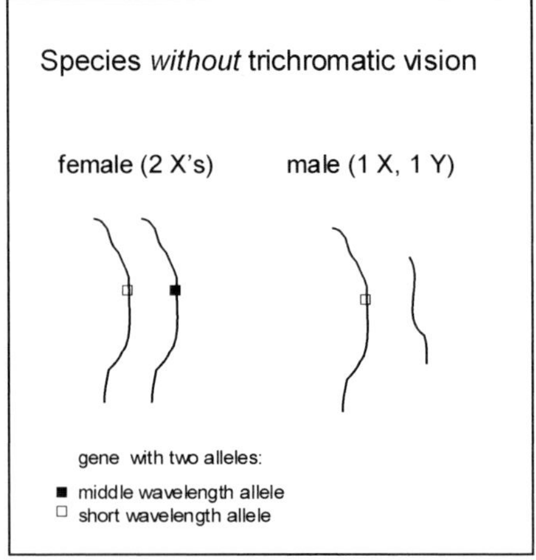

Figure C. The arrangement of genes in species with (diagram on left) and without (diagram on right) full trichromatic vision. Both kinds of species have a short-wavelength gene on one of their autosomes (not shown).

What about primate species that do not have full trichromatic vision? They all have the same autosomal (short-wavelength) gene. But on the X-chromosome, they have just one locus coding for a retinal pigment, not two loci. However, that single X-chromosome locus has two *different* alleles: one that codes for a middle-wavelength pigment and one that codes for a long-wavelength pigment. As a consequence, females that happen to be heterozygous at this locus *will* be able to see in full color, but females who are homozygous will not. And males will not have full color vision either, because with only one X-chromosome, they cannot possibly have both alleles. (Strictly speaking, males cannot be either homozygous or heterozygous for any X-chromosome gene; what they are is called hemizygous.)

Remember, the authors are categorizing primates into those that have full trichromatic vision and those that do not. The situation of having three separate loci (like we humans have) provides full trichromatic vision; the authors consider this to be the more complex visual adaptation. The condition of having only two loci does not give all members of the species full trichromatic vision and is thus considered to be the less complex visual adaptation. Figure C illustrates the configuration of genes in species with and without full trichromatic vision.

Now let's turn to olfaction; we need a measure of its complexity as well. Smells do not come in only short, medium and long; there are many different kinds of smells. Because you can smell so many different odors, you would be right to suspect there are many different genes coding for olfactory receptor proteins. There are over 1,000 olfactory receptor genes in mammals. But not all of these genes are functional in every species; some are "switched off." The "off" switch consists of one or more disruptions (errors) in the gene's coding sequence, which prevent the gene from sending a messenger RNA message (see Chapter 1 if you need to). When a gene is switched off in this way, the protein the gene would have coded for is never assembled; it is then called a "pseudogene" because it looks like a gene but it does not specify any protein the way real genes do. (We can still recognize that it used to be an olfactory receptor gene in the evolutionary past because its A,T,C,G sequence is still very similar to a known olfactory receptor gene.)

Each olfactory receptor gene that is switched off (converted to a pseudogene) deletes one smell element from the species' olfactory repertoire. The question we can ask for any given species of mammal or primate is, what proportion of their olfactory receptor genes have become pseudogenes? More complex olfactory systems have fewer olfactory receptor pseudogenes (i.e., more working genes), and simpler systems have more pseudogenes (i.e., fewer working genes).

The authors did not look at each of the 1,000 olfactory receptor genes in each species to determine which ones were real genes and which ones were pseudogenes. They did what people always do when they have a lot of cases to evaluate: they took a sample. If you wanted to estimate the results of an election, you would not ask every registered voter whom they were going to vote for; you would ask a sample of voters. In each of the primate species discussed in this paper, the authors looked at a sample of 100 olfactory receptor genes. This is a pretty big sample—10 %—and it should give a reliable estimate. In the first paragraph of the *Results and Discussion* section, the authors explain the biochemical techniques they used to take the sample, but this information is technical and you do not need to bother with it.

Figure 2 in the chapter shows the proportion of olfactory receptor pseudogenes in various species. In humans, about 50% of the olfactory receptor genes are pseudogenes (i.e., about half are switched off). In other Old-World anthropoid primates (African and Asian monkeys and apes), between 25% and 35% are pseudogenes. In New World primates (Central and South American species), a prosimian primate (lemur), and a non-primate (mouse), we see that generally only 15% to 18% are pseudogenes. But there is an obvious exception to this pattern. One New World monkey species, the howler monkey, has 31% pseudogenes; in this regard, howlers resemble the Old-World anthropoids. This exception (marked by the arrow in Figure 2) is critical to testing the hypothesis that increasing complexity of the visual systems allows some deterioration of the olfactory system. Here is why: among the New World monkeys, only howler monkeys have trichromatic vision!

If you look at Figure 3 you will see a phylogenetic tree of all the primates mentioned in Figure 2. It is a cladistic tree constructed using the methods you learned in Chapter 4. As you know, this kind of tree shows how closely related each species is to every other species. For example, our closest relative is the chimpanzee. The closest relative of the chimp-human group is the gorilla. The closest relative of the howler monkey is the spider monkey-wooly monkey group.

Based on this tree we can now ask how many times trichromatic vision evolved in the primates. The answer seems to be two. Natural selection twice solved the problem of getting three different retinal pigments into both male and female monkeys and apes: once in the common ancestor of all apes and Old World monkeys (indicated by the upper arrow in Figure 3), and a second time in the ancestor of howler monkeys (the lower arrow). This second solution was more recent; it probably did not occur in the ancestor of all New World monkeys because hardly any New World monkeys have it. Put in terms of the classes of similarities you learned in Chapter 4, trichromatic vision is primitive for the group that comprises Old World monkeys plus apes. But it is *not* primitive for the group that comprises New World monkeys; hence it is derived among howler monkeys.

Now, this makes the pattern we see in Figure 2 especially interesting. Trichromatic vision evolved twice in primates, and *both* times it was associated with an increase in the proportion of olfactory receptor pseudogenes. The authors conclude that when the visual system becomes more sophisticated, selection allows the olfactory system to become simpler. Here is the way to picture that happening. Mutations that switch off olfactory receptor genes can occur at any time. But if they occur in a species *without* trichromatic vision, selection is more likely to disfavor them than if the same disabling mutation occurred in a species *with* trichromatic vision. In terms of their high proportion of olfactory receptor pseudogenes, howler monkeys have converged on Old World monkeys and apes. Because this pairing of trichromatic vision and a degraded olfactory system occurred twice, our confidence is increased that there is an adaptive relationship between these two systems.

Chapter 5 Glossary

opsin: Retinal pigment allowing nerve cells to fire when they are struck by light; different opsins respond to different wavelengths of light.

PCR, primer: Tools used to handle and classify chunks of DNA. In this study they were used to identify olfactory receptor genes and determine whether or not they were pseudogenes.

primates: The order of mammals to which humans, other apes, monkeys and prosimians belong.

pseudogene: A gene that has been turned off as a result of changes in its A,T,C,G coding sequence.

trichromatic vision: The ability to see in full color as humans do; requires three different opsins.

vomeronasal pheromone transduction pathway: Part of a separate chemical sense, like olfaction, that is also situated in the nasal cavity.

Chapter 5
Loss of Olfactory Receptor Genes Coincides with the Acquisition of Full Trichromatic Vision in Primates (2004)

Yoav Gilad[1,2], Victor Wiebe[1], Molly Przeworski[1], Doron Lancet[2], Svante Pääbo[1]

Olfactory receptor (OR) genes constitute the molecular basis for the sense of smell and are encoded by the largest gene family in mammalian genomes. Previous studies suggested that the proportion of pseudogenes in the OR gene family is significantly larger in humans than in other apes and significantly larger in apes than in the mouse. To investigate the process of degeneration of the olfactory repertoire in primates, we estimated the proportion of OR pseudogenes in 19 primate species by surveying randomly chosen subsets of 100 OR genes from each species. We find that apes, Old World monkeys and one New World monkey, the howler monkey, have a significantly higher proportion of OR pseudogenes than do other New World monkeys or the lemur (a prosimian). Strikingly, the howler monkey is also the only New World monkey to possess full trichromatic vision, along with Old World monkeys and apes. Our findings

1 Max Planck Institute for Evolutionary Anthropology, Leipzig, Germany.

2 Department of Molecular Genetics, Weizmann Institute of Science, Rehovot, Israel.

Abbreviations: FET, Fisher's exact test; OR, olfactory receptor; ORF, open reading frame; OWM, Old World monkey; NWM, New World monkey
Academic Editor: David Hillis, University of Texas at Austin

Yoav Gilad, Victor Wiebe, Molly Przeworski, Doron Lancet, and Svante Pääbo, "Loss of Olfactory Receptor Genes Coincides with the Acquisition of Full Trichromatic Vision in Primates," from *PLoS Biology*, Vol. 2 Issue 1; January 2004, pp. 120–125.

suggest that the deterioration of the olfactory repertoire occurred concomitant with the acquisition of full trichromatic color vision in primates.

Introduction

Olfactory receptor (OR) genes provide the basis for the sense of smell (Buck and Axel 1991) and, with more than 1,000 genes, comprise the largest gene superfamily in mammalian genomes (Glusman et al. 2001; Zozulya et al. 2001; Young and Trask 2002; Zhang and Firestein 2002; Olender et al. 2003). OR genes are organized in clusters (Trask et al. 1998; Young and Trask 2002) and in humans are found on every chromosome save the Y and 20 (Glusman et al. 2001; Zozulya et al. 2001). On the basis of sequence similarity, they are classified into two major classes and 17 families (Glusman et al. 2001). All OR genes have an approximately 1 kb coding region that is uninterrupted by introns (Ben-Arie et al. 1994; Gilad et al. 2000).

Interestingly, approximately 60% of human OR genes carry one or more coding region disruptions and are therefore considered pseudogenes (Rouquier et al. 1998; Glusman et al. 2001; Zozulya et al. 2001). In nonhuman apes, the fraction of OR pseudogenes is only approximately 30% (Gilad et al. 2003). However, both humans and other apes have a significantly higher fraction of OR pseudogenes than do the mouse or the dog (approximately 20%) (Young et al. 2002; Zhang and Firestein 2002; Olender et al. 2003). Thus, there has been a decrease in the size of the intact OR repertoire in apes relative to other mammals, with a further deterioration in humans (Rouquier et al. 2000; Gilad et al. 2003).

Although the causes are unclear, it seems reasonable to speculate that the high fraction of OR pseudogenes in apes reflects a decreased reliance on the sense of smell in species for whom auditory and visual cues may be more important (e.g., Dominy and Lucas 2001). We were therefore interested in investigating whether the high fraction of OR pseudogenes is characteristic of primates as a whole and, if not, to pinpoint when the proportion of OR pseudogenes increased. To this end, we randomly selected subsets of 100 OR genes in 19 primate species, including a human, four apes, six Old World monkeys (OWMs), seven New World monkeys (NWMs) and one prosimian. We find that a decrease in the size of the intact olfactory repertoire occurred independently in two evolutionary lineages: in the ancestor of OWMs and apes, and in the New World howler monkey.

Results and Discussion

Owing to the high levels of DNA sequence divergence among the primate species in our sample, orthologous OR genes could not be amplified by primers designed based on human sequences (Gilad et al. 2003). Instead, we used two sets of degenerate primer pairs, constructed to amplify OR genes from all of the species studied (see Materials and Methods). We then cloned the PCR products and determined the sequences of clones until we had identified 100 distinct OR genes from each species. A danger of this approach is that degenerate primers may bind preferentially to certain OR genes, thereby resulting in a biased representation of the OR repertoire. To safeguard against this, we tested the degenerate primers on human and mouse, for which the entire OR gene repertoire is known, by using them to amplify 100 OR genes from the two species. The sample thus obtained faithfully represented the composition of the full OR gene repertoire in human and mouse with respect to the 17 OR gene families (Figure 1). Moreover, the sample estimates of the fractions of pseudogenes were accurate (see Materials and Methods; Figure 2). This pilot study demonstrates that the degenerate primers yield an unbiased representation of the OR gene repertoire, as measured by the family composition and pseudogene content of

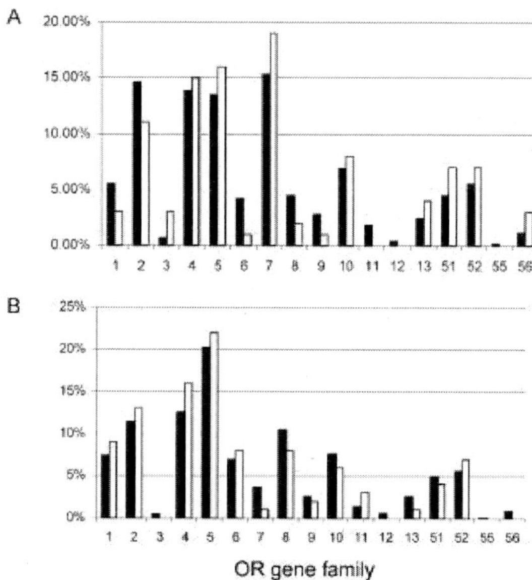

Figure 1. Results of the Pilot Study in Human and Mouse

The percentage of OR genes from each family is given for the entire repertoire (filled bars) and a sample of 100 genes amplified using PC1 and PC2 degenerate primers (open bars). (A) OR genes in human. (B) OR genes in mouse. None of the differences between the full repertoires and the samples are significant at the 5% level. Only full-length OR genes (larger than 850 bp) were considered. DOI: 10.1371/journal.pbio.0020005.g001

the human and mouse samples. Since the primers performed well both in human and a distantly related species, the mouse, there was no reason to assume that they would not do so in nonhuman primate species.

We therefore proceeded to sequence 100 genes from 18 nonhuman primates using these primer pairs. Since the genome sequence is not available for these species, we were not able to compare the familial composition of our samples of OR genes to that of the full OR repertoires. However, with the exception of OR families 3, 11, 12, and 55 (whose absence in a sample of 100 genes is not unlikely, as they represent less than 1.8% of human OR genes), we identified OR genes from all families in all species (Table 1). Moreover, the

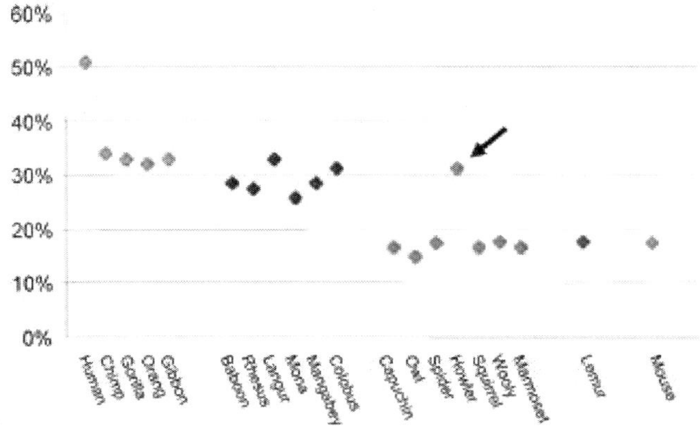

Figure 2. The Proportion of OR Pseudogenes in 20 Species

Primate species are color-coded according to family. The arrow points to the howler monkey. Datapoints (*from left to right*) are for apes (*green*): human (*Homo sapiens*), chimpanzee (*Pan troglodytes*), gorilla (*Gorilla gorilla*), orangutan (*Pongo pygmaeus*), gibbon (*Hylobates syndactylus*); for OWMs (*blue*): Guinea baboon (*Papio papio*), rhesus macaque (*Macaca mulatta*), silver langur (*Trachypithecus auratus*), mona (*Cercopithecus mona*), agile mangabey (*Cercocebus agilis*), black-and-white colobus (*Colobus guereza*); for NWMs (*red*): brown capuchin monkey (*Cebus apella*), southern owl monkey (*Aotus azarai*), spider monkey (*Ateles fusciceps*), black howler monkey (*Alouatta caraya*), squirrel monkey (*Saimiri sciureus*), wooly monkey (*Lagothrix lagotricha*), common marmoset (*Callithrix jacchus*); for one prosimian primate (*brown*): crowed lemur (*Eulemur mongoz*); and for the mouse (*Mus musculus*) (*grey*).
DOI: 10.1371/journal.pbio.0020005.g002

representation of the three largest OR gene families in the sample varied across species, again suggesting that there is no strong bias towards the amplification of specific families.

We then tabulated the proportion of OR pseudogenes in each species (Figure 2). Consistent with previous results based on direct sequencing of full-length OR orthologs (Gilad et al. 2003), we found that the proportion of OR pseudogene in the great apes and rhesus macaque is approximately 30% (Figure 2). Together, these findings confirm the validity of this degenerate primer approach.

We further found that the proportion of OR pseudogenes in OWMs (29.3% ± 2.4%) is very similar to that of nonhuman apes (33.0% ± 0.8%), but notably higher than that of NWMs (18.4% ± 5.6%). One NWM species, the howler monkey, was a conspicuous exception, with an elevated proportion of OR pseudogenes, similar to that of OWMs and apes (31.0%) (Figure 2) and significantly higher than any other NWM (one-tailed $p < 0.02$ for the difference between the howler monkey and the NWM with the second highest proportion of pseudogenes, the Wooly monkey, as assessed by a Fisher's exact test [FET]). Thus, it appears that a deterioration of the olfactory repertoire occurred in all apes and OWMs as well as, independently, in the howler monkey lineage.

Strikingly, a second phenotype is shared only by the howler monkey, OWMs, and apes: full (or "routine") trichromatic color vision. In primates, trichromatic color vision is accomplished by three opsin genes whose products are pigments sensitive to short, medium, or long wavelength ranges of visible light (Nathans et al. 1986). In OWMs and apes, the short-wavelength opsin gene is found on an autosome, while two distinct X-linked loci for medium and long wavelengths underlie full trichromatic color vision (and so are present in both males and females). In contrast, most NWM species carry an autosomal gene and only one X-linked gene, where different alleles encode for photopigment opsins that respond to medium or long wavelengths. Heterozygous females can therefore possess trichromatic vision, but males are dichromatic (Jacobs 1996; Boissinot et al. 1998; Hunt et al. 1998). The sole exception among NWMs is the howler monkey (Jacobs et al. 1996; Jacobs and Deegan 2001; Surridge et al. 2003), which has a duplication of the opsin genes on the X chromosome (Goodman et al. 1998; Jacobs and Deegan 2001) (Figure 3). Thus, full trichromatic vision arose twice in primates, once in the common ancestor of OWMs and apes and once in the howler monkey lineage.

While OWMs, apes, and the howler monkey carry 32.5% ± 6.3% OR pseudogenes in their OR gene repertoire, species without full trichromatic vision have 16.7% ± 1.0%, significantly fewer ($p < 10\text{-}4$, or, excluding humans from the full trichromatic group, $p < 10\text{-}3$, as assessed by a Mann-Whitney U test). This p value is only indicative since the species lineages are not all independent. However, if significance is instead assessed by a FET for all pairwise comparisons of species with full trichromatic color vision and without, the

Table 1. Distribution of OR Genes in Families across Species

OR Family	Chimp	Gorilla	Orangutan	Gibbon	Rhesus	Baboon	Colobus	Langur	Mangabey	Mona	Owl	Spider	Howler	Capuchin	Squirrel	Wooly	Marmoset	Lemur
1	5	7	10	8	12	10	10	8	8	9	8	12	8	9	8	9	8	3
2	15	17	19	12	14	15	19	20	21	14	12	11	10	13	10	13	9	22
3	1	1	3	1	0	3	3	3	1	3	1	1	3	1	1	3	4	1
4	11	9	6	5	9	7	6	9	12	14	13	9	13	14	12	9	13	7
5	16	15	7	18	14	7	16	14	9	11	14	14	15	18	17	13	15	18
6	5	3	4	2	2	1	2	2	1	2	3	2	3	1	2	3	3	2
7	18	19	19	19	12	10	6	8	11	7	7	5	4	4	5	4	6	20
8	4	3	4	7	7	6	2	3	7	9	7	2	4	4	7	12	9	5
9	3	3	2	3	1	1	1	1	1	3	4	3	3	3	4	3	3	0
10	10	8	11	12	13	8	12	12	7	8	9	13	12	8	12	12	13	7
11	0	1	0	1	0	1	1	3	2	2	0	4	1	2	2	2	1	1
12	0	0	0	0	0	1	1	0	0	0	0	0	0	0	0	0	0	1
13	3	2	1	1	3	8	11	5	7	8	8	7	8	8	4	4	4	1
51	5	5	8	4	5	7	4	3	6	4	7	9	7	8	7	6	6	2
52	2	4	5	5	7	11	3	8	5	5	5	7	7	5	8	6	3	9
55	0	0	0	0	0	0	0	0	0	0	0	0	0	0	0	0	0	0
56	2	3	1	2	1	4	3	1	2	1	2	1	2	2	1	1	3	1

DOI: 10.1371 /journal.pbio.0020005.t001

difference is again striking: 94 out of 96 comparisons are significant at the 5% level. Thus, the evolution of full trichromatic vision coincided with an increase in the fraction of OR pseudogenes, indicative of a deterioration of the sense of smell.

Apes and OWMs acquired trichromatic color vision approximately 23 million years ago (Yokoyama and Yokoyama 1989), while the duplication of the opsin genes in the howler monkey occurred approximately 7–16 million years ago (Jacobs 1996; Cortes-Ortiz et al.

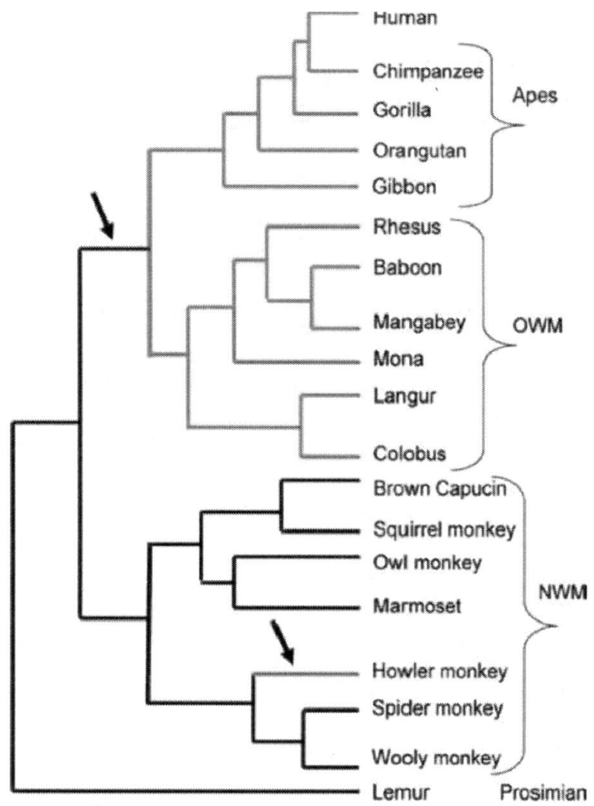

Figure 3. Phylogenetic Tree of Primates

Schematic phylogenetic tree of the primate species used in the current study. Phylogenetic relationships between species are based on Harada et al. (1995), Page et al. (1999), and Surridge et al. (2003). Arrows indicate on which lineages the acquisition of full trichromatic color vision occurred (Goodman et al. 1998; Jacobs and Deegan 2001). The grey color highlights lineages with a high proportion of OR pseudogenes. DOI: 10.1371/journal.pbio.0020005.g003

2003). In spite of this difference in timing, the proportion of OR pseudogenes in species from both lineages is very similar. We estimated the rate of fixation of neutral gene disruptions for OR genes to be approximately 0.12 per gene per million years (Y. Gilad, S. Pääbo, and G. Glusman, unpublished data). This estimate implies that both apes, OWMs and the howler monkey could have a much higher proportion of OR pseudogenes than observed (data not shown), indicating that the process of functional OR gene loss has decreased or stopped in these species. A plausible explanation for the similar proportion of OR pseudogenes in the different lineages is that while full trichromatic vision relaxed the need for a sensitive sense of smell, it did not render olfaction unnecessary. Accordingly, while some OR genes can accumulate coding region disruptions, others are still evolving under evolutionary constraint. This model predicts that the possession of full trichromatic color vision alone allows for the loss of some but not all OR genes. A natural next step would then be to identify which OR genes or families were lost after the acquisition of full trichromatic vision. The answer to this question awaits sequence from a large number of orthologous OR genes.

In this respect, it is interesting to note that the *TRP2* gene, a major component of the vomeronasal pheromone transduction pathway, was found to be intact in several NWM species, but is a pseudogene in OWMs and apes (Liman and Innan 2003; Zhang and Webb 2003). The authors raised the possibility of a connection between the acquisition of full trichromatic color vision and decreased pheromone perception, based on the difference between OWMs and apes on the one hand and NWMs on the other (Liman and Innan 2003; Zhang and Webb 2003). However, since many traits can potentially be mapped to the lineage that leads to OWMs and apes, the connection between full trichromatic vision and pheromone perception was tenuous. Furthermore, Liman and Innan (2003) did not find a coding region disruption in four exons of *TRP2* in the howler monkey. An intact *TRP2* gene in the howler monkey would be inconsistent with the hypothesis that the enhancement of color vision replaced pheromone signaling in primates.

In contrast, in the present study, we find that the deterioration of the olfactory repertoire occurred concomitant with the evolution of full trichromatic vision in two separate primate lineages. Thus, although at this point we are unable to demonstrate that the decline in the sense of smell is a direct result of the evolution of color vision, our results strongly suggest an exchange in the importance of these two senses in primate evolution. Future studies of the sensory cues involved in detection and selection of food (e.g., Smith et al. 2003), or the choice of a mate, may test this association directly.

Materials and Methods

Design and test of degenerate primers.

OR genes have a coding region that is approximately 1 kb long and contains no introns. In order to test the performance of degenerate primers, we sequenced 30 genes amplified with each primer pair in human and mouse and compared the composition of the different OR families in the sample to that of the full OR gene repertoire of these two species (Glusman et al. 2001; Zhang and Firestein 2002). We also compared the sample estimates of the proportion of pseudogenes to the proportion in the entire OR repertoire of human and mouse. Since the degenerate primers amplify only 670 bp of the approximately 1 kb coding region of the OR gene, a subset of the coding region disruptions will fall in segments of OR genes not amplified by our primers. As a result, the true fraction of OR genes carrying coding region disruptions will be underestimated by our approach. We therefore determined the proportion of OR genes with at least one disruption within the corresponding 670 bp in the entire human and mouse OR gene repertoires (47.7% and 16.3% in humans and mouse, respectively).

We first tested an existing set of primers, used by Rouquier et al. (2000), but found significant deviations from the family composition of the full OR repertoire in both species. As an illustration, among the 60 OR genes obtained in humans, 36.6 % were of the subfamily 7E (all pseudogenes), significantly more than expected given the true proportion of the 7E subfamily in the full human OR gene repertoire (12.4%, p = 2 3 10-6, assessed by FET). As a consequence of these biases, estimates of the proportion of pseudogenes in human and mouse obtained with these primers (Rouquier et al. 2000) differ significantly from the true value ($p < 0.01$, assessed by FET).

We proceeded by designing new pairs of degenerate primers for the OR gene family by using the program HYDEN (Fuchs et al. 2002; Linhart and Shamir 2002). The first primer pair, PC1 (PC1-5': CTSCAYSARCCCATGTWYHWYTTBCT, PC1-3': GTYYTSAYDCHRTARAYRAYRGGGTT), was designed based on class 1 human OR sequences only. The second primer pair, PC2 (PC2-5': YTNCAYWCHCCHATGTAYTTYTTBCT, PC2-3': TTYCTNARGSTRTAGATNANDGGRTT), was designed based on solely class 2 human OR sequences, excluding all genes that belong to subfamily 7E. Both primer pairs were designed to amplify a 670-bp product that approximately covers the region from transmembrane domains 2–7 of the OR protein. As a first step, we used each primer pair to amplify and sequence (see below) 30 genes from human genomic DNA. We found that PC1 primer pairs amplify OR class 1 and OR class 2 genes in roughly equal proportions. PC2 primer pairs amplified only OR class 2 genes, including members of the 7E OR subfamily. Based on the OR family composition that we observed for the 60 genes, we estimated that if we constructed a sample containing 25% of genes amplified with PC1 and 75% of genes amplified with PC2, we would obtain an unbiased representation of the familial composition of the human OR gene repertoire. This approach was validated by amplifying and examining 100 genes collected in the same way from human as well as from mouse.

PCR and DNA sequencing.

Each primer pair was used to amplify a set of eight reactions in each species using a temperature-gradient PCR. The use of several annealing temperatures for each species yielded a greater diversity of amplified OR genes. PCR was performed in a total volume of 25 μl, containing 0.2 μM of each deoxynucleotide (Promega, Madison, Wisconsin, United States), 50 pmol of each primer, 1.5 mM MgCl2, 50 mM KCl, 10 mM Tris (pH 8.3), 2 U of Taq DNA polymerase, and 50 ng of genomic DNA. Conditions for the PCR amplification from all species were as follows: 35 cycles of denaturation at 94°C, annealing at a gradient temperature of 48°C to 60°C, and extension at 72°C, each step for 1 min. The first step of denaturation and the last step of extension were 3 min each. The PCR products were separated and visualized in a 1% agarose gel. From each amplification set (a given primer pair in a given species), all successful products were mixed and subjected to cloning using a TA cloning kit (Boehringer, Mannheim, Germany). Cloning was followed by a touchdown PCR using the vector primers for amplifications from isolated bacterial colonies. Products were purified using the High Pure PCR Product Purification Kit (Boehringer). Sequencing reactions were performed in both directions on PCR products, using the vector primers and the dye-terminator cycle sequencing kit (Perkin Elmer, Wellesley, Massachusetts, United States) on an ABI 3700 automated sequencer (Perkin Elmer).

Sequence analysis.

After base calling with the ABI Analysis Software (version 3.0), the data were edited and assembled using the Sequencher program, version 4.0 (GeneCodes Corporation, Ann Arbor, Michigan, United States). Assembly of the clones was done using a similarity cutoff of 98%. This cutoff ensures that Taq-generated mutations that may have been sequenced in individual clones are not counted as independent genes. Clones that were collapsed to the same contig by the assembly process were counted as one gene. Once 25 and 75 genes (independent contigs) were identified from PC1 and PC2 primer pairs, respectively, a majority consensus was generated for each gene. In order to confirm that only OR genes were amplified from all the species, we used the consensus sequences of all genes from all species as queries in a BLAT search against the human genome sequence (http://genome.ucsc.edu/). In every case, the best hit was a human OR gene. This analysis was also used to insure that none of the genes were an artifact of ("jumping") PCR fusion. Finally, each consensus sequence was searched for an uninterrupted open reading frame (ORF) in all six possible frames. If an uninterrupted ORF was found, the gene was annotated as intact. If no ORF was identified, the gene was annotated as a pseudogene. This approach probably results in an underestimate of the proportion of pseudogenes, as not all OR genes with an intact coding region are functional. Mutations in promoter or control regions of OR genes may lead to reduced or no expression. Similarly, radical missense mutations in highly conserved positions of the OR protein may result in dysfunction (Menashe et al. 2003). Although it is known that there are several highly conserved positions among OR genes, it is not always straightforward to ascertain which, if any, of these positions is necessary to retain function. We therefore chose the most straight-forward definition of a pseudogene: a gene without a full ORF.

Supporting Information

Accession Numbers

Sequences for all OR genes from all primate species were deposited to GenBank (http://www.ncbi.nlm.nih.gov/Genbank/) as accession numbers AY448037-AY449380 and AY454789-AY455274.

Acknowledgments

We thank Christian Roos from the Primate Genetics German Primate Center in Göttingen for the primate DNA samples. We are also grateful to Chaim Linhart from Tel Aviv University for helping us to design the degenerate primer pairs. The experimental work was financed by the Bundesministerium für Bildung und Forschung (01KW9959-4) and by the Max Planck Gesellschaft. This research was completed while YG was supported by a Clore doctoral fellowship. DL holds the Ralph and Lois Silver Chair in Human Genomics and is supported by the Crown Human Genome Center at the Weizmann Institute of Science.

Author contributions.

YG and MP conceived and designed the experiments. YG and VW performed the experiments. YG and VW analyzed the data. SP contributed reagents/materials/analysis tools. YG, MP, DL, and SP wrote the paper.

References

Ben-Arie N, Lancet D, Taylor C, Khen M, Walker N, et al. (1994) Olfactory receptor gene cluster on human chromosome 17: Possible duplication of an ancestral receptor repertoire. Hum Mol Genet 3: 229–235.

Boissinot S, Tan Y, Shyue SK, Schneider H, Sampaio I, et al. (1998) Origins and antiquity of X-linked triallelic color vision systems in New World monkeys. Proc Natl Acad Sci U S A 95: 13749–13754.

Buck L, Axel R (1991) A novel multigene family may encode odorant receptors: A molecular basis for odor recognition. Cell 65: 175–187.

Cortes-Ortiz L, Bermingham E, Rico C, Rodriguez-Luna E, Sampaio I, et al. (2003) Molecular systematics and biogeography of the Neotropical monkey genus, *Alouatta*. Mol Phylogenet Evol 26: 64–81.

Dominy NJ, Lucas PW (2001) Ecological importance of trichromatic vision to primates. Nature 410: 363–366.

Fuchs T, Malecova B, Linhart C, Sharan R, Khen M, et al. (2002) DEFOG: A practical scheme for deciphering families of genes. Genomics 80: 295–302.

Gilad Y, Segre D, Skorecki K, Nachman MW, Lancet D, et al. (2000) Dichotomy of single-nucleotide polymorphism haplotypes in olfactory receptor genes and pseudogenes. Nat Genet 26: 221–224.

Gilad Y, Man O, Paabo S, Lancet D (2003) Human specific loss of olfactory receptor genes. Proc Natl Acad Sci U S A 100: 3324–3327.

Glusman G, Yanai I, Rubin I, Lancet D (2001) The complete human olfactory subgenome. Genome Res 11: 685–702.

Goodman M, Porter CA, Czelusniak J, Page SL, Schneider H, et al. (1998) Toward a phylogenetic classification of primates based on DNA evidence complemented by fossil evidence. Mol Phylogenet Evol 9: 585–598.

Harada ML, Schneider H, Schneider MP, Sampaio I, Czelusniak J, et al. (1995) DNA evidence on the phylogenetic systematics of New World monkeys: Support for the sister-grouping of *Cebusand Saimiri* from two unlinked nuclear genes. Mol Phylogenet Evol 4: 331–349.

Hunt DM, Dulai KS, Cowing JA, Julliot C, Mollon JD, et al. (1998) Molecular evolution of trichromacy in primates. Vision Res 38: 3299–3306.

Jacobs GH (1996) Primate photopigments and primate color vision. Proc Natl Acad Sci U S A 93: 577–81.

Jacobs GH, Deegan JF II (2001) Photopigments and colour vision in New World monkeys from the family Atelidae. Proc R Soc Lond B Biol Sci 268: 695–702.

Jacobs GH, Neitz M, Deegan JF, Neitz J (1996) Trichromatic colour vision in New World monkeys. Nature 382: 156–158.

Liman ER, Innan H (2003) Relaxed selective pressure on an essential component of pheromone transduction in primate evolution. Proc Natl Acad Sci U S A 100: 3328–3332.

Linhart C, Shamir R (2002) The degenerate primer design problem.Bioinformatics 18 (Suppl 1): S172–S181.

Menashe I, Man O, Lancet D, Gilad Y (2003) Different noses for different people. Nat Genet 34: 143–144.

Nathans J, Thomas D, Hogness DS (1986) Molecular genetics of human color vision: The genes encoding blue, green, and red pigments. Science 232: 193–202.

Olender T, Fuchs T, Linhart C, Shamir R, Adams M, et al. (2003) The canine olfactory subgenome. Genomics. In press.

Page SL, Chiu C, Goodman M (1999) Molecular phylogeny of Old World monkeys (*Cercopithecidae*) as inferred from gamma-globin DNA sequences. Mol Phylogenet Evol 13: 348–359.

Rouquier S, Taviaux S, Trask BJ, Brand-Arpon V, van den Engh G, et al. (1998) Distribution of olfactory receptor genes in the human genome. Nat Genet 18: 243–250.

Rouquier S, Blancher A, Giorgi D (2000) The olfactory receptor gene repertoire in primates and mouse: Evidence for reduction of the functional fraction in primates. Proc Natl Acad Sci U S A 97: 2870–2874.

Smith AC, Buchanan-Smith HM, Surridge AK, Osorio D, Mundy NI (2003) The effect of colour vision status on the detection and selection of fruits by tamarins (*Saguinus* spp.). J Exp Biol 206: 3159–3165.

Surridge AK, Osorio D, Mundy NI (2003) Evolution and selection of trichromatic vision in primates. Trends Ecol Evol 18: 198–205.

Trask BJ, Massa H, Brand-Arpon V, Chan K, Friedman C, et al. (1998) Large multichromosomal duplications encompass many members of the olfactory receptor gene family in the human genome. Hum Mol Genet 7: 2007–2020.

Yokoyama S, Yokoyama R (1989) Molecular evolution of human visual pigment genes. Mol Biol Evol 6: 186–197.

Young JM, Trask BJ (2002) The sense of smell: Genomics of vertebrate odorant receptors. Hum Mol Genet 11: 1153–1160.

Young JM, Friedman C, Williams EM, Ross JA, Tonnes-Priddy L, et al. (2002) Different evolutionary processes shaped the mouse and human olfactory receptor gene families. Hum Mol Genet 11: 535–546.

Zhang J, Webb DM (2003) Evolutionary deterioration of the vomeronasal pheromone transduction pathway in catarrhine primates. Proc Natl Acad Sci U S A 100: 8337–8341.

Zhang X, Firestein S (2002) The olfactory receptor gene superfamily of the mouse. Nat Neurosci 5: 124–133.

Zozulya S, Echevrri F, Nguyen T (2001) The human olfactory receptor repertoire. Genome Biol 2: RESEARCH0018.

SECTION 5

KIN SELECTION

Introduction to Chapter 6

Altruism has been demonstrated to evolve via two mechanisms. Kin selection, one of these mechanisms, was first described by W. D. Hamilton. Its role in shaping primate social behavior is summarized in this chapter.

An odd accident of history and perhaps personal prejudice is that a Nobel Prize in biology was never established. Be that as it may, another wealthy Swedish industrialist, Holger Crafoord, attempted to remedy Nobel's oversight in 1980 by founding the Crafoord Prize in Biosciences. In 1993, this esteemed prize was awarded to W. D. Hamilton for his development of kin selection theory.

The idea of kin selection is so central to modern evolutionary theory that you already met it in Chapter 1. Why is kin selection such a big idea? The answer is that it was the first logically coherent solution to the puzzle of how altruism might evolve. To biologists, "altruism" does not simply mean being nice. Just as the term "fitness" has a technical meaning for evolutionists, so does the term "altruism." An altruistic trait is one that reduces the reproductive success of the individual who manifests it while increasing the reproductive success of one or more neighbors of the altruist. The altruist sustains a fitness cost and the neighbor receives a fitness benefit. A simple example of altruism would be giving food to a hungry person, or (assuming there was a cost of doing so) warning someone of approaching danger.

The very definition of altruism (a fitness cost for the actor combined with a fitness benefit for the recipient) highlights the central evolutionary problem: How can a trait that lowers fitness spread, especially when it increases the fitness of potential competitors? The answer was explained in the last section of Chapter 1. If you do not remember it, you may find it helpful to reread that section before beginning Chapter 6.

We should emphasize that altruism is only one of four hypothetically possible kinds of traits. Trait X could increase or decrease the fitness of individuals who have it. (These effects would be shown to the right or to the left, respectively, of the origin in Figure D.) And the same trait, X, might simultaneously increase or decrease the fitness of the individuals' neighbors (above and below the origin, respectively). For example, if John has a mate-stealing trait, that would increase his fitness but decrease his (male) neighbor's fitness. The conjunction of such effects, on self and on neighbors, defines the four quadrants of Figure D and therefore the four kinds of traits. John's mate-stealing trait would fall in the selfish quadrant. Selfish traits are not difficult to explain evolutionarily, because genes for these traits will get a boost from their positive effects on the reproductive success of the individuals who have them. Keep in mind, however, that altruistic traits will decrease the fitness of those who have them. That is why evolutionists have struggled to explain altruism and, consequently, why the theory of kin selection is so important.

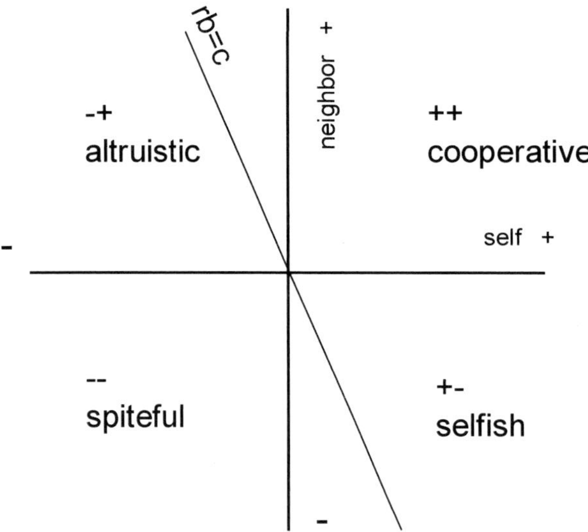

Figure D: Four kinds of traits, categorized by their fitness effects on self (horizontal axis) and on neighbors (vertical axis).

Kin selection theory does not predict that the altruistic quadrant will be fully occupied; it predicts only limited altruism. Altruism that satisfies *Hamilton's Rule* (rb>c) is favored by kin selection; altruism that does not is disfavored. We defined r, b, and c in Chapter 1, but to refresh your memory, b and c measure the benefit and cost (respectively), measured in fitness units, of the altruistic act. And r measures the degree of genetic similarity between the altruist and the recipient; specifically, it gives a numerical value to the chance that a randomly chosen gene in the altruist is also present in the recipient.

If you remember your analytic geometry, the distinction between altruism that is favored by kin selection (because it satisfies Hamilton's Rule) and altruism that is disfavored can be seen in Figure D. The diagonal line rb=c defines the boundary between altruism that is favored (above and to the right) and disfavored (below and to the left). When r is larger, as it is for more closely related kin, the rb=c line will have a shallower slope, thus bringing a larger wedge of the altruistic quadrant into the favored region. Translating back to English, kin selection theory predicts greater altruism to more closely related kin. To see if you fully understand the implications of kin selection, try to explain what it means to extend the diagonal line into the selfish quadrant.

Professor Silk begins by explaining the misstep, made by Darwin himself, of group selection. She shows why benefits to the group as a whole will *not* cause altruistic tendencies to spread. Then she shows how kin selection *would* cause altruistic tendencies to spread, *if and only if* the altruism provides benefits to the altruistic *genes* themselves. Her primary goal in this chapter is to see how kin selection works on the ground, so to speak, in contemporary primates. She makes no attempt to give an exhaustive review of all documented instances of kin selection, but instead focuses on several well studied examples. Pay attention to how kin selection influences the behavior of individuals, but also to how those resulting individual behavior patterns go on to shape the structure of whole social groups. In other words, groups are not random collections of individuals broadcasting indiscriminate altruism (as would be predicted by group selection). Instead, they are kinship-weighted webs of more and less altruistic associations among highly discriminating actors. The tendrils of evolution are everywhere.

Chapter 6 Glossary

callitrichid: The marmosets and tamarins; the smallest New World monkeys.

philopatry: Remaining to live as an adult near where you were born; failing to disperse from you natal area. Male philopatry means males do not disperse; female philopatry means that females do not.

Chapter 6
Kin Selection in Primate Groups (2002)

Joan B. Silk[1]

Altruism poses a problem for evolutionary biologists because natural selection is not expected to favor behaviors that are beneficial to recipients, but costly to actors. The theory of kin selection, first articulated by Hamilton (1964), provides a solution to the problem. Hamilton's well-known rule (br > c) provides a simple algorithm for the evolution of altruism via kin selection. Because kin recognition is a crucial requirement of kin selection, it is important to know whether and how primates can recognize their relatives. While conventional wisdom has been that primates can recognize maternal kin, but not paternal kin, this view is being challenged by new findings. The ability to recognize kin implies that kin selection may shape altruistic behavior in primate groups. I focus on two cases in which kin selection is tightly woven into the fabric of social life. For female baboons, macaques, and vervets maternal kinship is an important axis of social networks, coalitionary activity, and dominance relationships. Detailed studies of the patterning of altruistic interactions within these species illustrate the extent and limits of nepotism in their social lives. Carefully integrated analyses of behavior, demography, and genetics among red howlers provide an independent example of how kin selection shapes social organization and behavior. In red howlers, kin bonds shape the life histories and reproductive performance of both males and female. The two cases demonstrate that kin selection can be a powerful source of altruistic activity within

Key Words: altruism; kinship; kin selection; reciprocity.

---

[1] Department of Anthropology, University of California–Los Angeles, Los Angeles, California 90095; e-mail: Jsilk@anthro.ucla.edu.

Joan B. Silk, "Kin Selection in Primate Groups," from *International Journal of Primatology*, Vol. 23 No. 4; August 2002, pp. 849–875. Published by Springer New York LLC, 2002.

primate groups. However, to fully assess the role of kin selection in primate groups, we need more information about the effects of kinship on the patterning of behavior across the Primates and accurate information about paternal kin relationships.

The Problem of Altruism

Since Darwin's day biologists have been aware that animals perform some behaviors that enhance the fitness of others, but not themselves. In *The Descent of Man, and Selection in Relation to Sex*, Darwin (1871, p. 75) wrote:

> *"Social animals perform many little services for each other: horses nibble, and cows lick each other, on any spot which itches: monkeys search for each other's external parasites; and Brehm states that after a troop of the Cercopithecus griseo-viridus has rushed through a thorny brake, each monkey stretches itself on a branch, and another monkey sitting by "conscientiously" examines its fur and extracts every thorn or burr.*
>
> *Animals also render more important services to each other: thus wolves and some other beasts of prey hunt in packs, and aid each other in attacking their victims. Pelicans fish in concert. The Hamadryas baboons turn over stones to find insects, and when they come to a large one, as many as can stand round, turn it over together and share the booty ..."*

These examples intrigued, but troubled, Darwin because he realized that they contradicted the general logic of his theory of evolution by natural selection (Richards, 1987). Concurrently, however, he was convinced that the social instincts that produced behaviors like these played a fundamental role in social life and the evolution of moral sensibilities in modern humans (Darwin, 1871).

Eventually, Darwin worked out a solution to the problem. He suggested that "With strictly social animals, natural selection sometimes acts indirectly on the individual, through the preservation of variations which are beneficial only to the community. A community including a number of well-endowed individuals increases in number and is victorious over other and less well-endowed communities; although each separate member may gain no advantage over the other members of the same community" (Darwin, 1871:155).

Although this solution relieved Darwin's anxiety about the viability of his theory, we now know that his intuition misled him. Traits that confer advantages to the group do not persist unless certain conditions are met. To see where Darwin went wrong, imagine a hypothetical species of monkeys in which there is a genetically-inherited tendency to give alarm calls. Monkeys are distributed into groups at random with respect to the trait. Thus, the distribution of the trait in each group will be, on average, the same as the distribution in the population at large. Animals that inherit the alarm calling trait are inclined to give alarm calls when they are the first to spot predators (callers) while ones that do not inherit the trait are inclined to remain silent when they sight predators (noncallers). Callers make themselves conspicuous to predators and increase their own vulnerability, while animals that are alerted by alarm calls are more likely to escape attack. Thus, calling is costly to the actor and beneficial to the recipients.

Natural selection will favor the evolution of calling if callers have higher fitness on average than noncallers. Imagine a situation in which a caller is the first to spot the predator. She calls, allowing all the other members of the group to flee to safety and thereby gain a fitness advantage. Now imagine another group in which a noncaller sees the predator first, but does not alert the group. This reduces their chance of escaping the predator, and therefore reduces the fitness of all group members. Even though the members of the caller's group are better off on average than members of the noncaller's group, calling is not favored because calling is costly to the caller herself. Thus, the average fitness of callers will be lower than the average fitness of noncallers, and the trait will become less common in the population. In situations like these, alarm calling will not be favored by natural selection even if the costs of calling are small and the benefits of calling for other group members are quite substantial.

Solutions to Darwin's Problem

The first cogent explanation for the evolution of behaviors like alarm calling was provided by Hamilton (1964), who recognized that any process that would cause callers to interact selectively with other callers could facilitate the evolution of alarm calling behavior. More specifically, he suggested that selective interaction among kin, which are descended from a common ancestor, could promote the evolution of traits like alarm calling. He called the process kin selection. If callers live in groups composed of kin, then they enhance the fitness of others that are likely to carry copies of the same genes. Even though the caller reduces her own fitness, her call increases the fitness of her relatives, which may be callers themselves. In this situation, callers are more likely to benefit from calling than noncallers, so calling alters the relative fitness of callers and noncallers. At the same time, because kin aggregate together, noncallers are less likely to find themselves in groups with callers than expected by chance alone. The same logic can be applied to any form of behavior that is costly to the actor and beneficial to the recipient.

Selective interaction with other altruists is a necessary, but insufficient, condition for the evolution of behaviors like alarm calling. In the hypothetical situation, calling will only evolve if the benefits of calling sufficiently outweigh the costs of becoming more conspicuous to predators. The adaptive value of an alarm call or other altruistic act depends on the fitness costs to the donor and the benefits conferred on the recipient. Hamilton (1964) demonstrated that behaviors like alarm calling will be favored by selection if the costs of performing the behavior (c) are less than the benefits (b) discounted by the coefficient of relatedness between actor and recipient (r). The coefficient of relatedness is the average probability that two individuals acquire the same allele through descent from a common ancestor. This can be expressed simply in Hamilton's rule: $br > c$.

Hamilton's Rule generates two general predictions about the evolution of altruistic behavior via kin selection. First, altruism should be limited to kin, because the inequality can only be satisfied when $r > 0$. Second, costly altruism should be restricted to close kin. When $r = 0.5$, the degree of relateness between parents and offspring, the benefits must exceed just twice the costs to the actor in order to satisfy the inequality. But when $r = 0.125$, as it is among first cousins, the benefits must exceed 8 times the cost. Thus, close kinship facilitates costly altruism.

Kin selection plays a fundamental role in the organization of behavior in a variety of animal taxa. Perhaps the most obvious example of kin selection comes from studies of social insects, particularly eusocial species (Bourke, 1997 and Seger, 1991). In cooperatively breeding birds, kinship influences the likelihood of becoming a helper and the distribution of help given to group members (Emlen, 1991, 1997; Jaisson, 1991; Ligon, 1991). Similar patterns occur in eusocial naked mole rats (Jarvis *et al.*, 1994), cooperatively breeding lions (Packer and Pusey, 1997), brown hyenas (Owen and Owen, 1984), and dwarf mongooses (Creel *et al.*, 1991). In other social mammals, kinship influences the distribution of altruistic behaviors such as alarm calling in ground squirrels (Sherman, 1977) and allomaternal behavior in elephants (Lee, 1987).

Although kin selection is a powerful mechanism to generate altruism in nature, it is not the only possible means. Altruism can also evolve via reciprocal altruism if pairs of individuals balance the benefits and costs of altruistic acts over time (Axelrod and Hamilton, 1981; Dugatkin, 1997; Trivers, 1971). Reciprocal altruism works because individuals selectively aid reciprocating partners, and altruism is therefore restricted to reciprocators. Thus, kin selection and reciprocal altruism both rely on Hamilton's (1964) insight that altruistic behaviors can only evolve if there is some mechanism that causes altruists to interact selectively with other altruists.

Problems of Definition and Measurement

Behaviors like alarm calling are considered to be altruistic because they are costly to actors and beneficial to recipients. Some workers have complained about use of the word altruism in this context because behaviors that evolve through kin selection are phenotypically (or self-) sacrificing, but genotypically selfish (Alexander, 1974). This contradicts the common

English usage of the word altruism, which connotes unselfish, self-sacrificial acts (Fletcher, 1987). Alexander (1974) and Fletcher (1987) suggested that we use nepotism to refer to behavior that evolved via kin selection. However, this creates at least one new semantic problem. Nepotism implies preferential treatment of kin, but is silent about the nature of the effects on the actor. Thus, I use the term altruism to describe any behavior that reduces the fitness of the actor and increases the fitness of the recipients ($b > c$) and nepotism to describe preferential treatment of kin, regardless of the relative magnitude of b and c.

Practical difficulties arise when we try to test predictions derived from Hamilton's rule in nature. It is rarely possible to quantify the effects of a behavioral act or social interaction on lifetime fitness, particularly in long-lived animals like primates, and thus difficult actually to measure b and c. Testing predictions derived from Hamilton's Rule also requires information about genetic relatedness. Until recently, primatologists have relied on demographic data for this information. Thus, observers record births to known females and construct geneologies from them. This is a slow and painstaking task and still provides only half the information that is necessary to measure relatedness. Geneologies derived from demographic data trace relatedness through maternal lines. Thus, most studies that examine the effects of kinship on social behavior actually evaluate the effects of maternal kinship on behavior. This would not matter if monkeys were unable to recognize paternal kin, but it does matter if they can. Although new genetic techniques allow primatologists to identify paternity and to obtain more accurate measurements of relatedness, relatively few behavioral studies incorporating these kinds of data have been published.

How can we study kin selection if we can't measure the relevant parameters? This problem is common to almost all studies of the adaptive function of social behavior in animals. We rely on the phenotypic gambit (Grafen, 1991): the assumption that the short-term benefits that individuals derive from social interactions are ultimately translated into long-term differences in fitness. Animals that are regularly supported in agonistic confrontations, protected from harassment, or allowed to share access to desirable resources are expected to gain short-term benefits that are ultimately translated into fitness gains.

Assessing the Role of Kin Selection in Primate Groups

A review of the role of kin selection in the evolution of social behavior among primates should be carefully balanced across taxa and should cover the full range of relevant behavioral phenomena. Unfortunately, the empirical record is biased. We know much more about behavioral patterns in Old World monkeys than we do about the behavior of New World monkeys and prosimians. Few studies on New World monkeys or prosimians have continued long enough to construct the kinds of geneologies that are necessary to examine the effects of kinship on social behavior. Modern molecular genetic techniques shorten the time required to do this, but studies that include these sorts of data are limited in number and scope. This means that most of what we currently know about the effects of kinship on social behavior comes from a relatively small number of species and is limited to maternal kin.

To assess the role of kin selection we would also need to gauge the importance of kin selection across the full range of altruistic behaviors that occur in nature. However, the empirical record is uneven. We know much more about the distribution of relatively common behaviors like grooming and coalition formation than we do about less common behaviors like alarm calling and food sharing (Bernstein, 1991; Gouzoules and Gouzoules, 1987; Silk, 1987; Walters, 1987a). For example, I located only one primate study on the effects of kinship on the likelihood of giving alarm calls (Cheney and Seyfarth, 1985).

Consequently, I rely on a relatively limited set of behaviors in a relatively small number of species. I have deliberately chosen to focus on cases in which kin selection plays a crucial role because they illuminate how kin selection can shape the evolution of social organization, reproductive strategies, and social behavior. Moreover, by studying a small number of examples in depth we can get a better sense of how kinship is woven into the fabric of social life.

Kin Recognition

> *"In general ... finding of ability to discriminate [kin], even if uses made of it are still obscure is prima facie suggestion of the importance that kin selection is likely to have in nature" (Hamilton, 1987).*

The coefficient of relatedness, *r*, is the critical element to determine an adaptive course of action in social interactions (Hamilton, 1987). In order to meet the conditions of Hamilton's rule, animals must limit altruistic behavior to their kin ($r > 0$). For species in which kin are clustered in discrete locations, such as in burrows or nests, spatial location may provide sufficient information for kin discrimination (Blaustein *et al.*, 1987). However, for other animals the problem is more complicated. The ability to discriminate kin is expected to be most fully developed in species that live in social groups, when there are opportunities for costly fitness-reducing behaviors, such as egg dumping, and when simple cues for distinguishing kin from nonkin (such as location) are not likely to be effective (Hamilton, 1987).

Primates fit all three of these conditions. Most primates live in large, relatively stable social groups (Smuts *et al.*, 1987). Even the most solitary primates, like orangutans and galagos, have regular interactions with familiar conspecifics (Bearder, 1987; Delgado and van Schaik, 2000; Galdikas, 1988). Primates engage in a variety of fitness-reducing behaviors, including infanticide (van Schaik and Janson, 2000); severe intragroup aggression (Crockett, 1984; McGrew and McLuckie, 1986; Sauther *et al.*, 1999; Silk *et al.*, 1981; Vick and Pereira, 1989); and intense feeding competition (Dittus, 1979, 1988). Most primates live for extended periods of time in groups that include both relatives and nonrelatives, so context-driven mechanisms for distinguishing kin are likely to be of limited use. Thus, primates are expected to exhibit finely developed kin recognition abilities.

Several different perceptual mechanisms underlie kin recognition (Sherman *et al.*, 1997). For example, sea squirts are able to recognize other sea squirts that carry the same allele on the hypervariable histocompatability locus (Pfennig and Sherman, 1995). Some animals learn to identify their relatives during development, drawing cues about kinship from patterns of association and interactions. This is thought to be the most common mechanism for kin recognition, particularly among mothers and offspring (Holmes and Sherman, 1983).

Close association early in life is generally thought to be the basis for kin recognition in primate groups (Bernstein, 1991; Walters, 1987a). Early association may provide an efficient mechanism to learn to recognize maternal kin, but not for identifying paternal kin. This is because close associations between males and females are uncommon in many primate species, limiting infants' abilities to identify their paternal kin. Moreover, there may be considerable uncertainty about paternity in most primate species. Even in pair-bonded species, like gibbons and titis, females sometimes mate with males outside their groups (Mason, 1966; Palombit, 1994; Reichard, 1995). In some species that form one-male groups, such as patas and blue monkeys, incursions by nonresident males may occur during the mating season (Cords, 1987). In multimale species, male rank is often correlated with reproductive success, but the association is imperfect.

If primates rely on early association to identify their relatives and associations between males and infants are unreliable cues of paternity, then paternal kin recognition would have to be based on the ability to recognize familial alleles or phenotypic matching. Wu *et al.* (1980) caused a minor sensation when they reported that juvenile monkeys showed behavioral preferences for unfamiliar half-siblings over unfamiliar nonrelatives. This was a striking result, but subsequent efforts to replicate it were unsuccessful (Fredrickson and Sackett, 1984; Sackett and Fredrickson, 1987). Small and Smith (1981) reported that mothers were more tolerant of infant handling by their infants' paternal half siblings than by unrelated juveniles, which would imply that monkeys could identify paternal kin (Walters, 1987a). However, Bernstein (1991) found that Small and Smith's statistical analysis is flawed, and the effect they reported disappeared when he reanalyzed the data.

Subsequent studies have examined the independent effects of familiarity and kinship on interaction patterns among young monkeys (Erhart *et al.*, 1997; MacKenzie *et al.*, 1985; Welker *et al.*, 1987). In all 3 studies, monkeys showed clear preferences for familiar conspecifics over unfamiliar conspecifics. In 2 of the studies, monkeys did not discriminate among kin and nonkin when familiarity was held constant (Erhart *et al.*, 1997; Welker *et al.*, 1987). The results of the third study are anomalous: monkeys seemed to prefer paternal kin over unfamiliar nonkin when familiarity and rearing conditions were controlled, but showed no preference for familiar maternal kin (MacKenzie *et al.*, 1985). Several other researchers who examined the effects of kinship on mating preferences in captive populations reported strong inhibitions of mating with maternal kin, but no inhibition against mating with paternal kin (Inouye *et al.*, 1990; Kuester *et al.*, 1994; Smith, 1986).

Thus, most researchers have become convinced that primates rely on familiarity to distinguish kin from nonkin and therefore cannot recognize paternal kin. For example, in a review of the role of kinship in primate societies, Gouzoules and Gouzoules (1987, p. 304) concluded that available evidence from studies of baboons and macaques "cast considerable doubt on the ability of males to recognize their own infants independent of close behavioral association." Later, Chapais (1995, p. 117) wrote "Relatedness through the father, although of significant importance due to the prevalence of polygyny is not recognized in macaques: paternal half-siblings cannot recognize each other." And Mitani *et al.* (2000) reasoned, "… internal fertilization coupled with a promiscuous mating system … render it doubtful that male chimpanzees possess an ability to recognize paternal relatives."

Recent evidence suggests that the conventional wisdom may need to be reconsidered; nonhuman primates apparently recognize their own paternal kin in some situations. Widdig and her colleagues (Widdig *et al.*, 2001, in press) compared the rate and pattern of social interactions among maternal half-sisters, paternal half-sisters, and unrelated females among rhesus macaques on Cayo Santiago. Females showed strong affinities for maternal half-sisters, as expected. However, they also showed strong affinities for their paternal half-sisters, spending more time grooming and in close proximity to them than to unrelated females. Age may be a good proxy for paternal kinship as high-ranking males monopolize access to females and agemates are therefore likely to be paternal halfsiblings (Altmann, 1979). This means that monkeys might use age similarity as a context-dependent mechanism to distinguish kin from nonkin. In Widdig *et al.*'s study, females generally preferred agemates over others. Dunbar and Dunbar (1975), Pereira and Altmann (1985) and Walters (1987a,b) obtained similar results. However, Widdig and her colleagues found that female macaques also distinguished among their agemates, preferring paternal halfsiblings over nonkin.

These results are consistent with more limited evidence from a study of consort behavior among baboons in Amboseli, Kenya (Alberts, 1999). Although male dispersal typically limits opportunities for consortships among siblings, dispersal was delayed in one garbage-feeding group. Alberts (1999) found that consortships among agemates were typically less cohesive than consortships among nonagemates. However, the 3 pairs of agemates that were also paternal halfsiblings had the least cohesive consorts of all pairs of agemates, while the pairs of agemates with the most cohesive consorts were unrelated.

In Amboseli, adult female baboons also show affinities for age mates and preferences for paternal kin over unrelated individuals (Smith, 2000). Taken together, these studies suggest that cercopithecine females may use two rules of thumb to assess kinship: (*a*) treat as kin individuals known since birth, and (*b*) treat as kin individuals that bear familial cues (Smith, 2000).

Finally, there is tentative, but intriguing, evidence that primates may be able to recognize kinship from visual cues alone. Parr and de Waal (1999) found that chimpanzee females are able to match digitized photographs of unfamiliar females with their sons, but not with their daughters. Since the chimpanzees were unfamiliar with the individuals in the photographs and had no physical, auditory, or olfactory contact with them, their ability to identify mother-son pairs suggests that chimpanzees use visual cues to assess similarity. If the chimpanzee success in matching mothers and sons together is based on the ability to detect similarities in facial features, then it is possible that chimpanzees might also be able to match other kin pairs, such as fathers and sons, siblings, and so on. Of course, the chimpanzee inability to match mothers and daughters together raises some doubt about the likelihood that they can do so consistently. Moreover, it is not clear whether the chimpanzees that matched mothers and sons categorized them as kin.

Case 1: Nepotism in Macaques, Baboons, and Vervets

In macaques, baboons, and vervets matrilineal kinship underlies a suite of features, including female philopatry, well-differentiated relationships among females, matrilineal social networks, and stable matrilineal dominance hierarchies. This constellation of characteristics apparently evolved in the common ancestor of contemporary Old World monkey species and has been conserved subsequently in descendant species, even though they have radiated into diverse ecological niches throughout Africa and Asia (Di Fiore and Rendall, 1994; Rendall and Di Fiore, 1995). Thus, there are many similarities in the social structure of extant macaques, baboons, and vervets.

Matrilineal kinship bonds have a profound impact on the lives of female macaques, baboons, and vervets. Females, which remain in their natal groups throughout their lives, spend much of their time with their maternal kin, sitting near them while resting and feeding, grooming them, and handling their infants (Altmann, 1980; Chapais, 1983; Cheney, 1978; Defler, 1978; Gouzoules, 1984; Gouzoules and Gouzoules, 1987; Kapsalis and Berman, 1996a; Kurland, 1977; Missakian, 1974; Sade, 1965; Saunders, 1988; Silk, 1982,1999; Silk *et al.*, 1981,1999; Walters, 1981). They are also more likely to provide coalitionary support to members of their matrilines than to support others (Berman, 1983a,b,c; Bernstein and Ehardt, 1985,1986; Chapais, 1983a; Cheney, 1983; Datta, 1983a,b; de Waal, 1977; Kaplan, 1977, 1978; Kurland, 1977; Massey, 1977; Silk, 1982; Walters, 1981).

Although several studies indicate that female macaques are more tolerant of kin than nonkin during feeding (Belisle and Chapais, 2001; de Waal, 1986; Furiuchi, 1983; Imakawa, 1988), nepotism apparently does not extend to active food-sharing. Schaub (1996) examined female long-tailed macaques' willingness to forego feeding in order to provide food to related and unrelated group members. Females gained access to food by pulling on a counter-weighted bar. When females pulled the bar toward themselves, they simultaneously denied access to their partner. When females released the bar, they allowed their partner to feed. Schaub (1996) found that most females did not differentiate between kin and nonkin, giving them equal access to food. The significance of these results is difficult to evaluate because active food sharing is not part of their normal behavioral repertoire. Females in the experimental group showed nepotic biases in other domains, such as grooming (Schaub, 1996).

Surprisingly, kinship provides little protection against aggression, as rates of aggression are as high or higher among maternal kin than among members of different matrilines (Bernstein and Ehardt, 1985, 1986; Kurland, 1977; Silk *et al.*, 1981). Bernstein (1991) suggested that the disruptive effects of aggression on social relationships among kin may be limited because monkeys are more likely to reconcile with maternal kin than with members of other matrilines. This interpretation relies on the widely held assumption that reconciliation mends relationships that are damaged by conflict (Aureli and de Waal, 1999; *cf.* Silk, 1997).

Following Hamilton's Rule

Several lines of evidence suggest that macaques, baboons, and vervets are discriminating altruists, taking into account each of the parameters in Hamilton's rule. They seem to adjust their behavior in relation to the degree of relatedness between themselves and their partners. Thus, rhesus and Japanese macaques spend more time near close kin than near more distant kin and nonkin and groom and support close kin at higher rates than more distant kin and nonkin (Kapsalis and Berman, 1996a; Kurland, 1977). Macaques are more likely to intervene on behalf of close kin than distant kin (Chapais *et al.*, 1997; Datta, 1983c;

Kapsalis and Berman, 1996a; Kurland, 1977; Massey, 1977) and are also more tolerant of close kin than distant kin while feeding (Belisle and Chapais, 2001).

Several studies have demonstrated that altruism becomes less common as the degree of relatedness between actors and recipients declines (Belisle and Chapais, 2001; Berman, 1982; Chapais *et al.*, 1997, 2001; Kurland, 1977; Kapsalis and Berman, 1996a). Experimental and observational data suggest that macaques do not consistently discriminate between kin and nonkin when the degree of relatedness drops to <0.125 (Belisle and Chapais, 2001; Chapais *et al.*, 2001; Kapsalis and Berman, 1996a).

It is not clear whether the relatedness threshold reflects the fact that macaques do not recognize more distant relatives as kin (Kapsalis and Berman, 1996a) or that support for distant kin fails to meet the criteria for altruism specified by Hamilton's rule (Belisle and Chapais, 2001; Silk, 2000). The fact that Japanese macaques apparently apply a single criterion across several different behaviors that might have different benefit-cost structures—coalition formation, co-feeding, avoidance of homosexual interactions—suggests that the threshold is a function of kin recognition. This interpretation is also consistent with the finding that monkeys behave differently toward direct kin (great-grandmother-great-grandoffspring) and collateral kin (aunt-nephews), even though the degree of relatedness is the same ($r = 0.125$; Chapais *et al.*, 2001).

Studies of coalition formation provide further evidence that macaques are sensitive to variation in the parameters in Hamilton's Rule. Coalitions provide "the clearest evidence of primates engaging in behavior that benefits another at some risk and/or cost to self" (Bernstein, 1991), but not all agonistic encounters pose equal risks for potential allies and not all acts of support are likely to provide equal benefits to recipients (Prud'homme and Chapais, 1996; Silk, 1992; Widdig, 2000).

Females take greater risks and absorb higher costs on behalf of close kin than distant kin or nonkin. Monkeys are more likely to intervene on behalf of close kin against individuals that are higher-ranking than themselves (and therefore likely to launch counterattacks on allies) than on behalf of distant kin (Chapais *et al.*, 1997; Datta, 1983c). Moreover, when the risks to themselves are low, monkeys are more likely to intervene. Thus, members of high-ranking lineages, whose maternal kin are relatively invulnerable to retaliatory attacks, are supported by their relatives at higher rates than members of low-ranking lineages are (Berman, 1980; Chapais *et al.*, 1991; Cheney, 1977; Datta, 1983c; Horrocks and Hunte, 1983; Netto and van Hooff, 1986).

Careful studies of the process of rank acquisition in Japanese macaques suggest that even young females are sensitive to variation in cost-benefit ratios. As in other macaque species, young Japanese macaque females commonly rise in rank over their older sisters. This process is sometimes contentious, and younger sisters target their older sisters for rank reversals (Chapais *et al.*, 1994). When females intervene in disputes involving their older sisters and subordinate nonkin, they are as likely to intervene against their sisters as they are to support them. In contrast, when females intervene in conflicts involving kin that are not targeted for rank reversals, females are much more likely to intervene on behalf of their relatives than their opponents (Chapais *et al.*, 1994). Thus, females "apparently solve the conflict of interest between egotism and nepotism by maximizing their own rank among their kin on the one hand, and by maximizing the rank of their kin in relation to non-kin on the other" (Chapais, 1995, p. 129).

Nepotism Shapes Social Structure

Matrilineal biases in the construction and development of social networks and the patterning of support have a direct impact on the acquisition of dominance rank in macaques, baboons, and vervets (Chapais, 1992). Infants are protected and supported by their mothers and other close kin when they are threatened by other group members, particularly females lower-ranking than their own mothers (Berman, 1980; Datta, 1983a; de Waal, 1977; de Waal and Luttrell, 1985; Paul and Kuester, 1987; Walters, 1980). As they grow older, young juveniles receive support when they challenge peers whose mothers are lower-ranking than their own mothers and when they challenge adults that are subordinate to their own mothers. Initially, juveniles can defeat older and larger juveniles only when their own mothers are nearby (Datta, 1983a,b; Horrocks and Hunte, 1983). Later, they are able to defeat all group members that are subordinate to their own mothers, even when their mothers are not in the vicinity. Since juveniles are able to defeat everyone that their own mothers can defeat, but not their mothers themselves, offspring acquire ranks just below their mothers. The same process, repeated over generations and across families, generates corporate matrilineal dominance hierarchies. Thus, daughters acquire ranks below their mothers, which in turn occupy ranks below their own mothers. This means that all members of the same matriline occupy contiguous ranks. Moreover, all members of a given matriline rank above or below all the members of other matrilines. Matrilineal dominance hiearchies have been documented in ≥7 species of macaques (Chapais, 1992), savanna baboons (Hausfater *et al.*, 1982; Johnson, 1987; Lee and Oliver, 1979; Moore, 1978; Silk *et al.*, 1999), and vervets (Bramblett *et al.*, 1982; Fairbanks and McGuire, 1986; Horrocks and Hunte, 1983; Lee, 1983).

The matrilineal dominance hierarchies that characterize macaque, baboon, and vervet groups have 3 striking properties. They are transitive, linear, and very stable. Nearly all encounters between a particular pair of females have predictable outcomes: the higher-ranking female wins. Their dominance hierarchies are also very stable over time. Even though dominance hierarchies are sometimes disrupted by radical upheavals (Ehardt and

Bernstein, 1986; Samuels *et al.*, 1987; Samuels and Henrickson, 1983), long periods with few changes are common (Bramblett *et al.*, 1982; Chapais, 1992; Hausfater *et al.*, 1982; Samuels *et al.*, 1987; Silk, 1988).

Female dominance rank has important fitness consequences for females. In some groups, high-ranking females mature at earlier ages, give birth to healthier infants, and have shorter interbirth intervals than low-ranking females do (Harcourt, 1987; van Noordwijk and van Schaik, 1999; Silk, 1987). Although statistically significant associations between dominance rank and all reproductive parameters are not evident in every group (Altmann *et al.*, 1988; Cheney *et al.*, 1988; Gouzoules *et al.*, 1982; Packer *et al.*, 1995), there is little evidence that being low-ranking is advantageous.

The relationship between dominance rank and reproductive success may also contribute to the stability of dominance hierarchies over time. The power of a matrilineage is likely to be related to its size because larger lineages are able to muster more allies than smaller lineages can. Accordingly, differential reproductive success among females of different ranks will perpetuate power differences among matrilines. All other things being equal, high-ranking lineages are likely to become larger and more powerful, and to reproduce more successfully over time, while low-ranking lineages are likely to become smaller and less powerful, and to reproduce less successfully.

Although maternal kinship plays a central role in the daily lives of female macaques, baboons, and vervets, the extent of nepotism varies across species and groups (Cheney, 1992; Silk *et al.*, 1999; Thierry, 2000), within social groups over time (Kapsalis and Berman, 1996a), and among lineages within groups (Chapais and Primi, 1991; Cheney, 1977; Horrocks and Hunte, 1983; Kapsalis and Berman, 1996a; Netto and van Hooff, 1986; Silk, 1982; Silk *et al.*, 1999). For example, among female baboons in Botswana, members of high-ranking lineages devoted a greater fraction of grooming to maternal kin than members of lower-ranking lineages did. The basis for this variation is not well-established, though ecological (Cheney, 1992), demographic (Kapsalis and Berman, 1996b), and phylogenic factors (Thierry, 2000) may all play a role.

Kin Selection Is Not the Only Force at Work

There is no reason to expect kin selection to be the only force shaping female social relationships in baboons, macaques, and vervets. In fact, females sometimes groom reciprocally (Barrett *et al.*, 2000; Henzi and Barrett, 1999; Muroyama, 1991; Silk *et al.*, 1999) or exchange grooming for other benefits. Thus, low-ranking monkeys sometimes exchange grooming for coalitionary support from high-ranking individuals (Hemelrijk, 1994; Perry, 1996; Seyfarth, 1977, 1980; Seyfarth and Cheney, 1984; Silk, 1992a,b), though this pattern does not occur in all groups (Fairbanks, 1980; Kapsalis and Berman, 1996b; Silk, 1982).

Grooming might also be exchanged for tolerance at feeding sites (Cords, 1997; de Waal, 1991; Kapsalis and Berman, 1996b), access to newborn infants (Henzi, 2001; Muroyama, 1994), or reduced aggression (Silk, 1982).

Moreover, behaviors that might be altruistic in one context may not be altruistic in other contexts. For example, when Japanese macaques intervene in ongoing disputes among members of other matrilines, there is a strong tendency to support the higher-ranking of the two opponents (Chapais *et al.*, 1991; Prud'homme and Chapais, 1996). This kind of conservative support, which is also common among male bonnet and Barbary macaques (Silk, 1992b, 1993; Widdig *et al.*, 2000), may reinforce existing dominance relationships and enhance the status of the ally. If both allies and recipients benefit, support may be mutualistic, not altruistic.

In some cases, the ally may be the only party that benefits from intervention and support may actually be selfish. Prud'homme and Chapais (1996) argued that this is often the case when juvenile Japanese macaques intervene in ongoing disputes. Juvenile females are considerably more likely to defeat older and larger juveniles when they intervene in ongoing disputes than when they act alone. The costs of such intervention to the ally are relatively low because counterattacks are uncommon. Moreover, interventions do not necessarily help the recipients: juvenile females were as likely to intervene on behalf of monkeys that had already defeated their opponents, and presumably did not need additional help, as they were to intervene on behalf of monkeys that had not defeated their opponents. Prud'homme and Chapais (1996) noted that juvenile females are equally like to intervene against kin and nonkin and suggested that females place their own interests above those of others.

Some researchers have suggested that the strong bonds among maternal kin may reflect strong attraction to females of similar rank, not to females that share genes through common descent. Seyfarth (1977, 1983) first applied this idea to females, and he hypothesized that females would be attracted to high-ranking females because they provided the most effective coalitionary support. Competition over access to high-ranking females would force females to settle for partners of their own rank, producing high rates of interaction among females of adjacent rank. Later, de Waal (1991; de Waal and Luttrell, 1986) suggested that females will be attracted to others that most closely resemble them in rank, age, and kinship because they are the ones with which exchange relationships are most likely to be profitable. In both these models, reciprocal altruism is the selective force guiding the formation of social relationships among females.

Efforts to evaluate the relative importance of maternal kinship and rank distance in female relationships have been complicated by the fact that maternal kin usually occupy adjacent ranks, confounding the effects of maternal kinship and rank distance. One approach is to compare affinities between kin and unrelated females that occupy adjacent ranks. Female baboons and bonnet macaques show clear preferences for maternal kin over unrelated females that occupy adjacent ranks (Silk, 1982; Silk *et al.*, 1999). Using matrix correlation techniques, Kapsalis and Berman (1996b) untangled the effects of maternal kinship and rank distance on social relationships among female rhesus macaques. Their analysis suggests that maternal kinship is the primary organizing principle underlying female social relationships. Kin biases are complemented by a weaker and less consistent attraction to females of similar rank and in some years by an attraction to females of higher rank. Their data provide no support for predictions derived from the similarity model.

Case 2: Red Howlers

The second case study is drawn from studies of free-ranging red howlers (*Alouatta seniculus*). Red howlers represent an independent case for analysis because Old and New World primates diverged from a common ancestor ≥40 ma (Rosenberger, 1992). Red howlers have been studied at several different sites in Venezuela, producing a unique body of behavioral, ecological, demographic, and genetic data.

Red howlers form groups of 2–5 adult females, 1–3 adult males, and their offspring. Members of both sexes disperse, but the pattern of dispersal depends on sex and local demographic conditions. In most cases, females disperse at earlier ages and over longer distances than males do. Red howlers are fiercely territorial, and both sexes respond aggressively to incursions by strangers (Crockett and Pope, 1988, 1993). Females almost never join established groups, but male strategies are more variable. Males may attempt to take over established groups and to oust resident males or join migrating females as they establish new groups.

New groups are formed when unrelated, solitary migrating females meet, form social bonds, attract males, manage to establish a territory from which they exclude outsiders, and begin to reproduce (Pope, 2000a). Once females begin to reproduce within a group, they do not disperse again unless the group dissolves (Pope, 2000b). The number of females in red howler groups is confined within narrow limits. Groups with too few females are unable to defend their territories, while groups with too many females cannot secure access to adequate resources and become more attractive targets for male takeovers (Pope, 2000a). This means that female dispersal strategies are linked to the number of adult females present. Thus, in groups with 2 adult females, 50% of natal females disperse. In groups with 3 adult females, 90% disperse, while in groups with 4 adult females all natal females disperse (Crockett and Pope, 1993; Pope, 1998).

Dispersal is extremely costly for females, particularly when habitats are saturated and available territories are very limited. In these situations, females are forced to disperse over long distances and face uncertain prospects. This is reflected in female reproductive careers.

Females that mature and breed in their natal groups have higher quality diets and give birth at earlier ages than ones that emigrate from their natal groups (Crockett and Pope, 1993). Even though females leave their natal groups when they are 2 or 3 years old, they do not produce their first infant until they are 7 years old (Crockett, 1984; Crockett and Pope, 1993). Females that remain in natal groups to breed give birth to their first infants when they are only 5 years old (Crockett and Pope, 1993).

The high costs of dispersal generate intense competition among females over recruitment opportunities for their daughters. Adult females actively harass maturing females in an effort to force them to emigrate. In most cases, "only the daughters of a single presumably dominant adult female are successful at remaining to breed" (Pope, 2000b). Females actively intervene on behalf of their daughters in these contests (Crockett, 1984; Crockett and Pope, 1993).

Females emigrate alone, but may join up with migrants from other groups. Migrants that form new groups are initially unrelated ($r \approx 0$). Nonrandom recruitment of breeding females eventually leads to an increase in the average degree of relatedness among breeding females. Thus, in long-established groups, females represent a single matrilineage and the average degree of relatedness approaches that of mothers and daughters ($r \approx 0.43$; Pope, 1998, 2000a,b).

For females, membership in an established group is essential to achieve reproductive success. Females are often sexually active before they establish territories, but they never produce offspring until they have done so. This may reflect nutritional advantages enjoyed by females in established territories; the diets of solitary females are deficient in nutrients that limit reproduction (Pope, 2000b). There are further advantages gained from belonging to a group that contains closely related females. Females in newly-established groups have fewer surviving infants per year than females in well-established groups do (Pope, 2000a). Differences in reproductive success of females living in these groups may be due to differences in territory quality or differences in the availability of allomothers or both (Pope, 2000a). Whatever the cause, female reproductive success is correlated with the degree of relatedness within their groups (Pope, 2000a).

Males gain access to breeding females in a variety of ways. Males may join up with migrant, extragroup females and help them establish new territories. Once such groups are established, resident males must defend their positions and their progeny from alien males. Infanticidal attacks are a frequent element of both successful and unsuccessful takeover attempts, and account for nearly half of all infant mortality in some red howler populations (Crockett and Janson, 2000; Pope, 2000b).

As habitats become more saturated, male reproductive options change. First, males can only gain access to breeding females by taking over established groups and evicting male residents. Males that pursue this strategy gain immediate reproductive opportunities, but face serious risks. Males are often injured in takeover attempts, sometimes suffering debilitating or even lethal wounds (Crockett and Pope, 1988). Second, as habitats become more saturated and dispersal opportunities become more limited, males tend to remain in their groups longer (Pope, 2000b). Maturing natal males help their fathers defend their groups against takeover attempts. This makes it much harder for single males to succeed in takeover attempts.

When habitats are saturated, single males are at a distinct disadvantage in obtaining and maintaining access to breeding females. As a consequence, males form coalitions and cooperate in efforts to evict residents. After they have established residence, males collectively defend the group against incursions by extragroup males. Collective defense is crucial to males' success because single males are unable to defend groups against incursions by rival males.

The long tenure of male coalitions is remarkable because behavioral and genetic data demonstrate that only one male succeeds in siring offspring within the group. Thus, cooperation among males involves clear fitness costs. Not surprisingly, kinship influences the duration and stability of male coalitions. Coalitions that are made up of related males last on average 8.2 years, while coalitions among unrelated males last only 2.3 years (Pope, 1990). Coalitions composed of kin are also less likely to experience dominance changes than coalitions composed of unrelated males (Pope, 1990).

Pope's (1998, 2000) genetic analyses demonstrate that demographic conditions that influence the extent of intrasexual competition among both sexes also influence the opportunities for kin selection to operate. Kin selection relies on the nonrandom distribution of altruistic behavior to other altruists and the differential success of altruists over nonaltruists. For red howlers, the extent of genetic differentiation among groups within populations is partly a function of population density. When the density of local populations is low, and opportunities for dispersing females to establish new breeding opportunities are available, the average degree of relatedness within groups and the extent of genetic variation among groups in local populations are both low. But as groups mature, selective recruitment of breeding females leads to an increase in the degree of relatedness among breeding females. Moreover, as population density rises, and opportunities to establish new breeding groups decline, most groups become socially mature, producing higher variance in relatedness among groups. In red howler groups, female reproductive success increases as the degree of relatedness among them increases, and groups that recruit more daughters produce more offspring (Pope, 2000a). These are the conditions required for kin selection to favor the evolution of cooperative behavior, and behavioral data indicate that cooperative interactions among females directly influence both these outcomes. Thus, theory and behavior converge neatly in red howlers.

Conclusions

There is persuasive evidence that primates can recognize their kin, which suggests that kin selection plays an important role (Hamilton, 1987). In the two case studies that I reviewed, monkeys conform closely to predictions derived from Hamilton's rule, reserving altruism mainly for close kin and responding as predicted to variation in cost/benefit ratios and relatedness. These cases are instructive because they demonstrate the power of kin selection in shaping social organization and influencing reproductive strategies of individuals over the course of their lives.

This does not mean that kin selection is the only force that shapes the evolution of cooperative behavior in these primate species or in other primate groups; no behavior that is classified as altruistic is strictly limited to kin. For example, grooming is directed toward kin and reciprocating partners, even in the species that are most nepotistic. Grooming may also be traded for access to valuable commodities, including mating partners, preferred food items, and attractive neonates; or used to appease dominants (Silk, 1982) or to placate subordinates (Altmann *et al.*, 1998). The relative importance of kin selection and other forces may depend on local demographic conditions (Pope, 1998, 2000a), the availability of kin (Kapsalis and Berman, 1996b), the power of kin groups (Silk *et al.*, 1999), or the extent of inter group competition (Cheney, 1992).

It is also important to remember that kin selection does not imply that animals will always behave altruistically toward their relatives. Even in nepotistic species, like macaques, individuals sometimes behave selfishly (Prud'homme and Chapais, 1996), and kinship does not seem to dampen rates of aggression (Bernstein, 1991). In callitrichid groups, females typically suppress reproductive activities by subordinate females (Garber, 1997), even when they are closely related (Nievergelt *et al.*, 2000). Lemurs limit the size of social groups by evicting maturing females, and do not spare their own daughters from this fate (Digby, 1999; Vick and Pereira, 1989). Although severe aggression toward daughters and suppression of daughters' reproductive activities seems quite inconsistent with Hamilton's rule, mothers are only expected to allow their daughters to breed when the benefits to daughters of breeding in their natal groups, weighted by the degree of relatedness between mothers and daughters, are less than the costs to the mother herself. If ecological pressures limit group size, recruitment of daughters may not be favored.

One of the major limitations in assessing the role of kin selection in shaping the evolution of behavior in primate groups is that most analyses have been limited to what we know about maternal kinship. If primates can recognize paternal kin, as new data on baboons and macaques suggest, then our analyses of the effects of maternal kinship on social relationships may be seriously incomplete. For example, the conclusion that kin selection does not influence the evolution of cooperation among male chimpanzees (Mitani *et al.*,

2000) might have to be revised if we discover that male chimpanzees can recognize paternal kin and practice nepotism with a patrilineal bias. Moreover, evidence of affinities among agemates may be the product of kin selection in groups in which a single male sires all the offspring of a given cohort. Work on the role of paternal kinship in the structure of social relationships is badly needed, and the availability of new genetic techniques make such work feasible.

Another factor that limits efforts to assess the role of kin selection is that knowledge of social behavior is not evenly distributed across the primate order. We know much more about kinship relationships and social behavior of terrestial Old World primates than arboreal Old World primates and most New World primates. Male-biased dispersal strategies are relatively uncommon among New World primates (Strier, 2000), and this may alter the dynamics of female relationships and the potential for kin selection to operate within these groups. We clearly need more information about the patterning of social behavior in groups with well-established geneologies in a broader range of taxa.

Future work can fill existing gaps in our understanding of how kin selection shapes social organization and behavior in primates. Using the tools of molecular genetics, we can obtain accurate measures of genetic relatedness to assess the effects of kinship on behavior. Researchers making use of this technology can make an important contribution to our understanding of the mechanisms underlying kin recognition in primates, document the threshold for nepotism, and assess the relative importance of kinship and reciprocity in shaping social networks. We can extend our knowledge of social organization and behavior to a wider range of taxa and gather data on a wider range of behaviors. It would be useful to be able to compare the extent of nepotism in behavior of female-bonded and male-bonded groups, to examine the relative importance of kinship and reciprocity in taxa that vary in encephalization, and to examine thresholds for nepotism across behaviors with very different cost-benefit structures. Long-term population-level studies, like those conducted on red howlers, can illuminate the connections between behavior, demographic processes, and genetics. In the laboratory we can conduct carefully designed experiments to probe knowledge of kin relationships and to measure sensitivity to variation in the parameters in Hamilton's rule. These kinds of studies will broaden and deepen our understanding of the role of kin selection in the evolution of primate social behavior.

Acknowledgments

I thank Peter Kappeler and Dario Maestripieri for their invitation to write this paper and for their helpful suggestions on the text. I also thank Bernard Chapais and an anonymous reviewer for their constructive comments on the manuscript.

References

Alberts, S. A. (1999). Paternal kin discrimination in wild baboons. *Proc. R. Soc. Lond. B* 266: 1501–1506.

Alexander, R. D. (1974). The evolution of social behavior. *Annu. Rev. Ecol. Syst.* 5: 325–383.

Altmann, J. (1979). Age cohorts as paternal sibships. *Behav. Ecol. Sociobiol.* 6: 161–169.

Altmann, J. (1980). *Baboon Mothers and Infants*, Harvard University Press, Cambridge.

Altmann, J., Alberts, S. C., Haines, S. A., Dubach, J. D., Muruthi, P., Coote, T., Geffen, E., Cheesman, D. J., Mututua, R. S., Saiyalele, S. N., Wayne, R. K., Lacy, R. C., and Bruford, M. W. (1996). Behavior predicts genetic structure in a wild primate group. *Proc. Nat. Acad. Sci. USA* 93: 5797–5801.

Altmann, J., Hausfater, G., and Altmann, S. A. (1988). Determinants of reproductive success in savannah baboons, *Papio cynocephalus.* In Clutton-Brock, T. H. (ed.), *Reproductive Success*, University of Chicago Press, Chicago, pp. 403–418.

Altmann, J., Myles, B., and Combes, S. (1998). Grooming relationships in a primate group: Social cohesion or currying favors? Poster presented at *the annual meetings of the American Primatological Society.*

Aureli, F., and de Waal, E B.M. (eds.) (1999). *Natural Conflict Reconciliation,* California University Press, Berkeley.

Axelrod, R., and Hamilton, W D. (1981). The evolution of cooperation. *Science* 211:1390–1396.

Barrett, L., Henzi, S. P., Weingrill, T., Lycett, J E., and Hill, R. A. (1999). Market forces predict grooming reciprocity in female babons. *Proc. R. Soc. Lond. B* 266: 665–670.

Bearder, S. K. (1987). Lorises, bushbabies, and tarsiers: Diverse societies in solitary foragers. In Smuts, B. B., Cheney, D. L., Seyfarth, R. M., Wrangham, R. W., and Struhsaker, T. T. (eds.), *Primate Societies,* University of Chicago Press, Chicago, pp. 11–24

Belisle, P., and Chapais, B. (2001). Tolerated co-feeding in relation to degree of kinship in Japanese macaques. *Behaviour* 138: 487–510.

Berman, C.M. (1980). Early agonistic experience and rank acquisition among free-ranging infant rhesus monkeys. *Int. J. Primatol.* 1: 152–170.

Berman, C.M. (1982). The ontogeny of social relationshps with group companions among free-ranging infant rhesus monkeys: I. Social networks and differentiation. *Anim. Behav.* 20: 149–162.

Berman, C. M. (1983a). Matriline differences and infant development. In Hinde, R. A. (ed.), *Primate Social Relationships: An Integrated Approach,* Sinauer Associates, Sunderland, MA, pp. 132–134.

Berman, C. M. (1983b). Early differences in relationships between infants and other group members based on the mother's status: Their possible relationship to peer-peer rank acquisition. In Hinde, R. A. (ed.), *Primate Social Relationships: An Integrated Approach,* Sinauer Associates, Sunderland, MA, pp. 154–156.

Berman, C. M. (1983c). Influence of close female relations on peer-peer rank acquisition. In Hinde, R. A. (ed.), *Primate Social Relationships: An Integrated Approach,* Sinauer Associates, Sunderland, MA, pp. 157–159.

Bernstein, I. S. (1991). The correlation between kinship and behaviour in non-human primates. In Hepper, P. G. (ed.), *Kin Recognition,* Cambridge University Press, Cambridge, pp. 6–29.

Bernstein, I. S., and Ehardt, C. L. (1985). Agonistic aiding: Kinship, rank, age, and sex influences. *Am. J. Primatol.* 8: 37–52.

Bernstein, I. S., and Ehardt, C. L. (1986). The influence of kinship and socialization on aggressive behavior in rhesus monkeys *(Macaca mulatta). Anim. Behav.* 34: 739–747.

Blaustein, A. R., Bekoff, M., and Daniels, X (1987). Kin recognition in vertebrates (excluding primates): Empirical evidence. In Fletcher, D. X C., and Michener, C. D. (eds.), *Kin Recognition in Animals,* Wiley, New York, pp. 287–331.

Bramblett, C. A., Bramblett, S. S., Bishop, D., and Coelho, A. M., Jr. (1982). Longitudinal stability in adult hierarchies among vervet monkeys (*Cercopithecus aethiops*). *Am. J. Primatol.* 2:10–19.

Bourke, A.F.G. (1997). Sociality and kin selection in insects. In Krebs, X R., and Davies, N. B. (eds.), *Behavioural Ecology,* 4th edn., Blackwell, Oxford, pp. 203–227.

Chapais, B. (1983). Dominance, relatedness, and the structure of female relationships in rhesus monkeys. In Hinde, R. A. (ed.), *Primate Social Relationships: An Integrated Approach,* Sinauer Associates, Sunderland, MA, pp. 209–219.

Chapais, B. (1992). The role of alliances in social inheritance of rank among female primates. In Harcourt, A. H., and de Waal, F. B. M. (eds.), *Coalitions and Alliances in Humans and Other Animals,* Oxford Science Publications, Oxford, pp. 29–59.

Chapais, B. (1995). Alliances as a means of competition in primates: Evolutionary, developmental, and cognitive aspects. *Yrbk. Phys. Anthropol.* 38:115–136.

Chapais, B., Girard, M., and Primi, G. (1991). Non-kin alliances and the stability of matrilineal dominance relations in Japanese macaques. *Anim. Behav.* 41: 481–491.

Chapais, B., Gauthier, C., Prud'homme, J., and Vasey, P. (1997). Relatedness threshold for nepotism in Japanese macaques. *Anim. Behav.* 53: 1089–1101.

Chapais, B., Prud'homme, P., and Teijeiro, S. (1994). Dominance competition among silbings in Japanese macaques: Constraints on nepotism. *Anim. Behav.* 48:1335–1347.

Chapais, B., Savard, L., and Gauthier, C. (2001). Kin selection and the distribution of altruism in relation to degree of kinship in Japanese macaques (*Macaca fuscata*). *Behav. Ecol. Sociobiol.* 49: 403–502.

Cheney, D. L. (1977). The acquisition of rank and the development of reciprocal alliances among free-ranging immature baboons. *Behav. Ecol. Sociobiol.* 2: 303–318.

Cheney, D. L. (1978). Interactions of immature male and female baboons with adult females. *Anim. Behav.* 26: 389–408.

Cheney, D. L. (1983). Extrafamilial alliances among vervet monkeys. In Hinde, R. A. (ed.), *Primate Social Relationships: An Integrated Approach,* Sinauer Associates, Sunderland, MA, pp. 278–286.

Cheney, D. L. (1992). Intragroup cohesion and intergroup hostility: The relation between grooming distributions and intergroup competition among female primates. *Behav. Ecol.* 3: 334–345.

Cheney, D. L., and Seyfarth, R. M. (1985). Vervet monkey alarm calls: Manipulation through shared information? *Behaviour* 94:150–166.

Cheney, D. L., Seyfarth, R. M., Andelman, S. J., and Lee, P. C. (1988). Reproductive success in vervet monkeys. In Clutton-Brock, T. H. *(ed.), Reproductive Success,* University of Chicago Press, Chicago, pp. 384–402.

Cords, M. (1987). Male-male competition in one-male groups. In Smuts, B. B., Cheney, D. L., Seyfarth, R. M., Wrangham, R. W., and Struhsaker, T. T. (eds.), *Primate Societies,* University of Chicago Press, Chicago, pp. 98–111.

Cords, M. (1997). Friendship, alliances, reciprocity and repair. In Whiten, A., and Byrne, R. W. (eds.), *Machiavellian Intelligence II,* Cambridge University Press, Cambridge, pp. 24–49.

Creel, S. R., Monfort, S. L., Wildt, D. E., and Waser, P. M. (1991). Spontaneous lactation is an adaptive result of psuedo-pregnancy. *Nature* 351: 660–662.

Crockett, C. M. (1984). Emigration by female red howler monkeys and the case for female competition. In Small, M. F. (ed.), *Female Primates: Studied by Women Primatologists,* Alan R. Liss, New York, pp. 159–173.

Crockett, C. M., and Janson, C. H. (2000). Infanticide in red howlers: Female group size, male membership, and a possible link to folivory. In van Schaik, C. P., and Janson, X H. (eds.), *Infanticide by Males and its Implications,* Cambridge University Press, Cambridge, pp. 75–98.

Crockett, C. M., and Pope, T. R. (1988). Inferring patterns of aggression from red howler monkey injuries. *Am. J. Primatol.* 14:1–21.

Crockett, C.M., and Pope, T. R. (1993). Consequences for sex difference in dispersal for juvenile red howler monkeys. In Pereira, M. E., and Fairbanks, L. A. (eds.), *Juvenile Primates: Life History, Development, and Behavior,* Oxford University Press, Oxford, pp. 104–118.

Darwin, C. (1871). *The Descent of Man and Selection in Relation to Sex,* John Murray, London.

Datta, S. B. (1983a). Relative power and the acquisition of rank. In Hinde, R. A. (ed.), *Primate Social Relationships: An Integrated Approach,* Sinauer Associates, Sunderland, MA, pp. 93–103.

Datta, S. B. (1983b). Relative power and the maintenance of dominance. In Hinde, R. A. (ed.), *Primate Social Relationships: An Integrated Approach,* Sinauer Associates, Sunderland, MA, pp. 103–112.

Datta, S. B. (1983c). Patterns of agonistic interference. In Hinde, R. A. (ed.), *Primate Social Relationships: An Integrated Approach,* Sinauer Associates, Sunderland, MA, pp. 289– 297.

Defler, T. R. (1978). Allogrooming in two species of macaque (*Macaca nemestrina* and *Macaca radiata*). *Primates* 19: 153–167.

Delgado, R. A., Jr., and van Schaik, C. (2000). The behavioral ecology of the orangutan (*Pongo pygmaeus Pongo pygmaeus*): A tale of two islands. *Evol. Anthropol.* 9: 201–218.

de Waal, F. B. M. (1977). The organization of agonistic relations within two captive groups of Java-monkeys (*Macaca fasicularis*). *Z. Tierpsychol.* 44: 225–282.

de Waal, F. B. M. (1986). Class structure in a rhesus monkey group: The interplay between dominance and tolerance. *Anim. Behav.* 34:1033–1040.

de Waal, F. B. M. (1991). Rank distance as a central feature of rhesus monkey social organization: Sociometric analysis. Anim. Behav. 41: 383–395.

de Waal, F. B. M., and Luttrell, L. M. (1985). The formal hierarchy of rhesus monkeys: An investigation of the bared teeth display. *Am. J. Primatol.* 9: 73–85.

de Waal, F. B. M., and Luttrell, L. M. (1986). The similarity principle underlying social bonding among female rhesus monkeys. *Folia Primatol.* 46: 215–234.

Di Fiore, A., and Rendall, D. (1994). Evolution of social organization: A reappraisal for primates by using phylogenetic methods. *Proc. Nat. Acad. Sci. USA* 91: 9941–9945.

Digby, L. J. (1999). Targetting aggression in blue-eyed black lemurs (*Eulemur macaco flavifrons*). Primates 40: 613–617.

Dittus, W P. J. (1979). The evolution of behaviors regulating density and age-specific sex ratios in a primate population. *Behaviour* 69: 265–301.

Dittus, W P. J. (1988). Group fission among wild toque macaques as a consequence of female resource competition and environmental stress. *Anim. Behav.* 36: 1626–1645.

Dugatkin, L. A. (1997). *Cooperation Among Animals,* Oxford University Press, New York. Dunbar, R. I. M., and Dunbar, E. P. (1975). Social dynamics of gelada baboons. In *Contributions to Primatology, Vol. 6,* Karger, Basel.

Ehardt, C. L., and Bernstein, I. S. (1986). Matrilineal overthrows in rhesus monkeys groups. *Int. J. Primatol.* 7:157–181.

Emlen, S. T. (1991). Evolution of cooperative breeding in birds and mammals. In Krebs, J. R., and Davies, N. B. (eds.), *Behavioural Ecology,* 3rd edn., Blackwell, Oxford, pp. 301–337.

Emlen, S. T. (1997). Predicting family dynamics in social vertebrates. In Krebs, J. R., and Davies, N. B. (eds.), *Behavioural Ecology,* 4th edn., Blackwell, Oxford, pp. 228–253.

Erhart, E., Coelho, A. M., and Bramblett, C. A. (1997). Kin recognition by paternal half siblings in captive *Papio cyncocephalus. Am. J. Primatol.* 43:147–157.

Fairbanks, L. (1980). Relationships among adult females in captive vervet monkeys: Testing a model of rank-related attractiveness. *Anim. Behav.* 28: 853–859.

Fairbanks, L., and McGuire, M. T. (1986). Age, reproductive value, and dominance-related behavior in vervet monkeys: Cross-generational influences on social relationships and reproduction. *Anim. Behav.* 24:1710–1721.

Fletcher, D. J. C. (1987). The behavioral analysis of kin recognition: Perspectives on methodololy and interpretation. In Fletcher, D. J. C., and Michener, C. D. (eds.), *Kin Recognition in Animals,* Wiley, New York, pp. 19–54.

Fredrickson, W. T., and Sackett, G. P. (1984). Kin preferences in primates (*Macaca nemestrina*): Relatedness or familiarity? J. *Comp. Pyschol.* 98: 29–34.

Furiuchi, T. (1983). Interindividual distance and influence of dominance on feeding in a natural Japanese macaque troop. *Primates* 24: 445–455.

Galdikas, B. M. F. (1988). Orangutan diet, range, and activity at Tanjung Putting, Central Borneo. *Int. J. Primatol.* 9:1–35.

Garber, P. A. (1997). One for all and breeding for one: Cooperation and competition as a tamarin reproductive strategy. *Evol. Anthropol.* 5: 187–198.

Gouzoules, S. (1984). Primate mating systems, kin associations, and cooperative behavior: Evidence for kin recognition? *Yrbk. Phys. Anthropol.* 27: 99–134.

Gouzoules, S., and Gouzoules, H. (1987). Kinship. In Smuts, B. B., Cheney, D. L., Seyfarth, R. M., Wrangham, R. W., and Struhsaker, T. T. (eds.), *Primate Societies,* University of Chicago Press, Chicago, pp. 299–305.

Gouzoules, H., Gouzoules, S., and Fedigan, L. (1982). Behavioural dominance and reproductive success in female Japanese monkeys (*Macaca fuscata*). *Anim. Behav.* 30: 1138–1151.

Grafen, A. (1991). Modelling in behavioural ecology. In Krebs, X. R., and Davies, N. B. (eds.), *Behavioural Ecology,* 3rd edn., Blackwell, Oxford, pp. 5–31.

Hamilton, W. D. (1964). The genetical evolution of social behavior: I and II. J. *Theor. Biol.* 7: 1–52.

Hamilton, W. D. (1987). Discriminating nepotism: Expectable, common, overlooked. In Fletcher, D.J.C., and Michener, C. D. (eds.), *Kin Recognition in Animals,* Wiley, New York, pp. 417–637.

Harcourt, A. H. (1987). Dominance and fertility among female primates. J. *Zool. Lond.* 213: 471–487.

Hausfater, G., Altmann, J., and Altmann, S. A. (1982). Long-term consistency of dominance relations among female baboons (*Papio cynocephalus*). *Science* 217: 752–755.

Hemelrijk, C. K. (1994). Support for being groomed in long-tailed macaques, *Macaca fasicularis. Anim. Behav.* 48: 479–481.

Henzi, S. P. (2001). Baboons exchange grooming for tolerance around infants. Paper presented at the XVIIIth Congress of the International Primatological Society, Adelaide, Australia, Jan. 7–12, 2001.

Henzi, S. P., and Barrett, L. (1999). The value of grooming to female primates. Primates 40: 47–59.

Holmes, W. G., and Sherman, P. W. (1983). Kin recognition in animals. *Am. Nat.* 71: 46–55.

Horrocks, J., and Hunte, W. (1983). Maternal rank and offspring rank in vervet monkeys: An appraisal of the mechanisms of rank acquisition. *Anim. Behav.* 31: 772–782.

Imakawa, S. (1988). Development of co-feeding relationships in immature free-ranging Japanese monkeys (*Macaca fuscata fuscata*). *Primates* 29: 493–504.

Inouye, M., Takahata, A., Tanaka, S., Kominami, R., and Takenaka, O. (1990). Paternity discrimination in a Japanese monkeys group by DNA fingerprinting. *Primates* 31: 563–570.

Jaisson, P. (1991). Kinship and fellowship in ants and social wasps. In Hepper, P. G. (ed.), *Kin Recognition,* Cambridge University Press, Cambridge, pp. 60–93.

Jarvis, J.U.M., O'Riain, M. J., Bennett, N. C., and Sherman, P. W. (1994). Mammalian eusociality: A family affair. *Trends Ecol. Evol.* 9: 47–51.

Johnson, J.A. (1987). Dominance rank in olive baboons, *Papio anubis:* The influence of gender, size, maternal rank and orphaning. *Anim. Behav.* 35:1694–1708.

Kaplan, J.R. (1977). Patterns of fight interference in free-ranging rhesus monkeys. *Am. J. Phys. Anthropol.* 47: 279–288.

Kaplan, J.R. (1978). Fight interference and altruism in rhesus monkeys. *Am. J. Phys. Anthropol.* 49: 241–249.

Kapsalis, E., and Berman, C. M. (1996a). Models of affiliative relationships among free-ranging rhesus monkeys (*Macaca mulatta*): I. Criteria for kinship. *Behaviour* 133: 1209–1234.

Kapsalis, E., and Berman, C. M. (1996b). Models of affiliative relationships among free-ranging rhesus monkeys (*Macaca mulatta*): II. Testing predictions for three hypothesized organizing principles. *Behaviour* 133: 1235–1263.

Kuester, J., Paul, A., and Arnemann, X (1994). Kinship, familiarity and mating avoidance in Barbary macaques, *Macaca sylvanus. Anim. Behav.* 48:1183–1194.

Kurland, J.A. (1977). Kin selection in the Japanese monkey. In *Contributions to Primatology, Vol. 12,* Karger, Basel.

Lee, P. C. (1983). Context-specific predictability in dominance interactions. In Hinde, R. A. (ed.), *Primate Social Relationships: An Integrated Approach,* Blackwell, Oxford, pp. 35–44.

Lee, P. C. (1987). Allomothering among African elephants. *Anim. Behav.* 35: 278–291.

Lee, P. C., and Oliver, J.I. (1979). Competition, dominance, and the acquisition of rank in juvenile yellow baboons (*Papio cynocephalus*). *Anim. Behav.* 27: 576–585.

Ligon, J. D. (1991). Co-operation and reciprocity in birds and mammals. In Hepper, P. G. (ed.), *Kin Recognition,* Cambridge University Press, Cambridge, pp. 29–30.

MacKenzie, M. M., McGrew, W. C., and Chamove, A. S. (1985). Social preferences in stump-tailed macaques (*Macaca arcoides*): Effects of companionship, kinship, and rearing. *Dev. Psychobiol.* 18: 115–123.

Mason, W. A. (1966). Social organization of the South American monkey, *Callicebus molloch:* A preliminary report. *Tulane Stud. Zool.* 13: 23–28.

Massey, A. (1977). Agonistic aids and kinship in a group of pig-tail macaques. *Behav. Ecol. Sociobiol.* 2: 31–40.

McGrew, W. C., and McLuckie, E. C. (1986). Philopatry and dispersion in the cotton-top tamarin, *Saguinus (o.) oedipus:* An attempted laboratory simulation. *Int. J. Primatol.* 7: 401– 422.

Moore, J. (1978). Dominance relations among free-ranging female baboons in Gombe National Park, Tanzania. In Chivers, D. J., and Herbert, J. (eds.), *Recent Advances in Primatology I,* Academic Press, London, pp. 67–70.

Missakian, E. A. (1974). Mother-offspring grooming relations in rhesus monkeys. *Arch. Sex. Behav.* 3:135–141.

Mitani, J. C., Merriwether, D., and Zhang, C. (2000). Male affiliation, cooperation and kinship in wild chimpanzees. *Anim. Behav.* 59: 885–893.

Muroyama, Y. (1991). Mutual reciprocity of grooming in female Japanese macaques (*M. fuscata*). *Behavior* 119: 161–170.

Muroyama, Y. (1994). Exchange of grooming for allomothering in female patas monkeys. *Behaviour* 128:103–119.

Netto, W. J., and van Hooff, J. A. R. A. M. (1986). Conflict interference and the development of dominance relationships in immature *Macaca fasicularis*. In Else, X G., and Lee, P. C. (eds.), *Primate Ontogeny, Cognition and Social Behaviour*, Cambridge University Press, Cambridge, pp. 291–300.

Nievergelt, C. M., Digby, L. J., Ramakrishnan, U., and Woodruff, D. S. (2000). Genetic analysis of group composition and breeding system in a wild common marmoset (*Callithrix jacchus*) population. *Int. J. Primatol.* 21:1–20.

Owen, D. D., and Owen, M. J. (1984). Helping behaviour in brown hyenas. *Nature* 308: 843–846.

Packer, C., Collins, D. A., Sindimwo, A., and Goodall, X (1995). Reproductive constraints on aggressive competition in female baboons. *Nature* 373: 60–63.

Palombit, R. A. (1996). Pair bonds in monogamous apes: A comparison of the siamang *Hylobats syndactylus* and the white-handed gibbon *Hylobates lar*. *Behaviour* 133: 321–356.

Parr, L., and de Waal, F. B. M. (1999). Visual kin recognition in chimpanzees. *Nature* 399: 647–648.

Paul, A., and Kuester, X (1987). Dominance, kinship, and reproductive value in female Barbary macaques (*Macaca sylvanus*) at Affenberg, Salem. *Behav. Ecol. Sociobiol.* 21: 323–331.

Pereira, M. E., and Altmann, X (1985). Development of social behavior in free-living nonhuman primates. In Watts, E. (ed.), *Non-Human Primate Models for Human Growth and Development*, Alan R. Liss, New York, pp. 217–309.

Perry, S. (1996). Female-female social relationships in wild white-faced capuchin monkeys (*Cebus capucinus*). *Am. J. Primatol.* 40:167–182.

Pfennig, D. W., and Sherman, P. W (1995). Kin recognition. *Sci. Amer.* 272: 98–103.

Pope, T. R. (1990). The reproductive consequences of male cooperation in the red howler monkey: Paternity exclusion in multi-male and single-male troops using genetic markers. *Behav. Ecol. Sociobiol.* 27: 439–446.

Pope, T. R. (1998). Effects of demographic change on group kin structure and gene dynamics of populations of red howling monkeys. J. *Mammal.* 79: 692–712.

Pope, T. R. (2000a). Reproductive success increases with degree of kinship in cooperative coalitions of female red howler monkeys (*Alouatta seniculus*). *Behav. Ecol. Sociobiol.* 48: 253–267.

Pope, T. R. (2000b). The evolution of male philopatry in neotropical monkeys. In Kappeler, P. M. (ed.), *Primate Males,* Cambridge University Press, Cambridge, pp. 219–235.

Prud'homme, J., and Chapais, B. (1996). Development of intervention behavior in Japanese macaques: Testing the targeting hypothesis. *Intl. J. Primatol.* 17: 429–443.

Pusey, A. E., and Packer, C. (1997). The ecology of relationships. In Krebs, X R., and Davies, N. B. (eds.), *Behavioural Ecology,* 4th edn., Blackwell, Oxford, pp. 301–337.

Reichard, U. (1995). Extra-pair copulations in a monogamous gibbon (*Hylobates lar*). *Ethology* 100: 99–112.

Rendall, D., and Di Fiore, A. (1995) The road less traveled: Phylogenetic perspectives in primatology. *Evol. Anthropol.* 4: 43–52.

Richards, R.J. (1987). *Darwin and the Emergence of Evolutionary Theories of Mind and Behavior*, Chicago University Press, Chicago.

Rosenberger, A. L. (1992). Evolution of New World monkeys. In Jones, J., Martin, R., and Pilbeam, D. (eds.), *The Cambridge Encyclopedia of Human Evolution,* Cambridge University Press, Cambridge, pp. 209–216.

Sackett, G. P., and Fredrickson, W. T. (1987). Social preferences by pigtail macaques: Familiarity versus degree and type of kinship. *Anim. Behav.* 35: 603–607.

Sade, D. S. (1965). Some aspects of parent-offspring and sibling relations in a group of rhesus monkeys, with a discussion of grooming. *Am. J. Phys. Anthropol.* 23:1–18.

Samuels, A., and Henrickson, R. V. (1983). Outbreak of severe aggression in captive *Macaca mulatta. Am. J. Primatol.* 5: 277–281.

Samuels, A., Silk, J.B., and Altmann, J. (1987). Continuity and change in dominance relations among female baboons. *Anim. Behav.* 35: 785–793.

Saunders, C. D. (1988). *Ecological, Social, and Evolutionary Aspects of Baboon* (*Papio Cynocephalus*) Grooming Behavior, PhD Dissertation, Cornell University.

Sauther, M. L., Sussman, R. W., and Gould, L. (1999). The socioecology of the ringtailed lemur: Thirty-five years of research. *Evol. Anthropol.* 8:120–132.

Schaub, H. (1996). Testing kin altruism in long-tailed macaques (*Macaca fasicularis*) in a food-sharing experiment. *Int. J. Primatol.* 17: 445–467.

Seger, J. (1991). Cooperation and conflict in social insects. In Krebs, X R., and Davies, N. B. (eds.), *Behavioural Ecology,* 3rd edn., Blackwell, Oxford, pp. 338–373. Seyfarth, R. M. (1977). A model of social grooming among adult female monkeys. J. *Theor. Biol.* 65: 671–698.

Seyfarth, R. M. (1980). The distribution of grooming and related behaviours among adult female vervet monkeys. *Anim. Behav.* 28: 798–813.

Seyfarth, R. M. (1983). Grooming and social competition in primates. In Hinde, R. A. (ed.), *Primate Social Relationships: An Integrated Approach,* Blackwell, Oxford, pp. 182–190.

Seyfarth, R. M., and Cheney, D. L. (1984). Grooming, alliances, and reciprocal altruism in vervet monkeys. *Nature* 308: 541–543.

Sherman, P. W. (1977). Nepotism and the evolution of alarm calls. *Science* 197:1246–1253.

Sherman, P. W., Reeve, H. K., and Pfennig, D. W. (1997). Recognition systems. In Krebs, X R., and Davies, N. B. (eds.), *Behavioural Ecology,* 4th edn., Blackwell, Oxford, pp. 69–96.

Silk, J.B. (1982). Altruism among female *Macaca radiata:* Explanations and analysis of patterns of grooming and coalition formation. *Behaviour* 79: 162–168.

Silk, J.B. (1987). Social behavior in evolutionary perspective. In Smuts, B. B., Cheney, D. L., Seyfarth, R. M., Wrangham, R. W., and Struhsaker, T. T. (eds.), *Primate Societies,* University of Chicago Press, Chicago, pp. 318–329.

Silk, J.B. (1988). Maternal investment in captive bonnet macaques (*Macaca radiata*). *Am. Nat.* 132: 1–19.

Silk, J.B. (1992a). Patterns of intervention in agonistic contests among male bonnet macaques. In Harcourt, S., and de Waal, F. B. M. (eds.), *Coalitions and Alliances in Humans and Other Animals,* Oxford University Press, Oxford, pp. 215–232.

Silk, J.B. (1992b). The patterning of intervention among male bonnet macaque: Reciprocity, revenge, and loyalty. *Curr. Anthropol.* 33: 318–325.

Silk, J.B. (1997). The function of peaceful post-conflict contacts among primates. *Primates* 38: 265–279.

Silk, J. B. (1999). Why are infants so attractive to others? The form and function of infant handling in bonnet macaques. *Anim. Behav.* 57: 1021–1032.

Silk, J. B. (2000). Ties that bond: The role of kinship in primate societies. In Stone, L. (ed.), *New Directions in Anthropological Kinship,* Rowman and Littlefield, Lanham, pp. 71–92.

Silk, J. B., Cheney, D. L., and Seyfarth, R. M. (1999). The structure of social relationships among female savannah baboons in Moremi Reserve, Botswana. *Behaviour* 136: 679–703.

Silk, J. B., Samuels, A., and Rodman, P. S. (1981). The influence of kinship, rank, and sex upon affiliation and aggression among adult females and immature bonnet macaques (*Macaca radiata*). *Behaviour 78:* 112–137.

Small, M. F., and Smith, D. G. (1981). Interactions with infants by full-siblings, paternal half-siblings, and non relatives in a captive group of rhesus macaques (*Macaca mulatta*). *Am. J. Primatol.* 1: 91–94.

Smith, D. G. (1986). Incidence and consequences of inbreeding in three captive groups of rhesus macaques (*Macaca mulatta*). In Benirschke, K. (ed.), *Primates: The Road to Self-Sustaining Populations,* Springer-Verlag, New York, pp. 856–874.

Smith, K. L. (2000). *Paternal Kin Matter: The Distribution of Social Behavior Among Wild Adult Female Baboons,* PhD Dissertation, University of Chicago.

Smuts, B. B., Cheney, D. L., Seyfarth, R. M., Wrangham, R. W., and Struhsaker, T. T. (eds.) (1987). *Primate Societies,* University of Chicago Press, Chicago.

Strier, K. B. (2000). From binding brotherhoods to short-term sovereignty: The dilemma of male Cebidae. In Kappeler, P. M. (ed.), *Primate Males,* Cambridge University Press, Cambridge, pp. 72–83.

Thierry, B. (2000). Covariation of conflict management patterns across macaque species. In Aureli, F., and de Waal, F. B. M. (eds.), *Natural Conflict Resolution,* University of California Press, Berkeley, pp. 106–128.

Trivers, R. L. (1971). The evolution of reciprocal altruism. *Q. Rev. Biol.* 46: 35–57.

Van Schaik, C. P., and Janson, C. H. (2000). Infanticide by males: Prospectus. In van Schaik, C. P., and Janson, C. H. (eds.), *Infanticide by Males and its Implications,* Cambridge University Press, Cambridge, pp. 1–6.

Vick, L. G., and Pereira, M. E. (1989). Episodic targetting aggression and the histories of lemur social groups. *Behav. Ecol. Sociobiol.* 1: 3–12.

Walters, J. R. (1980). Interventions and the development of dominance relationships in female baboons. *Folia Primatol.* 34: 61–89.

Walters, J. R. (1981). Inferring kinship from behavior: Maternity determination in yellow baboons. *Anim. Behav.* 29: 126–136.

Walters, J. R. (1987a). Kin recognition in non-human primates. In Fletcher, D. J. C., and Michener, C. D. (eds.), *Kin Recognition in Animals,* Wiley, New York, pp. 359–393.

Walters, J. R. (1987b). Transition to adulthood. In Smuts, B. B., Cheney, D. L., Seyfarth, R. M., Wrangham, R. W., and Struhsaker, T. T. (eds.), *Primate Societies,* University of Chicago Press, Chicago, pp. 358–369.

Welker, C., Schwibbe, M. H., Shafer-Witt, C., and Visalberghi, E. (1987). Failure of kin recognition in *Macaca fasicularis. Folia Primatol.* 49: 216–221.

Widdig, A., Nürnberg, P., Krawczak, M., Streich, W.J., and Bercovitch, F.B. (2001). Paternal relatedness and age proximity regulate social relationships among adult female rhesus macaques. *Proc. Natl. Acad. Sci. USA* 98(24): 13769–13773.

Widdig, A., Nürnberg, P., Krawczak, M., Streich, W X, and Bercovitch, E (in press). Affiliations and aggression among adult female rhesus macaques: A genetic analysis of paternal cohorts. *Behavior.*

Widdig, A., Streich, W. X., and Tembrock, G. (2000). Coalition formation among male Barbary macaques *(Macaca sylvanus). Am. J. Primatol.* 50: 37–51.

Wu, H. M., Holmes, W. G., Medina, S. R., and Sackett, G. P. (1980). Kin preferences in infant *Macaca nemestrina. Nature* 285: 225–227.

SECTION 6

RECIPROCITY

Introduction to Chapter 7

Reciprocity provides a second evolutionarily plausible explanation for altruism. Reciprocal altruism is not nearly as widespread in the animal kingdom as is kin-based altruism, and it carries with it a set of specialized mental adaptations that are conspicuous in our own species.

Here we have an interesting parallel that further emphasizes the magnitude of the Darwinian puzzle posed by altruism. In 1993, W. D. Hamilton won the Crafoord prize for his development of kin selection theory; fifteen years later, R. L. Trivers won it for his work on "social evolution," including his formulation of the theory of reciprocal altruism. Trivers' reciprocal altruism offers a second evolutionary escape hatch from the dog-eat-dog world of perpetual competition and selfishness among individuals.

In social species like our own, we end up associating with our most serious competitors. This is true by definition. The members of any species share a set of adaptations geared to their particular ecology and naturally depend on the same resource base. The food I want is the best food for you. The same goes for mates and shelter; almost anything that would enhance my fitness would similarly enhance yours. And most of these resources are "zero-sum." Zero-sum simply means that what I use is unavailable to you. If I eat a piece of fruit or meat, it is gone; you can no longer eat it. Zero-sumness is precisely what causes the evolution of competitiveness, of selfishness. In the vast majority of circumstances, individuals whose *modus operandi* was, "No, you take it, please!" had lower fitness than individuals who said, "Get your paws off of it; it's mine!" My point here is not that I want to live in a mean and nasty world, but simply to remind you that you cannot take altruism for granted. Altruists seem destined to lose out in everything that matters to fitness. So we need special theories to explain how altruism can win out over selfishness.

Reciprocity works as an escape from selfishness because it can sometimes take the zero-sumness out of life. Let's imagine that we need to scratch up all our food from nature—by hunting animals and foraging for edible plants. As you will soon understand in much more detail, this is a very important thing to imagine because it was true for all humans until just a few thousand years ago. This way of making a living is challenging, and it entails very big ups and downs. Sometimes you get a bonanza: You kill a big animal that yields much more meat than you can eat before it rots. But sometimes you have a string of bad foraging luck that lasts for days. How wasteful to let the bonanza rot; and how painful to starve. If you just had a refrigerator you could save the leftover meat for the lean days that will inevitably come. Of course our foraging ancestors had no refrigerators. But they discovered what we might call the social refrigerator—reciprocity. Simply put, I give you the parts of my big kill that I do not need. Then, next week or next month, when I come up short on calories and you have a surplus, you pay me back.

Here is another way of thinking about it. What is five ounces of meat worth in fitness terms? This is a trick question, because the answer depends on how well fed you are at the moment. If you have just eaten 3 pounds of meat, five more ounces will not help you much. But if you have had nothing to eat for days, the very same five ounces could keep you from dying, a huge fitness benefit. This is how reciprocity lets individuals exploit non-zero-sum situations.

A very simple mathematical model will make the gambit clear. Here is a 10-day period in the lives of two stone-age foragers, Mald and Kleg. Mostly they each eat what they find, but interesting things happen on Day 2 and Day 9. When Mald has an especially good foraging day she gives food to her hungry neighbor, Kleg. Later, when Kleg has been fortunate in finding food but Mald has not, Kleg repays the favor. The numbers estimate the fitness consequences, negative numbers being fitness costs and positive numbers being fitness benefits. Even though they both accept costs along the way, they both come out ahead after the exchange.

	Mald	Kleg
Day 2	gives food -1	receives food +10
Day 9	receives food +10	gives food -1
Net result	+9	+9

Note that the non-zero-sumness of the situation is what that makes reciprocity work. In zero-sum situations, A loses whatever B gains. But here, because of their different nutritional situations, it costs Mald only 1 fitness unit to give Kleg 10. This asymmetry guarantees that if the situations are later reversed and the roles of giver and receiver are switched, both participants reap a substantial profit.

You might say that this kind of exchange is not altruism because both participants eventually end up with a net benefit. You would be right at one level; but remember, *all* evolutionary explanations of altruism must somehow convert the costs of altruism into benefits (you should be able to explain how kin selection makes this conversion); otherwise, selection will weed out altruism. Think about how this kind of reciprocity looks to an outside observer. A scientist would see that, on day 2, Mald does indeed pay a cost to provide a benefit to her neighbor; in other words, the scientist would see an instance of altruism. The scientist would only recognize that there was a net benefit to Mald if he also happened to be around on the day of the payback. Thus, as offered by Trivers, reciprocity is a *hypothesis* about how altruism can pay off—one which can be supported or falsified by observations of actual behavior over time.

The phrase "tit-for-tat" might be new to you. Tit-for-tat is a behavioral rule or strategy that, if employed by animals, would support the evolution of reciprocal altruism. It involves doing to your partner whatever he did on the previous round. For example, if your partner gave you food on the previous round, you should give him food on the next. But it needs to be just a bit more complicated. We need a way to get the tit-for-tat process started. If we begin with the premise that ordinary natural selection leads us to expect, the first round would be nothing but selfish withholding: I give you no food; then on the next round you give me the same, no food. In that scenario we are stuck in a selfish equilibrium. Therefore, the full tit-for-tat rule is as follows: Be altruistic on the first round and then do whatever your partner does. In other words, the kinds of advantages that Mald and Kleg reaped from reciprocity can only be launched if individuals are willing to take a chance on the reciprocal tendencies of new partners—as Mald did on day 2 of the example.

Just as reciprocity needs this altruistic push-start, it also involves stern withholding from non-reciprocators. If Mald starts out altruistic, but on Day 9 Kleg eats herself sick instead of giving any food to her now-hungry neighbor, Mald should not offer any of her next surplus to Kleg. "Should not offer" is not intended as a moral rule; it is simply a clarification of what must happen if reciprocity is to become established in the population. It is easy to see from our simple model (above) that those who offer benefits without getting paid back end up with net losses. Only those who receive altruism in return will come out ahead. So, the only way to avoid net losses is to terminate relationships with non-reciprocators. Even better, try to get others to terminate relationships with non-reciprocators as well; and best of all, try to prevent others from offering that initial push-start of generosity. "Don't bother to help him; he's a fair-weather friend." In this way, altruists take active steps to make sure that non-reciprocators cannot siphon benefits—cannot be what we might call social parasites.

By now you are probably realizing that for altruism to take hold in a population, a particular set of *mental* adaptations is required. "Mental adaptation" may be a new idea for you but it should not seem radical. For example, when selection shapes the equipment of a predator, that shaping is not limited to fangs, claws and speed. Selection also builds psychological adaptations for recognizing especially vulnerable prey, stalking into the wind and using all available cover, and knowing when to start the final rush, and how to anticipate the prey's escape tactics.

Likewise, we can specify the mental adaptations that are likely to be found in any species that has undergone selection for reciprocity. Some of these adaptations are obvious. Reciprocal altruists must be able to recognize and remember the past actions of their neighbors. Joan is not just one of many adult female members of my species. Instead, I recognize her as a unique individual and I know how often and how much she pays me back. But reciprocity is supported by more than a good memory for faces and exchanges. A growing body of research suggests that emotions are facultative mental adaptations designed to guide our behavior. Each emotion has either a positive or negative "valence." For this reason, emotions can be thought of as on-board reward and punishment systems. Positive emotions serve to reinforce behaviors that, on average, promote fitness, and negative emotions steer us away from or help correct behaviors or situations that are bad for fitness.

Let's make this more concrete. Most of us feel a little better—we get a little internal-happiness reward—when we help someone in need. This fuels that altruistic push-start and (unless we are badly treated by a non-reciprocator) keeps the favorable exchanges flowing. Likewise, the receiver feels a surge of gratitude, which functions to motivate her to return the favor when she can. On the other hand, an individual who does not reciprocate is likely to feel the negative emotion of guilt. Guilt often serves to trigger reconsideration and to motivate actions that will rebuild the altruistic partnership before it is too late. And what emotion do you feel when someone you have helped subsequently refuses to help you? Anger, perhaps even vengeance. The role of these negative emotions is to distance us from non-reciprocators and to reduce the future benefits that they might receive. For each possible outcome there is an emotion that serves either to motivate reciprocity or to prevent exploitation by social parasites.

This is an appropriate point to mention an analogy that appears a few times in this chapter: the analogy of "the rider and the elephant." In the book from which Chapter 7 is drawn, Haidt suggests we can think about our mental life as having two parts. Using our conscious, rational mind we can explicitly consider alternative courses of action, weigh the possible outcomes and make fully intentional decisions. The conscious mind is the rider. Our unconscious mind is not accessible to us; we cannot choose the alternatives it considers, nor feed it new weightings for the various possible outcomes. But it, like the elephant, has deeply seated priorities that guide its behavior. The emotions that underpin altruism come from the elephant—the unconscious mind.

Professor Haidt has given us a rich and fluid chapter which I selected over many fine alternatives, but I must resolve an apparent contradiction. Early on he says: "Because nearly all animals that live in cooperative groups live in groups of close relatives, most altruism in the animal kingdom reflects the simple axiom that shared genes equals shared interests." This sentence accurately summarizes the consensus among professionals that, outside of humans, nearly all the altruism we see in nature is the result of kin selection, not reciprocity. There are a few possible exceptions where animals do reciprocate—coalitions of savanna baboon males who trade roles in copulatory defense, or pairs of hermaphroditic black sculpin (fish) who alternate spawning as male and female—but reciprocity seems genuinely rare outside of our own species. However, Haidt later seems to contradict this view when he says: "Many species reciprocate, but only humans gossip." We can accept the second clause, but the first contains the contradiction. As I have stressed, there are very few examples of reciprocity outside of humans. I am not sure why Haidt wrote in this way, except perhaps to emphasize the uniqueness of gossip.

The functions of gossip, gossip's role in the evolution of language, and Robin Dunbar's "social brain" hypothesis are all topics to which we will return in later chapters.

Chapter 7 Glossary

fMRI: Functional Magnetic Resonance Imaging; a technique that allows researchers to see what areas of the brain are most active when a particular task is being performed.

reciprocity, reciprocal altruism: Accepting costs in order to benefit those neighbors who behave the same way towards you.

social-brain hypothesis: Robin Dunbar's proposal that evolution favors increases in brain size when the complexities of social life demand it.

tit-for-tat: A "nice" strategy that is largely immune to invasion by less nice strategies; it means to play altruistically on the first round and thereafter do whatever your partner did on the previous round.

ultrasociality: A form of highly integrated social behavior involving large social groups and division of labor among the members, with different individuals specializing in different tasks. Ultrasociality has apparently evolved only four times: twice in insects and twice in mammals.

Chapter 7
Reciprocity with a Vengeance (2006)

Jonathan Haidt

Zigong asked: "Is there any single word that could guide one's entire life?" The master said: "Should it not be reciprocity? What you do not wish for yourself, do not do to others."

—Analects of Confucius[1]

That which is hateful to you, do not do to your fellow; this, in a few words, is the entire Torah; all the rest is but an elaboration of this one, central point.

—Rabbi Hillel, 1st cent. bce[2]

When the sages pick a single word or principle to elevate above all others, the winner is almost always either "love" or "reciprocity." This chapter is about reciprocity. Both are, ultimately, about the same thing: the bonds that tie us to one another.

The opening scene of the movie *The Godfather* is an exquisite portrayal of reciprocity in action. It is the wedding day of the daughter of the Godfather, Don Corleone. The Italian immigrant Bonasera, an undertaker, has come to ask for a favor: He wants to avenge an assault upon the honor and body of his own daughter, who was beaten by her boyfriend and another young man. Bonasera describes the assault, the arrest, and the trial of the two boys. The judge gave them a suspended sentence and let them go free that very day. Bonasera is furious and feels humiliated; he has come to Don Corleone to ask that justice be done. Corleone asks what exactly he wants. Bonasera whispers something into his ear, which we can safely assume is "Kill them." Corleone refuses, and points out that Bonasera

Jonathan Haidt, "Chapter 3: Reciprocity with a Vengeance," from *The Happiness Hypothesis*, pp. 45–58, 250–251. Published by Basic Books, 2006.

has not been much of a friend until now. Bonasera admits he was afraid of getting into "trouble." The dialogue continues:[3]

> CORLEONE: I understand. You found paradise in America, you had a good trade, made a good living. The police protected you and there were courts of law. And you didn't need a friend like me. But now you come to me and you say, "Don Corleone give me justice." But you don't ask with respect. You don't offer friendship. You don't even think to call me "Godfather." Instead, you come into my house on the day my daughter is to be married, and you ask me to do murder, for money.
>
> BONASERA: I ask you for justice.
>
> CORLEONE: That is not justice; your daughter is still alive.
>
> BONASERA: Let them suffer then, as she suffers. [Pause]. How much shall I pay you?
>
> CORLEONE: Bonasera … Bonasera … What have I ever done to make you treat me so disrespectfully? If you'd come to me in friendship, then this scum that ruined your daughter would be suffering this very day. And if by chance an honest man like yourself should make enemies, then they would become *my* enemies. And then they would fear you.
>
> BONASERA: Be my friend—[He bows to Corleone]—Godfather? [He kisses Corleone's hand].
>
> CORLEONE: Good. [Pause.] Some day, and that day may never come, I'll call upon you to do a service for me. But until that day—accept this justice as a gift on my daughter's wedding day.

The scene is extraordinary, a kind of overture that introduces the themes of violence, kinship, and morality that drive the rest of the movie. But just as extraordinary to me is how easy it is for us to understand this complex interaction in an alien subculture. We intuitively understand why Bonasera wants the boys killed, and why Corleone refuses to do it. We wince at Bonasera's clumsy attempt to offer money when what is lacking is the right relationship, and we understand why Bonasera had been wary, before, of cultivating the right relationship. We understand that in accepting a "gift" from a mafia don, a chain, not just a string, is attached. We understand all of this effortlessly because we see the world through the lens of reciprocity. Reciprocity is a deep instinct; it is the basic currency of social life. Bonasera uses it to buy revenge, which is itself a form of reciprocity. Corleone uses it to manipulate Bonasera into joining Corleone's extended family. In the rest of this chapter I'll explain how we came to adopt reciprocity as our social currency, and how you can spend it wisely.

ULTRASOCIALITY

Animals that fly seem to violate the laws of physics, but only until you learn a bit more about physics. Flight evolved independently at least three times in the animal kingdom: in insects, dinosaurs (including modern birds), and mammals (bats). In each case, a physical feature that had potentially aerodynamic properties was already present (for example, scales that lengthened into feathers, which later made gliding possible).

Animals that live in large peaceful societies seem to violate the laws of evolution (such as competition and survival of the fittest), but only until you learn a bit more about evolution. Ultrasociality[4]—living in large cooperative societies in which hundreds or thousands of individuals reap the benefits of an extensive division of labor—evolved independently at least four times in the animal kingdom: among hymenoptera (ants, bees, and wasps); termites; naked mole rats; and humans. In each case, a feature possessing potentially co-operation-enhancing properties already existed. For all the nonhuman ultrasocial species, that feature was the genetics of kin altruism. It's obvious that animals will risk their lives for the safety of their own children: The only way to "win" at the game of evolution is to leave surviving copies of your genes. Yet not just your children carry copies of your genes. Your siblings are just as closely related to you (50 percent shared genes) as your children; your nephews and nieces share a quarter of your genes, and your cousins one eighth. In a strictly Darwinian calculation, whatever cost you would bear to save one of your children you should be willing to pay to save two nieces or four cousins.[5]

Because nearly all animals that live in cooperative groups live in groups of close relatives, most altruism in the animal kingdom reflects the simple axiom that shared genes equals shared interests. But because the sharing drops off so quickly with each fork in the family tree (second cousins share only one thirty-second of their genes), kin altruism explains only how groups of a few dozen, or perhaps a hundred, animals can work together. Out of a flock of thousands, only a small percentage would be close enough to be worth taking risks for. The rest would be competitors, in the Darwinian sense. Here's where the ancestors of bees, termites, and mole rats took the common mechanism of kin altruism, which makes many species sociable, and parlayed it[6] into the foundation of their uncommon ultrasociality: They are all siblings. Those species each evolved a reproduction system in which a single queen produces all the children, and nearly all the children are either sterile (ants) or else their reproductive abilities are suppressed (bees, mole rats); therefore, a hive, nest, or colony of these animals is one big family. If everyone around you is your sibling, and if the survival of your genes depends on the survival of your queen, selfishness becomes genetic suicide. These ultrasocial species display levels of cooperation and self-sacrifice that still astonish and inspire those who study them. Some ants, for example, spend their lives hanging from the top of a tunnel, offering their abdomens for use as food storage bags by the rest of the nest.[7]

The ultrasocial animals evolved into a state of ultrakinship, which led automatically to ultracooperation (as in building and defending a large nest or hive), which allowed the massive division of labor (ants have castes such as soldier, forager, nursery worker, and food storage bag), which created hives overflowing with milk and honey, or whatever other substance they use to store their surplus food. We humans also try to extend the reach of kin altruism by using fictitious kinship names for nonrelatives, as when children are encouraged to call their parents' friends Uncle Bob and Aunt Sarah. Indeed, the mafia is known as "the family," and the very idea of a godfather is an attempt to forge a kin-like link with a man who is not true kin. The human mind finds kinship deeply appealing, and kin altruism surely underlies the cultural ubiquity of nepotism. But even in the mafia, kin altruism can take you only so far. At some point you have to work with people who are at best distant relations, and to do so you'd better have another trick up your sleeve.

You Scratch My Back, I'll Scratch Yours

What would you do if you received a Christmas card from a complete stranger? This actually happened in a study in which a psychologist sent Christmas cards to people at random. The great majority sent him a card in return.[8] In his insightful book *Influence*,[9] Robert Cialdini of Arizona State University cites this and other studies as evidence that people have a mindless, automatic reciprocity reflex. Like other animals, we will perform certain behaviors when the world presents us with certain patterns of input. A baby herring gull, seeing a red spot on its mother's beak, pecks at it automatically, and out comes regurgitated food. The baby gull will peck just as vigorously at a red spot painted on the end of a pencil. A cat stalks a mouse using the same low-down, wiggle-close-then-pounce technique used by cats around the world. The cat uses the same technique to attack a string trailing a ball of yarn because the string accidentally activates the cat's mouse-tail-detector module. Cialdini sees human reciprocity as a similar ethological reflex: a person receives a favor from an acquaintance and wants to repay the favor. The person will even repay an empty favor from a stranger, such as the receipt of a worthless Christmas card.

The animal and human examples are not exactly parallel, however. The gulls and cats are responding to visual stimuli with specific bodily movements, executed immediately. The person is responding to the *meaning* of a situation with a motivation that can be satisfied by a variety of bodily movements executed days later. So what is really built into the person is a *strategy*: Play tit for tat. Do to others what they do unto you. Specifically, the tit-for-tat strategy is to be nice on the first round of interaction; but after that, do to your partner whatever your partner did to you on the previous round.[10] Tit for tat takes us way beyond kin altruism. It opens the possibility of forming cooperative relationships with strangers.

Most interactions among animals (other than close kin) are zero-sum games: One animal's gain is the other's loss. But life is full of situations in which cooperation would expand the pie to be shared if only a way could be found to cooperate without being exploited. Animals that hunt are particularly vulnerable to the variability of success: They may find far more food than they can eat in one day, and then find no food at all for three weeks. Animals that can trade their surplus on a day of plenty for a loan on a day of need are much more likely to survive the vagaries of chance. Vampire bats, for example, will regurgitate blood from a successful night of bloodsucking into the mouth of an unsuccessful and genetically unrelated peer. Such behavior seems to violate the spirit of Darwinian competition, except that the bats keep track of who has helped them in the past, and in return they share primarily with those bats.[11] Like the Godfather, bats play tit for tat, and so do other social animals, particularly those that live in relatively small, stable groups where individuals can recognize each other as individuals.[12]

But if the response to noncooperation is just noncooperation on the next round, then tit for tat can unite groups of only a few hundred. In a large enough group, a cheating vampire bat can beg a meal from a different successful bat each night and, when they come to him pleading for a return favor, just wrap his wings around his head and pretend to be asleep. What are they going to do to him? Well, if these were people rather than bats, we know what they'd do: They'd beat the hell out of him. Vengeance and gratitude are moral sentiments that amplify and enforce tit for tat. Vengeful and grateful feelings appear to have evolved precisely because they are such useful tools for helping individuals create cooperative relationships, thereby reaping the gains from non-zero-sum games.[13] A species equipped with vengeance and gratitude responses can support larger and more cooperative social groups because the payoff to cheaters is reduced by the costs they bear in making enemies.[14] Conversely, the benefits of generosity are increased because one gains friends.

Tit for tat appears to be built into human nature as a set of moral emotions that make us *want* to return favor for favor, insult for insult, tooth for tooth, and eye for eye. Several recent theorists[15] even talk about an "exchange organ" in the human brain, as though a part of the brain were devoted to keeping track of fairness, debts owed, and social accounts-receivable. The "organ" is a metaphor—nobody expects to find an isolated blob of brain tissue the only function of which is to enforce reciprocity. However, recent evidence suggests that there really could be an exchange organ in the brain if we loosen the meaning of "organ" and allow that functional systems in the brain are often composed of widely separated bits of neural tissue that work together to do a specific job.

Suppose you were invited to play the "ultimatum" game, which economists invented[16] to study the tension between fairness and greed. It goes like this: Two people come to the lab but never meet. The experimenter gives one of them—let's suppose it's not you—twenty one-dollar bills and asks her to divide them between the two of you in any way she likes. She then gives you an ultimatum: Take it or leave it. The catch is that if you leave it, if you say no, you both get nothing. If you were both perfectly rational, as most economists would predict, your partner would offer you one dollar, knowing that you'd prefer one dollar to no dollars, and you'd accept her offer, because she was right about you. But the economists were wrong about you both. In real life, nobody offers one dollar, and around half of all people offer ten dollars. But what would you do if your partner offered you seven dollars? Or five? Or three? Most people would accept the seven dollars, but not the three. Most people are willing to pay a few dollars, but not seven, to punish the selfish partner.

Now suppose you played this game while inside an fMRI scanner. Alan Sanfey[17] and his colleagues at Princeton had people do just that; the researchers then looked at what parts of the brain were more active when people were given unfair offers. One of the three areas that differed most (when comparing responses to unfair vs. fair offers) was the frontal insula, an area of the cortex on the frontal underside of the brain. The frontal insula is known to be active during most negative or unpleasant emotional states, particularly anger and disgust. Another area was the dorsolateral prefrontal cortex, just behind the sides of the forehead, known to be active during reasoning and calculation. Perhaps the most impressive finding from Sanfey's study is that people's ultimate response—accept or reject—could be predicted by looking at the state of their brains moments before they pressed a button to make a choice. Those subjects who showed more activation in the insula than in the dorsolateral prefrontal cortex generally went on to reject the unfair offer; those with the reverse pattern generally accepted it. (It's no wonder that marketers, political consultants, and the CIA are so interested in neural imaging and "neuromarketing.")

Gratitude and vengefulness are big steps on the road that led to human ultrasociality, and it's important to realize that they are two sides of one coin. It would be hard to evolve one without the other. An individual who had gratitude without vengefulness would be an easy mark for exploitation, and a vengeful and ungrateful individual would quickly alienate all potential cooperative partners. Gratitude and revenge are also, not coincidentally, major forces holding together the mafia. The Godfather sits at the center of a vast web of reciprocal obligations and favors. He accumulates power with each favor he does, secure in the knowledge that nobody who values his own life will fail to repay at a time of the Godfather's choosing. Revenge for most of us is much less drastic, but if you have worked long enough in an office, restaurant, or store, you know there are many subtle ways to retaliate against those who have crossed you, and many ways to help those who have helped you.

You Stab His Back, I'll Stab Yours

When I said that people would beat the hell out of an ingrate who failed to repay an important favor, I left out a qualification. For a first offense, they'd probably just gossip. They'd ruin his reputation. Gossip is another key piece in the puzzle of how humans became ultrasocial. It might also be the reason we have such large heads.

Woody Allen once described his brain as his "second favorite organ," but for all of us it's by far the most expensive one to run. It accounts for 2 percent of our body weight but consumes 20 percent of our energy. Human brains grow so large that human beings must be born prematurely[18] (at least, compared to other mammals, who are born when their brains are more or less ready to control their bodies), and even then they can barely make it through the birth canal. Once out of the womb, these giant brains attached to helpless baby bodies require somebody to carry them around for a year or two. The tripling of human brain size from the time of our last common ancestor with chimpanzees to today imposed tremendous costs on parents, so there must have been a very good reason to do it. Some have argued that the reason was hunting and tool making, others suggest that the extra gray matter helped our ancestors locate fruit. But the only theory that explains why animals in general have particular brain sizes is the one that maps brain size onto social group size. Robin Dunbar[19] has demonstrated that *within* a given group of vertebrate species—primates, carnivores, ungulates, birds, reptiles, or fish—the logarithm of the brain size is almost perfectly proportional to the logarithm of the social group size. In other words, all over the animal kingdom, brains grow to manage larger and larger groups. Social animals are smart animals.

Dunbar points out that chimpanzees live in groups of around thirty, and like all social primates, they spend enormous amounts of time grooming each other. Human beings ought to live in groups of around 150 people, judging from the logarithm of our brain size; and sure enough, studies of hunter-gatherer groups, military units, and city dwellers' address books suggest that 100 to 150 is the "natural" group size within which people can know just about everyone directly, by name and face, and know how each person is related to everybody else. But if grooming is so central to primate sociality, and if our ancestors began living in larger and larger groups (for some other reason, such as to take advantage of a new ecological niche with high predation risks), at some point grooming became an inadequate means of keeping up one's relationships.

Dunbar suggests that language evolved as a replacement for physical grooming.[20] Language allows small groups of people to bond quickly and to learn from each other about the bonds of others. Dunbar notes that people do in fact use language primarily to talk about other people—to find out who is doing what to whom, who is coupling with whom, who is fighting with whom. And Dunbar points out that in our ultrasocial species, success is largely a matter of playing the social game well. It's not what you know, it's who you know. In short, Dunbar proposes that language evolved because it enabled gossip. Individuals who could share social information, using any primitive means of communication, had an advantage over those who could not. And once people began gossiping, there was a runaway competition to master the arts of social manipulation, relationship aggression, and reputation management, all of which require yet more brain power.

Nobody knows how language evolved, but I find Dunbar's speculation so fascinating that I love to tell people about it. It's not good gossip—after all, you don't know Dunbar—but if you are like me you have an urge to tell your friends about anything you learn that amazes or fascinates you, and this urge itself illustrates Dunbar's point: We are *motivated* to pass on information to our friends; we even sometimes say, "I can't keep it in, I have to tell somebody." And when you do pass on a piece of juicy gossip, what happens? Your friend's reciprocity reflex kicks in and she feels a slight pressure to return the favor. If she knows something about the person or event in question, she is likely to speak up: "Oh really? Well, I heard that he …" Gossip elicits gossip, and it enables us to keep track of everyone's reputation without having to witness their good and bad deeds personally. Gossip creates a non-zero-sum game because it costs us nothing to give each other information, yet we both benefit by receiving information.

Because I'm particularly interested in the role of gossip in our moral lives, I was pleased when a graduate student in my department, Holly Hom, told me that she wanted to study gossip. In one of Holly's studies,[21] we asked fifty-one people to fill out a short questionnaire each time over the course of a week that they took part in a conversation that went on for at least ten minutes. We then took only the records in which the topic of conversation was another person, which gave us about one episode of potential gossip per day per person. Among our main findings: Gossip is overwhelmingly critical, and it is primarily about the moral and social violations of others. (For college students, this meant a lot of talk about the sexuality, cleanliness, and drinking habits of their friends and roommates.) People do occasionally tell stories about the good deeds of others, but such stories are only one tenth as common as stories about transgressions. When people pass along high-quality ("juicy") gossip, they feel more powerful, they have a better shared sense of what is right and what's wrong, and they feel more closely connected to their gossip partners.

A second study revealed that most people hold negative views of gossip and gossipers, even though almost everyone gossips. When we compared people's attitudes about gossip to the social functions that gossip serves, Holly and I came to believe that gossip is underappreciated. In a world with no gossip, people would not get away with murder but they would get away with a trail of rude, selfish, and antisocial acts, often oblivious to their own violations. Gossip extends our moral–emotional toolkit. In a gossipy world, we don't just feel vengeance and gratitude toward those who hurt or help us; we feel pale but still instructive flashes of contempt and anger toward people whom we might not even know. We feel vicarious shame and embarrassment when we hear about people whose schemes, lusts, and private failings are exposed. Gossip is a policeman and a teacher. Without it, there would be chaos and ignorance.[22]

Many species reciprocate, but only humans gossip, and much of what we gossip about is the value of other people as partners for reciprocal relationships. Using these tools, we create an ultrasocial world, a world in which we refrain from nearly all the ways we could take advantage of those weaker than us, a world in which we often help those who are unlikely ever to be able to return the favor. We *want* to play tit for tat, which means starting out nice without being a pushover, and we *want* to cultivate a reputation for being a good player. Gossip and reputation make sure that what goes around comes around—a person who is cruel will find that others are cruel back to him, and a person who is kind will find that other others are kind in return. Gossip paired with reciprocity allow karma to work here on earth, not in the next life. As long as everyone plays tit-for-tat augmented by gratitude, vengeance, and gossip, the whole system should work beautifully.

Use the Force, Luke

In offering reciprocity as the best word to guide one's life, Confucius was wise. Reciprocity is like a magic wand that can clear your way through the jungle of social life. But as anyone who has read a Harry Potter book knows, magic wands can be used against you. Robert Cialdini spent years studying the dark arts of social influence: He routinely answered ads recruiting people to work as door-to-door salesmen and telemarketers, and went through their training programs to learn their techniques. He then wrote a manual[23] for those of us who want to resist the tricks of "compliance professionals."

Cialdini describes six principles that salespeople use against us, but the most basic of all is reciprocity. People who want something from us try to give us something first, and we all have piles of address stickers and free postcards from charities that gave them to us out of the goodness of their marketing consultants' hearts. The Hare Krishnas perfected the technique: They pressed flowers or cheap copies of the *Bhagavad Gita* into the hands of unsuspecting pedestrians, and only then asked for a donation. When Cialdini studied the Krishnas at O'Hare Airport in Chicago, he noticed that they routinely went around the garbage pails to collect and recycle the flowers that they knew would be thrown away. Few people wanted the flowers, but in the early days of the technique, most were unable just to accept them and walk on without giving something in return. The Krishnas grew wealthy by exploiting people's reciprocity reflexes—until everyone learned about the Krishnas and found ways to avoid taking the "gift" in the first place.

But legions of others are still after you. Supermarkets and Amway dealers give out free samples to boost sales. Waiters and waitresses put a mint on the check tray, a technique that has been shown to boost tips.[24] Including a five-dollar "gift check" along with a survey sent in the mail increases people's willingness to complete the survey, even more than does promising to send them fifty dollars for completing the survey.[25] If you get something for nothing, part of you may be pleased, but part of you (part of the elephant-automatic processes) moves your hand to your wallet to give something back.

Reciprocity works just as well for bargaining. Cialdini was once asked by a boy scout to buy tickets to a movie he didn't want to see. When Cialdini said no, the scout asked him to buy some less expensive chocolate bars instead. Cialdini found himself walking away with three chocolate bars that he didn't want. The scout had made a concession, and Cialdini automatically reciprocated by making a concession of his own. But rather than getting mad, Cialdini got data. He conducted his own version of the encounter, asking college students walking on campus whether they would volunteer to chaperone a group of juvenile delinquents to the zoo for a day. Only 17 percent agreed. But in another condition of the study, students were first asked whether they would volunteer to work for two hours a week for two years with juvenile delinquents. All said no, but when the experimenter then asked about the day trip to the zoo, 50 percent said yes.[26] Concession leads to concession. In financial bargaining, too, people who stake out an extreme first position and then move toward the middle end up doing better than those who state a more reasonable first position and then hold fast.[27] And the extreme offer followed by concession doesn't just get you a better price, it gets you a happier partner (or victim): She is more likely to honor the agreement because she feels that she had more influence on the outcome. The very process of give and take creates a feeling of partnership, even in the person being taken.

So the next time a salesman gives you a free gift or consultation, or makes a concession of any sort, duck. Don't let him press your reciprocity button. The best way out, Cialdini advises, is to fight reciprocity with reciprocity. If you can reappraise the salesman's move for what it is—an effort to exploit you—you'll feel entitled to exploit him right back. Accept the gift or concession with a feeling of victory—you are exploiting an exploiter—not mindless obligation.

Reciprocity is not just a way of dealing with boy scouts and obnoxious salespeople; it's for friends and lovers, too. Relationships are exquisitely sensitive to balance in their early stages, and a great way to ruin things is either to give too much (you seem perhaps a bit desperate) or too little (you seem cold and rejecting). Rather, relationships grow best by balanced give and take, especially of gifts, favors, attention, and self-disclosure. The first three are somewhat obvious, but people often don't realize the degree to which the disclosure of personal information is a gambit in the dating game. When someone tells you about past romantic relationships, there is conversational pressure for you to do the same. If this disclosure card is played too early, you might feel ambivalence—your reciprocity reflex makes you prepare your own matching disclosure, but some other part of you resists sharing intimate details with a near-stranger. But when it's played at the right time, the past-relationships-mutual-disclosure conversation can be a memorable turning point on the road to love.

Reciprocity is an all-purpose relationship tonic. Used properly, it strengthens, lengthens, and rejuvenates social ties. It works so well in part because the elephant is a natural mimic. For example, when we interact with someone we like, we have a slight tendency to copy their every move, automatically and unconsciously.[28] If the other person taps her foot, you are more likely to tap yours. If she touches her face, you are more likely to touch yours. But it's not just that we mimic those we like; we like those who mimic us. People who are subtly mimicked are then more helpful and agreeable toward their mimicker, and even toward others.[29] Waitresses who mimic their customers get larger tips.[30]

Mimicry is a kind of social glue, a way of saying "We are one." The unifying pleasures of mimicry are particularly clear in synchronized activities, such as line dances, group cheers, and some religious rituals, in which people try to do the same thing at the same time. A theme of the rest of this book is that humans are partially hive creatures, like bees, yet in the modern world we spend nearly all our time outside of the hive. Reciprocity, like love, reconnects us with others.

Notes

1. *Analects,* 15.24. In Leys, 1997.
2. Babylonian Talmud, Tractate Shabbos, Folio 31a, Schottenstein edition, A. Dicker, trans. (New York: Mesorah Publications, 1996).
3. *The Godfather,* directed by F. F. Coppola, 1972. Paramount Pictures. Based on the novel by Mario Puzo.
4. Campbell, 1983; Richerson and Boyd, 1998.
5. Hamilton, 1964, first worked out the details of kin selection. We all share most of our genes with all people, and even with most chimpanzees, mice, and fruit flies. What matters here is only the subset of genes that vary within the human population.
6. Of course, the ancestors did no "parlaying"; they just survived better than their competitors, and in the process, reproduction shifted over to a queen and ultrasociality emerged.
7. Described in Ridley, 1996.
8. Kunz and Woolcott, 1976.
9. Cialdini, 2001.
10. Axelrod, 1984.
11. Wilkinson, 1984.
12. Trivers, 1971.
13. Ridley, 1996.
14. Panthanathan and Boyd, 2004; Richerson and Boyd, 2005.
15. Cosmides and Tooby, 2004.
16. Guth, Schmittberger, and Schwarze, 1982.
17. Sanfey et al., 2003.
18. Bjorklund, 1997.
19. Dunbar, 1993.
20. Dunbar, 1996.
21. Hom and Haidt, in preparation.
22. For a defense of gossip, see Sabini and Silver, 1982.
23. Cialdini, 2001.
24. Cialdini, 2001, cites an unpublished study by Lynn and McCall, 1998.
25. James and Bolstein, 1992.
26. Cialdini et al., 1975.
27. Benton, Kelley, and Liebling, 1972.
28. Lakin and Chartrand, 2003.
29. van Baaren et al., 2004.
30. van Baaren et al., 2003.

SECTION 7

SEXUAL SELECTION

Introduction to Chapter 8

Sexual selection is a force that often pushes male and female phenotypes apart. This happens whenever when one sex finds mating more difficult to obtain than does the other. Predicting the direction of that imbalance has taken 120 years of study.

Selection crafts the adaptations of a species to meet the challenges of its environment. This seems to suggest that, within each population, phenotypes will become very similar to each other as they converge on whatever best meets the local challenges. A more precise way to say this is that selection generally causes the mean (average) phenotype to approach the optimum phenotype. To a large degree this is what we see in the world. We all have the same numbers of hands and feet, noses and eyes; our hearts are in the same place and have the same arrangement of parts. Surgeons can confidently rely on this uniformity. But there is a conspicuous class of exceptions. Many species have not one but two "typical" phenotypes, one for males and one for females. This could only happen if selection were favoring different traits in the two sexes; but why would it?

Twelve years after he published *On the Origin of Species*, Darwin wrote another large work, one volume of which—*Selection in Relation to Sex*—was dedicated to answering this question. His touchstone example was the peacock, or more precisely, the peacock's tail. Does the resplendent train of a male peafowl help him find food? Avoid predators? Fight off parasites and pathogens? No, it actually hinders all of these fitness-serving goals. Then how have the genes that build this seemingly worse-than-useless tail been preserved? The answer is simple: The tail is attractive to females.

Think about how selection works. Mere survival gets precisely zero genes into the next generation. To be evolutionarily successful, an individual must survive to adulthood *and then mate*. Even if a trait decreased the chances of survival—as a large, heavy, flashy tail probably would—it could still be favored by selection, as long as it provided a big enough mating boost during one's (admittedly shorter) lifetime. Sexual selection, as defined by

Darwin and as still understood today, is selection for traits that increase mating success. Live fast, die young—and leave plenty of offspring! (Once you have assimilated all the ideas in this introduction and in the accompanying chapter by British biologists Tim Clutton-Brock and Amanda Vincent, you could try to explain why men's lives average seven years shorter than women's.)

There are several broad categories of sexually selected traits. The two categories that will most concern us in this course are courtship traits and aggressive traits: the phrase "make love or make war" may help you grasp the dichotomy. Let's stick with the male perspective for the moment (and then we'll throw that open for evaluation, as the chapter does). Selection could favor traits that allow a male to dazzle—to hypnotize—females so that other males essentially disappear. Or, selection could favor traits that allow a male to beat up or so thoroughly intimidate his competitors that they do not even approach the females. Either kind of trait—hypnotic or dominating—would be favored by sexual selection as long as it helped in getting mates. Chapter 8 does not try to solve the question of whether sexual selection will favor courting or fighting in any given species. Instead, our British friends take up the equally challenging question of which sex will evolve these mate-monopolizing traits—which sex will court or fight.

What is your intuition? Which sex will evolve sexually competitive traits? The peacock example or your broader experience may lead you to suspect that the answer is always the male. Alternatively, if you think it through from first principles, you may come to a different conclusion: In any sexual species, males and females are equally dependent on getting a mate (because a male cannot reproduce without a female, and a female cannot reproduce without a male). Yes, a male might benefit from traits that help him to get more females, but a female should *equally* benefit from traits that help her to get more males. If that were true, the two sexes would compete with equal intensity for mates. What do we actually see in the world?

In reality, all possible patterns occur. In other words, there are many species where males have either courtship or aggressive traits that females completely lack. There are also many species in which these sexually selected traits—bright coloration or weapons—are present to approximately the same degree in both sexes. And, though they are rare, there are species where only the females are flamboyant or aggressive. The point is not that some females are aggressive. The point is that there are entire species where the females are consistently more aggressive than the males. What can explain these patterns? What would we have to know about a species in order to predict which sex—males, females, or both—will be the target(s) of sexual selection? Put simply, which sex will compete more intensely for mates? This is what Chapter 8 answers in a simple and elegant way.

Both Charles Darwin and Robert Trivers, the developer of the reciprocal altruism theory, had made earlier attempts to answer this question. All the answers, including the one offered by Clutton-Brock and Vincent in Chapter 8, have a certain logical framework in common, so let's try to understand that framework. Darwin knew that when only one sex had sexually competitive traits (courtship or aggressive structures), it was almost always the male. He suggested that an unbalanced sex ratio could be the cause. In particular, he argued that if males were common and females were scare, competition for mates would be asymmetrical. Females would find an abundance of mates and would gain no advantage from competing; but males would find few females and could benefit by competing for them. Darwin was both a good theorist and a good observer. Thus he was able to discover that his hypothesis was wrong; sex ratios are not generally unbalanced in nature. Females are not scarce, so this is not the reason that males compete.

One hundred years later, Robert Trivers made another suggestion: It is not the numbers of males and females that is unbalanced; it is the reproductive work they do in forming the offspring. Let's take a typical mammalian example. What does a female deer do in the course of reproducing? Besides producing the egg, she gestates the fetus for about six months and lactates for her fawn through another five. And what does her mate do? He contributes a tiny sperm cell, and then walks away. This, too, is an imbalance. But on this view it is not females themselves who are scarce; it is female reproductive work. Sperm are cheap and abundant compared to eggs, uteruses and milk. Following the core Darwinian logic, that imbalance in reproductive work means that sperm makers will need to compete for access to the nurturing capacities of uteruses and mammary glands.

Trivers' theory was a good theory because it predicted the full range of observed possibilities. It predicted sexually competitive males in species where females do most of the reproductive work. It predicted that both sexes would have sexually competitive traits in species where males and females share the reproductive work equally. And, importantly, it predicted sexually competitive females in species where males do most of the reproductive work. In 99.9% of cases, Trivers' predictions were accurate; as a result, his theory held sway for two decades. But the 0.1% of cases, the exceptions, continued to bother people. Specifically, the exceptions were cases where males appear to perform *all* the parental care but nevertheless still compete for mating access more than females do. According to Trivers' theory, that should never happen.

All good scientists care disproportionately about the (sometimes) tiny percent of cases where a theory does not fit. That is how Einstein was able to improve on Newton's ideas. In Chapter 8, Clutton-Brock and Vincent concentrate on species that have uniparental care by males (species that have no parental care by females). According to Trivers, females should be the sexual competitors in all of these species. In actuality, they are in some, but not all. The authors of Chapter 8 develop a theory that predicts which sex will be the sexual competitor in these critical test cases. Try to see what general principle this theory has in common with the ideas of both Darwin and Trivers.

Once you understand how sexual selection works in general, try to say how it has acted in humans. Which sex is the predominant sexual competitor and, in terms of Clutton-Brock and Vincent's theory, why?

Chapter 8 Glossary

ectotherm: A cold-blooded animal; one that does not regulate its body temperature chemically.

endotherm: A warm-blooded animal; one that maintains a relatively constant body temperature by chemical means.

operational sex ratio: The ratio of females ready and able to begin a reproductive venture to males in the same position. This is not automatically equal to the raw sex ratio because females (or males) may be unavailable because of commitments to ongoing reproductive ventures (e.g., because of pregnancy).

parental investment: Anything done or contributed by a parent that increases the survival or reproductive prospects of a particular offspring at a cost to the parent's future reproductive capacity. Parental investment is what economists call a "cost function;" this means that what is spent on one offspring is unavailable to be spent on another.

Chapter 8
Sexual Selection and the Potential Reproductive Rates of Males and Females (1991)

T. H. Clutton-Brock and A. C. J. Vincent

Pronounced sex differences in mating competition are a prominent feature of many animal breeding systems. These differences are widely attributed to sex differences in parental investment[1,2] which bias the ratio of sexually receptive females to males[3] (the operational sex ratio), generating more intense competition between members of one sex, usually males[3–5]. Unfortunately, relative parental investment[1] is usually impossible to measure in species where both sexes invest in their offspring[6,7] and there is currently no empirical basis for predicting the pattern of mating competition in these species. In contrast, the potential rate of reproduction by males and females (measured as the maximum number of independent offspring that parents can produce per unit time) is both more directly related to the operational sex ratio and more easily estimated in natural populations[7]. Here we show that among species where males care for the young, the sex with the higher potential reproductive rate competes more intensely for mates than the sex with the lower potential rate of reproduction.

In animals without parental care or where females are responsible for all care, the potential reproductive rate of males usually exceeds that of females. As a result, the operational sex ratio is biased towards males and males are the predominant competitors for mates[1,7,14], (except in a few cases where males contribute resources used in the production of zygotes[8–11]). In contrast, in species where males are responsible for all parental care while females pay the costs of egg production (which include some teleost fishes[14–16], anurans[17], urodeles[18], invertebrates[19,20] and a few birds[21,22]), the direction of mating competition differs between species. In some, females compete intensely for mates, males are choosey in selecting partners and females are brighter than males[23–26]. In others, males compete intensely for females, females are choosey in selecting partners, and males are brighter than females[27,28]. An explanation of these differences could be that only in some of these species does the involvement of males in parental care depress their potential reproductive rate below that of females[7].

To test whether differences in the direction of mating competition depend on which sex has the higher potential rate of reproduction, we extracted data on the maximal reproductive rates of males and females for 29 species where males were responsible for parental care, there was a clear sex difference in the intensity of mating competition, and data were available (Tables 1 and 2). With only two possible exceptions, males had potentially higher reproductive rates than females in all 'predominant male competitors' (Table 1). The most highly developed examples of predominant male competition combined with male parental care are found in fish and frogs where males can care for multiple clutches simultaneously or in quick succession[27–29]. For example, in the three-spined stickleback, *Gasterosteus aculeatus,* males can guard 10 or more clutches of eggs at a time and do so for about 2.weeks, whereas females can lay one clutch every 3–5 days[28]. Consequently, the potential reproductive rate of males is higher than that of females, the operational sex ratio is male-biased and males compete intensely for mates.

By contrast, in all species that we identified as 'predominant female competitors', females were able to achieve higher rates of reproduction than males. The clearest examples occur in small polyandrous shorebirds, where the potential reproductive rate of males is low because incubation is prolonged and brood size is small[21]. For example, in the polyandrous spotted sandpiper *Actitis macularia,* where females compete intensely for mating partners, males do not raise more than one clutch of four eggs during the breeding season, whereas females can produce an egg a day and lay clutches for up to four different males in the course of the season[23,30]. Predominant female competition also occurs in some fish where males carry eggs or young for lengthy periods and their reproductive rate is constrained by the number of eggs they can carry, including the pipefishes, *Nerophis ophidion* and *Syngnathus typhle*[25,26,31,32], and some cardinal fishes[33]. Further examples can be expected in other animals where males bear eggs or young.

Both possible exceptions in Table 1 are instructive as they illustrate the need to calculate reproductive rates over different periods in different species. In the greater rhea, *Rhea americana,* males incubate broods of 20–30 eggs laid by several females and compete vigorously for mating access to female groups[36]. The potential reproductive rate of females calculated over the entire breeding season may be higher than that of males. During the period of mating and brood production however, males can fertilize and accept eggs

Table 1 Relationship between reproductive rates and mating competition for species in which males are responsible for parental care

Female rate / Male rate	Competition for mates more intense in males	Competition for mates more intense in females
<1	Fish *Cottus (2 spp)* *Oxylebius pictus* *Chromis notata* *Chrysiptera cyanea* *Badis badis* *Pimephales promelas* *Etheostoma olmstedi* *Gasterosteus aculeatus* *Forsterygion varium* Frogs *Alytes obstetricans* *Hyla rosenbergii* *Eleutherodactylus coqui*	
>1	Fish *Hippocampus spp* Birds *? Rhea americana*	Fish *Apogon notatus* *Nerophis ophidion* *Syngnathus typhle* Birds *Actitis macularia* *Phalaropus (2 spp)* *Eudromias morinellus* *Jacana (5 spp)* *Rostrathula benghalensis* *Turnix sylvaticus*

Males compete more than females for access to mates in all but two of the species in which a male has a higher potential reproductive rate than a female (mainly ectotherms). Females are the more competitive sex (sex roles are 'reversed') in species where the potential reproductive rate of females exceeds that of males (primarily endotherms).

faster than females can lay them and the operational sex ratio is probably male-biased. In seahorses (*Hippocampus* spp.), the operational sex ratio is biased towards males despite a prolonged male gestation period because the reproductive rate of females is constrained by monogamous pair bonds and by limited periods of receptivity[12].

The potential rates of reproduction by males and females thus provide a basis for predicting the direction of mating competition in the two sexes and thus the direction of sexual selection. Several other factors, however, can bias the operational sex ratio and influence the relative intensity of mating competition. These include behavioural adaptations to competition in the sex with the potentially higher reproductive rate, such as precopulatory guarding of multiple mates and earlier eclosion, emergence or arrival times[24,37–40]. Conversely, biases in the operational sex ratio may be reduced by sex differences in life expectancy[41], which can reflect the costs of increased competition in the potentially faster sex[7]. Variation in the time necessary to find mates may constrain mating competition in some species[42] (G. Parker, personal communication), while the form of competitive behaviour may be affected by variation in the costs and benefits of particular tactics to the two sexes. Finally, where the potential rate of reproduction is similar in the two sexes, the relative benefits of acquiring qualitatively superior mates[43,44], rather than the operational sex ratio, may determine the comparative intensity of mating competition in the two sexes.

Species shown are allocated to two categories on the basis of reports of mating competition: predominant male competitors (*a*) and predominant female competitors (*b*). Although both sexes may compete for particular mating partners, most species could be allocated to the groups without difficulty. Records of reproductive rate ignore the possibility of 'stolen' copulations by males. Abbreviations: M, male; F, female; MM, males; FF, females. Columns show the best available estimates of: (1) the duration of male care of eggs (incubation) and/or young and of the time between successive broods where remating does not follow immediately on independence of the previous brood; (2) average clutch size laid by females (*C*) and the average brood size cared for by males (*B*). Where males are known to care for several clutches simultaneously, this is noted; (3) the approximate inter-clutch interval for females or the maximum number of successful breeding partners per season; (4) maximum recorded female reproductive rate (eggs per unit time) divided by the maximum recorded rate of reproduction by males (independent young reared per unit time). For most species, estimates of reproductive rate were only adequate to indicate whether the potential reproductive rate of males exceeded that of females or vice versa; (5) whether males or females are recorded as the primary competitors for mates or breeding territories. * In congenerics/other Jacana spp.

Table 2 Maximum observed reproductive rates in species where males are responsible for parental care

Predominant male competitors	Male care duration	Clutch (C) and brood (B) size	Interclutch interval	Max. F/max. M rate of reproduction	Competing sex	Ref.
Alytes obstetricans (Discoglossidae: Midwife toad)	2–3 weeks	M can carry > 1 clutch at a time	FF breed 2–4 times per summer at ~ monthly intervals	<1	M	45–47
Hyla rosenbergii (Hylidae)	4 days	*B* = 2,350	23 days	«1 (0.25)	M	27
Eleutherodactylus coqui (Leptodactylidae)	17–26 days of care 8–9 month season	*B* = up to 5 x *C* at once *C* =16–43	up to 6 clutches per season	<1	M	29
Cottus hangiongensis (Cottidae: river sculpin)		*B* = 3.4–5.3 x *C* up to 13 x *C*	2 per season	<1	M	49
Cottus gobio (Cottidae: river bullhead)	4 weeks	*B* = 2.15 x C *C* = 75–200	2 per season	<1	M	50
Oxylebius pictus (Hexagrammidae: greenling)	2.5–3.5 weeks 30 days between spawnings up to 7.5 x C per season	*B* = 0–10 x *C* per cycle *B* = 0–22 x *C* per season *C* = 1,500–5,000	3 per season	<1	M	51, 52
Chromis notata (Pomacentridae: damselfish)	4–12 days (depends on temperature) 8.2–17.8 days between spawnings	*B* = 1–4 x *C* 2.8–4.6 nests per season *C* = 10,000–27,500	7.2–18.4 days	<1	M*	15, 53
Chrysiptera cyanea (Pomacentridae: damselfish)	4 days MM spawn continuously	*B* = up to 12,255 eggs per cycle *C* = 900–2,500 eggs per cycle	4 days	<1	M	54
Badis badis (Nandidae)	2 days egg 3–4 days larvae 7–8 days between spawnings	*B* = 2–3 x *C*	4–7 days	<1	M	55, 56
Pimephales promeias (Cyprinidae)	4–8 days males spawn continuously for 3–5 weeks	*B* = max. 6,000 eggs per nest *C* = 200–700 eggs	3–4 days	<1	M	57, 58
Etheostoma oimstedi (Percidae: tessellated darter)	4 days	*B* = max. 2,000 eggs *C* = 19–324 (season $\bar{x}$ = 727)	5–16 days ($\bar{x}$ = 7.6)	«1	M*	15, 59
Gasterosteus aculeatus (Gasterosteidae: stickleback)	2 weeks at 21 °C	*B* = up to 10 x *C* *B* » *C* = 51–150	3–5 days	<1	M	28
Forsterygion varium (Tripterygidae)	7–10 days spawn up to 15 times per season	*B* = 20–7,080 ($\bar{x}$ = 2,245)eggs *C* = 20–1.680 ($\bar{x}$= 796) eggs	100% spawn once 31% spawn > once never > 5 times per season	«1 (0.3)	M	60
Hippocampus fuscus (Syngnathidae: Seahorse)	13–14 days	*C* > *B*	<13–14 days	>1	M	12
Rhea americana (Greater Rhea)	incubation 36–37 days plus care one brood per season	*B* = 26.5 C = 2–3	up to 12 MM per year	eggs per season > 1 eggs per laying period < 1	M	34–36

Predominant female competitors	Male care duration (including incubation]	Clutch (C) and brood (B) size	Interclutch interval	Max. F/max. M rate of reproduction	Competing sex	Ref.
Actitis macularia (Spotted sandpiper)	Incubation 21 days max. 8.1 eggs per season usually one brood per season	$C = B = 4$ 1 egg per day	max. 11 eggs per season	>1	F	23, 30
Phalaropus lobatus (Red-necked phalarope)	incubation 17–21 days male care = 33 days usually one brood per season	$C = B = 4$ 1 egg per day	10 days up to 2 clutches per season	>1	F	24, 61
Phalaropus fulicarius (Grey phalarope)	incubation 18–20 days male care = 37 days usually one brood per season	$C = B = 4$	up to 2 per season	>1	F	61, 62
Eudromias morineflus (Dotterel)	incubation 24–28 days male care = 61 days usually one brood per season	$C = B = 3$	5–11 days up to 3 clutches per season	>1	F	61
Jacana spinosa (American jacana)	male care = 59 days total	$C = B = 4$	up to 3 MM per year (≥4 clutches in few weeks')	>1	F	63
Jacana jacana (Wattled jacana)	about 60 days*	$C = B = 4$ 1 egg per day	minimum = 2–4 days up to 6 clutches per season (up to 2 MM)	>1	F	64, 65
Hydrophasianus chirurgus (Pheasant tailed jacana)	about 60 days*	$C = B = 4$	several MM per F at same time	>1	F	66. 67
Metopidius indicus (Bronze winged jacana)	about 60 days*	$C = B = 4$*	several MM per F at same time	>1	F	68
Actophilornis africana (African jacana)	incubation 24 days male care >60 days	$C = B = 4$	up to 4 MM per F at same time	>1	F	69, 70
Rostrathula benghalensis (Painted snipe)	incubation 15–19 days 1–2 months care (62 days)	$C = B = 4$	up to 4 MM per F at same time	>1	F	69
Turnix sylvaticus (Little button quail)	incubation 12–15 days care 18–20 days male cycle = 53 days total	$C = B = 3.5$	not known but estimated that F can breed with up to 5 MM per year	>1	F	69, 71
Apogon notatus (Apogonidae: cardinalfish)	8 days care plus 6–15 days = 14–23 days between spawning	$C = B$	10–19 days (= 13.8)	>1	F	33
Nerophis ophidion (Syngnathidae: pipefish)	28–37 days	$C = 1.8 \times B$ M = 204 eggs per season F = 396 eggs per season		>1 (1.8)	F	25, 31
Syngnathus typhle (Syngnathidae: pipefish)	28–45 days	$C = 1.9 \times B$ M = 91 eggs per season F = 219 eggs per season		>1 (1.9)	F	26, 31

References

1. Trivers, R. L. in *Sexual Selection and the Descent of Man* (ed. B. Campbell) 136–179 (Aldine, Chicago, 1972).
2. Trivers, R. L. *Social Evolution* (Cummings, California. 1985).
3. Emlen, S. T. & Oring, L. W. *Science* 197, 215–223 (1977).
4. Thornhill, R. in *Evolution of Animal Behaviour: Paleontological and Field Approaches* (eds Nitecki, M. H. & Hitchell, J. A.) 113–135 (Oxford University Press, Oxford, 1986).
5. Krebs, J. R. & Davies, N. B. *An Introduction to Animal Ecology* (Blackwell Scientific, Oxford, 1987).
6. Knapton, R. W. *Can. J. Zool.* **62,** 2673–2674 (1984).
7. Clutton-Brock, T. H. *The Evolution of Parental Care* (Princeton University Press, New Jersey, in the press).
8. Gwynne, D. T. *Trends Ecol. Ecol.* **6,** 118–121 (1991).
9. Gwynne, D. T. *Behavl Ecol. Sociobiol.* **16,** 355–361 (1985).
10. Gwynne, D. T. & Simmons, L. W. *Nature* **346,** 172–174 (1990).
11. Thornhill, R. & Gwynne, D. T. *Am. Scient.* **74,** 382–389 (1986).
12. Vincent, A. C. J. thesis, Univ. Cambridge (1990).
13. Baylis, J. R. *Nature* **276,** 278 (1978).
14. Baylis, J. R. *Envir. Biol. Fish.* **6,** 223–251 (1981).
15. Breder, C. M. Jr & Rosen, D. E. *Modes of Reproduction in Fishes* (Natural History Press, New York, 1966).
16. Thresher, R. E. *Reproduction in Reef Fishes* (T. F. H. Publications, Neptune City, New Jersey, 1984).
17. Wells. K. D. in *Natural Selection and Social Behavior* (eds Alexander, R. D. & Tinkle, D. W.) 184–197 (Chiron Press, New York, 1981).
18. Nussbaum, R. A. *Misc. Publs. Mus. Zool. Univ. Mich.* **169,** 1–50 (1985).
19. Wilson, E. O. *Insect Societies* (Harvard University Press, Cambridge, Massachusetts, 1971).
20. Thornhill, R. & Alcock, J. *The Evolution of Insect Mating Systems* (Harvard University Press, Cambridge, Massachusetts, 1983).
21. Erckmann, W. J. thesis, Univ. Washington (1981).
22. Handford, P. & Mares, M. A. *Biol. J. Linn. Soc. Lond.* **25,** 77–104 (1985).
23. Oring. L. W., Lank, D. B. & Maxson, S. J. *Auk* **100,** 272–285 (1983).
24. Reynolds, J. D., Colwell, M. A. & Cooke, F. *Behavl. Ecol. Sociobiol.* **18,** 303–410 (1986).
25. Rosenqvist, G. *Anim. Behav.* **39,** 1110–1115 (1990).

26. Berglund. A. *Evolution* (in the press).
27. Kluge, A. G. *Misc. Publs. Mus. Zool. Univ. Mich.* **160,** 1–170 (1981).
28. Kynard, B. E. *Behaviour* **67,** 178–207 (1978).
29. Townsend, D. S, *Am. Nat.* **133,** 266–272 (1989).
30. Oring, L. W. & Knudson, M. L *Living Bird* **11,** 59–73 (1972).
31. Berglund, A., Rosenqvist, G. & Svensson, I. *Am. Nat.* **133,** 506–516 (1989).
32. Berglund, A., Rosenqvist, G. & Svensson, I. *Mar. Ecol. Prog. Ser.* **29,** 209–215 (1986).
33. Kuwamura. T. *Envir. Biol. Fish.* **13,** 17–24 (1985).
34. Bruning, D. F. *Nat. Hist.* **82,** 68–75 (1973).
35. Bruning. D. F. *Living Bird* **13,** 251–294 (1974).
36. Bruning, D. F. thesis, Univ. Colorado (1974).
37. Iwasa, Y., Odendaal, F. J., Murphy, D. D., Ehrlich, P. R. & Launer, A. E. *Theor. Populat. Biol.* **23,** 363–379 (1983).
38. Gregory, P. T. *Can. J. Zool.* **52,** 1063–1069 (1974).
39. Michener, G. R. *Behavl. Ecol. Sociobiol.* **14,** 29–38 (1983).
40. Myers, J. P. *Can. J. Zool.* **59,** 1527–1534 (1981).
41. Breitwisch, R. *Curr. Onithol.* **6,** 1–50 (1989).
42. Sutherland, W. J. *Anim. Behav.* **33,** 1349–1352 (1985).
43. Burley, N. *Proc. natn. Acad. Sci. US.A.* **74,** 3476–3479 (1977).
44. Burley, N. *Am. Nat.* **127,** 415–445 (1986).
45. Duellman, W. E. & Trueb, L. *Biology of Amphibians* (McGraw-Hill, New York, 1986).
46. Crespo, J. thesis, Univ. Lisbon (1979).
47. McDiarmid, R. W. in *The Development of Behavior: Comparative and Evolutionary Aspects* (eds Burghardt, C. M. & Bekoff, N.) 127–147 (Garland, New York, 1978).
48. Smith, B. G. *Biol. Bull. Mar. biol. Lab., Woods Hole* **13,** 5–39 (1907).
49. Goto, A. *Copeia* 1987, 32–40 (1987).
50. Marconato, A. & Bisazza, A. *J. Fish. Biol.* **33,** 905–916 (1988).
51. DeMartini, E. E. *Anim. Behav.* **35,** 1145–1158 (1987).
52. DeMartini, E. E. *Copeia* 1985, 966–975 (1985).
53. Ochi, H. *Envir. Biol. Fish.* **17,**117–123 (1986).
54. Gronell, A. M. *Ethology* **81,** 89–122 (1989).
55. Barlow, G. W. *Copeia* 1962, 346–360 (1962).
56. Barlow, G. W. *Z. Tierpsychol.* **21,** 99–123 (1964).
57. Unger, L. M. *Behavl. Ecol. Sociobiol.* **13,**125–130 (1983).
58. Sargent, R. C. *Behavl. Ecol. Sociobiol.* **25,** 379–385 (1989).
59. Gale, W. F. & Deutsch, W. G. *Trans. Am. Fish. Soc.* **224,** 220–229 (1985).
60. Thomson, S. *Anim. Behav.* **34,** 580–589 (1986).

61. Cramp, S. *et al. Handbook of the Birds of Europe, the Middle East and North Africa* Vol. Ill (Oxford University Press, Oxford, 1983).
62. Ridley, M. W. *Ibis* **122,** 210–226 (1980).
63. Jenni, D. A. & Collier, C. *Auk* **89**, 743–765 (1972).
64. Osborne, D. R. *Wilson Bull.* **94,** 206–208 (1982).
65. Osborne, D. R. & Bourne, G. R. *Condor* **79,** 98–105 (1977).
66. Hoffman, A. *Scop. Zool. Jahrb. Abt. Syst. Oekol. Geogr. Tiere.* **78,** 367–403 (1949).
67. Hoffman, A. *Orn. Ber.* **2,** 119–126 (1950).
68. Matthew, D. N. *J. Bombay nat. Hist. Soc.* **61,** 295–301 (1964).
69. Urban, E. K., Fry, C. H. & Keith, S. *The Birds of Africa* Vol. II (Academic, New York, 1986).
70. Vernon, C. J. *Ostrich* **44,** 85 (1973).
71. Wintle, C. C. *Honeyguide* **82,** 27–30 (1975).

Acknowledgements

The work arose from discussion of mating competition in pipefish with I. Ahnesjö. For comments, advice, discussion, criticism or access to unpublished material, we thank S. Albon, M. Andersson, A. Balmford, A. Berglund, N. Davies, A. Desrochers, A. Grafen, D. Gwynne, P. Harvey, G. Parker, J. Lazarus, J. Maynard Smith, G. Rosenqvist, and also P. Cassidy for her secretarial help.

Part II
ADAPTATIONS

SECTION 8

ANCESTRAL HUMANS

Introduction to Chapter 9

This chapter introduces the cast of characters of human evolution, discusses some traits that seem to set modern humans apart, and asks which extinct species share enough of these traits to be classified in our genus.

With the previous eight chapters, we have completed our review of evolutionary processes. Armed with these ways of thinking, we now turn our attention to the evolution of a species that holds special fascination for us: our own. Our focus will be on the suite of adaptations that define us, as well as on how, when, and why those adaptations were formed. Evidence useful in answering these questions comes from a variety of sources, for example, from the kinds of comparative approaches we explored in Chapter 5. The fossil record is another very important—though incomplete—source of evidence. In Chapter 9 we get an overview of that fossil record and of the extent to which our various extinct relatives share important adaptations with us.

Professors Wood and Collard are primarily concerned with the genus to which we belong (*Homo*) and, in particular, with the definition of that genus. In the course of wrestling with this question they will demonstrate a variety of approaches and methods. For example, they will apply both kinds of classification techniques you studied in Chapter 4. As we follow their line of argument we will become more familiar with the timeline of human evolution. And we will also get some hands-on practice in applying the evolutionary-process thinking, developed in the first eight chapters, to an actual body of data.

Remember that classification is hierarchical. A genus, such as *Homo*, can include several species (e.g., *H. sapiens* and *H. erectus*). Likewise, genera (the plural of genus) can be collected together to form higher level groupings. Tribe is the next higher level. Likewise, tribes (which usually have an "ini" ending) can be grouped together to create families. For example, the Hominini is grouped together with the various tribes of African and Asia great apes (chimpanzees, gorillas and orangutans) to form the family Pongidae. The listing below shows how the Hominini, discussed in this chapter, fit with our closest living relatives.

Family Pongidae: all great apes.
- Tribe Pongini (orangutans and their close relatives).
- Tribe Gorillini (gorillas and their close relatives)
- Tribe Panini (chimpanzees and their close relatives)
- Tribe Hominini (humans and their close relatives)
    - Genus *Praeanthropus*
    - Genus *Ardipithecus*
    - Genus *Australopithecus* (with multiple species)
    - Genus *Paranthropus* (with multiple species)
    - Genus *Homo* (with multiple species)

As shown in Table 1 of Chapter 9, each of the genera in the Hominini has one or more species assigned to it. This chapter asks one question: Which members of the tribe Hominini belong in the genus *Homo*? For example, it is possible that a species presently assigned to a different genus, perhaps the species *africanus* currently placed in *Australopithecus*, would fit better in *Homo*. Likewise, it could be that a species currently assigned to *Homo*, such as *habilis*, would fit better in *Australopithecus*. A central focus of chapter 9 is to understand what the phrase "fits better" means. Perhaps it will not ruin the plot too much if I tell you that Wood and Collard think there are good reasons to remove some species, like *habilis*, from *Homo*.

This might seem like a "who-cares?" kind of exercise. Let's explore what is right and wrong with that intuition. It is true that the practice of classification began well before evolution was established. Linnaeus, the founder of biological classification, believed—as did all of his contemporaries—that each type of organism was fixed and unchanging. As long as organisms did not change, it was simple and justifiable to create a name, a pigeon hole, a museum drawer for each type. Classification was just a matter of recognizing these fixed types and then grouping the types into higher-level categories on the basis of similarity. In a hypothetical world where organisms do not change, a name, like *Homo rudolfensis*, would simply be the name of a type. If your newfound specimen is enough like *H. rudolfensis*, then it goes in the same pigeon hole. If it is not, you will need to determine, based on the specimen's similarities and differences with known types, which other pigeon hole it belongs in.

But the classification landscape changed once the idea of evolution began to shape our thinking. As evolutionists, we realized that the population to which our *H. rudolfensis* specimen belonged probably changed over time. And if that population persisted long enough, it probably changed sufficiently that it would be regarded as something else, not *H. rudolfensis* anymore. Let's think about what this means. If populations change over time, how does that affect our approach to naming and classification?

I am going to use an analogy here. (It is not my analogy, but I am having trouble reconstructing where it came from; my apologies to the original analogist.) Imagine you attend an event in a large circular or oval-shaped stadium. You go in and take your seat. You also bought a ticket for your mother, who sits in the next seat, immediately to your right. She thoughtfully bought a ticket for her mother (your grandmother) who sits to your mother's right. Your grandmother bought a ticket for her mother and so on, all the way around the stadium! They all come in and sit down. Whom do you see when you look to your left? Well, obviously you see your great, great, great, great ... (enough "greats" to get all the way around the stadium) grandmother. But if this is a big enough stadium, with enough seats, then you are in for a surprise: The "woman" sitting on your left will not be a member of your species; she will not fit in the pigeon hole called *Homo sapiens*.

This is *not* a trick. If we accept modern evolutionary theory, this is exactly what we should expect to see from a hypothetically perfect fossil record. Now let's drive home the key aspect of this thought experiment. You and your mother are members of the same species; your mother and her mother are members of the same species; and that same claim is true for the occupants of *every* adjacent pair of seats (except yours and the one to your left). Assuming that Professor Dawkins convinced you about the gradualist perspective (in Chapter 3), then you understand why *no* mother ever gave birth to an offspring that was a member of a different species from her. Mother and offspring are always a little bit different because they have different genotypes, but not nearly different enough to be members of different species. So this creates an apparent paradox. Each adjacent pair shows only minor differences, but if we add up the small mother–child differences all the way around the stadium, we have accumulated enough differences that the end points of the continuum could not interbreed. Think about why this is similar to the real-world example of ring species.

The notion that many accumulated small changes add up to a big change is not hard to understand. You grew from a tiny infant to the adult you are today. Looking in the mirror on any two consecutive days you would see no noticeable change; but the sum of those daily changes is large. Many other examples could be given. The Himalayas are roughly five miles high but that towering height has grown at a rate of about 5mm (about one-fifth of an inch) per year as the Indian Plate crashed into the Eurasian plate.

The point is that gradualism and classification are also on a collision course back in the stadium. You and the "person" on your left are not members of the same species. But everyone else is a member of the same species as the person on her right, her mother. So, as we move around the stadium, where are we going to draw the species dividing line? We know that we have (at least) two distinct species, so some individuals must be in one species and some in the other. *Where is the boundary?* Because we are not saltationists, *there is no rationally defensible dividing line.*

To summarize, we have been talking about recognizing and naming different species. Considering a single ancestor–descendant lineage (as we have been doing in our stadium analogy), if we look at forms that are well-separated in time, we can see that those forms may well be different species. And this can be true, even though we cannot designate a particular point in time when speciation happened—there was no such event, just a long summation of tiny non-speciation events.

Now, suppose that instead of looking at a single lineage gradually changing over time we consider a lineage that is gradually splitting into two. Again, we will not be able to precisely identify the bifurcation point. We will not be able to say that in generation 741 the individuals were still similar enough to interbreed but in generation 742 they were no longer able to. This is not because our ability to assess such things is poor; it is because the separation is gradual and statistical. It might be that in generation 741 54.3% of the randomly chosen pairs can interbreed and in generation 742 the equivalent figure is 54.1%. In other words, the reproductive isolation that defines different species emerges gradually.

This same framework applies not only to species, but also to genera and to still higher levels of classification. Two genera are just two species that separated longer ago, and have had more time to accumulate differences between them. Follow this comparison. Even though we believe that *Homo heidelbergensis* populations were ancestral to *Homo sapiens* populations (i.e., the former provided most of the genes the latter caries), we could not draw a sharp species boundary between them if we had a complete fossil record. Likewise, we believe that the genus *Australopithecus* is ancestral to the genus *Homo*, with the same implication about their genetic connectedness: There was no sharp dividing line between them, even though we now classify them as different genera. Just as mothers do not have offspring that belong to a different species, they even more surely do not have offspring that belong to a different genus. Species diverge gradually; when they have been diverging long enough they will be sufficiently distinct such that we may want to classify them in different genera.

Against this gradualist background, let's now reconsider Wood and Collard's goal. How can we define the genus *Homo* in a consistent and useful way that will allow us to decide which species to include? As you will see, Wood and Collard use several methods, including both cladistic analysis (in Figures 1 and 2 and in Table 2) and numerical taxonomy (most explicitly in Tables 5 and 6). My Figure E is designed to help you think about their goal in cladistic terms. Most all anthropologists agree that the sister genus of *Homo* is *Australopithecus*

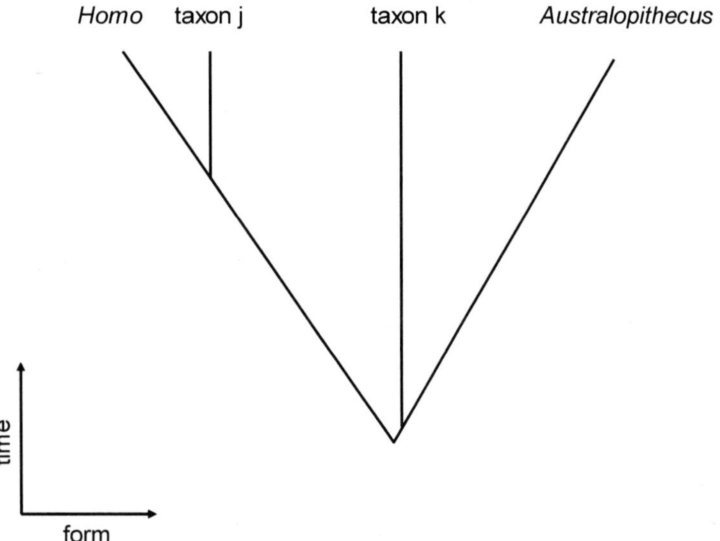

Figure E. Hypothetical cladeogram showing possible branching patterns.

and this is what Figure E depicts: the two genera share a common ancestor. As a reminder, Wood and Collard's question is, What species belong in *Homo* (and, by implication, what species belong in *Australopithecus*)? A good case could be made that "taxon j" belongs in *Homo* because it branched off from the line that leads to *Homo* long after the *Homo* line separated from the *Australopithecus* line. What about "taxon k"? It branched off from the line leading to *Australopithecus*, but only a short time after the *Homo* and *Australopithecus* lines separated. Let's agree that, in principle, taxon k does belong in *Australopithecus*. It is more closely related to Australopithecus, and this is the key cladistic criterion. The fact that it branched off only shortly after the *Homo–Australopithecus* divergence is irrelevant. But it does make a major difference in our ability to confidently apply the principle.

Let's be clear about the gap between theory and application. As discussed above, when two genera first diverge, they are just two closely related—and hence quite similar—species. If a third species, like taxon k, branched off near this divergence point it would necessarily be a lot like *both* of the other two. In other words, we can agree that in reality a taxon like k must have branched off one lineage or the other. But we should also recognize that in such cases it may be difficult to determine which lineage it was part of because of the minimal divergence between them.

A brief discussion of some specific concepts will help you integrate these evolutionary perspectives with your reading of the chapter. The trickiest new concept is "monophyletic genus." A genus is monophyletic if all of its member species are more closely related to each other than they are to any member of any other genus. This definition is easier to understand in picture form. Look at Figure 1 in the Wood and Collard chapter. In cladograms C, D, and F, *Homo* is a monophyletic genus. Take a highlighter and mark all the lines leading to a *Homo* species in cladograms C, D, and F. You will see that in each of these three cladograms, the highlighted lines converge on a single common ancestor which has only *Homo* descendants. Now take a different color highlighter and do the same for the remaining three cladograms. The patterns are quite different; in particular, *Homo* and *Australopithecus* species are interspersed. For example, in cladogram A, the common ancestor of all *Homo* would also include some members of the genus *Australopithecus*. Thus in cladograms A, B, and E, *Homo* is not a monophyletic genus.

The question is not whether *Homo* (or any genus) *should be* monophyletic. If we are cladists, *all genera should be monophyletic*. The question is, what species would need to be included in or excluded from the genus *Homo* to make it monophyletic? That is what Wood and Collard are trying to determine.

A bit more on methods: Each of the individual cladograms shown in Figure 1 (A–F) is based on multiple trials of the outgroup comparison method you learned in Chapter 4. To get more analytical power, those multiple trials used different traits ("character states") and different outgroups. The notion of "parsimony" refers to the fact that each of these trials (each trait/outgroup pairing) produces a "vote" in favor of the particular cladogram it specifies. After all the trials, the votes are tallied and the one that gets the most votes—the most parsimonious cladogram—is declared the winner. The differences among cladograms A–F result from different choices by the various authors about which traits and which outgroups to use in their analyses and which species to include in the process.

Table 2 examines the differences in parsimony among various hypothetical cladograms. The targets of this analysis are the three cladograms (C, D, and F), which indicate *Homo* is monophyletic and all species currently assigned to *Homo* really do belong in that genus. How much is parsimony insisting on that arrangement? In other words, how much does the parsimony score go down when one or another species is removed from *Homo* and placed with *Australopithecus* instead? The analysis reported in Table 2 tells us that the score does not go down much, especially if it's *H. rudolfensis* or *H. habilis* that is moved to *Australopithecus*. (The L, CI, and RI scores are simply components of the overall parsimony score.)

In most of the rest of the chapter, the authors revert to the methods of numerical taxonomy—looking at overall similarity among the various species rather than focusing exclusively on shared derived traits. This is inconsistent with their focus on a cladistic (monophyletic) definition of the genus. If you are a cladist you should limit yourself to cladistic methods. Nevertheless, it is important to pay attention to the six traits (summarized in Table 7) that the authors choose for making comparisons among the candidate *Homo* species.

What general conclusions should you draw from this chapter? Our genus, *Homo*, is roughly 2 million years old and includes at least four and perhaps as many as seven species. While it is easy to distinguish most species of *Homo* from most species of *Australopithecus*, the species that lived around the time the two lineages were separating—between 2 and 2.5 million years ago—can be challenging to distinguish because they are inevitably quite similar to each other. In short, attaching static names to the outcomes of a dynamic process (evolution) is like putting a square peg in a round pigeon hole. Nevertheless, please do not lose sight of the ways in which *Homo* is derived with respect to *Australopithecus*.

Chapter 9 Glossary

bipedal: Walking on two legs; bipedality is a highly derived state for a mammal.

gnatchic: Having to do with jaws and teeth.

humerofemoral index: Ratio of the length of the humerus (the upper arm bone) to the length of the femur (the upper leg bone); often this ratio is multiplied by 100 to make it a whole number. In either case, the ratio tends to be large in climbing species (whose arms tend to be longer than their legs) and small in bipedal species (whose arms tend to be shorter than their legs).

hypodigm: A specimen, often very incomplete in the case of extinct species, from which the characteristics of the population from which it came are inferred.

monphyletic group: A group whose member species are more closely related to each other than they are to any member of any other such group. Look at Figure E, above. Homo plus taxon j comprise a monophyletic group; Australopithecus plus taxon k comprise another monophyletic group. In contrast, a group that included any three of those four species would *not* be monophyletic.

Pleistocene: Geological epoch immediately following the Pliocene and lasting from about 2.6 million years ago to about 12 thousand years ago.

Pliocene: Geological epoch immediately preceding the Pleistocene and lasting from 5.3 to 2.6 MYA (million years ago).

relative brain size: The size of the brain compared to the size of something else, often the whole body. In this chapter the authors compare the size of the brain to the size of the orbits (the eye sockets) because they feel that estimating the body size of fossils is unreliable. This is an odd claim because they do estimate body size just a few paragraphs beforehand, and they include both body size and "relative brain size" (based on orbit size) in Table 7. See also Chapter 10.

taxon (plural, taxa): A named biological unit at any level in the classification system; a species, a genus, a family, etc.

type species: First species (sometimes the only species) of a genus to be scientifically described and named.

senu lato: Literally, loose sense; a more inclusive use of a taxon. For example, some taxonomists think *Australopithecus* and *Paranthropus* are two distinct genera, but others think they should be lumped together and both called *Australopithecus*; in the latter case the correct term would be *Australopithecus, senu lato.*

Chapter 9
The Human Genus (1999)

Bernard Wood[1] and Mark Collard[2]*

A general problem in biology is how to incorporate information about evolutionary history and adaptation into taxonomy. The problem is exemplified in attempts to define our own genus, *Homo*. Here conventional criteria for allocating fossil species to *Homo* are reviewed and are found to be either inappropriate or inoperable. We present a revised definition, based on verifiable criteria, for *Homo* and conclude that two species, *Homo habilis* and *Homo rudolfensis*, do not belong in the genus. The earliest taxon to satisfy the criteria is *Homo ergaster*, or early African *Homo erectus*, which currently appears in the fossil record at about 1.9 million years ago.

For more than a century, the fossil record for human evolution was interpreted as a ladderlike series of time-successive species, with an apelike ancestor at the base and modern humans at the top. Within this scenario, the problem of where to place the lower boundary of our own genus was resolved by using stone tool manufacture as a proxy for humanity. Thus, the hominin species contemporary with the first evidence of stone tools was deemed to have made them and thus merited inclusion in the genus *Homo*. However, from the 1960s on, when it began to become apparent that at several stages in human evolution

Large Animal Research Group, Department of Zoology, University of Cambridge, Cambridge CB3 0DT, UK

[1] Department of Anthropology, George Washington University, 2110 G Street NW, Washington, DC 20052, USA, and Human Origins Program, National Museum of Natural History, Smithsonian Institution, Washington, DC, 20560, USA.

[2] Department of Anthropology, University College London, Gower Street, London WC1E 6BT, UK.

Bernard Wood and Mark Collard, "The Human Genus," from *Science*, Vol. 284; April 2, 1999, pp. 65–71.

there were as many as three contemporaneous hominin species, the identification of the toolmaker became more difficult. More recently, fossil species have been assigned to *Homo* on the basis of absolute brain size, inferences about language ability and hand function, and retro-dictions about their ability to fashion stone tools. With only a few exceptions (*1*, *2*), the definition and use of the genus within human evolution, and the demarcation of *Homo*, have been treated as if they are unproblematic. But are the criteria set out above appropriate and workable, and is this a proper use of the genus category? (*3–5*). We provide an overview of the genus category and show that recent data, fresh interpretations of the existing evidence, and the limitations of the paleoanthropological record invalidate existing criteria for attributing taxa to *Homo*.

Species of *Homo*

Established by Linnaeus in 1758, *Homo* is one of five genera currently assigned to the tribe Hominini (Table 1). The type species, *Homo sapiens*, is the one to which living humans are assigned. Opinions differ about the number of species represented by the fossils assigned to *Homo* (*5*). Some researchers advocate using *H. sapiens* to include most or all of the fossil species shown in Table 1 (*6*), whereas more speciose interpretations allocate them to *H. neanderthalensis*, *H. erectus*, *H. heidelbergensis*, *H. habilis*, *H. ergaster*, and *H. rudolfensis* (*2*, *5*, *7*). Because there are both theoretical and practical reasons for erring on the side of too many rather than too few taxa (*8*), we have adopted the latter, more speciose, taxonomy for this review.

The species name *H. neanderthalensis* was introduced in 1864, but it has only recently been widely used (4) for fossils that have skulls with a projecting face, a large rounded cranial vault, and robust limb bones. Before this, fossils that are now assigned to *H. neanderthalensis* were included as a subspecies within *H. sapiens*. Material assigned to *H. neanderthalensis* has been found throughout Europe as well as in central and southwest Asia. Current evidence indicates that the species was extant from 250,000 to 30,000 years ago.

The first evidence of *H. erectus* was recovered in Indonesia in the early 1890s. Subsequently, numerous crania with distinctive brow ridges, a low cranial vault, and a sharply angled occipital region have been located elsewhere in Indonesia as well as in mainland Eurasia and Africa. The earliest *H. erectus* material may be 1.9 million years old, and the youngest reliably dated specimens are around 200,000 years old. The specific name *H. heidelbergensis* was introduced for the Mauer jaw, but the taxon has only been revived in the past decade (*4*, *7*). Previously, Mauer and related material were incorporated in the grade-based taxon "archaic *H. sapiens*." *Homo heidelbergensis* is known from a number of African and European Middle Pleistocene sites.

Table 1. Current hominin taxonomy, including formal taxonomic designations and approximate geographical ranges. The symbol † indicates that the taxon is extinct. Brackets around a citation indicate that the generic attribution of the taxon differs from the original one. *Praeanthropus* is, for the time being, accepted as the correct generic nomen for the specimens hitherto assigned to *Australopithecus afarensis* (*17*). Some researchers treat *Paranthropus* as a junior synonym of *Australopithecus*.

Genus †*Ardipithecus* White *et al.*, 1995. Pliocene, East Africa.
    Species † *Ardipithecus ramidus* (White *et al.*, 1994). Pliocene, East Africa.

Genus †*Australopithecus* Dart, 1925 [includes †*Plesianthropus* Broom, 1938]. Pliocene, Africa.
    Species †*Australopithecus africanus* Dart, 1925. Pliocene, Africa.
    Species †*Australopithecus anamensis* M. G. Leakey et *al.*, 1995. Pliocene, East Africa.

Genus *Homo Linnaeus*, 1758 [includes, for example, †Pithecanthropus Dubois, 1894; †Protanthropus Haeckel, 1895; †*Sinanthropus* Black, 1927; †*Cyphanthropus* Pycraft, 1928; †*Meganthropus* Weidenreich, 1945; †*Atlanthropus* Arambourg, 1954; and †*Telanthropus* Broom and Robinson, 1949]. Pliocene to the present, worldwide.
    Species †*Homo ergaster* Groves and Mazák, 1975, Plio-Pleistocene, Africa and Eurasia.
    Species †*Homo erectus* (Dubois, 1892). Pleistocene, Africa and Eurasia.
    Species †*Homo habilis* L. S. B. Leakey *et al.*, 1964. Pliocene, Africa.
    Species †*Homo heidelbergensis* Schoetensack, 1908. Pleistocene, Africa and Eurasia.
    Species †*Homo neanderthalensis* King, 1864. Pleistocene, western Eurasia.
    Species †*Homo rudolfensis* (Alexeev, 1986). Pliocene, East Africa.
    Species *Homo sapiens* Linnaeus, 1758. Pleistocene to the present, worldwide.

Genus †*Paranthropus* Broom, 1938 [includes †*Zinjanthropus* L. S. B. Leakey, 1959, and †*Paraustralopithecus* Arambourg and Coppens, 1967]. Pliocene-Pleistocene, Africa.
    Species †*Paranthropus aethiopicus* (Arambourg and Coppens, 1968). Pliocene, East Africa.
    Species †*Paranthropus boisei* (L.S.B. Leakey, 1959). Pliocene-Pleistocene, East Africa.
    Species †*Paranthropus robustus* Broom, 1938. Pleistocene, southern Africa.

†*Praeanthropus* Senyürek, 1955. Pliocene, East Africa.
    Species †*Praeanthropus africanus* (Weinert, 1950). Pliocene, East Africa.

Material now assigned to *H. habilis* was first recovered at Olduvai Gorge in Tanzania in the early 1960s. Additional specimens have since been discovered at a number of localities in East and, more controversially, southern Africa. Current dating indicates that *H. habilis* certainly appeared by 1.9 million years ago (Ma), and perhaps as early as 2.3 Ma, and was last seen 1.6 Ma. The species name *H. ergaster* was introduced in 1975. However, it did not come into use until researchers suggested that the specimens conventionally referred to as "early African *H. erectus*" may be sufficiently distinct to be considered a different species (*9*). The best-known specimens assigned to *H. ergaster* come from the Lake Turkana region in Kenya. Radiometric and faunal dating indicate that *H. ergaster* was extant 1.9 to 1.5 Ma. Originally proposed by Alexeev, the species name *H. rudolfensis* was not used until the 1990s, when it was suggested that part of the *H. habilis sensu lato* hypodigm should be recognized as a separate species (*2*, *7*). There is still some debate over the distinctiveness and composition of the hypodigm of *H. rudolfensis*, but most workers who recognize the taxon accept that it includes the cranium KNM-ER 1470. To date, *H. rudolfensis* specimens have been found in deposits in Kenya, Malawi, and possibly Ethiopia, and date from 2.4 to 1.8 Ma.

Criteria for Membership in Homo

Regardless of any formal definitions, in practice fossil hominin species are assigned to *Homo* on the basis of one or more out of four criteria. The first is an absolute brain size of 600 cm^3 (*10*). The second is the possession of language, as inferred from endocranial casts (*10*). The third and fourth criteria are, respectively, the possession of a modern, humanlike precision grip involving a well-developed and opposable pollex and the ability to manufacture stone tools (*10*). It is now evident, however, that none of these criteria is satisfactory. The Cerebral Rubicon is problematic because absolute cranial capacity is of questionable biological significance (*11*). Likewise, there is compelling evidence that language function cannot be reliably inferred from the gross appearance of the brain, and that the language-related parts of the brain are not as well localized as earlier studies had implied (*12*). Thus, although it may be attractive to link the first evidence of language to the appearance of the genus *Homo*, there is little sound verifiable evidence to support such a scenario. Functional morphological analyses of the hands of the early hominins have either suggested that a modern humanlike grip is not restricted to *Homo* or indicated that we cannot yet be certain about the potential range of precision grips of any of the early hominin species (*13*). Lastly, the connection between *Homo* and stone tool manufacture is also difficult to substantiate because the earliest stone tools, which come from deposits in East Africa that are 2.6 to 2.3 million years old, were almost certainly contemporaneous with both early *Homo* and with one of the australopith genera, *Paranthropus* (*14*).

What Is a Genus?

Systematists are debating the definition of the genus category as part of a wider discussion about the taxonomic implications of recent developments in phylogenetic analysis (*15*). There are two main interpretations of the genus category. In the first (evolutionary systematic) interpretation, a genus is a species or a group of species of common ancestry that occupies an ecological situation, or adaptive zone, that is different from that occupied by the species of another genus (*3*). A group of species of common ancestry under this definition can be either monophyletic, comprising a common ancestor and all its descendants, or paraphyletic, comprising a subset of a monophyletic group. In the second (cladistic) definition, a genus is a group of species that are more closely related to one another than to species assigned to another genus (*15*). Thus, this interpretation insists that a genus must be monophyletic; it cannot be paraphyletic.

The evolutionary systematic definition of the genus is rejected by those who subscribe to cladistic classification, because they do not accept that paraphyletic taxa are real evolutionary units. However, defining genera solely on the basis of monophyly is equally problematic because there is no criterion for specifying how many species should be included in a genus. A pragmatic solution is to revise the first, gradistic, definition of the genus category (*3*) so that paraphyletic taxa are inadmissible. Because phylogenetic methods are unable to distinguish between ancestor-descendant and sister group relationships, the problem of how to classify an ancestral species that has a different adaptive strategy from those of its descendants simply does not arise. The problem of how to classify a terminal species that forms a monophyletic group with one taxon but shares an adaptive strategy with another can be overcome by recognizing the terminal species as an adaptively coherent evolutionary unit and classifying it as a monotypic genus. We suggest, therefore, that a genus should be defined as a species, or monophylum, whose members occupy a single adaptive zone.

Cladistics is the method of choice for identifying monophyletic groups, but there is no equivalent system for identifying adaptive strategies. Nevertheless, for a species to emerge and persist, the individuals belonging to it have to flourish in the face of the challenges posed by their environment and produce sufficient fertile offspring to repeat the process. The ways in which a hominin species meets these fundamental requirements are clearly important components of its adaptive strategy. Thus, if *H. neanderthalensis, H. erectus, H. heidelbergensis, H. habilis, H. ergaster*, and *H. rudolfensis* have been allocated to the correct genus, two conditions must be met. First, cladistic analyses should confirm that these species are more closely related to *H. sapiens* than they are to any of the australopith genera—*Australopithecus, Paranthropus, Praeanthropus* (*16*), and *Ardipithecus*. Second, assessments of function should indicate that the adaptive strategies used by fossil Homo species to maintain homeostasis, acquire food, and produce offspring are more similar to the strategies used by the *H. sapiens* than they are to the strategies employed by the australopiths.

Is *Homo* Monophyletic?

If *Homo* is a monophylum, cladistic studies should consistently and strongly indicate that the fossil species assigned to it are more closely related to *H. sapiens* than they are to the australopiths. Six recent studies have adequately tested the monophyly of *Homo* (*2, 9, 17–20*). Three of them (Fig. 1, C, D, and F) suggest that *Homo* is monophyletic, but the same number suggest that it is paraphyletic (Fig. 1, A, B, and E). In Chamberlain and Wood's (*19*) most parsimonious cladogram, *H. habilis* is the sister taxon of a clade comprising *Australopithecus africanus*, the "robust" australopiths, and the other *Homo* species; and *H. rudolfensis* is the sister taxon of the "robust" australopiths. In Chamberlain's (*18*) most parsimonious cladogram, *H. rudolfensis* is more closely related to A. africanus and the "robust" australopiths than to *H. sapiens*. In Lieberman et al.'s (*20*) most parsimonious cladogram, *H. rudolfensis* is the sister taxon of a clade comprising A. africanus as well as H. habilis and H. ergaster.

How robust are the results of the three cladistic analyses (*2, 9, 17*) that support *Homo* monophyly? To assess their reliability, we used the program MacClade (*21*) to alter the most parsimonious cladograms so that the fossil *Homo* species were consecutively positioned as the sister taxon of the nearest australopith clade. The resulting cladogram lengths, consistency indices, and retention indices were compared with those associated with the most parsimonious cladograms. As shown in Table 2, relocating *H. rudolfensis* has little effect on the explanatory power of the cladogram. Removing *H. habilis* from the *Homo* clade has slightly more effect, as does the removal of *H. ergaster*. Relocating *H. erectus* has the greatest impact on the cladogram's explanatory power. To further assess the reliability of the results, each matrix was bootstrapped 1000 times using a 70% confidence region (*22*). The bootstrap analyses of Wood's (*2, 9*) matrices supported only one clade comprising *P. boisei* and *P. robustus* (98%). The 70% majority-rule consensus cladogram derived from Strait *et al.*'s (*17*) matrix contained four clades. One linked the three *Paranthropus* species to the exclusion of the other taxa (97%). Another linked *H. ergaster* and *H. sapiens* to the exclusion of the other taxa (98%). A third linked *Paranthropus* and *Homo* to the exclusion of *A. africanus* and *Praeanthropus africanus* (73%). The last clade linked *Paranthropus, Homo*, and *A. africanus* to the exclusion of *Praeanthropus africanus* (100%). These results suggest that *Homo* monophyly is only weakly supported by the three studies.

Taken together, the parsimony, MacClade, and bootstrap analyses suggest that *H. ergaster* and *H. heidelbergensis* are more closely related to *H. sapiens* than either of them is to *Praeanthropus africanus, A. africanus, P. aethiopicus, P. boisei*, or *P. robustus*. They also suggest that *H. erectus* probably shares a common ancestor with *H. sapiens* to the exclusion of the australopiths, although the relationship is possibly less reliable than those linking *H. ergaster* and *H. heidelbergensis* to *H. sapiens*. None of the analyses included *H. neanderthalensis*. Nevertheless, the number of almost certainly derived cranial and postcranial similarities between *H. neanderthalensis* and *H. sapiens* (8) is such that it is highly unlikely that H. neanderthalensis is more closely related to the australopiths than it is to *H. sapiens*. In contrast, neither *H. habilis* nor *H. rudolfensis* can be assumed with any degree of reliability to be more closely related to *H. sapiens* than to the australopiths. The cladograms favored in the parsimony analyses do not consistently indicate that *H. habilis* and *H. rudolfensis* share a common ancestor with H. sapiens to the exclusion of the australopiths. Even in the cladograms in which H. habilis and H. rudolfensis are grouped with the other *Homo* species, the links are weak. Thus, the current interpretation of the genus *Homo* does not satisfy the condition that the fossil species within it unequivocally form a monophyletic group with *H. sapiens* to the exclusion of the australopiths (Fig. 2).

Is *Homo* Adaptively Coherent?

Many aspects of the ontogeny and phenotype of a primate are adaptations to help it maintain homeostasis, acquire food, and produce offspring; however, not all of them can be reliably reconstructed from the fossil record. Arguably, the most important of those that can be determined using paleontological evidence are body size and shape, the skeletal concomitants of locomotor behavior, relative brain size, the rate and pattern of development, and the relative size of the masticatory apparatus.

Body size in primates correlates with numerous ecological and life history variables, including population density, home range size, social organization, and age at first breeding (*23*), whereas body shape is closely linked to temperature regulation, water balance, and habitat (*24*). Indicative mean body masses for the fossil hominins can be estimated by using skeletal surrogates (*23*). The data (Table 3) show a clear separation between *H. sapiens* (excluding secondarily dwarfed populations), *H. neanderthalensis, H. erectus, H. heidelbergensis,* and *H. ergaster,* on the one hand, and *A. africanus, P. boisei, P. robustus, Praeanthropus africanus,* and *H. habilis,* on the other. The smallest species in the former group is *H. sapiens*, which has a mean body mass of 53 kg, whereas the largest species in the latter group, *P. boisei*, is estimated to have had a body mass of 44 kg. *Homo habilis* is the smallest of the species in the second group, with an estimated body mass of just 34 kg. Body shape, in the form of limb proportions, can be reconstructed for just five fossil hominin species: *Praeanthropus africanus, A. africanus, H. ergaster, H. neanderthalensis,* and *H. habilis.* On the basis of the associated skeleton AL 288-1, *Praeanthropus africanus* was, in overall size and limb proportions, more

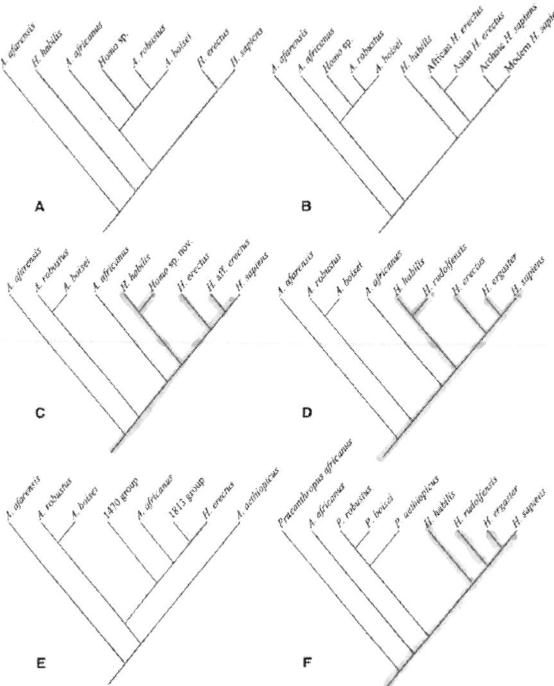

Fig. 1. Cladograms favored in recent early hominin parsimony analyses. (A) Most parsimonious cladogram recovered by Chamberlain and Wood (***19***) using Chamberlain's (***18***) operational taxonomic units. ***Homo*** sp. = ***H. rudolfensis***. (B) Most parsimonious cladogram obtained in Chamberlain (***18***). African ***H. erectus = H. ergaster.*** (C) Cladogram favored in Wood (***9***). ***Homo*** sp. nov. = ***H. rudolfensis*** and ***H***. aff. ***erectus = H. ergaster***. (D) Most parsimonious cladogram recovered by Wood (***2***). ***A. boisei*** includes ***A. aethiopicus***. (E) Most parsimonious cladogram obtained by Lieberman ***et al***. (***20***). 1470 group = ***H. rudolfensis***; 1813 group = ***H. habilis***. (F) Cladogram favored by Strait ***et al***. (17).

similar to living great apes than to modern humans (24). What can be gleaned from the fragmentary skeleton Sts 14 indicates that A. africanus had a body shape similar to that of Praeanthropus africanus (*24*). In contrast, the nearly complete skeleton KNM-WT 15000 suggests that *H. ergaster* had a body shape closer to that of modern humans (*24*). The numerous associated skeletons of *H. neanderthalensis* indicate that their body shape was within the range of variation seen in modern humans. If OH 62 and KNM-ER 3735 (*2, 9*) are properly attributed to *H. habilis*, then that species had body proportions similar to those of the australopiths (*24*). Thus, not all the fossil species currently assigned to *Homo* are more similar in body size and shape to *H. sapiens* than they are to the australopiths.

Table 2. Results of analysis in which *Homo* polyphyly was imposed on matrices that returned a *Homo* clade when subjected to parsimony analysis. L1, CI1, and RI1 indicate the length, consistency index, and retention index, respectively, of the most parsimonious cladogram. L2, CI2, and RI2 indicate the length, consistency index, and retention index, respectively, of the cladogram in which *Homo* is polyphyletic. In the Wood (2, 9) cladograms, *Homo* sp. nov. = *H. rudolfensis* and *Homo* aff. *erectus* = *H. ergaster*.

Matrix	Species moved	L1	L2	CI1	CI2	RI1	RI2
Wood (*9*)	*H. habilis*	292	298	0.65	0.64	0.41	0.38
	Homo sp. nov.		294		0.65		0.40
	H. erectus		299		0.64		0.37
	H. aff. erectus		298		0.64		0.38
Wood (*2*)	*H. habilis*	320	326	0.64	0.63	0.45	0.42
	Homo sp. nov.		322		0.64		0.44
	H. erectus		328		0.63		0.41
	H. aff. *erectus*		327		0.63		0.42
Strait *et al.* (*6*)	*H. habilis*	199	202	0.59	0.58	0.68	0.67
	H. rudolfensis		201		0.59		0.67
	H. ergaster		214		0.55		0.62

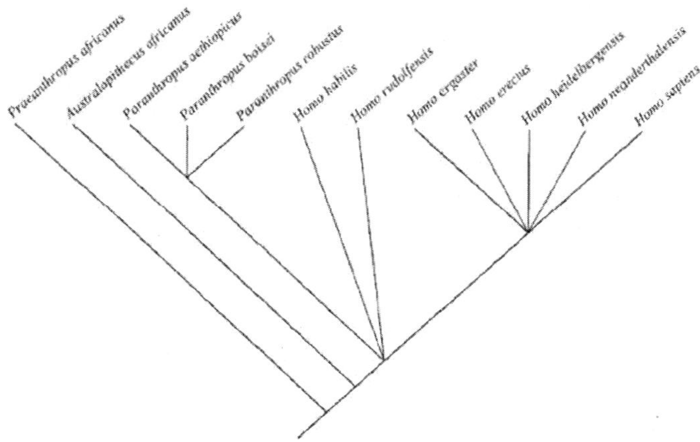

Fig. 2. Hominin phylogenetic relationships. The pattern of relationship among *Praeanthropus africanus, A. africanus, P. aethiopicus, P. boisei, P. robustus, H. habilis, H. rudolfensis, H. ergaster,* and *H. sapiens* was obtained in a bootstrap analysis of Strait et al.'s (17) character state data. The lack of resolution within *Homo* is in line with an analysis in which Stringer's (*50*) data were bootstrapped after reallocation to *H. ergaster, H. erectus, H. heidelbergensis, H. neanderthalensis,* and *H. sapiens.*

Evidence about the locomotor repertoire of fossil hominins comes from a variety of sources, some of which (limb proportions, for example) also influence other aspects of hominin adaptation. In practice, most inferences about locomotion have to be drawn from functional interpretations of postcranial evidence. Currently, evidence about locomotion is available for *Praeanthropus africanus, A. africanus, P. robustus, P. boisei, H. habilis, H. ergaster, H. erectus, H. heidelbergensis,* and *H. neanderthalensis.* Among the australopiths, the postcranium of *Praeanthropus africanus* is the best preserved and it presents a combination of traits that is not seen among living primates. Some workers suggest that it had a modern humanlike posture and a commitment to terrestrial bipedalism (*25*), whereas others claim that its relatively long and markedly curved proximal phalanges, high humerofemoral index, and highly mobile joints indicate that its locomotor repertoire included suspensory and climbing activities (*26*). Likewise, a reconstruction of the thoracic cage of AL 288-1 suggests that it was funnel-shaped, a trait that is associated in the great apes with a pectoral girdle musculature that is adapted for climbing (*26*). Overall, it appears that *Praeanthropus africanus* combined terrestrial bipedalism with an arboreal facility. Recent analyses have indicated that the postcranium of *A. africanus* was similar to that of *Praeanthropus* (*27*), which suggests that it too combined proficient climbing with terrestrial bipedalism. The hypothesis of a mixed locomotor repertoire is supported by recent analyses of foot bones and tibial fragments that have been assigned to the species (*27*).

The postcranial skeleton of *P. robustus* is poorly known, and opinions differ over the functional interpretation of what material there is. On the one hand, the foot bones and hip of *P. robustus* point to a more humanlike form of locomotion than that of *Praeanthropus* (*28*). On the other hand, the upper limbs of the type specimen (TM 1517) seem to have been longer in relation to its lower limbs than is the case in *H. sapiens*, which suggests that *P. robustus* was adapted, to some extent, for climbing (30). It would appear that even if *P. robustus* was not as arboreal as *Praeanthropus* or *Australopithecus*, it is likely that its postcranial morphology would have allowed it some arboreal capability. Few limb bones can be definitely attributed to *P. boisei*. Nevertheless, forelimb bones assigned to the species suggest that, like Praeanthropus and Australopithecus, it too could climb proficiently (*27*). Similarly, various indices taken on the skeletal fragments of KNM-ER 1500, which some assign to *P. boisei* (*9, 28*), show that this fossil falls midway between modern humans and the great apes in its limb proportions and is similar in these proportions to Praeanthropus (30). Therefore, *P. boisei* is also likely to have combined bipedal locomotion with proficient climbing. The hand bones associated with OH 7, the type specimen of *H. habilis*, have been interpreted as implying apelike climbing ability (*29*). Likewise, the relatively long arms of OH 62 and KNM-ER 3735 (*24*) suggest that *H. habilis* was capable of proficient climbing.

Together these data suggest that *H. habilis* was capable of both terrestrial bipedalism and efficient arboreal activity.

The relevant evidence for *H. ergaster* suggests that it was an obligate terrestrial biped, much like *H. sapiens* (*31*). Remains of the lower limbs and pelvis indicate that it had a commitment to bipedal locomotion that was equivalent to that seen in modern humans, and there is no evidence in the upper limb bones for the sort of climbing abilities possessed by the australopiths and *H. habilis*. Furthermore, it is likely that the barrel-shaped thoracic cage and narrow waist of *H. ergaster* were also components of an adaptation for efficient bipedal walking and running (*31*). The postcranial skeleton *of H. erectus* is relatively poorly known, with most of the available and relevant evidence consisting of pelves and femora. These bones differ from those of modern humans in some character states; for example, the femora exhibit greater robusticity and platymeria and have a narrower medullary canal, but they are nonetheless considered to be consistent with a modern humanlike posture and gait. The evidence for the postcranial skeleton of *H. heidelbergensis* has recently been augmented by discoveries at Atapuerca in Spain, and although there is some evidence that the cortical bone may be thicker than that seen in modern humans (*32*), there is no evidence that the posture and gait of *H. heidelbergensis* differed from those of modern humans. Contrary to the suggestions of early commentators who depicted *H. neanderthalensis* as apelike, it is now clear that their posture, foot structure, and limb and muscle function were essentially the same as those of modern humans (*33*). Most of the postcranial differences between *H. neanderthalensis* and *H. sapiens* relate to the greater muscularity of the former; the few that may relate to posture and locomotion, such as the long and thin pubis of *H. neanderthalensis*, are not interpreted as indicating substantial behavioral differences, and there is no evidence to suggest that Neanderthals were more adept at climbing than adult modern humans are (*33*).

Thus, on the basis of the locomotor inferences that can be made from their postcranial morphology, the fossil hominins can be divided into two groups. The first group displays a mixed strategy, combining a form of terrestrial bipedalism with an ability to climb proficiently. This group comprises *Praeanthropus, Australopithecus, Paranthropus,* and *H. habilis*. The second group consists of *H. erectus, H. ergaster, H. heidelbergensis,* and *H. neanderthalensis* and is characterized by a commitment to modern human-like terrestrial bipedalism and a very limited arboreal facility. The hypothesized contrast between the locomotor repertoires of the two groups is supported by a recent computed tomography study of the hominin bony labyrinth (*34*).

Relative brain size is also a proxy for neocortex size, which has been linked with important aspects of social behavior (35). We derived relative brain size by dividing the cube root of the mean cranial capacity of the species by the square root of the mean of the species' orbital area, and multiplying the product by 10 (Table 4). We used a body size proxy rather than the conventional approach of expressing brain size in relation to the estimated brain volume of a generalized placental mammal of the same body mass, because of the problems associated with the use of body mass estimates in the latter type of analysis (*36*). Although there are substantial differences in the mean absolute brain size of the australopiths on the one hand and the *Homo* species on the other (Table 4), some of these differences are almost certainly not meaningful when differences in the body size proxy are taken into account. When this adjustment is made, four *Homo* species—*H. ergaster, H. habilis, H. heidelbergensis*, and *H. rudolfensis*—are more similar to *Australopithecus* than they are to *H. sapiens*, and the relative brain size of H. erectus is intermediate between those of *A. africanus* and *H. sapiens*. The only fossil *Homo* species whose relative brain size is more similar to *H. sapiens* than it is to that of *A. africanus* is *H. neanderthalensis*.

It is well established that the period of maturation of *H. sapiens* is nearly twice as long as those of *Gorilla gorilla* and *Pan troglodytes* (*37*). This extended ontogeny is believed to be important for the transmission of the numerous additional learned behaviors that modern humans exhibit as compared to the African apes. Recent analyses of dental and femoral development in the fossil hominins have indicated that *Australopithecus* is more similar to the African apes in its rate of development than it is to modern humans, whereas the developmental schedules of *H. ergaster* and *H. neanderthalensis* are more similar to that of H. sapiens than they are to the developmental schedules of *G. gorilla* and *P. troglodytes* (*37*). Do *H. habilis* and *H. rudolfensis* display a pattern of growth that is apelike, or is it more modern human-like? Using incremental lines and periradicular bands to analyze tooth root formation times, researchers have found that the rate of root development exhibited by the *H. habilis* specimen OH 16 was more similar to those of the great apes than it was to the human rate of root development (*38*). Similarly, an independent analysis of crown development patterns indicated that the *H. rudolfensis* specimen, KNM-ER 1590, exhibits an apelike rather than a humanlike pattern of development (*37*). Thus, both *H. habilis* and *H. rudolfensis* are apparently more similar in their dental development to the African great apes than they are to *H. sapiens*, which indicates that neither species is likely to have displayed an extended period of dependence. To date, no comparative analysis of hominin development has included *H. erectus* or *H. heidelbergensis*, but the dental development of *H. neanderthalensis* is more like that of *H. sapiens* than that of the living apes (*37*).

Table 3. Estimates of hominin body mass. The figure for *H. sapiens* is the average of the male and female values given for modern Africans (*49*). The fossil hominin estimates are derived from postcranium-based regression equations. The estimates for *A. africanus, P. boisei, P. robustus, Praeanthropus africanus, H. ergaster,* and *H. habilis* are from (*23*). The figure for *H. erectus* was calculated from those given for the OH 28 (*31*) and Trinil (*23*) specimens. The *H. heidelbergensis* estimate was computed with the use of the *Homo* equation for tibial circumference/body mass and values for tibial midshaft circumference from the Boxgrove and Kabwe specimens and two specimens from Atapuerca (*32, 49*). The figure for *H. neanderthalensis* was taken from (*31*). There are no postcranial fossils that can be reliably linked to *H. rudolfensis*.

Taxon	Body mass (kg)	Taxon	Body mass (kg)
H. habilis	34	*H. sapiens*	53
A. africanus	36	*H. erectus*	57
P. robustus	36	*H. ergaster*	58
Praeanthropus africanus	37	*H. heidelbergensis*	62
P. boisei	44	*H. neanderthalensis*	76

The relative size of the masticatory apparatus of a species is linked to the effectiveness with which the food items consumed are rendered suitable for chemical digestion. For example, other things being equal, the relative size of the contact area, or occlusal surface, of the cheek teeth determines how efficiently a given quantity of food will be broken down. Likewise, the cross-sectional area of the mandibular body is positively correlated with the amount of chewing-induced stress it can withstand, so that an individual with a large mandibular corpus can either break down tougher food items or process larger quantities of less resistant food more readily than one with a more slender mandibular body. Absolute values for 11 variables from the mandible and lower posterior dentition for *H. sapiens* and eight fossil hominins are given in Table 5. Relative size for variables 1 through 10 was calculated by dividing the species mean for each variable by a body size proxy—the square root of the species' mean orbital area (*23*). Relative size for variable 11 was calculated by dividing the square root of the species mean by the body size proxy. When pairwise Euclidean distances are calculated from the data after normalization (Table 6), it is evident that *H. habilis* and *H. rudolfensis* are more similar to the type species of *Australopithecus* and *Paranthropus* than they are to *H. sapiens*. Thus, even though the teeth and jaws of *H. habilis* are comparatively small in absolute terms, when related to a body size proxy the components of the masticatory apparatus match those of *Australopithecus* and *Paranthropus* more closely than they do those *of H. sapiens*. The other fossil *Homo* species examined (*H. erectus, H. ergaster*, and *H. neanderthalensis*) are more similar to *H.*

Table 4. Hominin brain size. The cranial capacities and orbital areas were taken from (*23*), and the hypodigms of *P. aethiopicus, P. boisei, A. africanus, H. habilis,* and *H. rudolfensis* are those used in those studies. *Homo ergaster* consists of specimens KNM-WT 15000 and KNM-ER 3733 and 3883. *Homo heidelbergensis* comprises the Kabwe and Steinheim specimens. *Homo erectus* comprises the Sangiran 17 and Zhoukoudian XI and XII specimens. *Homo neanderthalensis* comprises the Amud I, Gibraltar 1, La Chapelle, La Ferrassie, Le Moustier, and Saccopastore specimens. The figures for *H. sapiens* are the averages of the male and female values given in Kappelman (23). Relative brain size was computed by dividing the cube root of absolute brain size by the square root of orbital area and multiplying the product by 10. Orbital area is not available for *Praeanthropus africanus*.

Taxon	Absolute size (cm^3)	Orbital area (cm^2)	Relative
P. aethiopicus	410	968	2.39
P. boisei	513	1114	2.40
A. africanus	457	839	2.66
H. habilis	552	908	2.72
H. ergaster	854	1180	2.76
H. rudolfensis	752	1084	2.76
H. heidelbergensis	1198	1403	2.84
H. erectus	1016	1225	2.87
H. neanderthalensis	1512	1404	3.06
H. sapiens	1355	1289	3.08

sapiens than they are to *A. africanus* or *P. robustus*. These results concur with those of a recent examination of mandibular scaling in early hominins (*39*). Together, these analyses suggest that the diets of *H. habilis* and *H. rudolfensis* required considerably more bite force and processing than does that of *H. sapiens*, whereas the diets of *H. erectus*, *H. ergaster*, and *H. neanderthalensis* had mechanical properties similar to those of the modern human diet.

Adaptive Strategies

Knowledge about the adaptations of the fossil hominins is necessarily sketchy. However, what is known about their body size and shape, locomotion, development, and relative size of their masticatory apparatus suggests that fossil hominin adaptive strategies fall into two broad groups. The first is characterized by a relatively low body mass; a body shape that, in terms of thermoregulation, is better suited to a relatively closed environment; and a postcranial skeleton that suggests a mode of locomotion that combined a form of terrestrial bipedalism with proficient climbing. It is also distinguished by teeth and jaws that are probably adapted to a diet that was considerably more mechanically demanding than that of

Table 5. Hominin species means for 11 gnathic variables. The variables are (1) symphyseal height, (2) symphyseal breadth, (3) corpus height at M_1, (4) corpus width at M_1, (5) P_4 mesiodistal diameter, (6) P_4 buccolingual diameter, (7) M_1 mesiodistal diameter, (8) M_1 buccolingual diameter, (9) M_2 mesiodistal diameter, (10) M_2 buccolingual diameter, and (11) M_3 area. OA indicates orbital area (*23*). The specimen values were obtained from several sources and are available from the authors on request. Orbital area is not available for *Praeanthropus africanus*.

Taxon	Variables											OA
	1	2	3	4	5	6	7	8	9	10	11	
A. africanus	41	20	33	23	9.3	11.0	13.2	12.9	14.9	14.1	218	839
P. boisei	51	29	42	29	14.2	15.5	16.7	15.7	20.4	18.5	327	1114
P. robustus	50	28	39	27	11.7	14.0	15.1	14.1	16.6	15.7	254	1066
H. erectus	37	19	36	22	8.9	11.3	12.4	12.0	13.3	12.7	145	1225
H. ergaster	33	20	31	19	8.7	11.0	13.1	11.6	13.8	12.3	170	1180
H. habilis	27	19	29	271	9.8	10.5	13.9	12.3	14.9	12.6	201	908
H. neanderthalensis	42	15	34	18	7.1	8.7	10.6	10.7	110.71	10.7	131	1404
H. rudolfensis	36	23	36	23	10.5	12.0	14.0	13.2	16.4	13.7	250	1084
H. sapiens	34	14	29	13	7.1	8.4	11.2	10.5	10.8	10.5	113	1289

H. sapiens and a developmental schedule that was more apelike than modern human-like. The second group differs from the first in having a larger body mass, a modern human-like physique that would have been adaptive in more open habitats, and a postcranial skeleton consistent with terrestrial bipedalism with a limited ability for arboreal travel in adults. The teeth and jaws of the second group were apparently adapted to a diet that, when ingested, had similar mechanical properties to that of *H. sapiens*, and its developmental pattern was more modern human-like. Relative brain size does not group the fossil hominins in the same way as the other variables. This pattern suggests that the link between relative brain size and adaptive zone is a complex one (*40*). With varying degrees of certainty, the australopiths (with the exception of *Ardipithecus*, for which there is as yet insufficient information), *H. habilis*, and *H. rudolfensis* can all be assigned to the first group, whereas *H. neanderthalensis*, *H. erectus*, *H. heidelbergensis*, and *H. ergaster* can be confidently assigned to the second.

Homo Is Not a Good Genus

When these functional interpretations are combined with the uncertainty over the phylogenetic relationships of *H. habilis* and *H. rudolfensis*, it is clear that the species currently assigned to *Homo* do not form a monophylum whose members occupy a single adaptive

Table 6. Normalized Euclidean distances between fossil *Homo* species and the type species of *Homo, Australopithecus*, and *Paranthropus*, which are respectively, *H. sapiens, A. africanus*, and *P. robustus*, based on 11 size-corrected gnathic variables.

Species name	*H. sapiens*	*A. africanus*	*P. robustus*
H. rudolfensis	5.5	1.9	2.6
H. habilis	5.3	2.7	3.6
H. erectus	3.1	4.0	4.7
H. ergaster	2.9	4.3	5.0
H. neander-thalensis	1.3	6.4	7.2

zone (Table 7). In other words, with the hypodigms of *H. habilis* and *H. rudolfensis* assigned to it, the genus Homo is not a good genus. Thus, *H. habilis* and *H. rudolfensis* (or *Homo habilis sensu lato* for those who do not subscribe to the taxonomic subdivision of "early *Homo*") should be removed from *Homo*. The obvious taxonomic alternative, which is to transfer one or both of the taxa to one of the existing early hominin genera, is not without problems, but we recommend that, for the time being, both *H. habilis* and *H. rudolfensis* should be transferred to the genus *Australopithecus*. This reverts to a taxonomy that was initially considered by Tobias, Howell, and Walker (*1, 10, 41, 42*), among others, and was supported by Robinson (*43*). The transfer will almost certainly make *Australopithecus* paraphyletic, and the genus will subsume an impressive range of cranial morphology (*9, 44*), but we favor this option because it is taxonomically conservative. The generic allocation of the two taxa should be reviewed when associated postcranial evidence is available for *Australopithecus rudolfensis* and when we are more confident about the use of morphological data for resolving cladistic relationships among early hominin taxa (*45*).

Conclusion

We suggest that a fossil species should be included in *Homo* only if it can be demonstrated that it (i) is more closely related to *H. sapiens* than it is to the australopiths, (ii) has an estimated body mass that is more similar to that of *H. sapiens* than to that of the australopiths, (iii) has reconstructed body proportions that match those of *H. sapiens* more closely than those of the australopiths, (iv) has a postcranial skeleton whose functional morphology is consistent with modern human-like obligate bipedalism and limited facility for climbing, (v) is equipped with teeth and jaws that are more similar in terms of relative size to those of modern humans than to those of the australopiths, and (vi) shows evidence for a modern human-like extended period of growth and development. The adoption of these criteria would mean that *Homo* would have both phylogenetic and adaptive significance.

Table 7. Summary of the results of functional analyses of fossil *Homo* species. (1) body size, (2) body shape, (3) locomotion, (4) jaws and teeth, (5) development, and (6) brain size. H, modern human-like; A, australopith-like; I, intermediate. The question mark indicates that data are unavailable.

Species name	1	2	3	4	5	6
H. rudolfensis	?	?	?	A	A	A
H. habilis	A	A	A	A	A	A
H. ergaster	H	H	H	H	H	A
H. erectus	H	?	H	H	?	I
H. heidelbergensis	H	?	H	H	?	A
H. neanderthalensis	H	H	H	H	H	H

Researchers can then explore whether this adaptive shift in hominin evolution corresponds with changes in climate, analogous evolutionary changes in other large mammal groups (*46*), particular innovations in the hominin cultural record (*47*), substantial expansions in geographic range, or changes in ecological tolerance, as reflected in reconstructions of hominin habitats (*48*).

References and Notes

1. A. Walker, in *Earliest Man and Environments in the Lake Rudolf Basin*, Y. Coppens, F. C. Howell, G. L I. Isaac, R. E. Leakey, Eds. (Univ. of Chicago Press, Chicago, IL, 1976), pp. 484–489; F. C. Howell, in *The Evolution of African Mammals*, V. J. Maglio and H. B. S. Cooke, Eds. (Harvard Univ. Press, Cambridge, MA, 1978), pp. 154–248; I. Tattersall, *Evol. Anthropol.* 3, 114 (1994); *J. Hum. Evol.* **22**, 351 (1992).
2. B. A. Wood, *Nature* 355, 783 (1992).
3. E. Mayr, *Quant. Biol.* 15, 109 (1950).
4. I. Tattersall, J. *Hum. Evol.* 15, 165 (1986).
5. B. A. Wood, *Bioessays* 18, 945 (1996).
6. M. H. Wolpoff, A. G. Thorne, J. Jelinek, Zhang Yinyun, *Cour. Forschungsinst. Senckenb.* 171, 341 (1994); M. Henneberg and J. F. Thackeray, *Evol. Theory* **11**, 31 (1995).
7. C. P. Groves, *A Theory of Human and Primate Evolution* (Oxford Univ. Press, Oxford, 1989); G. P. Rightmire, J. *Hum. Evol.* **31**, 21 (1996).
8. I. Tattersall, J. *Hum. Evol.* 22, 341 (1992).
9. B. A. Wood, *Koobi Fora Research Project, Volume 4* (Clarendon Press, Oxford, 1991).
10. L. S. B. Leakey, P. V. Tobias, J. R. Napier, *Nature* **202**, 7 (1964); P. V. Tobias, *The Skulls, Endocasts and Teeth of* Homo habilis. *Olduvai Gorge Volume 4* (Cambridge Univ. Press, Cambridge, 1991).
11. R. D. Martin, *Human Brain Evolution in an Ecological Context* (American Museum of Natural History, New York, 1983).
12. A. M. Galaburda and D. N. Pandya, in *Primate Brain Evolution*, E. Armstrong and D. Falk, Eds. (Plenum, New York, 1982), pp. 203–216; P. J. Gannon, R. L. Holloway, D. C. Broadfield, A. R. Braun, *Science* **279**, 220 (1998).
13. R. L. Susman, *Science* **265**, 1570 (1994); M. W. Marzke *Am. J. Phys. Anthropol.* **102**, 91 (1997); R. L. Susman, J. *Hum. Evol.* **35**, 23 (1998).
14. M. Kibunjia, *J. Hum. Evol.* **27**, 159 (1994); S. Semaw et *al.*, *Nature* **385**, 333 (1997); B. A. Wood, C. G. Wood, L. W. Konigsberg, *Am. J. Phys. Anthropol.* **95**, 117 (1994).
15. W. D. Clayton, *Kew Bull.* **38**, 149 (1983); P. F. Stevens, *ibid.* **40**, 457 (1984); K. De Queiroz and J. Gauthier, *Trends Ecol. Evol.* 9, 27 (1994); J. W. Valentine and C. L. May, *Paleobiology* **22**, 23 (1996); E. B. Knox, *Biol. J. Linn. Soc.* **63**, 1 (1998).

16. We are convinced by the arguments set out in (17) and thus use *Praeanthropus africanus* to refer to the hypodigm previously known as *Australopithecus afarensis.*
17. D. S. Strait, F. E. Grine, M. A. Moniz, *J. Hum. Evol.* **32**, 17 (1997).
18. A. T. Chamberlain, thesis, University of Liverpool (1987).
19. _____ and B. A. Wood, *J. Hum. Evol.* **16**, 118(1987).
20. D. E. Lieberman, D. Pilbeam, B. A. Wood, *J. Hum. Evol.* **30**, 97 (1996).
21. W. P. Maddison and D. R. Maddison, *MacClade: Analysis of Phylogeny and Character Evolution, Version 3* (Sinauer, Sunderland, MA, 1992).
22. J. Felsenstein, *Evolution* **39**, 783 (1985); D. M. Hillis and J. J. Bull, *Syst. Biol.* **42**, 182 (1993); D. L. Swofford, *Phylogenetic Analysis Using Parsimony 3.0s* (Illinois Natural History Survey, Champaign, IL, 1991).
23. H. M. McHenry, / *Hum. Evol. 27*, 77 (1994); *Am. J. Phys. Anthropol.* **86**, 445 (1991); J. Kappelman, *J. Hum. Evol.* **30**, 243 (1996); L. Aiello and B. A. Wood, *Am. J. Phys. Anthropol.* 95, 409 (1994).
24. P. E. Wheeler, *J. Hum. Evol.* **24**, 13 (1993); C. B. Ruff, *Yearb. Phys. Anthropol.* **37**, 65 (1994); D. C. Johanson *et al., Nature* **327**, 205 (1987).
25. B. Latimer, in *Origine(s) de la Bipedie Chez les Hominidés,* Y. Coppens and B. Senut, Eds. (Cahiers de Paléoanthropologie, Editions du CNRS, Paris, 1991), pp. 169–176; J. C. Ohman, T. J. Krochta, C. O. Lovejoy, R. P. Mensforth, B. Latimer, *Am. J. Phys. Anthropol.* **104**, 117 (1997).
26. M. M. Abitbol, / *Hum. Evol.* **28**, 211 (1994); K. D. Hunt, S. *Afr. J. Sci.* **92**, 77 (1996); P. Schmid, in *Origine(s) de la Bipédie Chez les Hominidés*, Y. Coppens and B. Senut, Eds. (Cahiers de Paléoanthropologie, Editions du CNRS, Paris, 1991), pp. 225–234.
27. H. M. McHenry, in *Integrative Paths to the Past. Paleoanthropological Advances in Honor of F. Clark Howell*, R. S. Corruccini and R. L. Ciochon, Eds. (Prentice Hall, NJ, 1994), pp. 251–268; M. M. *Abitbol, Am J. Phys. Anthropol.* **96**, 143 (1995); R. Clarke and P.V. Tobias, *Science* **269**, 521 (1995); L. R. Berger and P. V. Tobias, J. *Hum. Evol.* **30**, 343 (1996).
28. L. M. MacLatchy, J. Hum. Evol. **31**, 455 (1996); H. M. Grausz, R. E. Leakey, A. C. Walker, C. V. Ward, in *Evolutionary History of the "Robust" Australopithecines*, F. E. Grine, Ed. (Aldine de Gruyter, New York, 1988), pp. 127–132.
29. R. L. Susman and N. Creel, *Am. J. Phys. Anthropol.* **51**, 311 (1979).
30. L. C. Aiello and C. Dean, *An Introduction to Human Evolutionary Anatomy* (Academic Press, London, 1990); L. C. Aiello and P. E. Wheeler, *Curr. Anthropol.* **36**, 199 (1995).

31. C. B. Ruff and A. Walker, in *The Nariokotome* Homo erectus *Skeleton*, A. Walker and R. E. Leakey, Eds. (Harvard Univ. Press, Cambridge, MA, 1993), pp. 234–265; C. B. Ruff, E. Trinkaus, T. W. Holliday, *Nature* **387**, 173 (1997); H. Preuschoft and H. Witte, in *Origine(s) de la Bipedie Chez Les Hominides*, Y. Coppens and B. Senut, Eds. (Cahiers de Paleonathropologie, Editions de CNRS, Paris, 1991), pp. 59–77.
32. M. B. Roberts, C. B. Stringer, S. A. Parfitt, *Nature* **369**, 311 (1994).
33. E. Trinkaus, C. B. Ruff, S. E. Churchill, in Neandertals and Modern Humans in Western Asia, T. Akazawa, K. Aoki, O. Bar-Yosef, Eds. (Plenum, New York, 1998), pp. 391–404.
34. F. Spoor, F. W. Zonneveld, B. A. Wood, Nature 369, 645 (1994).
35. R. E. Passingham and G. A. Ettlinger, *Int. Rev. Neurobiol.* **16**, 233 (1974); R. I. M. Dunbar, J. *Hum. Evol.* **28**, 287 (1995).
36. R. Smith, *Curr. Anthropol.* 37, 309 (1996).
37. B. H. Smith, *Am. J. Phys. Anthropol.* **94**, 307 (1994); M. C. Dean, C. B. Stringer, T. G. Bromage, *ibid.* **70**, 301 (1986); C. Tardieu, *ibid.* **107**, 163 (1998).
38. M. C. Dean, in *Aspects of Dental Biology: Palaeontology, Anthropology and Evolution*, J. Moggi-Cecchi, Ed. (International Institute for the Study of Man, Florence, Italy, 1995), pp. 239–265; J. Moggi-Cecchi, P. V. Tobias, A. D. Beynon, *Am. J. Phys. Anthropol.* **106**, 425 (1998); J. Moggi-Cecchi, in *The Origin of Humankind*, M. Aloisi, B. Battaglia, E. Carafoli, G. A. Danieli, Eds. (Istituto Veneto di Scienze, Lettere, Arti Series, vol. II, IOS Press, Amsterdam, in press).
39. B. A. Wood and L. C. Aiello, *Am. J. Phys. Anthropol.* **105**, 523 (1998).
40. T. W. Deacon, *Int. J. Primatol.* **11**, 237 (1990).
41. P. V. Tobias, quoted by S. L. Washburn, in *Classification and Human Evolution*, S. L. Washburn, Ed. (Aldine, Chicago), p. 196.
42. F. C. Howell, *Curr. Anthropol.* 6, 399 (1965).
43. J. T. Robinson, *Nature* **205**, 121 (1965).
44. M. C. Dean and B. A. Wood, *Am. J. Phys. Anthropol.* **59**, 157 (1982).
45. R. S. Corruccini, in *Integrative Pathways to the Past. Paleoanthropological Advances in Honor of F. Clark Howell*, R. S. Corruccini and R. L. Ciochon, Eds. (Prentice-Hall, NJ, 1994), pp. 167–183.
46. E. S. Vrba, in *Paleoclimate and Evolution, with Emphasis on Human Origins*, E. S. Vrba, G. H. Denton, T. C. Partridge, L. H. Burkle, Eds. (Yale Univ. Press, New Haven, CT, 1995), pp. 24–48; A. K. Behrensmeyer, N. E. Todd, R. Potts, G. E. McBain, *Science* **178**, 1589 (1997).

47. H. Roche, *Ossa* **14**, 97 (1989); in *The First Humans and Their Cultural Manifestations,* F. Facchini, Ed. (Forli, A.B.A.C.O., 1996), pp. 55–68.
48. K. Reed, *J. Hum. Evol.* **32**, 289 (1997).
49. B. A. Wood, in *Paleoclimate and Evolution, with Emphasis on Human Origins*, E. S. Vrba, G. H. Denton, T. C. Partridge, L. H. Burkle Eds. (Yale Univ. Press, New Haven, CT, 1995), pp. 438–448; S. Hartwig-Schrerer, *Am. J. Phys. Anthropol.* 92, 17 (1993).
50. C. B. Stringer, *J. Hum. Evol.* 16, 135 (1987).
51. B.W. was supported by the NERC and the Leverholme Trust and is now supported by the Henry Luce Foundation; M.C. is supported by the Wellcome Trust. We are grateful to A. Cain for the translation of Linnaeus' *Systema Naturae* (10th edition, 1758); A. Chamberlain for making his data available; and A. Chamberlain, W. Kimbel, D. Lieberman, and D. Strait for commenting on the manuscript.

Introduction to Chapter 10

We know that Homo and Australopithecus are sister genera; now the task is to explore what their essential differences are, as well as when, why, and how those differences emerged.

The fossil record is tantalizingly fragmentary. Many extinct populations are surely not represented at all. And those that are may be represented by a few bone fragments from just one individual. The job of paleoanthropologists is to extract as much valid information as they can from that very fragmentary record. To do so, they need to walk a tightrope between creativity and scientific rigor. Each researcher will find his or her own unique balance point. I have intentionally given you two chapters that address quite similar questions so you can appreciate the diversity of approaches that have been used in interpreting the fossil record. The task I have set for myself in this introduction is twofold: to give you the tools to keep you from getting bogged down in those "style" differences, and to help you understand some of the more technical (e.g., mathematical and statistical) approaches used by McHenry and Coffing.

Rather than organizing their chapter by species—describing the features of each taxon—McHenry and Coffing have collected the available information in terms of traits. For each of the traits on which *Homo* and *Australopithecus* differ, the authors tabulate which fossil specimens show the primitive versus the derived version of the trait. Because they are explicitly interested in the *Australopithecus-to-Homo* transition, they define the species of interest—their cast of characters—as those surrounding that transition. Thus they ignore hominins before *Australopithecus*, and they also omit members of the genus *Homo* after *H. ergaster* (for example, *H. erectus* and *H. heidelbergensis*). The exceptions to this inclusion criterion are that common chimpanzees (*Pan troglodytes*) and modern humans (*Homo sapiens*) are used as anchoring points. Also, in discussing brain size (e.g., Figures 2 and 3), the authors include more recent members of the genus *Homo* to show the relative position of the transitional species that represent the main focus of this chapter. The set of species covered by their analysis is shown in their Table 1. In that table, you will see three more species of *Australopithecus* than in Wood and Collard's Table 1: *A. afarensis*, *A. garhii*, and *A. aethiopicus* (Wood and Collard actually do include *A. aethiopicus* but classify it as *Paranthropus aethiopicus*).

Remember that Wood and Collard showed considerable ambivalence about estimating the body size of fossil species, sometimes relying on such estimates and sometimes avoiding them. In case this has left you skeptical, you should know that McHenry is probably *the* living expert on methods for performing and validating such body-size estimates. Of course, that does not mean that his numbers are perfect. My own personal statistical guru gave me many mantras, and my favorite among them is "all measurements are estimates." My point is that McHenry's body-size estimates are the best that you will find.

Another "style" difference between Chapters 9 and 10 is that McHenry and Coffing like to describe the traits and fossils by referring to specimen numbers. This is actually a "clean" way to do things, even though it might seem a bit more confusing initially. The reason specimen numbers are useful is that fossils are physical objects with a complex array of features, but they do not come out of the ground with taxonomic labels like *Homo thisus* or *Australopithecus thatus*. Nevertheless, as each fossil is discovered (however fragmentary it may be, even a single tooth!), it must be assigned to a taxon—either an existing one or a new one. Of course, those species names are just a guess and they might not be correct. As time goes by and more fossils are discovered, our opinions can shift about the amount of variability a given taxon shows and therefore about what specimens fit within it. For example, Wood and Collard's comments about "*H. habilis, sensu lato*" suggest that they think some *H. habilis* specimens are misnamed and properly belong to some other taxon. (You can infer this from Wood and Collard's Figure 1E; the relevant distinction is the "1470 group" versus the "1813 group," both of which refer to particular specimen numbers.) This is why I say that describing a fossil by its specimen number (which will never change) rather than by its current taxonomic label (which may change next year) is a clean way of doing business. When I say "KNM-ER 1808," everyone will know (as Paul Simon sang in "Diamonds on the Soles of her Shoes") exactly what I'm talking about. And we will all be able to use the evidence that the fossil presents to discuss what species it might have belonged to.

In both Chapters 9 and 10, the discussion focuses on the place of *H. habilis* and *H. rudolfensis* in human evolution. Given the suite of fossils that have been discovered thus far, these two taxa jointly fall between *Australopithecus* and later *Homo* on a number of important dimensions. McHenry and Coffing separate these dimensions into two categories: the body, which most of their chapter focuses on, and the mind, which is included in the last few pages. This latter category covers, more precisely, what can be inferred about the mind from fossil skulls. As a result of this game plan, McHenry and Coffing make many references to "*Australopithecus* + *habilis*" and explicitly contrast this set with "later *Homo*" (in which they include *H. rudolfensis*, *H. eregaster* and the other species of *Homo* that appear even more recently in the fossil record but are largely ignored in this chapter). Consequently, you may expect McHenry and Coffing to conclude that *habilis* belongs in *Australopithecus*; they have two reasons for not drawing this conclusion. First, they are not very interested in the "where-does-it-belong?" problem that boggled Wood and Collard. Second, the brains tell a different story than the bodies. With respect to the mind dimension, *habilis* is more like later *Homo* than *rudolfensis* is!

This is an interesting conclusion, especially because some paleoanthropologists have argued that *habilis* and *rudolfensis* really represent only a single species. Instead, McHenry and Coffing are suggesting a much more complicated story: *habilis* has some derived features of *Homo*, *rudolfensis* has others, and they share almost none!

Because McHenry and Coffing are anatomists who depend on their anatomical expertise to analyze and interpret the fossils, you will meet many new terms in this chapter. The most essential ones are defined and their relevance briefly interpreted in the Glossary, below). Other than these technicalities, some discussion of Figures 2 and 3 might be helpful to you.

Figure 2 is a standard X-by-Y graph. Each species is marked by one data point, which represents its average body weight and its average brain weight. The only slightly tricky aspect of this graph is that both brain weight and body weight are given not as raw numbers, but as logarithms of those raw numbers. The reason for this is technical but will emerge as we go along. Please take a pencil (or something erasable) and a ruler, and lay the ruler across the graph diagonally from lower left to upper right. Wiggle the ruler around a bit, trying to find a position where every point is as close to the ruler as it can possibly be. The points do not fall on a straight line so this is not an easy task. (Holding the ruler on edge rather than flat on the page will at least help you to see what you are doing.) The line that I think looks best goes roughly through the *africanus* x-mark in the lower left and through the "0.1–0.15 MYA" right-pointing solid triangle in the upper right. I'm not going to fuss if yours looks a little different.

What you have just done is the visual equivalent of a statistical technique called regression analysis. The goal of regression analysis is to find the average relationship between two variables, in this case the average relationship between brain weight and body weight. The useful thing about determining the average relationship is that it lets you see whether a particular species falls above or below the average. Species above the line have larger-than-average brains and those below the line have smaller-than-average brains. McHenry and Coffing want to emphasize that *H. habilis* falls above the line.

In Figure 3, the x-axis is time, moving backwards from the present. The y-axis is *relative* brain size. In other words, the y-axis compresses together the information from both axes of Figure 2 by dividing brain weight by body weight. There is one more complexity however: The actual calculation is not (brain weight divided by body weight). Insetad it is (brain weight divided by 11.22 times body weight to the 0.76 power). That is why the y-axis is labeled "encephalization quotient" instead of "brain weight/body weight". Why so complicated?

When we drew a line on Figure 2, we were trying to find out the average relationship between brain weight and body weight. Our simple ruler-and-pencil method was good enough to show that *habilis*, for example, had an unusually large brain. But if we want a precise estimate of the average brain weight–body weight relationship, we would get brain weight and body weight from lots of species and use the formal mathematical method of regression. If you do that, you get an equation that describes the average relationship between brain weight and body weight. This is the encephalization quotient (EQ). The EQ equation tells you what mathematical operations you need to perform on the body mass of any species of mammal to determine its expected brain mass.

What we see in Chapter 10 is that in the early Pleistocene, between 2 and 2.5 million years ago, there were several different species of hominins exhibiting different suites of adaptations. Using later *Homo* to define our derived adaptations, some of these early Pleistocene hominins were more derived in terms of relative brain size and relative cheek tooth size, but were more primitive in aspects of their anatomy related to locomotion; other contemporaneous hominins show the reverse pattern, being more primitive in their cranial and dental anatomy but relatively derived in terms of their locomotor adaptations.

Chapter 10 Glossary

acetabular width: The acetabulum is the socket in the hip where the head of the femur rests. The width is simply a measure of the size of this socket. Its size is thought to give information about the nature of an animal's gait—the way it walks. This is useful for extinct animals whose gait we cannot observe directly.

Acheulean: Stone tools that are more sophisticated than Oldowan tools; Acheulean tools first appear about 1.4 million years ago (MYA).

arborealism: A mode of life that depends on spending a lot of time in trees as opposed to on the ground.

autapomorphy: A unique derived trait; a trait not shared with any other taxon and therefore useless for determining cladistic relationships.

cheek teeth: Chewing teeth as opposed to biting teeth. Molars and premolars are cheek teeth; incisors and canines are not. When adjusted for body size (see the last column of Table 1), the chewing-surface area of the cheek teeth gives information about an animal's diet. Large chewing surface area is thought to reflect a high-fiber diet.

Oldowan: The oldest kind of stone tools. They first appear about 2.6 MYA. Early tools are the topic of Chapter 14.

hominid: McHenry and Coffing use this term to refer to the group of apes we are calling hominins. The continued existence of both terms reflects a difference of opinion about whether this group of apes represents a family or a tribe.

masticatory apparatus: The functionally linked set of anatomical traits involved in chewing, including the teeth, the jaws in which they sit, and the muscles that operate those jaws.

synapomorphy: A shared derived trait that is useful for determining cladistic relationships (see Chapter 4).

phalanx (plural, phalanges): The bones comprising the fingers and toes. Curved phalanges are common in species that do a lot of tree climbing.

Chapter 10
Australopithecus to *Homo*: Transformations in Body and Mind (2000)

Henry M. McHenry and Katherine Coffing

Abstract

Significant changes occurred in human evolution between 2.5 and 1.8 million years ago. Stone tools first appeared, brains expanded, bodies enlarged, sexual dimorphism in body size decreased, limb proportions changed, cheek teeth reduced in size, and crania began to share more unique features with later *Homo*. Although the two earliest species of *Homo*, *H. habilis* and *H. rudolfensis*, retained many primitive features in common with australopithecine species, they both shared key unique features with later species of *Homo*. Two of the most conspicuous shared derived characters were the sizes of the brain and masticatory apparatus relative to body weight. Despite the shared derived characters of *H. habilis* and *H. rudolfensis*, one unexpected complication in the transition from australopithecine to *Homo* was that the postcranial anatomy of *H. habilis* retained many australopithecine characteristics. *H. rudolfensis*, however, seems to have had a more human-like body plan, similar to later species of *Homo*. *H. rudolfensis* may therefore represent a link between *Australopithecus* and *Homo*.

Key Words: postcranium, craniodental morphology, encephalization

---

Department of Anthropology, University of California, Davis, California 95616;
e-mail: hmmchenry@ucdavis.edu, kecoffing@ucdavis.edu

Introduction

When Kamoya Kimeu discovered the early *Homo* skeleton KNM-WT 15000 in 1984, something that had been vaguely understood before snapped into sharper focus: The evolutionary transition from australopithecine to *Homo* involved not only an expansion of the brain and a reduction of the cheek teeth, but a change in walking and climbing behavior (Walker & Leakey 1993a). Arguments remain about which early *Homo* species gave rise to later *Homo*, but the origin of the genus is becoming of greater interest.

New discoveries and new analyses of *Homo* include three major monographs (Tobias 1991, Walker & Leakey 1993a, Wood 1991). Most paleoanthropologists (e.g. Groves 1989; Tobias 1991; Wood 1991, 1992; Skelton & McHenry 1992; Walker & Leakey 1993a; McHenry 1994c; Strait et al 1997; Asfaw et al 1999a; Klein 1999; Wolpoff 1999; Wood & Collard 1999), but not all (e.g. Oxnard 1975), agree that *Homo* evolved from *Australopithecus*, but there is less consensus on which species of *Australopithecus* is the most likely ancestor and which fossils are the earliest members of *Homo*.

The search for the immediate ancestor of *Homo* among known species of *Australopithecus* may be fruitless because all the possible candidates have unique specializations (i.e. autapomorphies). It is more useful to search for the species whose unknown ancestor most recently branched off from the stem leading to *Homo*. The closeness of two species can be determined on the basis of morphological resemblances that are unique relative to other species (shared derived characters or synapomorphies). The closest branches in the evolutionary tree are referred to as sister clades. Unfortunately, there is little consensus on which species of *Australopithecus* is the closest to *Homo*. An analysis using most of the information on craniodental morphology of early hominids available in 1999 found that the sister clade to *Homo* was that containing the "robust" australopithecines (in their terminology, *Paranthropus aethiopicus, Paranthropus robustus*, and *Paranthropus boisei*), with *Australopithecus africanus* and *Australopithecus garhi* more distantly related to *Homo* (Strait & Grine 1999). Not all agree (Asfaw et al 1999b, McCollum 1999). Nor is there agreement on who are the earliest members of the genus *Homo* (Grine et al 1996) or whether the species known as *Homo habilis* and *Homo rudolfensis* should be put into Australopithecus (Wood & Collard 1999).

Even without unanimity of opinion on hominid taxonomy and phylogeny, there are some important generalizations that can be made about the origin of the genus *Homo*. Between 2.5 and 1.8 million years ago (mya) stone tools first appeared, brains expanded, bodies enlarged, sexual dimorphism in body size decreased, limb proportions changed, cheek teeth reduced in size, and crania began to share more unique features with later *Homo*. This paper reviews what can be said, and with what level of certainty, about these transformations.

Cast of Characters

Table 1 presents one version of who's who in the early Plio-Pleistocene. The taxonomy is mostly from Klein (1999), who provides discussions of alternative views that are beyond the scope of this review. This taxonomic scheme recognizes three genera of hominid. *Australopithecus* and *Paranthropus* are often referred to informally as australopithecines, in contrast to members of the genus *Homo*. The body sizes, brain volumes, tooth dimensions, and other variables derive from sources given in the footnotes to the table.

Transformations of Body

All species of hominid appear to be accomplished bipeds, but there are noticeable differences in body plan. Bipedal adaptations have so profoundly altered the general body plan of hominids away from that seen in other members of the superfamily Hominoidea (apes and people) that differences between species of hominid are often not emphasized (e.g. Lovejoy 1988, Latimer 1991). By most accounts there are important differences in postcranial anatomy between australopithecine species, and especially between australopithecines and *Homo ergaster* (McHenry 1994b, Stern 2000). Some of the most conspicuous changes between the australopithecines and *H. ergaster* include a sharp increase in body size (especially among females), a reduction in relative forelimb size, a lengthening of the thigh, a narrowing of the pelvis, a side-to-side expansion of the femoral shaft, and the development of a more barrel-shaped chest.

When did the body transform from the patterns seen in australopithecine species to the one manifest in *H. ergaster?* The first evidence of an *H. ergaster*-like body occurred at 1.95 mya with the pelvic bone KNM-ER 3228. About 60,000 years later there were several hindlimb specimens that were more like KNM-WT 15000 than like any australopithecine. These include the two well-preserved femora, KNM-ER 1472 and 1481, and the proximal and distal tibia and distal fibula of 1481. These derive from the Upper Burgi Member of Area 131 in Koobi Fora at the same time and place as the KNM-ER 1470 cranium of *H. rudolfensis*. It has always seemed reasonable to assume that these legs go with that head (Leakey 1973, Wood 1992), but the postcrania are not directly associated with the cranium. Wood & Collard (1999) reject Wood's (1992) earlier attribution of these femora to *H. rudolfensis*. However, the assumption that these femora do belong to the same species as *H. rudolfensis* is strengthened by the fact that there is no other *Homo* species at that site, although there are two P. boisei mandibles there (Wood 1991). The most common hominid craniodental specimens at the site are those that Wood refers to as *H. rudolfensis* (i.e. KNM-ER 1470, 1482, 1483, 1801, and 1802). The legs (KNM-ER 1472 and 1481) might belong to *P. boisei*, but that appears unlikely because they are unlike the one known *P. boisei*

TABLE 1 Species, dates, body size, brain size, and posterior tooth size in early hominids[a]

Taxon	Dates (mya)	Mass (kg) Male	Mass (kg) Female	Stature (cm³) Male	Stature (cm³) Female	ECV (cc)	Brain weight (g)	Postcanine tooth area	EQ	MQ
Pan troglodytes	Extant	49	41	—	—	—	395	294	2.0	0.9
Australopithecus anamensis	4.2–3.9	51	33	—	—	—	—	428	—	1.4
Australopithecus afarensis	3.9–3.0	45	29	151	105	438	434	460	2.5	1.7
Australopithecus africanus	3.0–2.4	41	30	138	115	452	448	516	2.7	2.0
Australopithecus aethiopicus	2.7–2.2	—	—	—	—	—	—	688	—	—
Paranthropus boisei	2.3–1.4	49	34	137	124	521	514	756	2.7	2.7
Paranthropus robustus	1.9–1.4	40	32	132	110	530	523	588	3.0	2 2
Australopithecus garhi	2.5–?	—	—	—	—	450	446	—	—	—
Homo habilis	1.9–1.6	37	32	131	100	612	601	478	3.6	1.9
Homo rudolfensis	2.4–1.6	60	51	160	150	752	736	572	3.1	1.5
Homo ergaster	1.9–1.7	66	56	180	160	871	849	377	3.3	0.9
Homo sapiens	Extant	58	49	175	161	—	1350	334	5.8	0.9

[a]Taxonomy is based on Klein (1999). *Ardipithecus* and later extinct species of *Homo* are beyond the scope of this paper. Dates are from Klein (1999). mya, Million years ago. Body mass estimates are from McHenry (1992), except for the following: *A. anamensis* male is from Leakey et al (1995), *A. anamensis* female is calculated from the ratio of male and female in *A. afarensis*, and *H. ergaster* is from Ruff et al (1998). Statures are from McHenry (1991), except *H. ergaster*, which is from Ruff & Walker (1993). ECV is cranial capacity from sources listed in McHenry (1994), with the addition of A.L. 444-2 (540 cc) to *A. afarensis* (WH Kimbel, personal communication), Stw 505 (515 cc) to *A. africanus* (Conroy et al 1998), KGA 10-525 (545 cc) to *P. boisei* (Suwa et al 1997), and BOU-VP-12/130 (450 cc) to *A. garhi* (Asfaw et al 1999a). Brain weight is calculated from Ruff et al (1998). Postcanine tooth area (in square millimeters) is the sum of products of the mesiodistal and buccolingual dimensions lengths of P_4, M_1, and M_2 and is taken from McHenry (1994), with the addition of *A. anamensis* from Leakey et al (1995). Encephalization quotient (EQ) is calculated as brain mass divided by (11.22 x body mass$^{0.76}$), from Martin (1981). Megadontia quotient (MQ) is the postcanine tooth area divided by (12.15 x body mass$^{0.86}$), from McHenry (1988).

partial skeleton, KNM-ER 1500 (Grausz et al 1988). If it is true that these femora belong to *H. rudolfensis*, then it becomes more likely that the KNM-ER 3228 pelvic bone also belongs to that species. It is morphologically compatible with the femora. *H. rudolfensis* appears in the fossil record before 1.95 mya, but *H. ergaster* does not. The specimen comes from the earliest hominid-bearing levels in Area 102 and no other hominids have been found in those levels at that site.

As is discussed below, however, what is known of the body of *H. habilis* is much more like that of *Australopithecus* than *H. rudolfensis* or later *Homo*. The primitiveness of the *H. habilis* postcranium was one of the reasons Wood & Collard (1999) suggested transferring that species to the genus *Australopithecus*.

Hands and Tools

It has long been assumed that the morphology of the hand will reveal something about the manual dexterity required to make stone tools (Napier 1962, Leakey et al 1964), but interpretation of the hominid fossils is not simple (Marzke 1997). The earliest known stone tools appeared between 2.6 and 2.5 mya from Kada Gona, Hadar (Semaw et al 1997), which predates the first known appearance of *Homo*. Evidence of tool use comes from 2.5-million-year-old sediments at Bouri on the Middle Awash River, with cut and percussion marks on mammalian bones made by stone tools (de Heinzelin et al 1999). These sediments also contained remains of only one species of hominid, *A. garhi* (Asfaw et al 1999a). Slightly later in time (2.4–2.3 mya) stone tools appeared at Afar Locality 666 (Kimbel et al 1996) associated with a maxilla of a hominid resembling some of the *H. habilis* specimens at Olduvai (i.e. specimens O.H. 16 and 39). Tools also made their earliest known appearance in the lower Omo River valley [Member F of the Shungura Formation (Howell et al 1987)] and at West Turkana [Kalochoro Member of the Nachukui Formation (Roche et al 1999)] at about that time. The richest collection of early stone tools occurred between 2 and 1.6 mya at Olduvai (Leakey 1971) and Koobi Fora (Harris & Isaac 1976). All of these are part of the Oldowan Industrial Complex, but those from before about 2 mya are more crudely flaked than the later Oldowan tools (Kibunjia 1994). Perhaps by 1.6 mya, but certainly by 1.4 mya, the Acheulean Industrial Complex appears in the record with more sophisticated tools, such as hand axes and cleavers (Asfaw et al 1992).

Oldowan tools

Is there a detectable change in hand morphology at the time tools first appeared or when they become more sophisticated? Hand bones are known for most species of *Australopithecus*. Within the collection of the earliest species, *Australopithecus anamensis*, is a proximal hand phalanx that is curved and has strong ridges for the attachment of the flexor sheath (Leakey et al 1998). Both features are present in *Australopithecus afarensis* and are considered primitive and possibly indicative of climbing ability (Stern & Susman 1983, Susman et al 1984). The capitate of *A. anamensis* is even more primitive than *A. afarensis* in that it has an ape-like, laterally facing metacarpal II facet (Leakey et al 1998). The hands of *A. afarensis* have many primitive features that are associated with arborealism, including strongly curved proximal phalanges, strong ridges for the flexor sheath, an elongated and rod-shaped pisiform, and expanded heads and bases of the metacarpals

(Tuttle 1981, 1988; Stern & Susman 1983; Susman et al 1984, 1985; Susman & Stern 1991; Susman 1994, 1998). *A. afarensis* also possessed several derived features that would allow two distinctively human precision grips important to stone tool manufacture but it lacked the human mobility of the thumb. This lack may have limited its tool-making ability (Marzke 1997). *A. africanus* also combined primitive characteristics [e.g. its capitate had a dorsally placed trapezoid facet, mediolaterally constricted metacarpal III facet, prominent palmar beak, and reduced area for the styloid process of metacarpal III (McHenry 1983)], with derived features associated with the human pad-to-side precision pinch and handling grips (Marzke 1997). Remains of both of these species have been found in sediments that are distinctly lacking in stone tools.

At Olduvai, Koobi Fora, and elsewhere, stone tools are abundant in sediments containing *H. habilis*, yet in many respects the hand bones attributed to the type specimen of this species (O.H. 7) retain numerous primitive features (Susman & Creel 1979; Susman & Stern 1982; Susman 1994, 1998). That hand did have some key features associated with the firm precision pinch and handling grips used in making stone tools (Marzke 1983, 1986, 1997; Marzke & Shackley 1986; Marzke & Marzke 1987; Marzke et al 1992). A partial skeleton of *H. habilis*, KNM-ER 3735, has two fragments of proximal phalanges that are curved and strongly built (Leakey & Walker 1985). Stone and bone tools are also abundant at Swartkrans, and the hand bones there have traits associated with the ability to make tools (Susman 1988a–c, 1989, 1993, 1994, 1998; Marzke 1997). This may imply that *P. robustus*, by far the most common hominid at that site, was a toolmaker. However, a species of *Homo* is also present in Members 1 and 2 (but not 3), Swartkrans, and it is possible that the tools were made by it (Clark 1993).

There are few hand bones of *H. ergaster* and none that can be attributed with any certainty to *H. rudolfensis*. There are two phalanges (one proximal pollex, 15000 BQ, and one middle that is not from the thumb, 15000 BO) associated with KNM-WT 15000 (Walker & Leakey 1993b). Neither shows curvature. There are two juvenile thumb metacarpals that probably belong to KNM–WT 15000, but their association is uncertain (Walker & Leakey 1993b). If part of the skeleton, they are significant in that they are long and straight like those of modern humans and one of the Swartkrans specimens (SKW 5020), although the 15000 specimens have palmar beaks on their distal end formed by the diaphysis, not by the epiphysis, as it is in SK 84. There are two proximal phalanges of KNM-ER 164, a specimen that also has enough of a skull bone to allow Wood (1991) to classify it as *Homo sp. indet.* The phalanges do not have the strong curvature and markings for the flexor sheath that characterize *A. afarensis*. The KNM-ER 803 partial skeleton of *H. ergaster* preserves the proximal end of a metacarpal V, but it is not complete enough to show whether its hand had shed arboreal features. The lack of hand bones in early species of *Homo* is especially frustrating because other evidence points to important changes between australopithecines + habilines and later *Homo*.

Forelimb Transformations

The evidence from the hand is confusing and incomplete, but the forelimb as a whole shows profound modification between *Australopithecus* + *habilis* and later *Homo*: The former had big, robust arms and the latter was relatively petite. There are no associated limb bones of *A. anamensis*, but the well-preserved radius KNM-ER 20419 is very long [265–275 mm (Heinrich et al 1993)]. The humeri of *A. afarensis* are not exceptionally long but are exceptionally robust (Johanson et al 1982a; Jungers 1982, 1991, 1994; Lovejoy et al 1982; Jungers & Stern 1983; Susman et al 1984, 1985; White et al 1993; Kimbel et al 1994; White 1994). Forearms of *A. afarensis* appear to be very long relative to humeral length, however. Kimbel et al (1994) estimate an ulnar/femoral index of 91% for A.L. 438-1/137-50 and 92.5% for A.L. 288–1 that is closer to that of chimps (95%) than humans (80%). *H. ergaster* is closer to the human condition [85% (Ruff & Walker 1993)]. *A. garhi* also has a long forearm relative to humeral length. For BOU-VP 12/1, Asfaw et al (1999a) estimate a radial length of 231 mm and a humeral length of 236 mm, which makes a ratio of 98, more similar to chimps [87–100 (Napier & Napier 1967)] than modern tropical people (76–79) or *H. ergaster* [80 (Ruff & Walker 1993)].

The limbs of *A. africanus* are too fragmentary to be able to reconstruct total lengths with accuracy, but judging from the sizes of the articular ends, forelimb length is probably greater relative to hindlimb length than is true for modern people (McHenry & Berger 1998b). Joint breadths of the forelimbs are much larger than expected from human proportions relative to the joints of the hindlimb (McHenry & Berger 1998a). In fact, *A. africanus* had relatively larger forelimb breadths than did *A. afarensis* (McHenry & Berger 1998a).

Relatively large forelimbs characterize *H. habilis* as well. This is certainly true comparing shaft breadths, and according to some (Johanson et al 1987, Hartwig-Scherer & Martin 1991), but not all (Korey 1990, Asfaw et al 1999a), is probably true of estimated humeral and femoral lengths.

Unfortunately, no forelimb specimens are definitely attributed to *H. rudolfensis*, although the proximal humerus KNM-ER 1473 is from the Upper Burgi Member of Area 131 and may belong to that species. The ratio of its head diameter to the femoral head diameters of KNM-ER 1471 and 1481a are 1.07 and 0.99, respectively, which is at the upper range of variation seen in modern humans and well below the ratio in any modern apes.

As noted above, the size of the arm relative to the forearm in the *H. ergaster* skeleton KNM-WT 15000 is very human-like and not at all similar to any species of *Australopithecus* (Ruff & Walker 1993). This is a conspicuous change and adds weight to the argument favoring a dramatic alteration in locomotor behavior between the australopithecines + *H. habilis* and later *Homo*. Both the humerus-to-femur length index (74%) and the ulnar-to-humeral length ratio (85%) of this specimen are human-like. Other partial skeletons of *H. ergaster* confirm the observation that forelimbs dramatically decreased in relative size. The clavicle and humerus of the KNM-ER 1808 partial skeleton are approximately the same size as those of KNM-WT 15000, but the KNM-ER 1808 femur is much larger. The KNM-ER 803 fore-to-hindlimb proportions are also very human-like (McHenry 1978).

Shoulders and Trunks

What many would consider climbing features are also retained in the shoulder and trunk of *Australopithecus* + *H. habilis* but not in later *Homo*. The shoulder joint appears to be directed more superiorly in *A. afarensis* (Jungers & Stern 1983; Stern & Susman 1983, 1991; Susman et al 1984, 1985; Susman & Stern 1991), but this appearance may not be related to locomotor behavior (Inouye & Shea 1997). The thorax of *A. afarensis* is distinctly pongid-like in its funnel shape (Schmid 1983, 1989, 1991; Berge et al 1984), but the thorax is barrel shaped in *H. ergaster* and later humans (Jellema et al 1993). Perhaps the more pongid shape of the A. afarensis thorax is simply an artifact of its wider hips, but it is also interpreted as an indication that this species' back muscles were specially adapted to climbing (Schmid 1983).

Hips

Hips transform dramatically between *Australopithecus* and *Homo*. Here, the fossil sample includes a rich collection of pelvic and femoral specimens, including those that we argue belong to *H. rudolfensis* (i.e. the KNM-ER 3228 pelvic bone and the KNM-ER 1472 and 1481a femora). The pelvic girdles show key bipedal adaptations, such as shortening of the pelvic blades and anterior rotation of the sacrum. The big alterations from the pongid condition resulted from changes in the morphogenesis of the limb (Lovejoy et al 1999). Still, there are conspicuous differences between *Australopithecus* and *Homo* that are important but harder to explain in terms of genetic alterations.

The most obvious change from *Australopithecus* to *Homo* is in relative hipjoint size. Figure 1 plots pelvic height against acetabular width to illustrate how very small the hips were in *Australopithecus* and how human-like *H. rudolfensis* was in this respect. But there

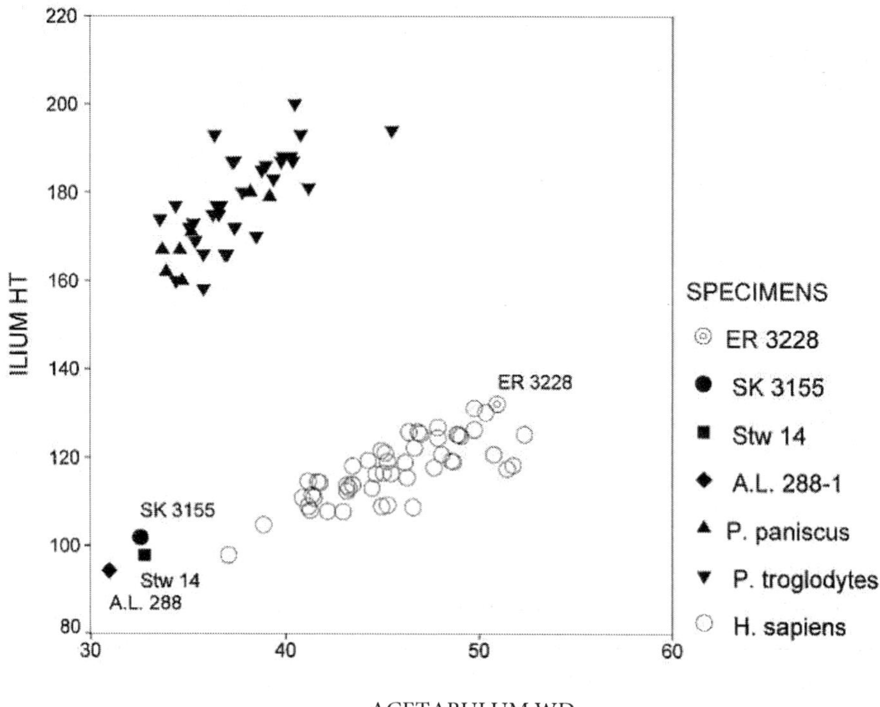

Figure 1. Scatter plot of hip joint size against height of the pelvic blade. Measurements and samples are from McHenry (1975b). Like most mammals, the pelvic girdle of bonobos (*Pan paniscus*) and common chimps (*Pan troglodytes*) have small acetabulae and long iliac blades relative to the conditions seen in humans. The australopithecines are represented by the pelvic bones of *Australpithecus afarensis* (A.L. 288-1), *Australpithecus africanus* (Sts 14), and *Paranthropus robustus* (SK 3155) and are smaller in size than modern humans but decidedly human in shape. The specimen referred to, *Homo rudolfensis* (KNM-ER 3228), is indistinguishable from modern humans in this regard. Unfortunately, this part of the anatomy has not yet been recovered for *Homo habilis.*

were interesting changes between the hips of early *Homo* and later *Homo* as well. Changes in the pattern of gait explain most of the changes in pelvic morphology between the last common ancestor of African apes and humans, but changes within the human lineage also involve birth. The shortening of the pelvic blades to make bipedalism possible reduced the front-to-back dimension of the birth canal. This may (Berge et al 1984, Tague & Lovejoy 1986, Berge 1991) or may not (Leutenegger 1987) have affected the birth process of small-brained australopithecines, but it became a painful reality to *Homo*. It probably explains the difference between early and late *Homo* hips.

Unfortunately, no pelvic remains are known for *H. habilis* except for a very eroded sacrum associated with KNM-ER 3735 (Leakey et al 1989). Something can be discerned about the *H. habilis* hip on the basis of its femoral shafts. Analyses using engineering principles show interesting contrasts between the proximal femora attributed to australopithecines + *H. habilis* and *H. rudolfensis* + later species of archaic *Homo* (Ruff 1995, 1998). The ratio of mediolateral bending strength to the anteroposterior bending strength is much higher in *H. rudolfensis* and later species of archaic *Homo* than in the australopithecines. The one femoral shaft that can definitely be attributed to *H. habilis*, O.H. 62, is australopithecine-like in this regard. Ruff (1995) provides one explanation for this difference that involves femoral neck length and the shape of the pelvic inlet. In australopithecine hips, long femoral necks compensate for the high hip-joint reaction forces generated by the abductor muscles. These high forces are due to the relatively wide mediolateral dimension of the birth canal. In *H. rudolfensis* and later archaic members of the genus *Homo*, the hip-joint reaction force increased, as indicated by relatively large joints, and so did the mediolateral strain of the femoral shafts. This implies, according to Ruff (1995), that early Homo retained the platypelloid pelvic outlet of *Australopithecus* and compensated by increasing the abductor force and mediolateral strain on the femoral shafts. Only by Middle Pleistocene times did the rounder pelvic inlet typical of modern humans evolve, a change that was made possible by the rotation during birth of the infant's head.

Femoral Length

It is known with certainty that relative to humeral length, the femur of *A. afarensis* was short (Johanson & Taeib 1976; Johanson et al 1982a, b; Jungers 1982, 1988a; Jungers & Stern 1983; Susman et al 1984, 1985) and that of *H. ergaster* was long (Ruff & Walker 1993). There is less certainty about relative femoral length in other early hominid species because of the fragmentary nature of the fossils, but enough is preserved to indicate that *A. africanus* (McHenry & Berger 1998b) and *H. habilis* (Johanson 1989, Leakey et al 1989, Korey 1990, Hartwig-Scherer & Martin 1991) also had relatively short femora. Associated fore- and hindlimbs from the Hata beds of Ethiopia's Middle Awash probably belong to *A. garhi* and appear to show femoral lengthening relative to humeral length (Asfaw et al 1999a). Relative to radial length, however, the length of this femur is intermediate between humans and apes.

Legs

The tibia and fibula of the australopithecines + *H. habilis* are variable, decidedly more human-like than ape-like, but there remains a debate as to the precise kinematics of the knee and ankle (Susman & Stern 1982, 1991; Stern & Susman 1983, 1991; Tardieu 1983, 1986, 1998; Susman et al 1985; Latimer et al 1987; Latimer 1988, 1991; Berger & Tobias 1996; Tardieu & Preuschoft 1996; Crompton et al 1998). These elements are variable in modern human populations, but all relevant specimens of australopithecines + *H. habilis* show the key adaptations to bipedalism, particularly a horizontally oriented talar facet.

Feet

There are numerous primitive features reported from the pedal remains of *A. afarensis*, including relatively long and curved toes and the lack of side-to-side widening of the dorsal region of the metatarsal heads (Johanson & Edey 1981; Turtle 1981; Stern & Susman 1983; Susman et al 1984, 1985; Susman & Stern 1991). Primitive features have also been emphasized in the description of foot remains from Member 2 of Sterkfontein that might belong to *A. africanus* (Clarke & Tobias 1995, Clarke 1998). The primitive qualities of the Olduvai Hominid 8 foot have been noted (Oxnard 1972, 1973; Lisowski et al 1974, 1976; Oxnard & Lisowski 1978; Lewis 1980, 1989; Kidd et al 1996), and this foot probably belongs to *H. habilis* (Day & Napier 1964; Day & Wood 1968; Day 1973, 1976; Susman & Stern 1982). Unfortunately, there are no foot specimens that can be attributed to *H. rudolfensis* and only a few scraps to *H. ergaster*. A very human-looking talus from East Turkana, KNM-ER 813, derives from strata dated to 1.85 mya (Feibel et al 1989) and may belong to *H. ergaster*, but it is not directly associated with taxonomically diagnostic craniodental material (Wood 1974). There is evidence that the toes of *H. ergaster* were shorter and less curved than those of *A. afarensis*. One of the partial skeletons of *H. ergaster*, KNM-ER 803, preserves two intermediate toe phalanges (803k and 803l) that are relatively short and straight compared with the equivalent parts of *A. afarensis* [A.L. 333x-21a and 333-115k & l (Day & Leakey 1974, Latimer et al 1982)]. The footprints attributed to early *Homo* at Koobi Fora may be more human-like than those attributed to *A. afarensis* (Behrensmeyer & Laporte 1981), but given the controversy over the interpretation of the Laetoli footprints (Clarke 1979; Tuttle 1981, 1985, 1987, 1988, 1994; Jungers & Stern 1983; Stern & Susman 1983, 1991; Susman et al 1984, 1985; Deloison 1985; White & Suwa 1987; Susman & Stern 1991; Tuttle et al 1991a, b, 1992, 1998), such contrasts may not be important. A first metatarsal (KNM-WT 15000 BX) may belong to the Strapping Youth, but it is not closely associated with the rest of the skeleton, and it contains peculiarities that make the original describers doubt its attribution (Walker & Leakey 1993b).

Body Size

Table 1 presents estimates of body weights for males and females of each species. Most of these are based on the relationship between known body weight and hindlimb joint size in modern humans (McHenry 1992a). Many other estimates appear in the literature (e.g. McHenry 1974, 1975a, 1988, 1991a–c, 1992b, 1994a, 1996; Jungers 1988b, 1991; Hartwig-Scherer & Martin 1992; Hartwig-Scherer 1993, 1994; Ruff & Walker 1993; McHenry & Berger 1998a, b; Ruff et al 1998). Until the appearance of *H. rudolfensis*, the male averages are small by modern human standards (37–51 kg) and female averages are tiny (29–37 kg). By 1.95 mya, modern-sized hindlimbs appear in the record. Although it is still uncertain what isolated limb bones belong to *H. rudolfensis*, by 1.8 mya there are partial associated skeletons of *H. ergaster* that are from big-bodied individuals (i.e. KNM-ER 803 and 1808). What is particularly striking is the apparent increase in the size of the *H. ergaster* female compared with that seen in earlier species of hominid.

Craniodental

The high level of heterogeneity in craniodental morphology among australopithecine species and among specimens attributed to *H. habilis* and *H. rudolfensis* makes it difficult to generalize about specific transformations between the australopithecines and *Homo*. In a formal cladistic analysis of 60 craniodental characters, Strait et al (1997) found only four synapomorphies defining the *Homo*-clade, and two of these were reversals or parallelisms. Their most parsimonious cladogram placed *H. habilis* as the sister clade to all later species of *Homo*, including *H. rudolfensis*. Lieberman et al (1996) did a similar analysis and found *H. habilis* to be the closest clade to later *Homo* to the exclusion of *H. rudolfensis*. In one analysis, Chamberlain & Wood (1987) found *H. habilis* to be the sister of all other species of *Homo*, including *H. rudolfensis*. Wood (1991) preferred a cladogram in which *H. habilis* and *H. rudolfensis* are on sister clades and their combined branch is sister to other *Homo*. Wood & Collard (1999) reanalyzed these and other data sets and showed that four clades are equally close, including that of *Paranthropus* species, *H. habilis*, *H. rudolfensis*, and all later *Homo* species. If genus names were to be applied strictly on the basis of monophyly, their cladogram suggests that either all species of *Paranthropus* should be included in the genus Homo (because relative to other species of hominid, *Paranthropus, H. habilis, H. rudolfensis*, and all other *Homo* are monophyletic), or each of the four clades should be given different genus names.

For the purposes of this review, we assumed that *H. habilis, H. rudolfensis, H. ergaster*, and all later species of *Homo* are monophyletic relative to species of australopithecines. When scaled to body size, they all share two distinctive and fundamentally important characteristics not found in combination in any other hominid species: All species of *Homo* have both a relatively reduced masticatory system and an expanded brain.

The reduction in absolute size of the masticatory system is clearly evident in *H. habilis*. One measure of this reduction is given in Table 1 (postcanine tooth area). The absolute sizes of cheek teeth expand through successively younger species of australopithecine, from the oldest, *A. anamensis* (428 mm^2), to *A. afarensis* (460 mm^2), *A. africanus* (516 mm^2), *P. robustus* (588 mm^2), and *P. boisei* (756 mm^2). The trend is reversed in successively younger species of *Homo*, from *H. rudolfensis* (572 mm^2) to *H. habilis* (478 mm^2), *H. ergaster* (377 mm^2), and *Homo sapiens* (334 mm^2).

The absolute size of the cheek teeth is correlated to the morphology of much of the skull, including mandibular corpus robusticity, position and robusticity of the zygomatic arches, attachment areas and buttressing for the chewing muscles, and many features of the face. *H. rudolfensis* resembles some of the australopithecines in retaining absolutely larger cheek teeth and related features (Wood 1991), but when scaled to body weight, its teeth are relatively much smaller than any australopithecine.

The relative size of the cheek teeth can be estimated by comparing postcanine tooth area with body size. This can be done by comparing postcranial dimensions of associated skeletons with cheek-tooth size (McHenry 1984), but there are few specimens. Although there are methodological problems (Smith 1996), it is heuristically interesting to compare tooth area directly with estimated body weight to find a measure of relative tooth size. Table 1 presents one measure of relative cheek-tooth size by way of the ratio of actual postcanine tooth area to predicted tooth area based on scaled body weight [the megadontia quotient (MQ)]. By this measure, the average extant hominoid has an MQ of 1. Both modern chimps and humans are slightly below this average and have a value of 0.9. The australopithecine species expand through time from the earliest, *A. anamensis*, with 1.4, to *A. afarensis* with 1.7, *A. africanus* with 2.0, *P. robustus* with 2.2, and *P. boisei* with 2.7. This trend is reversed in the *Homo* lineage. The earliest species of *Homo* show some reduction from late *Australopithecus* (*H. habilis* has an MQ of 1.9 and *H. rudolfensis* one of 1.5). The values for *H. rudolfensis* depend on the assumption that the large hindlimbs of Area 103 at Koobi Fora belong to that species and thereby provide valid body weight estimates. Attempts have been made to estimate body weight directly from the skull (Aiello & Wood 1994, Kappelman 1996), and these range between 46 and 54 kg for the skull of *H. rudolfensis*. These are slightly smaller than the 60-kg estimate derived from the postcranium of the presumptive male of that species. The lower body weight estimates would raise the MQ value slightly. Because of its large body size, the relative size of the cheek teeth of *H. ergaster* is the same as that of modern humans (i.e. 0.9).

Transformations of Mind

There was probably significant internal reorganization of the brain between *Australopithecus* and *Homo*, but the fossil record preserves only the exterior shape. The external morphology of the KNM-ER 1470 endocast appears to have a reorganized frontal lobe with a distinctively human-like Broca's area (Holloway 1995). The most conspicuous change in the human fossil record through time is in brain size. Table 1 gives the average endocranial volume for each species and provides the calculated brain size. The brain size of *A. afarensis* ranges from 342 to 540 cc and averages 434 cc, which is about that of modern chimpanzees and one third that of modern humans. The range for *A. africanus* is from 424 to 508 cc, with an average of 448 cc. The one endocast so far reported for *A. garhi* would predict a brain size of 446 cc, and the one for *Australopithecus aethiopicus* would predict 407 cc. There is, therefore, little difference between these representatives of early species (3.2–2.5 mya). The specimens recovered from slightly later than 2 mya are larger. There are four endocranial casts of *P. boisei*, ranging from 494 to 537 cc, with an average brain size of 514 cc. The one specimen of *P. robustus* is 523 cc. There are six specimens of *H. habilis* that range from 503 to 661 cc, with an average of 601 cc. The single representative of *H. rudolfensis*, KNM-ER 1470, is 736.cc. Brain size jumps to 849 cc with *H. ergaster*, although there is one specimen (O.H. 12) that is as small as 712 cc and one (O.H. 9) as large as 1035 cc.

These absolute values for brain weight are instructive, but they should be viewed in the context of body weight to determine relative size. Figure 2 is a plot of brain and body weight. The small body sizes of the australopithecines and *H. habilis* shift them strongly to the left of the plot, but within that group there are three distinct grades of brain size, with small-sized *A. afarensis* and *A. africanus*, medium-sized *P. robustus* and *P. boisei*, and larger-sized *H. habilis*. The larger body size of *H. rudolfensis* aligns it more with later Homo. There are four distinct grades of brain size among the later *Homo* and *H. rudolfensis* sample: (*a*) *H. rudolfensis* is distinctly smaller; (*b*) *H. ergaster* and other hominids from between 0.6 and 1.15 mya are a step larger; (*c*) those from between 0.2 and 0.55 mya are intermediate; and (*d*) the early late Pleistocene (0.1–0.15 mya) and Neanderthal samples are large brained like the anatomically modern *H. sapiens* samples (Skhul-Qafzeh and modern). A strong case can be made for separating the Neanderthals and other late Pleistocene archaics from the anatomically modern sample on the basis of brain size relative to body weight using encephalization quotients (EQ) (Ruff et al 1998).

The EQ is the ratio of actual brain weight divided by brain weight predicted from scaled body weight. The method has its limitations (Smith 1996) but is certainly a useful heuristic tool. Table 1 gives EQ values for the hominid species, and Figure 3 plots these values against time. The same pattern emerges except for the position of *H. habilis*. Because of its very small body size, the relative size of its brain is strikingly enlarged relative to its

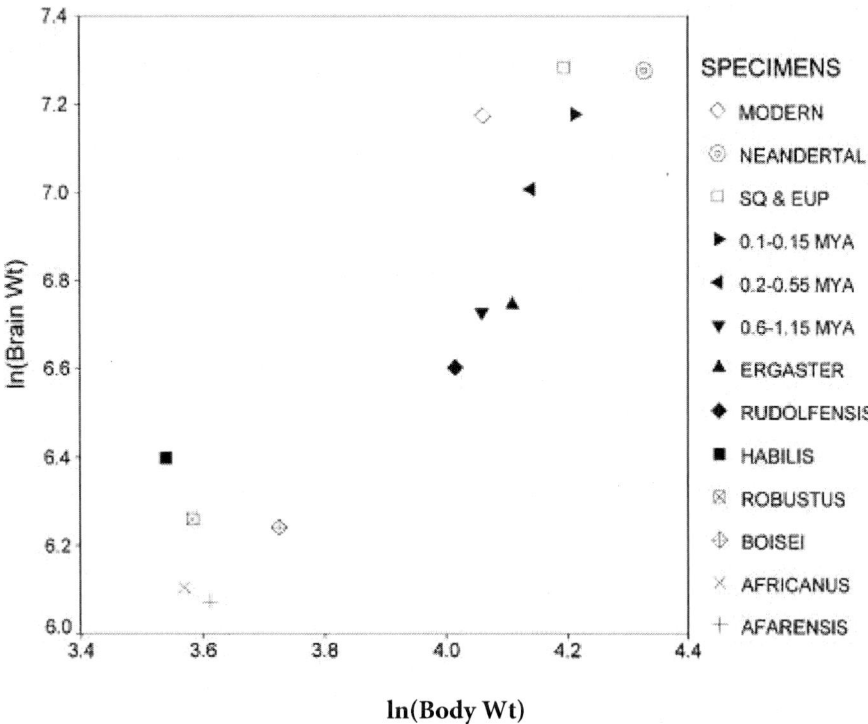

Figure 2. Scatter plot of brain and body size. This is an expanded version of Figure 3 of Ruff et al (1998), with data from Table 1. The two species ***of Australopithecus, A. afarensis*** and ***A. africanus***, are similar to one another. The two species of ***Paranthropus*** are similar, but the one specimen representing ***P. robustus*** has a larger brain size than ***P. boisei*** relative to its diminutive body mass. ***Homo habilis*** combines a very small body with a brain larger than that seen in any australopithecine species. ***Homo rudolfensis*** has an absolutely larger brain than the australopithecines or ***H. habilis,*** but this may be due primarily to its larger body size. MYA, Million years ago; SQ, Skhul/Qafzeh; EUP, European Upper Paleolithic.

contemporaries. *H. rudolfensis* has a larger body, and therefore a smaller relative brain size. The contrast between anatomically modern *H. sapiens* and Neanderthals becomes clear with the use of EQ. Accompanying this expansion in brain through time is an ever-increasing complexity of material culture. Neither brain size nor material culture complexity increases at a gradual rate. The paleoanthropological record is dense enough now to reveal a pattern of stasis in certain characteristics over long periods within species, as well as rapid shifts between species.

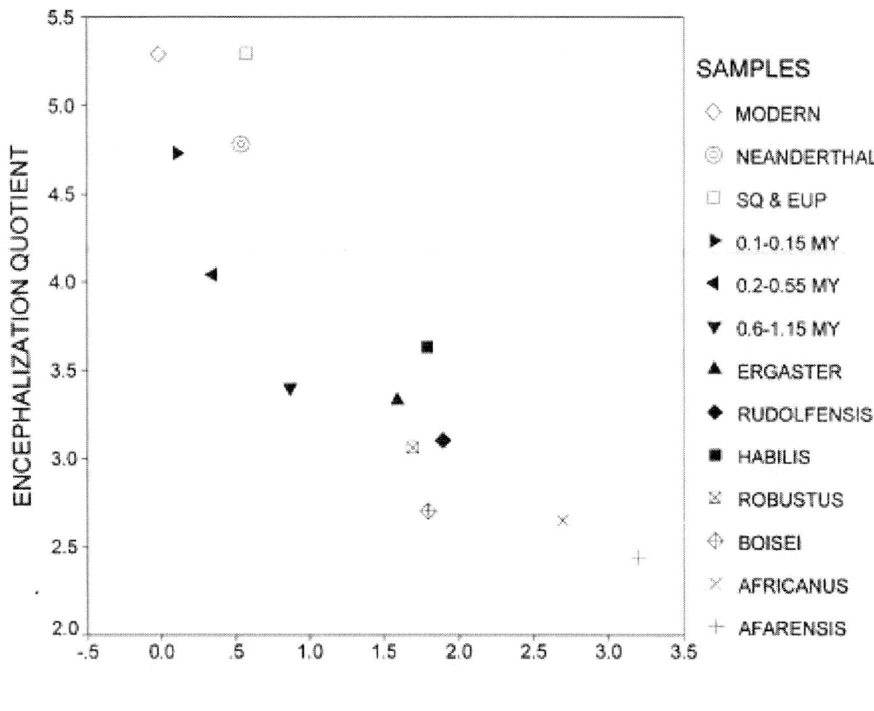

Figure 3. Scatter plot of relative brain size against time. Note the high level of variability around 1.8 million years ago (mya) and the apparent fact that *Homo ergaster* did not have a higher encephaliza

Summary and Conclusions

Before about 2.6 mya, stone tools were absent at sites containing hominid fossils, brain sizes were chimp-like, cheek teeth and supporting masticatory structures were enormous, numerous primitive traits were retained in all parts of the body, including the skull, bodies were small, there was strong sexual dimorphism in body size, and hindlimbs were small relative to forelimbs. By 1.8 mya, *H. ergaster* stepped into view with its more human-like body and behavior. What is known about this transformation and with what certainty? Stone tool manufacture and the use of them on animal carcasses certainly appears in the record by about 2.6 mya. Perhaps brains expanded at that time, but specimens attributed to early *Homo* that are nearly that old do not preserve enough of the skull to show this. In *H. rudolfenisis*, by 1.9 mya, brains were significantly expanded and there was a more human-like form to their frontal lobes. Brain size relative to body weight expanded further in specimens attributed to *H. habilis*, which began to appear in the record by 1.8 mya. The size of the cheek teeth and other parts of the chewing apparatus reduced in *H. habilis* perhaps as early as 2.3 mya, but certainly by 1.8 mya. Although *H. rudolfensis* appeared to have retained the megadontia of its ancestor, scaled to body weight its cheek-tooth size is reduced and similar to that of *H. ergaster*.

The transformations of the body below the head are profound between the australopithecines and *H. ergaster*, but the intermediate stages are not well established. What is known of the body of *H. habilis* reveals a remarkably australopithecine morphology, including (*a*) small body size, (*b*) relatively small hindlimbs and large forelimbs, (*c*) an australopithecine-like femoral-shaft morphology that is probably related to a walking mechanism different from that seen in *H. ergaster* and later species of *Homo*, (*d*) hands lacking the morphology relating to some precision and power grips characteristic of later *Homo*, and (*e*) more flexible feet. If the fossil limbs discovered at the same geological area and time as the skull fragments of *H. rudolfensis* belong to that taxon, then the link between *Australopithecus* and *H. ergaster* becomes clearer. The size and morphology of these limbs are very much like that of *H. ergaster* and unlike the australopithecines and *H. habilis*.

Acknowledgments

We thank all those whose work led to the discovery of the fossils and especially CK Brain, FC Howell, DC Johanson, MG and RE Leakey, JF Thackeray, PV Tobias, and T White for many kindnesses and for permission to study the original fossil material. We thank the curators of the comparative samples used in this study. Partial funding was provided by the Committee on Research of the University of California, Davis, and a University of California President's Postdoctoral Fellowship.

Literature Cited

Aiello LC, Wood BA. 1994. Cranial variables as predictors of hominine body mass. *Am. J. Phys. Anthropol.* 95:409–26

Asfaw B, Beyene Y, Suwa G, Walter RC, White TD, et al. 1992. The earliest Acheulean from Konso-Gardula. *Nature* 360:732–35

Asfaw B, White T, Lovejoy O, Latimer B, Simpson S, Suwa G. 1999a. *Australopithecus garhi*: a new species of early hominid from Ethiopia. *Science* 284:629–35

Asfaw B, White T, Lovejoy O, Latimer B, Simpson S, Suwa G. 1999b. Cladistics and early hominid phylogeny. *Science* 285:1210–11

Behrensmeyer AK, Laporte LF. 1981. Footprints of a Pleistocene hominid in Northern Kenya. *Nature* 289:167–69

Berge C. 1991. Size- and locomotion-related aspects of hominid and anthropoid pelves: an osteometrical multivariate analysis. *Hum. Evol.* 6:365–76

Berge C, Orban-Segebarth R, Schmid P. 1984. Obstetrical interpretation of the australopithecine pelvic cavity. *J. Hum. Evol.* 13:573–87

Berger LR, Tobias PV. 1996. A chimpanzee-like tibia from Sterkfontein, South Africa and its implications for the interpretation of bipedalism in *Australopithecus africanus*. *J. Hum. Evol.* 30(4):343–48

Brain CK, ed. 1993. *Swartkrans: A Cave's Chronicle of Early Man*. Pretoria: Transvaal Mus.

Chamberlain AT, Wood BA. 1987. Early hominid phylogeny. *J. Hum. Evol.* 16:119–33

Clark JD. 1993. Stone artifact assemblages from members 1–3, Swartkrans cave. See Brain 1993, pp. 167–94

Clarke RJ. 1979. Early hominid footprints from Tanzania. *S. Afr. J. Sci.* 75:148–49

Clarke RJ. 1998. First ever discovery of a well-preserved skull and associated skeleton of *Australopithecus*. *S. Afr. J. Sci.* 94(10):460–63

Clarke RJ, Tobias PV. 1995. Sterkfontein Member 2 foot bones of the oldest South African hominid. *Science* 269:521–24

Conroy GC, Weber GW, et al. 1998. Endocranial capacity in an early hominid cranium from Sterkfontein, South Africa. *Science* 280:1730–31

Coppens Y, Senut B, eds. 1991. *Origine(s) de la bipedie chez les hominides*. Paris: Cah. Paleoanthropol., CNRS

Corruccini RS, Ciochon RL, eds. 1994. *Integrative Paths to the Past: Paleoanthropological Advances in Honor of F. Clark Howell*. Englewood Cliffs, NJ: Prentice Hall

Crompton RH, Yu L, Weijie W, Gunther M, Savage R. 1998. The mechanical effectiveness of erect and "bent-hip, bent-knee" bipedal walking in *Australopithecus afarensis*. *J. Hum. Evol.* 35(1):55–74

Day MH. 1973. Locomotor features of the lower limb in hominids. *Symp. Zool. Soc. London* 33:29–51

Day MH. 1976. Hominid postcranial material from Bed I, Olduvai Gorge. In *Human Origins: Louis Leakey and the East African Evidence*, ed. GL Isaac, ER McCown, pp. 363–74. Menlo Park, CA: Benjamin

Day MH, Leakey REF. 1974. New evidence of the genus *Homo* from East Rudolf, Kenya III. *Am. J. Phys. Anthropol.* 41:367–80

Day MH, Napier JR. 1964. Hominid fossils from Bed I, Olduvai Gorge, Tanganyika: fossil footbones. *Nature* 201:969–70

Day MH, Wood BA. 1968. Functional affinities of the Olduvai hominid 8 talus. *Man* 3:440–55

de Heinzelin J, Clark JD, White T, Hart W, Renne P, et al. 1999. Environment and behavior of 2.5-million-year-old Bouri hominids. *Science* 284:625–29

Deloison Y. 1985. Comparative study of calcanei of primates and *Pan-Australopithecus-Homo* relationship. See Tobias, pp. 143–47

Else JG, Lee PC, eds. 1986. *Primate Evolution*. Cambridge, UK: Cambridge Univ. Press

Feibel CS, Brown FH, McDougall I. 1989. Stratigraphic context of fossil hominids from the Omo group deposits: Northern Turkana Basin, Kenya and Ethiopia. *Am. J. Phys. Anthropol.* 78:595–622

Giacobini G, ed. 1989. *Hominidae: Proc. 2nd Int. Congr. Hum. Paleontol., Turin, September 28–October 3, 1987*. Milan: Jaka

Grausz HM, Leakey REF, Walker AC, Ward CV. 1988. Associated cranial and postcranial bones of *Australopithecus boisei*. See Grine 1988, pp. 127–32

Grine FE, ed. 1988. *Evolutionary History of the "Robust" Australopithecines*. New York: Gruyter

Grine FE, Jungers WL, Schultz J. 1996. Phenetic affinities among early *Homo* crania from East and South Africa. *J. Hum. Evol.* 30(3): 189–225

Groves CP. 1989. *A Theory of Human and Primate Evolution*. Oxford, UK: Clarendon

Harris JWK, Isaac G. 1976. The Karari industry: early Pleistocene archaeological evidence from the terrain east of Lake Turkana, Kenya. *Nature* 262:102–7

Hartwig-Scherer S. 1993. Body weight prediction in early fossil hominids: towards a taxon-"independent" approach. *Am. J. Phys. Anthropol.* 92:17–36

Hartwig-Scherer S. 1994. Body weight prediction in fossil *Homo*. In *100 Years of Pithecanthropus: The Homo erectus Problem*, ed. JL Franzen, pp. 257–79. Frankfurt: Forschungsinst. Senckenberg

Hartwig-Scherer S, Martin RD. 1991. Was "Lucy" more human than her "child"? Observations on early hominid postcranial skeletons. *J. Hum. Evol.* 21:439–49

Hartwig-Scherer S, Martin RD. 1992. Allometry and prediction in hominoids: a solution to the problem of intervening variables. *Am. J. Phys. Anthropol.* 88:37–57

Heinrich RE, Rose MD, Leakey RE, Walker AC. 1993. Hominid radius from the middle Pliocene of Lake Turkana, Kenya. *Am. J. Phys. Anthropol.* 92:139–48

Holloway RL. 1995. Toward a synthetic theory of human brain evolution. In *Origins of the Human Brain*, ed. J-P Changeux, J Chavaillon, pp. 42–60. Oxford, UK: Clarendon

Howell FC, Haesaerts P, de Heinzelin J. 1987. Depositional environments, archaeological occurrences and hominid from Members E and F of the Shungura Formation (Omo basin, Ethiopia). *J. Hum. Evol.* 16:665–700

Inouye SE, Shea BT. 1997. What's your angle? Size correction and bar-glenoid orientation in "Lucy" (A.L. 288-1). *Int. J. Primatol.* 18(4):629–50

Jellema LM, Latimer BM, Walker A. 1993. The rib cage. See Walker & Leakey 1993a, pp. 294–325

Johanson DC. 1989. A partial *Homo habilis* skeleton from Olduvai Gorge, Tanzania: a summary of preliminary results. See Giacobini 1989, pp. 155–66

Johanson DC, Edey M. 1981. *Lucy: The Beginnings of Humankind.* New York: Simon & Schuster

Johanson DC, Lovejoy CO, Kimbel WH, White TD, Ward SC, et al. 1982a. Morphology of the Pliocene partial hominid skeleton (A.L. 288-1) from the Hadar Formation, Ethiopia. *Am. J. Phys. Anthropol.* 57:403–52

Johanson DC, Massao FT, Eck GG, White TD, Walter RC, et al. 1987. New partial skeleton of *Homo habilis* from Olduvai Gorge, Tanzania. *Nature* 327:205–9

Johanson DC, Taeib M. 1976. Plio-Pleistocene hominid discoveries in Hadar, Ethiopia. *Nature* 260:293–97

Johanson DC, Taieb M, Coppens Y. 1982b. Pliocene hominids from the Hadar Formation, Ethiopia (1973–1977): stratigraphic, chronologic, and paleoenvironmental contexts, with notes on hominid morphology and systematics. *Am. J. Phys. Anthropol.* 57:373–402

Jungers WL. 1982. Lucy's limbs: skeletal allometry and locomotion in *Australopithecus afarensis*. *Nature* 297:676–78

Jungers WL. 1988a. Lucy's length: stature reconstruction in *Australopithecus afarensis* (A.L. 288-1) with implications for other small-bodied Hominids. *Am. J. Phys. Anthropol.* 76:227–32

Jungers WL. 1988b. New estimations of body size in australopithecines. See Grine 1988, pp. 115–26

Jungers WL. 1991. A pygmy perspective on body size and shape in *Australopithecus afarensis* (A.L. 288-1, "Lucy"). See Coppens & Senut, pp. 215–24

Jungers WL. 1994. Ape and hominid limb length. *Nature* 369:194

Jungers WL, Stern JT. 1983. Body proportions, skeletal allometry and locomotion in the Hadar hominids: a reply to Wolpoff. *J. Hum. Evol.* 12:673–84

Kappelman J. 1996. The evolution of body mass and relative brain size in fossil hominids. *J. Hum. Evol.* 30(3):243–76

Kibunjia M. 1994. Pliocene archaeological occurrences in the Lake Turkana basin. *J. Hum. Evol.* 27:159–71

Kidd RS, O'Higgins P, Oxnard CE. 1996. The OH8 foot: a reappraisal of the functional morphology of the hindfoot utilizing a multivariate analysis. *J. Hum. Evol.* 31(3):269–91

Kimbel WH, Johanson DC, Rak Y. 1994. The first skull and other new discoveries of *Australopithecus afarensis* at Hadar, Ethiopia. *Nature* 368:449–51

Kimbel WH, Walter RC, Johanson DC, Reed KE, Aronson JL, et al. 1996. Late Pliocene *Homo* and Oldowan tools from the Hadar Formation (Kada Hadar Member), Ethiopia. *J. Hum. Evol.* 31(6): 549–61

Klein RG. 1999. *The Human Career: Human Biological and Cultural Origins.* Chicago: Univ. Chicago Press

Korey KA. 1990. Deconstructing reconstruction: the OH 62 humerofemoral index. *Am. J. Phys. Anthropol.* 83:25–33

Latimer BM. 1988. *Functional analysis of the Pliocene hominid ankle and pedal bones recovered from the Hadar Formation, Ethiopia: 1974–1977 collections.* Ann Harbor, MI: UMI Dissertat. Inf. Serv.

Latimer BM. 1991. Locomotor adaptations in *Australopithecus afarensis*: the issue of arboreality. See Coppens & Senut 1991, pp. 169–76

Latimer BM, Lovejoy CO, Johanson DC, Yves Coppens. 1982. Hominid tarsal, metatarsal, and phalangeal bones recovered from the Hadar Formation: 1974–1977 collections. *Am. J. Phys. Anthropol.* 57:701–20

Latimer BM, Ohman JC, Lovejoy CO. 1987. Talocrural joint in African hominoids: implication for *Australopithecus afarensis. Am. J. Phys. Anthropol.* 74:155–75

Leakey LSB, Tobias PV, Napier JR. 1964. A new species of the genus *Homo* from Olduvai Gorge. *Nature* 202:7–9

Leakey MD. 1971. *Olduvai Gorge: Excavations in Beds I and II, 1960–1963.* Cambridge, UK: Cambridge Univ. Press

Leakey MG, Feibel CS, et al. 1995. New four-million-year-old hominid species from Kanapoi and Allia Bay, Kenya. *Nature* 376:565–71

Leakey MG, Feibel CS, McDougall I, Ward C, Walker A. 1998. New specimens and confirmation of an early age for *Australopithecus anamensis. Nature* 393:62–66

Leakey REF. 1973. Evidence for an advanced Plio-Pleistocene hominid from East Rudolf, Kenya. *Nature* 242:447–50

Leakey REF, Walker A, Ward CV, Grausz HM. 1989. A partial skeleton of a gracile Hominid from the Upper Burgi Member of the Koobi Fora Formation, East Lake Turkana, Kenya. See Giacobini 1989, pp. 167–74

Leakey REF, Walker AC. 1985. Further hominids from the Plio-Pleistocene of Koobi Fora, Kenya. *Am. J. Phys. Anthropol.* 67:135–63

Leutenegger W. 1987. Neonatal brain size and neurochemical dimensions in Pliocene hominids: implications for obstetrics. *J. Hum. Evol.* 16:291–96

Lewis OJ. 1980. The joints of the evolving foot. III: The fossil evidence. *J. Anat.* 131:275–98

Lewis OJ. 1989. *Functional Morphology of the Evolving Hand and Foot.* Oxford, UK: Clarendon

Lieberman DE, Wood BA, Pilbeam DR. 1996. Homoplasy and early *Homo*: an analysis of the evolutionary relationships of *H. habilis sensu stricto* and *H. rudolfensis*. *J. Hum. Evol.* 30(2):97–120

Lisowski FP, Albrecht GH, Oxnard CE. 1974. The form of the talus in some higher primates: a multivariate study. *Am. J. Phys. Anthropol.* 41:191–215

Lisowski FP, Albrecht GH, Oxnard CE. 1976. African fossil tali: further multivariate morphometric studies. *Am. J. Phys. Anthropol.* 45:5–18

Lovejoy CO. 1988. Evolution of human walking. *Sci. Am.* 259:118–26

Lovejoy CO, Cohn M, White TD. 1999. Morphological analysis of the mammalian postcranium: a developmental perspective. *Proc. Natl. Acad. Sci. USA* 96(23): 13247–52

Lovejoy CO, Johanson DC, Coppens Y. 1982. Hominid upper limb bones recovered from the Hadar Formation: 1974–1977 collection. *Am. J. Phys. Anthropol.* 57:637–50

Martin RD. 1981. Relative brain size and basal metabolic rate in terrestrial vertebrates. *Nature* 293:57–60

Marzke MW. 1983. Joint functions and grips of the *Australopithecus afarensis* hand, with special reference to the region of the capitate. *J. Hum. Evol.* 12:197–211

Marzke MW. 1986. Tool use and the evolution of hominid hands and bipedality. See Else & Lee 1986, pp. 203–9

Marzke MW. 1997. Precision grips, hand morphology, and tools. *Am. J. Phys. Anthropol.* 102(1):91–110

Marzke MW, Marzke RF. 1987. The third metacarpal styloid process in humans: origin and function. *Am. J. Phys. Anthropol.* 73:415–31

Marzke MW, Shackley MS. 1986. Hominid hand use in the Pleistocene: evidence from experimental archaeology and comparative morphology. *J. Hum. Evol.* 15:439–60

Marzke MW, Wullstein KL, Viegas SF. 1992. Evolution of the power ("squeeze") grip and its morphological correlates in hominids. *Am. J. Phys. Anthropol.* 89:283–98

McCollum M. 1999. Cladistics and early hominid phylogeny. *Science* 285:1211

McHenry H. 1991a. Femoral lengths and stature in Plio-Pleistocene hominids. *Am. J. Phys. Anthropol.* 85:149–58

McHenry HM. 1974. How large were the Australopithecines? *Am. J. Phys. Anthropol.* 40:329–40

McHenry HM. 1975a. Fossil hominid body weight and brain size. *Nature* 254:686–88

McHenry HM. 1975b. A new pelvic fragment from Swartkrans and the relationship between the robust and gracile australopithecines. *Am. J. Phys. Anthropol.* 43:245–62

McHenry HM. 1978. Fore- and hindlimb proportions in Plio-Pleistocene hominids. *Am. J. Phys. Anthropol.* 49:15–22

McHenry HM. 1983. The capitate of *Australopithecus afarensis* and *Australopithecus africanus*. *Am. J. Phys. Anthropol.* 62:187–98

McHenry HM. 1984. Relative cheek-tooth size in *Australopithecus*. *Am. J. Phys. Anthropol.* 64:297–306

McHenry HM. 1988. New estimates of body weights in early hominids and their significance to encephalization and megadontia in "robust" australopithecines. See Grine 1988, pp. 133–48

McHenry HM. 1991b. Petite bodies of the "robust" Australopithecines. *Am. J. Phys. Anthropol.* 86:445–54

McHenry HM. 1991c. Sexual dimorphism in *Australopithecus afarensis*. *J. Hum. Evol.* 20:21–32

McHenry HM. 1992a. Body size and proportions in early hominids. *Am. J. Phys. Anthropol.* 87:407–31

McHenry HM. 1992b. How big were early hominids? *Evol. Anthropol.* 1:15–19

McHenry HM. 1994a. Behavioral ecological implications of early hominid body size. *J. Hum. Evol.* 27:77–87

McHenry HM. 1994b. Early hominid postcrania: phylogeny and function. See Corruccini & Ciochon 1994, pp. 251–68

McHenry HM. 1994c. Tempo and mode in human evolution. *Proc. Natl. Acad. Sci. USA* 91:6780–86

McHenry HM. 1996. Sexual dimorphism in fossil hominids and its socioecological implications. In *The Archaeology of Human Ancestry Power, Sex, and Tradition*, ed. J Steele, S Shennan, pp. 91–109. London/New York: Routledge.

McHenry HM, Berger LR. 1998a. Body proportions in *Australopithecus afarensis* and *A. africanus* and the origin of the genus *Homo*. *J. Hum. Evol.* 35(1):1–22

McHenry HM, Berger LR. 1998b. Limb lengths in *Australopithecus* and the origin of the genus *Homo*. *S. Afr. J. Sci.* 94:447–50

Napier JH. 1962. Fossil hand bones from Olduvai Gorge. *Nature* 196:409–11

Napier JR, Napier P. 1967. *A Handbook of Living Primates*. New York: Academic

Oxnard CE. 1972. Some African fossil foot bones; a note on the interpolation of fossils into a matrix of extant species. *Am. J. Phys. Anthropol.* 37:3–12

Oxnard CE, ed. 1973. *Form and Pattern in Human Evolution: Some Mathematical, Physical, and Engineering Approaches*. Chicago: Univ. Chicago Press

Oxnard CE. 1975. The place of the australopithecines in human evolution: grounds for doubt. *Nature* 258:389–95

Oxnard CE, Lisowski FP. 1978. The Olduvai foot. *Anat. Res.* 190:499–50

Roche H, Delagnes A, Brugal J-P, Feibel C, Kibunjia M, et al. 1999. Early hominid stone tool production and technical skill 2.34 myr ago in West Turkana, Kenya. *Nature* 399:57–60

Ruff C. 1995. Biomechanics of the hip and birth in early *Homo*. *Am. J. Phys. Anthropol.* 98(4):527–74

Ruff C. 1998. Evolution of the hominid hip. See Strasser et al 1998, pp. 449–69

Ruff CB, Trinkaus E, Holliday TW. 1998. Body mass and encephalization in Pleistocene *Homo*. *Nature* 387:173–76

Ruff CB, Walker A. 1993. Body size and body shape. See Walker & Leakey 1993a, pp. 234–65

Schmid P. 1983. Eine Rekonstruktion des skelettes von A.L. 288-1 (Hadar) und deren Konsequenzen. *Fol. Primatol.* 40:283–306

Schmid P. 1989. How different is Lucy? See Giacobini 1989, pp. 109–14

Schmid P. 1991. The trunk of the Australopithecines. See Coppens & Senut 1991, pp. 225–34

Semaw S, Renne P, Harris JWK, Feibel CS, Bernor RL, et al. 1997. 2.5-million-year-old stone tools from Gona, Ethiopia. *Nature* 385:333–36

Skelton RR, McHenry HM. 1992. Evolutionary relationships among early hominids. *J. Hum. Evol.* 23:309–49

Smith RJ. 1996. Biology and body size in human evolution: statistical inference misapplied. *Curr. Anthropol.* 37(3):451–60

Stern JT. 2000. Climbing to the top: a personal memoir of *Australopithecus afarensis*. *Evol. Anthropol.* In press

Stern JT, Susman RL. 1983. The locomotor anatomy of *Australopithecus afarensis*. *Am. J. Phys. Anthropol.* 60:279–318

Stern JT, Susman RL. 1991. "Total morphological pattern" versus the "magic trait": conflicting approaches to the study of early hominid bipedalism. See Coppens & Senut 1991, pp. 99–112

Strait DS, Grine FE. 1999. Cladistics and early hominid phylogeny. *Science* 285:1210

Strait DS, Grine FE, Moniz MA. 1997. A reappraisal of early hominid phylogeny. *J. Hum. Evol.* 32(1): 17–82

Strasser E, Fleagle J, Rosenberger A, McHenry H, eds. 1998. *Primate Locomotion: Recent Advances.* New York: Plenum

Susman RL. 1988a. Hand of *Paranthropus robustus* from I, Swartkrans: fossil evidence for tool behavior. *Science* 240:781–82

Susman RL. 1988b. New postcranial fossils from Swartkrans Member 1: implications for the behavior of *Paranthropus robustus. Annu. Rev. Am. Assoc. Phys. Anthropol.* 75: 77

Susman RL. 1988c. New postcranial remains from Swartkrans and their bearing on the functional morphology and behavior of *Paranthropus robustus.* See Grine 1988, pp. 149–74

Susman RL. 1989. New hominid fossils from the Swartkrans Formation (1979–1986 excavations): postcranial specimens. *Am. J. Phys. Anthropol.* 79:451–74

Susman RL. 1993. Hominid postcranial remains from Swartkrans. See Brain 1993, pp. 117–36

Susman RL. 1994. Fossil evidence for early hominid tool use. *Science* 265:1570–73

Susman RL. 1998. Hand function and tool behavior in early hominids. *J. Hum. Evol.* 35(1):23–46

Susman RL, Creel N. 1979. Functional and morphological affinities of the subadult hand (O.H. 7) from Olduvai Gorge. *Am. J. Phys. Anthropol.* 51:311–32

Susman RL, Stern JT. 1982. Functional morphology of *Homo habilis. Science* 217:931–34

Susman RL, Stern JT. 1991. Locomotor behavior of early hominids: epistemology and fossil evidence. See Coppens & Senut 1991, pp. 121–32

Susman RL, Stern JT, Jungers WL. 1984. Arboreality and bipedality in the Hadar hominids. *Fol. Primatol.* 43:113–56

Susman RL, Stern JT, Jungers WL. 1985. Locomotor adaptations in the Hadar hominids. In *Ancestors: The Hard Evidence*, ed. E Delson, pp. 184–92. New York: Liss

Suwa GB, Asfaw B, et al. 1997. The first skull of *Australopithecus boisei. Nature* 389:489–92

Tague RG, Lovejoy CO. 1986. The obstetric pelvis of A.L. 288-1 (Lucy). *J. Hum. Evol.* 15:237–55

Tardieu C. 1983. *L'articulation du genou. Analyse morpho-fonctionelle chez les primates et les hominides fossiles.* Paris: Cah. Paleoanthropol. 108 pp.

Tardieu C. 1986. Evolution of the knee intra-articular menisci in primates and some hominids. See Else & Lee 1986, pp. 183–90

Tardieu C. 1998. Short adolescence in early hominids: infantile and adolescent growth of the human femur. *Am. J. Phys. Anthropol.* 107(2):163–78

Tardieu C, Preuschoft H. 1996. Ontogeny of the knee joint in humans, great apes and fossil hominids: pelvi-femoral relationships during postnatal growth in humans. *Fol. Primatol.* 66:68–81

Tobias PV, ed. 1985. *Hominid Evolution: Past, Present and Future.* New York: Liss

Tobias PV. 1991. *Olduvai Gorge.* Vol. 4: *The Skulls, Endocasts and Teeth of Homo habilis.* Cambridge, UK: Cambridge Univ. Press

Tuttle RH. 1981. Evolution of hominid bipedalism and prehensile capabilities. *Philos. Trans. R. Soc. London Ser. B* 292:89–94

Tuttle RH. 1985. Ape footprints and Laetoli impressions: a response to SUNY claims. See Tobias 1985, pp. 129–34

Tuttle RH. 1987. Kinesiological inferences and evolutionary implications from Laetoli bipedal trails G-1, G-2/3 and A. In *Laetoli: A Pliocene Site in Northern Tanzania,* ed. MD Leakey, JM Harris, pp. 503–23. Oxford, UK: Clarendon

Tuttle RH. 1988. What's new in African anthropology. *Annu. Rev. Anthropol.* 17:391–426

Tuttle RH. 1994. Up from electromyography: primate energetics and the evolution of human bipedalism. See Corruccini & Ciochon 1994, pp. 269–84

Tuttle RH, Hallgrimsson B, Stein T. 1998. Heel, squat, stand, stride: function and evolution of hominoid feet. See Strasser et al 1998, pp. 435–48

Tuttle RH, Webb DM, Baksh M. 1991a. Laetoli toes and *Australopithecus afarensis. Hum. Evol.* 6:193–200

Tuttle RH, Webb DM, Tuttle NI. 1991b. Laetoli footprint trails and the evolution of hominid bipedalism. See Coppens & Senut 1991, pp. 187–98

Tuttle RH, Webb DM, Tuttle NI, Baksh M. 1992. Footprints and gaits of bipedal apes, bears, and barefoot people: perspective on Pliocene tracks. In *Topics in Primatology,* ed. S Matano, RH Tuttle, H Ishida, M Goodman, 3:221–42. Tokyo: Univ. Tokyo Press

Walker A, Leakey R, eds. 1993a. *The Nariokotome Homo erectus Skeleton.* Cambridge, MA: Harvard Univ. Press

Walker A, Leakey R. 1993b. The postcranial bones. See Walker & Leakey 1993a, pp. 95–160

White TD. 1994. Ape and hominid limb length, reply. *Nature* 369:194

White TD, Suwa G. 1987. Hominid footprints at Laetoli: facts and interpretations. *Am. J. Phys. Anthropol.* 72:485–514

White TD, Suwa G, Hart WK, Walter RC, Wolde Gabriel G, et al. 1993. New discoveries of *Australopithecus* at Maka in Ethiopia. *Nature* 366:261–65

Wolpoff MH. 1999. *Paleoanthropology*. Boston: McGraw-Hill

Wood B, Collard M. 1999. The human genus. *Science* 284:65–71

Wood BA. 1974. Evidence on the locomotor pattern of *Homo* from early Pleistocene of Kenya. *Nature* 251:135–36

Wood BA, ed. 1991. *Koobi Fora Research Project IV: Hominid Cranial Remains From Koobi Fora*. Oxford, UK: Clarendon

Wood BA. 1992. Origin and evolution of the genus *Homo*. *Nature* 355:783–90

SECTION 9

BIPEDALISM

Introduction to Chapter 11

Walking and running on two legs is the first uniquely human trait to appear in the fossil record. This bipedalism radically reorganized our body plan but also affected our patterns of infant development and the relations between the sexes.

None of our great ape relatives—chimpanzees, gorillas, or orangutans—move the way we do. Orangutans use all four of their limbs to clamber around the canopy of tropical forests. Chimpanzees and gorillas walk quadrupedally on the ground, carrying their weight on the soles of their feet and the knuckles of their hands. Humans are striding bipeds, using only our hind limbs for locomotion. As you saw in Chapters 9 and 10, this shift in mode of locomotion is the first derived hominin trait to appear in the fossil record, and it produced, over time, a variety of changes in the anatomy of the trunk and both limbs. This chapter highlights the effects of bipedalism on the pelvis and the surprising consequences of those pelvic changes.

Unless they are running very fast, quadrupedal animals have two or three feet in contact with the ground at all times. But even when walking rather slowly, bipeds often have only one foot touching the ground. Thus, there are dramatic weight-bearing and balance differences between these two modes of locomotion, which require different sets of muscular connections between the pelvis and the hind limb. As a result of these different requirements, the hominin pelvis has become twisted and compressed compared to the arrangement we see in the other apes (see Figure 4 in the chapter). This kind of evolutionary modification is not at all unusual; as you know, selection modifies existing structures to meet new demands. But the pelvis is not only involved in balance and weight-bearing, but also in the birth process—human infants have to pass through the pelvis as they are born. The same pelvic twisting and compression that was necessary for bipedalism has also constricted the birth canal. Rosenberg and Trevathan do a thorough job of explaining how humans and other primates transit the birth canal. Here I want to concentrate on the associated causes and consequences of this "obstetrical dilemma."

Clearly, the logical question is, why did our lineage become bipedal in the first place? Since bipedality causes obstetrical problems, it must have provided some pretty important benefits. Otherwise, selection would not have favored it. What were those benefits? Paleoanthropologists have several plausible ideas and all of them ultimately trace back to the effects of a long-term climate change. Beginning in the Miocene Epoch, roughly 20 million years ago, the earth's climate began an accelerating series of cooling and drying cycles that have continued until the end of the Pleistocene, a mere 12,000 years ago. In Africa, where almost all human evolution occurred, this cooling and drying caused dramatic habitat changes. The forests shrank, and there was an expansion of more open habitats dominated by grasses and scattered trees. These more open habitats, called savanna and woodland, differ in many ways from forests; they are hotter, sunnier, dryer, and support more large game animals, including ones that form herds. They also have more large predators such as lions, leopards, cheetahs, hyenas and the dreaded cape hunting dog.

The other great apes are all forest dwellers, and their fortunes shrank along with the forests: there are an estimated 300 thousand chimpanzees in the wild versus 6.75 billion people. We humans are the apes that left the dwindling forests to take advantage of those new niches in the expanding woodlands and savannas of a progressively cooler and dryer Africa. So, our question about the advantages of bipedalism must be framed in terms of this new niche.

There are four hypothesized advantages of bipedalism, and they are not in any way mutually exclusive; in other words, multiple selection pressures could have simultaneously pushed our ancestors toward bipedalism. The first possible advantage concerns getting around in an extensive two-dimensional habitat (forests are three-dimensional). Resources can be far-flung and patchy in savanna and woodland habitats, and therefore early hominins may have needed to forage over long distances. Bipedalism may have been an energetically efficient way to cover these long distances. Second, bipedalism is cooler, literally. It exposes less body area to the hottest perpendicular rays of the sun—just the top of the head and the shoulders, as compared to the entire trunk in quadrupeds—and additionally it raises more of the body farther from the ground where the temperatures are lower and there is more cooling wind. Third, by extending the vertical reach, bipedalism allows foraging from the smaller trees and bushes that are common in these open habitats. Finally, perhaps the strongest selection pressure, bipedalism frees the fore limbs for other purposes, such as carrying food or other resources, and for wielding tools and weapons that could have aided in hunting herd animals or in fending off predators.

Whatever the combination, the various selection pressures for bipedalism were strong enough to produce a significant resculpting of the relevant bones and muscles. The associated obstetric problems would have been minor at first, simply because bipedalism emerged well before large brains in the human lineage. But the birth canal constriction that is an inevitable side effect of bipedalism began to impose more serious costs as selection for large brains became more intense. The skull must be large enough to accommodate the infant brain and that skull needs to pass through the birth canal without damage to the skull's precious contents. Selection is a great tinkerer, throwing in any bit of junk—any mutation—that happens to improve the design. Two types of mutations were favored as bigger brains began to collide, literally, with bipedal pelves (the plural of pelvis).

The first type of mutation adjusted the timing of birth. If selection is favoring large brains but the birth canal cannot be expanded because of locomotor constraints, a possible solution is to bring the infant through the birth canal earlier, before its brain has finished growing. Of course, this tactic produces less-developed infants who may have a harder time surviving the first weeks and months after birth. But this is one route that selection took, and, as a consequence, we humans have very helpless—the technical word is "altricial"—newborns. Human babies are much less mature than, for example, chimpanzee infants; newborn chimps can ordinarily walk, climb and cling to their mothers without help or support. Partly because of our "hind-start," we humans grow up much more slowly than the other great apes.

A second type of mutation also helped in addressing the big-brain-versus-bipedal-pelvis problem. Altricial, hind-start infants are at great risk, especially out on the savanna. A mother chimpanzee can care for her well-developed infant on her own. But mothers have their hands full with altricial infants. This situation might favor dads who offered some material help. To spell this argument out more completely, let's think back to our discussions about sexual selection. Clutton-Brock and Vincent argued that sexual selection favors sexually competitive traits in the fast sex—the sex that has the potential to reproduce more rapidly. Because male mammals never gestate nor lactate they have potentially much higher reproductive rates than female mammals. This leads to the generally correct prediction that male mammals will compete to fertilize as many females as possible. That is precisely what we see in chimpanzees, gorillas and orangutans.

But consider this hypothetical situation: Imagine, for example, that because her offspring was so helpless, a mother absolutely could not rear it alone. In such a hypothetical case, a male who fertilized females and then went off to search for additional mating partners doomed each and every one of his offspring to death. My intention is not to suggest that the human case is, or ever was, that extreme. No, I just want to suggest that human males hurt their offsprings' survival chances when they abandoned their mating partners. More precisely, they hurt those survival chances more than a similarly-abandoning chimpanzee father does. That is the kind of selection pressure that could drive the evolution of paternal care. This argument—which is intended to explain why humans are among the tiny minority of mammals that have paternal care—is discussed in Chapter 16.

Chapter 11 Glossary

altricality: The state of being born (or hatched) at an early stage of development; altricial young are relatively helpless and need extra care. (See precociality, below).

anterior: Front, first; the opposite of posterior.

apes: Our closest relatives among the primates; ape species discussed in Chapter 11 include the lesser apes in the genus *Hylobates* (the gibbons), as well as the four great ape genera: *Pongo* (the orangutan), *Pan* (the chimpanzee), *Gorilla* (you guessed it!) and *Homo*.

mentum: The chin.

monkeys: Many species of mostly quadrupedal primates; monkey species discussed in Chapter 11 include the genera *Ateles*, *Nasalis*, *Macaca*, and *Papio*.

occiput: The back of the skull.

posterior: Back, last; the opposite of anterior.

precociality: The state of being born (or hatched) at an advanced stage of development; precocial young are relatively independent and need less care.

sagittal dimension: From the front of the body to the back, from your nose to the back of your head, or from your belly button to your spine.

secondary altricality: Altritiality in a species whose close relatives have precocial young; derived altriciality.

transverse dimension: Across the body, from your right side to your left side

ventral: The front side of the body; the chest side or belly side.

Chapter 11
Bipedalism and Human Birth: The Obstetrical Dilemma Revisited (1995)

Karen Rosenberg and Wenda Trevathan

... adaptation to bipedal locomotion decreased the size of the bony birth-canal at the same time that the exigencies of tool use selected for larger brains. This obstetrical dilemma was solved by delivery of the fetus at a much earlier stage of development. (Washburn[1])

... there can be no doubt that many of the obstetrical problems of Mrs. H. Sapiens are due to the combination of a narrower pelvis and a bigger head in the species. (Krogman[2])

Although Washburn described it as as a "dilemma" and Krogman called it a "scar of human evolution," both authors recognized that the unique way that humans give birth is the result of a set of constraints imposed by several exclusively human attributes: bipedalism, a large brain, and "secondary altriciality," or the delivery of the infant in a helpless state. Although human birth has long been seen as a single compromise between locomotion and brain size, we now know that the particularly complex series of twists and turns that human babies make in the process of emerging from their mothers' birth canals is the result of a history of continual compromises, adapting first to one constraint and then to another.

Birth in Nonhuman Primates

Contrary to popular perceptions, humans are not the only animals that have difficulty during childbirth. One important characteristic of primates as a group is a large head and

Key Words: Birth, obstetrics, australopithecines, Homo, bipedalism

Karen Rosenberg and Wenda Trevathan, "Bipedalism and Human Birth: The Obstetrical Dilemma Revisited," from *Evolutionary Anthropology: Issues, News, and Reviews*; Vol. 4 Issue 5, pp. 161–168.

brain relative to body size (i.e., a high encephalization quotient). For most primates this means that their infants, at birth, have heads that are close to the size of the maternal birth canal through which they must pass. This is especially true of monkeys, lesser apes, and humans. Schultz[3,4] depicted this relationship in a classic figure, redrawn here as Figure 1, showing the size of the maternal pelvic inlet and the infant cranium in *Ateles*, *Nasalis*, *Macaca*, *Hylobates*, the great apes, and humans. The close correspondence between the size of the maternal pelvis and the size of neonatal cranium is obvious for monkeys, gibbons, and humans, whereas chimpanzees, gorillas, and orangutans appear to have spacious birth canals, probably as a result of their large bodies. As one would expect from examining these drawings, birth is reported to be difficult for the smaller-bodied primates (monkeys and gibbons), as well as for humans,[5–9] but somewhat easier for the larger-bodied (great) apes.[10]

Although observations of wild animals giving birth are rare, we know that neonatal death resulting from cephalopelvic disproportion, when a fetal head is too large to pass through the mother's birth canal, is not uncommon in species such as marmosets, squirrel monkeys,[11] baboons,[8] and macaques.[12] Cephalopelvic disproportion is also, of course, a relatively frequent cause of death for human infants and can be the cause of death for their mothers.[13] Because the cephalopelvic constraints in monkeys are greater than those in great apes, the comparisons made herein between nonhuman primates and humans will use monkeys, rather than the phylogetically closer great apes, to represent nonhumans.

It is not only the size of the pelvic aperture that is important to the birth process, but also its shape. The birth canal can be seen as a passageway with an entrance (the inlet) and an exit (the outlet) and a space between (the midplane) through which the infant must pass. For most primate species, the entrance (see Table 1), the exit, and the passageway between them are longer in the sagittal dimension than in the transverse dimension. The neonatal cranium is largest in the sagittal dimension in all primate species, including humans. Furthermore, the back of the infant cranium is broadest, so that it fits best against the broader back of the monkey pelvis.

Until recent work by Stoller,[14] it had been assumed that in monkeys the sagittal dimension of the infant cranium lines up with the sagittal dimension of the pelvis, the infant facing the ventral side of the mother's body (Fig. 2) and passing straight through the birth canal without rotating. The infant is born in a position obstetricians describe as occiput posterior. Based on observations that included radiographs of laboratory animals during parturition, Stoller[14] has shown that squirrel monkey and baboon infants may rotate during birth, albeit in a different way than human infants do. In the four baboons (*Papio anubis*) and seven squirrel monkeys (*Saimiri sciureus*) Stoller studied, the fetuses entered the birth canal in various positions, but then rotated to exit face first (mentum anterior), facing the maternal pubic bones and with their heads in an extended position.

Monkey mothers usually deliver in a squatting position. As the infant is born, the mother typically reaches down to guide it out of the birth canal and toward her nipples, and may wipe mucus from the baby's mouth and nose to assist its breathing.[10] Other animals may observe the birth process from a distance but do not assist the mother or infant. The newborns of most monkey species have sufficiently developed motor skills that an infant can assist in its own delivery once its hands are free.

Monkeys and apes generally give birth wherever and whenever other group members and predators are least likely to be present. Laboring mothers typically seek seclusion, often among trees, which provide protection from terrestrial predators. Diurnal species generally give birth at night; nocturnal species tend to give birth during the day.[15] For nonhuman primates, birth generally is a solitary event.

Birth in Modern Humans

Although, as shown in Figure 1, the close correspondence between the infant cranium and maternal pelvis in monkeys is also characteristic of humans, the orientation of the pelvic diameters differs. In monkey pelves, both the inlet and the outlet are greatest in the sagittal dimension. In contrast, the human birth canal is "twisted" in the middle so that the greatest breadth at the inlet is in the transverse dimension, while the outlet is largest in the sagittal dimension. In other words, the long axes of the inlet and outlet lie perpendicular to each other in humans, whereas in other primates they are parallel to each other.

The human infant's head, like the monkey's, is greatest in the sagittal dimension. The extremely close correspondence between the fetal head and the maternal pelvic dimensions requires that these dimensions line up so that the head enters in the transverse plane (facing to the side) (Fig. 2), but then rotates to emerge in the sagittal plane, usually facing to the back in a position obstetricians refer to as occiput anterior (Fig. 3). The head must rotate again after it passes through the outlet so that the shoulders, which, as in the great apes, are fairly broad and rigid, can follow the head through the maximum diameters of the birth canal.

In addition to the differences in cross-sectional shape, human and nonhuman primate pelvic morphologies differ in another way. The broadest part of the monkey pelvis is at the back, whereas the human pelvis is also spacious in the front. As with monkeys, the human infant's occiput is the largest, most rigid part of its head. Thus, rather than lining up with the back of its head against the maternal sacrum as monkeys do, the human infant more commonly lies so that its occiput is against the pubic bones, and toward the front of the pelvis as it exits the birth canal, its convex frontal bone passing along the concave anterior surface of the sacrum. The smallest diameter of the human fetal head is

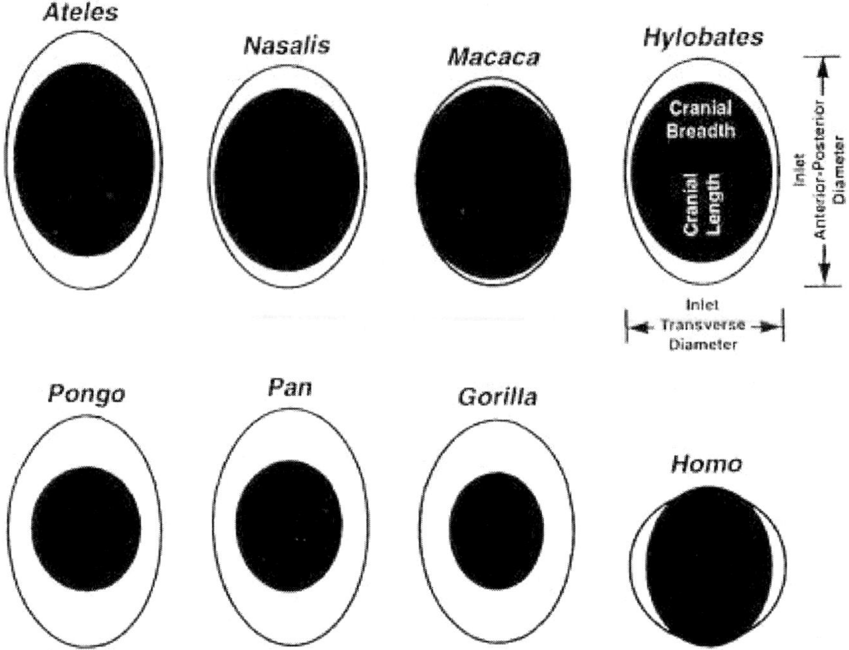

Figure 1. A redrawing of Schultz' classic diagram relating the size of the maternal pelvic inlet and the size of the neonatal head in different primate species. Maternal pelvic and infant cranial outlines are diagrammatic, but scaled so that the transverse diameter of all maternal pelvic inlets are constant and all dimensions are correctly scaled relative to one another. For each species, the outlined oval represents the average maternal pelvic inlet, the black oval represents the average infant's cranium. Note that in the monkeys and gibbon, the dimensions of the infant cranium are only slightly smaller than the dimensions of the mother's pelvis. In great apes, the pelvic inlet is relatively spacious. In humans, the infant cranium is actually longer than the anterior-posterior dimension of the pelvic inlet, requiring the head to enter the inlet facing sideways.

the sub-occipito-bregmatic diameter (from the back of the head to the top of the head). In order to make this minimum cross-sectional diameter pass through the plane of the maximum diameter of the outlet, the fetal head must be in an occiput anterior presentation as it exits the birth canal. This means that the head not only rotates from its original sideways facing orientation as it passes through the birth canal, but emerges facing in the opposite direction from the mother.

TABLE 1. Average transverse diameter of female pelvic inlet, newborn cranial breadth, and relative breadth of newborn cranium for primate species (from Leutenegger[11])

	Adult females		Newborns		
	N	Transverse Diameter of Inlet (mm)	N	Cranial Breadth (mm) Relative	Cranial Breadth[1]
Species					
Callithrix jacchus	15	17.2	4	18.0	104.5
Saimiri sciureus	7	23.1	3	28.0	121.1
Cebus capucinus	4	35.1	2	43.0	118.2
Alouatta villosa	2	47.0	1	38.0	80.8
Lagothrix lagothricha	4	44.3	1	48.0	108.3
Ateles geoffroyi	7	54.4	8	52.2	95.9
Macaca mulatta	41	50.9	28	50.7	99.6
Nasalis larvatus	15	51.8	1	49.0	94.6
Hylobates lar	87	55.9	6	52.7	94.3
Pongo pygrnaeus	26	102.5	4	74.9	73.1
Pan troglodytes	29	98.0	9	71.0	72.4
Gorilla gorilla	10	122.6	4	79.0	64.4
Homo sapiens	10	121.6	10	123.8[2]	101.8

1. Relative cranial breadth is newborn cranial breadth as a percentage of the transverse diameter of the maternal pelvis. Index is calculated for the means of each species.
2. Cranial length rather than breadth is included here, since that is the dimension that passes through the transverse diameter of the inlet in humans.

In summary, the mechanism of birth in nonhuman primates differs from that most common in humans in two fundamental ways. The orientation of the fetal head as it enters the birth canal is different, that of nonhuman primates usually facing forward or backward and that of humans facing sideways. The change in orientation of the fetal head as it passes through the birth canal is also different, that of nonhuman primates rotating to a variable degree but emerging facing forward with the head flexed and that of humans rotating to exit facing backward with the head extended.

These two distinctions account for significant differences in maternal behavior at birth. For humans, birth is a social activity. Unlike nonhuman primates, which seek solitude at this time, human mothers actively seek assistance in childbirth.[16] We suggest that this distinction is related to the mechanical differences in the birth process, which are the result of the previously discussed anatomical differences. Like nonhuman primate mothers, human mothers often squat during delivery, although they also assume a wide range of other postures. Because the human fetus emerges from the birth canal facing in the opposite direction from its mother, it is difficult for the mother, whatever her position, to reach down, as nonhuman primate mothers often do, to clear a breathing passage for the infant or remove the umbilical cord from around its neck. If a human mother tries to assist in delivery by guiding the infant from the birth canal, she risks pulling it against the body's angle of flexion, possibly damaging the infant's spinal cord, brachial nerves, and muscles.[16]

The adaptation that humans have made to this situation is to seek assistance during birth. Today, virtually all women in all societies seek assistance at delivery from relatives, midwives, or obstetricians. In a survey of 296 cultural groups in which attendance at childbirth has been described, ethnographers for 24 such groups noted that delivery may, under certain circumstances, take place unattended. For example, first births may be attended and subsequent ones unattended, or attendance may occur only at births involving complications. Even among the !Kung, a woman who gives birth alone arouses interest and concern,[17] suggesting that solitary birth is not as routine as some ethnographers have reported. Howell[18] reported that although giving birth alone is the cultural ideal for !Kung women, most have their mothers, sisters, or other women with them. So, while there are rare exceptions,[19] it is a phenomenon that comes close to being a "cultural universal." At some point in the evolutionary past of humans, the benefits of having assistance during birth outweighed the costs, so that the species-typical pattern of "obligate midwifery" emerged. Human birth is a social, rather than a solitary event.

When Did the Human Pattern of Birth Emerge?

In contrast to our understanding of human evolution fifty years ago, we now know that bipedalism is independent of encephalization and secondary altriciality in the human evolutionary record. Although all of these human characteristics affect the birth process, their influence is sequential rather than a single compromise to conflicting constraints.[20]

The series of rotations that the human infant must undergo during birth is related to the locomotor pattern, bipedalism, as well as to another characteristic aspect of human morphology, a relatively large brain. The close relationship between the size and shape of the maternal birth canal and the size and shape of the infant skull means that in humans the mechanism of birth can be inferred from the morphology of the bony birth canal.[21] Fortunately, some aspects of this morphology are preserved in the fossil record.

Our knowledge of the pelvic anatomy of the earliest bipeds comes principally from two australopithecine specimens, both sexed as female: Sts 14[22–24] from Sterkfontein, South Africa, and A.L. 288-1[25] (Lucy) from Hadar, Ethiopia. Although controversy surrounds

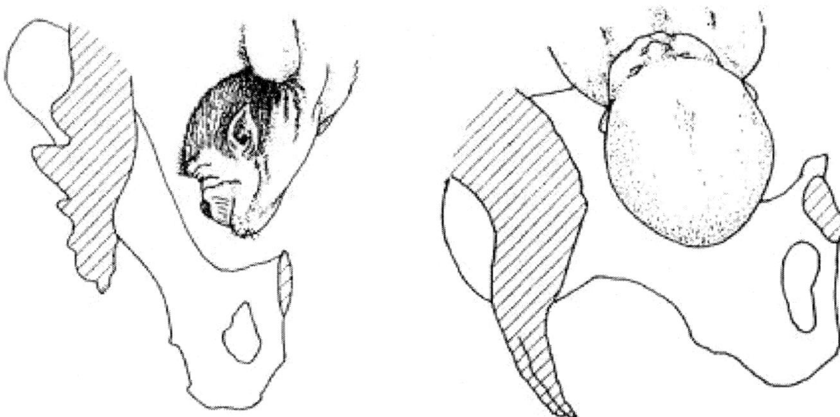

Figure 2. Comparison of the entry of the fetal head (seen in lateral view) into the birth canal in a baboon (left) and a human (right). The figure on the left was drawn from a radiograph taken of Papio anubis by Melissa Stoller.[8, 14] The traditional understanding of monkey birth mechanics was that because the longest axis of the neonatal head and the longest axis of the maternal pelvic inlet are in the sagittal dimension, the fetal head enters the birth canal with its sagittal axis aligned with the mother's sagittal axis. The infant is positioned with its occiput against the internal surface of the maternal sacrum and remains in that orientation as it passes through to the outlet. Stoller's recent work on nonhuman primate birth[8, 14] has shown that the neonatal head may enter the pelvic inlet in other positions, such as the one shown here, but that it exits the birth canal face first, facing the front of the mother's body. In humans,[10] because the longest axis of the neonatal head is the sagittal dimension and the longest axis of the maternal pelvic inlet is the transverse dimension, the fetal head enters the birth canal with its sagittal axis aligned with the mother's transverse axis (i.e., facing to the side). Because the birth canal is not a straight tube of unchanging shape, the human fetus must rotate as it passes through (See Fig. 3). (Note that these drawings are not scaled correctly relative to one another.)

the fine details of the locomotor system of these earliest hominid,[26,27] it is clear that their anatomy represents a significant departure from the pattern in apes and that they were bipedal (Fig. 4). The pelvis of both australopithecine specimens includes a birth canal that is extremely wide (i.e., platypelloid), both absolutely and relative to stature. Tague and Lovejoy[21] showed that in contrast to the twisted birth canal of modern humans, the australopithecine birth canal maintains the same shape throughout its passage from inlet to outlet. This makes it similar to the straight passageway of the nonhuman primate birth canal, but with the significant difference in the orientation of its longest diameter.

An important point is that the modifications in morphology visible in the bony fossil remains and footprints of early hominids occurred primarily because of locomotor rather than obstetrical demands. However, these locomotor changes had important consequences with regard to the way that early hominids gave birth.

Studies of the birth process in australopithecines yeilded diverse conclusions: that the process was "quick and easy"; that it was similar to the modern human process in degree of difficulty[28] or in "mechanism of birth"[29,30]; or that it was unlike the process in any living human or nonhuman primates. Tague and Lovejoy[21] assumed that australopithecine infants had cranial dimensions similar to those of a modern chimpanzee infant[31,32] and that "the shape of the maternal pelvis directs that pattern of birth." Using the morphology of known australopithecines, they inferred a mechanism of birth. The australopithecine infant cranium would have been too long to enter the pelvic inlet if it were oriented in the same direction as a nonhuman primate (i.e., facing either forward or backward, but with its sagittal axis aligned with the sagittal axis of the mother's body). At the inlet, then, the australopithecine infant cranium would have had a human-like orientation. Tague and Lovejoy[21] suggested, however, that because the australopithecine birth canal had a constant shape throughout, there would have been no "bony resistance to fetal descent" and the infant would have moved through the passageway in this sideways facing orientation. Although they suggested that birth may have been "slow and difficult," rotation within the birth canal would have been unnecessary, given the size of the infant head, and impossible, given the platypelloid[16] shape of each pelvic plane.

Fetal rotation in modern human births, however, is not simply a mechanism to accommodate a large cranium. An additional characteristic that may have had an impact on birth in hominids may have been important first in australopithecines. Hominoids as a group have broad, rigid shoulders, which are associated with their locomotor adaptations. In modern humans, shoulder dystocia, or obstruction of an infant's shoulders, is associated with increased mortality for both mothers and infants, especially when the pelvis is platypelloid. Although this does not present a problem to the large-bodied great apes because of their spacious birth canals, it may have been a source of difficulty and, hence, selection, in early hominids. It is possible that after the australopithecine fetal head passed through the pelvic outlet without rotating within it, it had to rotate so that the wide shoulders at a ninety-degree angle to the long axis of the head, could also pass through the pelvic passageway. This hypothesis remains untested, but we suggest that shoulder size may have been an important constraint during hominid birth and, along with increased infant cranial size, may have been among the causes of selection for the more rounded pelvis of later hominids.

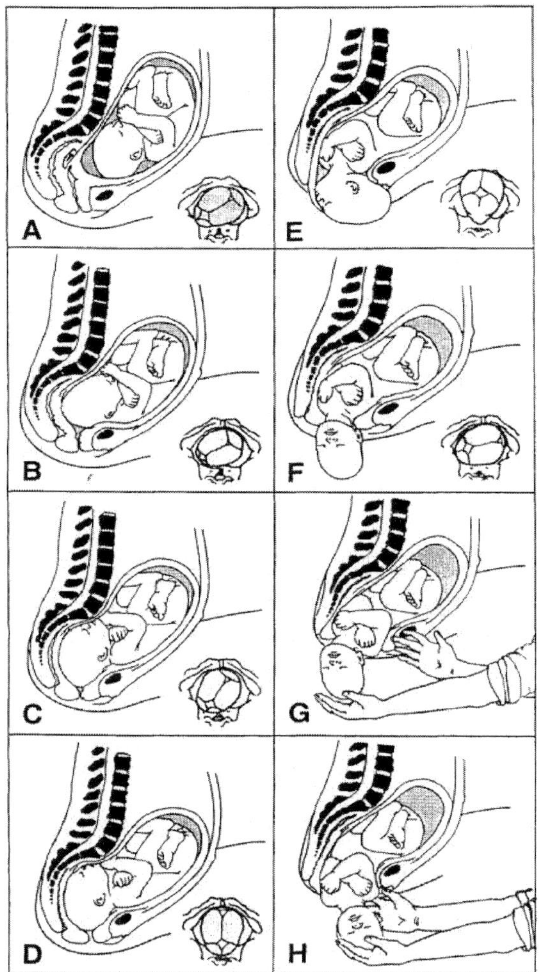

Figure 3. The passage of the human fetus through the maternal birth canal. Each box shows a sagittal section through the maternal body of a woman squatting during labor. The maternal pubic bone, sacrum, and vertebrae are shown in black (other parts of the bony skeleton are not visible in this midline view). In the lower right corner of each box is a "midwife's-eye" view of the fetus as it rotates within and emerges from the birth canal.

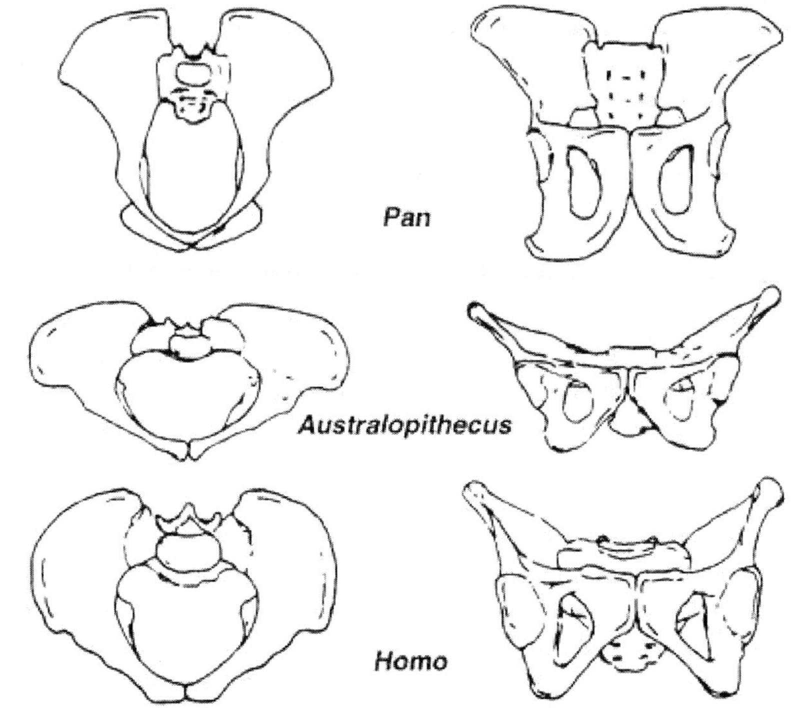

Figure 4. A chimpanzee (top), australopithecine (the reconstructed pelvis of A.L. 288-1) (middle), and the pelvis of a modern human female (bottom) in approximately superior (left) and anterior (right) views. Note the shape of the pelvic inlet in the superior views. The chimpanzee inlet is long in the sagittal plane whereas both hominid inlets are broad transversely (though the modern human is also more spacious in the sagittal plane than is the australopithecine).

Recently, based on their reconstructions of A.L. 288-1 and STS 14, Häusler and Schmid[33] have proposed that birth in *Australopithecus* may have involved rotation of the fetus in a manner similar to modern human birth. In addition, these authors offer the provocative hypothesis that A.L. 288-1 may have been male. (Because of the small size of the specimen, that suggestion would require the presence of two australopithecine species at Hadar.) Ruff[40] has pointed out that, regardless of the sex of A.L. 288-1, Häusler and Schmid's estimates of the birth canal size and shape in australopithecines are, in fact, consistent with a nonrotational birth mechanism, at least as far as the head is concerned, though not necessarily the shoulders.

Birth and Encephalization

Humans are often described as being secondarily altricial. In many ways, our species is typical of precocial mammals in having small litters, a long gestation, hemochorial placentas, and large brains, and thus probably evolved from prehominid ancestors that gave birth to more precocial young. However, modern human young typically are altricial, being extremely undeveloped at birth as compared with infants of other primate species. This observation has led to speculation about the gestation length that would have been characteristic of past hominids. Some authors[34–36] have suggested that in the past gestation was longer, either absolutely, or relatively, than it is at present The human 38-week gestation is not very different from the gestation periods of our close relatives, the great apes—35–39 weeks for orangutans, 32 weeks for chimpanzees, and 37 weeks for gorillas—and probably is close to the length of primitive hominoid gestation.[20] However, humans are born at a stage of development at which they are more helpless than the neonates of our relatives. Montagu[37] referred to the period immediately after the birth of human infants as "exterogestation," suggesting that the human neonate continues for some time to function more as a fetus than an infant. Clearly, the extreme helplessness of human newborns has important behavioral implications for such areas as parental behavior and social relationships.

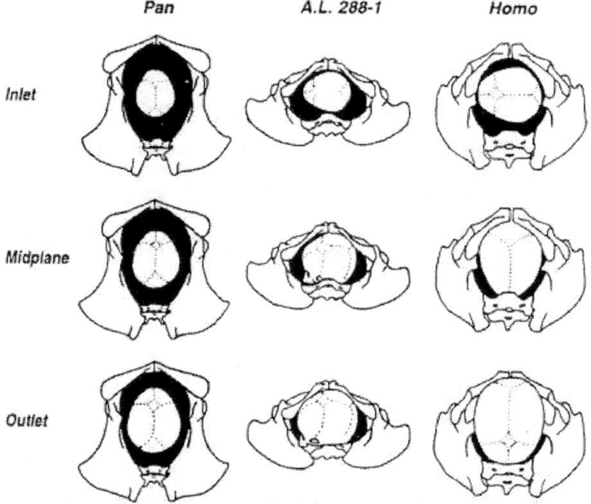

Figure 5. Comparisons of the mechanisms of birth in *Pan, Australopithecus afarensis* and modern *Homo*. This diagram shows the "midwife's-eye" view of a neonatal head passing through the birth canal. In each drawing, the maternal pelvis and fetal head are shown in inferior view, with the sacrum at the bottom of the picture and the pubic symphysis at the top. This view corresponds to the drawing in the lower right hand corner of each box in Figure 3. Redrawn from Tague and Lovejoy.[21]

When did secondary altriciality evolve in humans? Martin[38] proposed that approximately 1.5 mya, the pelvic size placed a limit on prenatal brain growth. Until that time, brain size could have increased simply by increasing the fetal rate of growth rather than by altering the postnatal rate. Two changes could have allowed encephalization to continue: for human infants to become secondarily altricial (that is, to have a smaller percentage of adult brain size at birth), or for birth to occur at a relatively earlier time in fetal development. The only other possibility would have been alteration of the shape of the pelvis and change in the mechanism of birth.

Unfortunately, no complete pelvic apertures of early *Homo* are available. Based on the fragmentary adolescent male skeleton WT 15000 from Kenya, dated at 1.5 mya, Walker and Ruff[39] estimated the pelvic capacity of an adult female *Homo erectus* and suggested that it could accommodate a modern fetus at 32 to 33 weeks of gestation. They concluded that in order to achieve adult *Homo erectus* cranial capacity, this species must have been characterized by a modern human-like pattern of growth in which rapid brain growth continues after birth rather than an ape-like pattern of growth in which the timing of birth corresponds to a decline in the rate of brain growth. This would mean that *Homo erectus* birth was nonrotational, as in australopithecines, but that secondary altriciality was present.

Ruff[40] has recently suggested, based on biomechanical concomitants of pelvic expansion in the femur, that early *Homo*, like *Australopithecus*, had a wide, platypelloid pelvis and a non-rotational birth mechanism like that proposed for australopithecines. He further suggests that the increases in cranial capacity above the average of 900 cc reached in *Homo* by 1–1.5 mya became possible only when a rotational mechanism of birth had evolved. This would mean that secondary altriciality evolved in humans some time after 1.5 mya. If this is correct, *Homo habilis*, with an adult cranial capacity of approximately 700 cc, was the last hominid to deliver infants with the typical mammalian pattern in which half of brain growth has been completed. If, as suggested earlier, shoulder dystocia was a significant source of selection in australopithecines, necessitating rotation of the head after its passage through the bony birth canal, this would have been true of *Homo erectus* as well. Hence these early hominids may have had a rotational form of birth. This rotation may have been different from that in modern humans, however, in that it would have been necessary to accommodate only the broad shoulders of *Australopithecus* and early *Homo* rather than both the large head and broad shoulders of the modern human fetus.

Speculation About Birth in Archaic *Homo*, Including Neandertals

In Neandertals and other archaic humans, the anterior portion of the pelvis generally is elongated.[41] Moreover, this portion of the pelvis is expanded in modern females relative to males. Several hypotheses about the functional significance of this morphology suggested that archaic and modern humans differ in such aspects of reproductive biology as gestation length,[34] accelerated fetal growth,[42] and maternal-fetal size relationship.[43] It is clear now that female archaic humans fall within the modern female human range for pubis length and size of the birth canal relative to body size. It can be thus concluded that these archaic humans probably gave birth much as modern humans do, not only with respect to the mechanism of birth (i.e., rotation of the fetus as it passes through the birth canal and emergence of the infant from the birth canal in the occiput anterior position), but also in the behavior associated with birth (i.e., obligate midwifery[10]). Differences between male archaic humans (Neandertals) and modern males exist, but remain unexplained, although hypotheses focusing on locomotor differences have been proposed.[44]

A corollary issue that arises from discussion of the evolution of human birth is the question of when the modern human pattern of pelvic sexual dimorphism arose.[45] Modern human sex differences in the pelvis are a reflection of differing balances of the selective constraints on males and females imposed by locomotion and birth. It seems probable that, like the modern pattern of birth, the evolution of pelvic sexual dimorphism took place in a mosaic fashion.

One result of the anatomical changes in the pelvis and concomitant changes in the way human babies are born is that birth has been transformed from the solitary event that it is for nonhuman primates and other mammals into a social and cultural event. This is a result of the fact that the human infant emerges from the birth canal facing away from the mother, which, as noted previously, hinders her ability to help her child. The presence of another individual who can assist in the final stage of delivery reduces the risk of mortality for the infant and probably for the mother as well. Thus, as the modern process of birth evolved, selection began to favor hominid females who sought the assistance of others during birth. Although the proximate causes of seeking companionship during birth include pain, fear, other emotional stress, or conformity to cultural norms, the ultimate cause of this behavior may be that it reduces mortality. The evolutionary process has resulted in heightened emotional needs during labor, which lead women to seek companionship at this time. This suggests that the desire for supportive, familiar people at birth is deeply rooted in human evolutionary history.

Acknowledgments

For access to unpublished material, we are grateful to Melissa Stoller. For helpful comments on the manuscript, we thank Tracey Crummett, John Fleagle, Melissa Stoller, and Dana Walrath. Barbara Tidman did the illustrations.

About the Author

Karen Rosenberg is Associate Professor of Anthropology at the University of Delaware. She is a paleoanthropologist who has worked on fossils in Europe, the Near East and Eastern Asia. Her research interests are in the origin of modern humans and the evolution of modern human childbirth. Wenda Trevathan is Associate Professor of Anthropology at New Mexico State University. Her major research interests are the evolution of human female reproductive behavior, including sexuality, pregnancy, childbirth, and menopause. Her major publications include *Human Birth: An Evolutionary Perspective* and articles on menstrual synchrony, sexuality, and evolutionary medicine. Email: KRR@UDEL.EDU

References

1. Washburn SL (1960) Tools and human evolution. Sci Am *203*:3–15.
2. Krogman WM (1951) The scars of human evolution. Sci Am *184*:54–57.
3. Schultz AH (1969) *The Life of Primates*. Weidenfeld and Nicolson.
4. Schultz A (1949) Sex differences in the pelves of primates. Am J Phys Anthropol *7*:401423.
5. Bowden D, Winter P, Ploog D (1967) Pregnancy and delivery behavior in the squirrel monkey (*Saimiri sciureus*) and other primates. Folia Primatol (Basel) *5*:1–42.
6. Leutenegger W (1982) Encephalization and obstetrics in primates with particular reference to human evolution. In Armstrong E, Falk D (eds.) *Primate Brain Evolution: Methods and Concepts*. Plenum Press, pp 85–95.
7. Lindburg DG (1982) Primate obstetrics: The biology of birth. Am J Primatol *1*:193–199.
8. Stoller M (1995) The obstetric pelvis and mechanism of labor in nonhuman primates. Am J Phys Anthropol Supplement *20*:204.
9. Mitchell G, Brandt EM (1975) Behavior of the female rhesus monkey during birth. In Bourne GH (ed) *The Rhesus Monkey, Volume II: Management, Reproduction, and Pathology*. Academic Press, pp 231–244.
10. Trevathan W (1987) *Human Birth: An Evolutionary Perspective*. Aldine de Gruyter.
11. Leutenegger W (1974) Functional aspects of pelvic morphology in simian primates. J Hum Evol *3*:207–222.
12. Goodlin BI, Sackett GP (1983) Parturition in *Macaca nemestrina*. Am J Primatol *4*:283–307.
13. Oxorn H (1986) *Oxorn-Foote Human Labor and Birth*, 5th ed. Norwalk, CT Appleton-Century-Crofts.
14. Stoller M (1995) *The Obstetric Pelvis and Mechanism of Labor in Nonhuman Primates*. Ph.D. Dissertation, University of Chicago.
15. Jolly A (1972) Hour of birth in primates and man. Folia Primatol (Basel) *18*:108–121.
16. Trevathan W (1988) Fetal emergence patterns in evolutionary perspective. Am Anthropol *90*:674–681.
17. Shostak, M (1981) *Nisa: The Life and Words of a !Kung Woman*. Cambridge MA: Harvard University Press.
18. Howell N (1979) *Demography of the Dobe !Kung*. Academic Press.
19. Konner M, Shostak M (1981) Timing and management of birth among the !Kung: Biocultural interaction in reproductive adaptation. Cultural Anthropol *14*:11–28.
20. Rosenberg KR (1992) The evolution of modern human childbirth. Yearbook Phys Anthropol *35*:89–124.

21. Tague RG, Lovejoy CO (1986) The obstetric pelvis of A. L. 288-1 (Lucy). J Hum Evol *15*:237–255.
22. Broom R, Robinson JT, Schepers GWH (1950) Sterkfontein Ape-Man *Plesianthropus*. Transvaal Museum Memoirs *4*:58–63.
23. Robinson JT (1972) *Early Hominid Posture and Locomotion*. Chicago: University of Chicago Press.
24. Abitbol, MM (1995) Reconstruction of the STS 14 (*Australopithecus africanus*) pelvis. Am J Phys Anthropol *96*:143–158.
25. Johanson DC, Lovejoy CO, Kimbel WH, White TD, Ward SC, Bush ME, Latimer BM, Coppens Y (1982) Morphology of the Pliocene partial hominid skeleton (A. L. 288-1) from the Hadar formation, Ethiopia. Am J Phys Anthropol *57*:403–451.
26. Lovejoy CO (1988) Evolution of human walking. Sci Am *259*:118–125.
27. Susman RL, Stern JT, Jungers WL (1984) Arboreality and bipedality in the Hadar hominids. Folia Primatol *43*:113–156.
28. McHenry HM (1986) The first bipeds: A comparison of the *A. afarensis* and *A. africanus* postcranium and implications for the evolution of bipedalism. J Hum Evol *15*:177–191.
29. Abitbol MM (1987) Obstetrics and posture in pelvic anatomy. J Hum Evol *16*:243–255.
30. Berge C, Orban-Segebarth R, and Schmid P (1984) Obstetrical interpretation of the australopithecine pelvic cavity. J Hum Evol *13*:573–587.
31. Leutenegger W (1972) Newborn size and pelvic dimensions of *Australopithecus*. Nature *240*: 568–569.
32. Leutenegger W (1987) Neonatal brain size and neurocranial dimensions in Pliocene hominids: Implications for obstetrics. J Hum Evol *16*:291–296.
33. Häusler M, Schmid P (1995) Comparison of the pelves of Sts 14 and AL 288-1: Implications for birth and sexual dimorphism in australopithecines. J Hum Evol *29*:363–383.
34. Trinkaus E (1984) Neandertal pubic morphology and gestation length. Curr Anthrol *25*:509–514.
35. Gould SJ (1975) Allometry in primates, with emphasis on scaling and the evolution of the brain. In Szalay F (ed.) *Approaches to Primate Paleobiology*, Contributions to Primatology 5:244–292.
36. Shipman P, Walker A (1989) The costs of becoming a predator. J Hum Evol *18*:373–392.
37. Montagu A (1961) Neonatal and infant immaturity in man. JAMA *178*:56–57.

38. Martin RD (1983) Human brain evolution in an ecological context. Fifty-second James Arthur lecture on the evolution of the human brain. American Museum of Natural History.
39. Walker A, Ruff C (1993) The reconstruction of the pelvis. In Walker A, Leakey RE (ed) *The Nariokotome* Homo erectus *Skeleton*. Cambridge, MA Harvard University Press, pp 221–233.
40. Ruff C (1995) Biomechanics of the hip and birth in Early *Homo*. Am J Phys Anthrol *98*:527–574.
41. Trinkaus E (1976) The morphology of European and Southwest Asian Neandertal pubic bones. Am J Phys Anthropol *44*:95–104.
42. Dean MC, Stringer CB, Bromage T (1986) Age at death of the Neandertal child from Devil's Tower, Gibraltar and the implications for studies of general growth and development in Neanderthals. Am J Phys Anthropol *70*:301–309.
43. Rosenberg KR (1988) The functional significance of Neandertal pubic length. Curr Anthropol *29*:595–617.
44. Rak Y (1990) On the differences between two pelvises of Mousterian context from the Qafzeh and Kebara Caves, Israel. Am J Phys Anthrol *81*:323–332.
45. Hager L (1989) *The Evolution of Sex Differences in the Hominid Bony Pelvis*. Ph.D dissertation, University of California at Berkeley. University Microfilms, Ann Arbor.

SECTION 10

COSTLY BRAINS

Introduction to Chapter 12

Animals are energetic systems that must meet all their needs with the calories that they can harvest. The energy budgets of animals depend on their activity levels and on the total costs of running the individual components of their bodies, some of which are more expensive than others. It seems that the evolution of Homo involved some major component swaps.

Like your car, organisms need fuel; but unlike your car, they must harvest that fuel themselves. And if an organism spends more resources doing the harvesting than the harvesting actually yields—at least if it operates at that kind of deficit for very long—it dies. Indeed, not only do organisms need to show enough of a harvesting profit to pay for their ongoing fuel costs, at some times in their lives they need to pay the additional costs of growth and reproduction. Chapter 12 is about the energy needs and efficiencies of modern and ancestral humans. We are going to do the paleoanthropological equivalent of "kicking the tires" while the authors take us on a tour of a used hominin lot. How much fuel did these creatures need, how far did they travel to get it, and how efficiently did they use it?

Just as you can discuss the fuel efficiency of various kinds of cars, biologists can compare the energetic efficiency of different species. Miles/gallon is a well known efficiency measure for cars. For example, a Hummer gets, say, 4 miles/gallon and a Prius about 50 miles/gallon. We could easily invert that calculation and talk about gallons/mile; that would be 0.25 gallons/mile for the Hummer and 0.02 gallons/mile for the Prius. Either form—miles/gallon or gallons/mile—is equally informative, but (assuming you want efficiency) you have to notice that high numbers are good on the miles/gallon scale, and low numbers are good on the gallons/mile scale. I mention this inversion because the standard efficiency measure for animals, called resting metabolic rate (RMR), is more like the gallons/mile measure. It measures how many calories are burned over some standard time period like an hour; in Chapter 12, the form used is kilocalories/day.

The analogy with cars can carry us a little further. The Environmental Protection Agency gives each kind of car a sort of standard efficiency rating based on an average of driving conditions and speed. But, as you probably recognize, your car's actual efficiency depends on how you drive it, and especially on how fast you go. It turns out that RMR is equivalent to your car's efficiency at idle: How fast would you burn up a gallon if you just ran your engine in the parking lot? RMR is a useful measure because it represents a baseline that allows us to compare any set of animals fairly, even if in real life they have very different activity levels. Put another way, there are factors that make some animals more costly to run than others even at rest, and then there are activity-level factors (like driving speed) that are added on top of those baseline differences.

Let's talk about the baseline differences first. Bigger animals burn more calories than smaller ones. (In fact, the relationship between body weight and RMR has essentially the same exponent, 0.75, as the relationship between body weight and brain weight; compare equations in Chapters 10 and 12). So, because it had a smaller body, *Homo habilis* needed fewer calories than *H. rudolfensis* or *H. ergaster*. Moreover, even at rest, your metabolic rate (your RMR) depends on your body composition. Here is the core idea that has made Leslie Aiello famous among paleoanthropologists: Some kinds of tissue are more expensive to operate than others. In other words, body weight alone does not tell the whole story; it matters whether that body weight is made up of cheap or expensive tissues. Remember, to evaluate "cheap" or "expensive," we are still measuring in kilocalories per day, at rest. On this RMR scale, the cheapest kind of tissue is fat. Next comes muscle, but this is a big jump. At rest, muscle is a bit more than four times more expensive to maintain than fat. But most expensive of all is organs, things like intestines and brains. This should strike a chord with you because you know that brains expanded dramatically over human evolution. That means the energy budgets of hominins were increasing as their brains got larger. In modern humans, where we can measure these things directly, the brain amounts to about 2.5% of total body weight, but it consumes roughly 20% of RMR! That is a costly organ; your brain is a "Hummer in your head."

As mentioned at the outset, all these caloric bills need to be paid; otherwise the organism dies. How do hominins pay for such big brains? Aiello has argued that there is a trade-off among different kinds of similarly costly tissues. You could not save enough calories to pay for a bigger brain by reducing the amount of some cheap tissue like fat; that would be like trying to pay for your mortgage by drinking less coffee. (In fact, there are good reasons, which we will come to later, why fat must *increase*, not decrease, when brains increase.) The only way to pay for a big brain is by significantly cutting back on some other costly tissue.

Following that line of thinking, Aiello convincingly argues that big hominin brains were paid for by a reduction in hominin guts—digestive tissue. Of course, you cannot blithely delete your digestive system because that is how you extract calories from your food. So, if you want to reduce caloric expenditures on guts in order to afford a bigger brain, you would need to switch to a higher quality—more calorically dense—diet. That way, you could still extract lots of calories, but do so with less digestive processing, with less gut.

This is a clever argument, and it probably is at least partially correct. For example, we do have evidence—both from fossil teeth and from fossilized food remains—that our hominin ancestors were moving away from an almost completely vegetarian diet, like that of chimpanzees, to a diet that included more animal prey. We also have evidence that the expanding tool kit of early hominins (see Chapter 14) was used in acquiring these new foods. Thus, there may have been a kind of ongoing feedback system, with brain evolution supporting tool use, and tool use supporting a shift to higher quality foods, thus allowing the brain to be paid for by digestive savings. All of this would have had to occur gradually, in small steps.

We can get pretty good estimates of brain size for fossil taxa, because the brain more or less fills the skull. But what about gut size estimates? Aiello has an interesting perspective. Remember from Chapters 9 and 10 that *Australopithecus* has a funnel shaped thorax, narrow at the shoulder and wide at the gut, but that *Homo* generally has a barrel-shaped thorax, without the widening toward the waist. Aiello suggests that perhaps these shape differences are a direct consequence of *Homo*'s smaller gut.

This argument works fine for the species listed in Aiello and Wells' Table 1. On the other hand, some of the most important evidence is missing; what about our two nemesis species, *habilis* and *rudolfensis*? We have some limb bones that are attributed to each of these taxa, and from these it seems that *rudolfensis* had the more derived (*sapiens*-like) limb proportions and mode of locomotion, while *habilis* retained a more *Australopithecus*-like configuration. *If* (and this is just a conjecture) that pattern extended to the rest of the body, with *habilis* also having an *Australopithecus*-like thorax, we would have a contradiction of Aiello's hypothesis, because *habilis* had a larger relative brain size (larger EQ) than *rudolfensis*. However, we do not have any actual thoracic fossils for either taxon at present, so we should probably not assume that their thorax and limbs conform to one of the two patterns we know. If they did not conform, for example if *habilis* turned out the have long arms and short legs like *Australopithecus*, but a barrel-shaped thorax and large EQ like *Homo*, that mosaic pattern would be interesting new evidence in favor of the expensive tissue hypothesis.

Evidence of that general type might be read from another part of the anatomy. Though teeth themselves are not on the list of expensive tissues, they can reflect dietary quality. In

general, a larger surface area of the cheek teeth, as reflected in the megadontia quotient (MQ; see Chapter 10), is associated with a high-fiber, low-quality diet. So, if your diet is improving in quality, your MQ should go down. As would be expected if their diets were improving (and their guts were shrinking), both *habilis* and *rudolfensis* have MQ's that fall between those of *Australopithecus* and later *Homo*. Unfortunately, the more fine-grained hypothesis fails because *rudolfensis* had both smaller cheek teeth and a smaller brain than *habilis*. Be sure you understand why this fact is problematic for Aiello's view that dietary quality must increase as brain size increases.

Let's now return to fat. Remember that fat is relatively cheap, although it does add to the costs of locomotion, because every pound of fat has to be lugged around. (You have surely noticed that heavier people tend to get out of breath climbing up stairs.) Nevertheless, for some reason selection has favored fat accumulation in a wide array of species. Aiello and Wells believe that reason is insurance against periodic food shortages. They suggest that fat is like a savings account where occasional foraging surpluses can be banked, to be later burned for calories during periods of food scarcity. This is certainly part of the story, because it is a pattern we see in a wide variety of animals; they put on a little fat in the good season and use it up when times are tough. But it cannot be the whole story, because humans are nearly unique among land mammals in how *much* fat they store. And I am not referring to the obesity epidemic; I am talking about normal, healthy people. Let's look at some numbers.

The way to measure this is simply to express fat as a percentage of total body weight. As noted in Chapter 12, for men this number is around 14%, and for women it is 26-28%. If you weigh 150 pounds and you are an average man, about 21 of those pounds would be fat; if you are a woman of the same weight (150), roughly 40 pounds would be fat. What Aiello and Wells neglect to mention are any comparative figures for other animals, though they do acknowledge that humans are fatter. The fact is that humans are *much* fatter. Appropriate comparisons might be other mammals that live in savanna habitats like those where *Homo* evolved. For example, ungulates (hoofed mammals)—whose ancestors' bones we find in hominin butchery sites—have 2–3% body fat (a 150-pound ungulate would have roughly 4 pounds of fat). Open country primates such as baboons have 3–5%. On the view that fat represents a caloric savings account, one would need to explain two facts: 1) why humans face so much greater food scarcity risks than other animals living in the same habitat, and 2) why women face so much greater food-scarcity risk than men. The first challenge seems daunting. Regarding the second, one could argue that the caloric demands of pregnancy and lactation dictate that women must have more stored resources. But if this were true, all mammals should exhibit sex differences in body fat—but only humans do.

Ok then, why are humans so fat? There may be other functions of fat than guarding against starvation in tough times. In fact, we know there are. For example, the brain—there it is again—is the fattiest organ in the body. Fat, and lots of it, is essential to the operation of every single nerve cell in the brain. This is true of all brains, not just human brains. But because we have such big brains, we need more fat to build and maintain them than other animals. Now you see why women are fatter than men. Over their reproductive careers, women will build multiple large brains. So the pregnancy-and-lactation argument was sniffing up the right tree, but for the wrong reason. Women do not burn their extra fat for calories to pay the energetic costs of baby making; they use it as essential materials for constructing that quintessential hominin adaptation, a huge brain.

Chapter 12 Glossary

DEE: daily energy expenditure; higher than RMR (below); how much higher will depend on activity levels.

Expensive tissue hypothesis (ETH): The idea that evolution can only increase the size of one expensive kind of tissue (e.g., the brain) if it reduces the size of some other kind of expensive tissue.

RMR: Resting metabolic rate; the "fuel efficiency" of an organism, measured in calories per unit time.

Chapter 12
Energetics and the Evolution of the Genus *Homo* (2002)

Leslie C. Aiello[1] and Jonathan C. K. Wells[2]

Abstract

The genus *Homo* as represented by *Homo ergaster* (= early African *Homo erectus*) is characterized by a pattern of features that is more similar to modern humans than to the earlier and contemporaneous australopithecines and paranthropines. These features include larger relative brain sizes, larger bodies, slower rates of growth and maturation, dedicated bipedal locomotion, and smaller teeth and jaws. These features are phenotypic expressions of a very different lifestyle for the earliest members of the genus *Homo*. This paper considers the energetic correlates of the emergence of the genus *Homo* and suggests that there were three major changes in maintenance energy requirements. First, there was an absolute increase in energy requirements due to greater body size. Second, there was a shift in the relative requirements of the different organs, with increased energy diverted to brain metabolism at the expense of gut tissue, possibly mediated by changes in the proportion of weight comprised of fat. And third, there was a slower rate of childhood growth, offset by higher growth costs during infancy and

Key Words : human evolution, metabolic rate, diet, growth, *Homo erectus*, *Homo ergaster*, australopithecines, brain evolution

[1] Department of Anthropology, University College London, Gower Street, London WC1E 6BT; email: L.Aiello@ucl.ac.uk

[2] MRC Childhood Nutrition Research Centre, Institute of Child Health, 30 Guilford Street, London WC1N 1EH; email: J.Wells@ich.ucl.ac.uk

adolescence. These changes, as well as energetic requirements of reproduction and bipedal locomotion, are considered in a discussion of one of the major transitions in adaptation in human evolution, the appearance of our own genus.

Introduction

Modern humans are very different than our closest living relatives, the African apes. Among other traits, we have larger brains, walk on two legs, have slower rates of growth and maturation, longer lifespans, a long period of post reproductive life for females, differently shaped bodies, different foraging behaviors, and higher quality diets. These features are all phenotypic expressions of the human life history pattern and reflect the pace and energetic requirements of human life. Humans, as well as all other organisms, are confronted by constraining relationships, or trade-offs, in terms of how energy is invested in either growth, maintenance, activity, or reproduction (Stearns 1992). Natural selection operates very strongly on these trade-offs because of their overall influence on lifetime reproductive success (Wells 2002).

This paper reviews the energetic consequences of the evolution of *Homo*. It identifies the features of the modern human life history pattern that were present at the first appearance of our genus and considers their costs and benefits in relation to adaptive fitness. The assumption underlying this is that features should only be selected for when the cost/benefit ratio is optimal (Ulijazek 1995). Physical and behavioral adaptations seen in our early *Homo* ancestors should minimize their use of energy and optimally balance expenditure to achieve optimal reproductive success.

When the genus *Homo* first appeared is a matter of debate that depends largely on how the genus is defined. Wood & Collard (1999) convincingly argue that *Homo ergaster* (= early African *Homo erectus*), as defined by Wood (1992) and best known from the Turkana basin in Kenya between 1.9 and 1.5 Ma, is the first known species in the genus *Homo*. *Homo ergaster* is distinguished from earlier possible members of the genus *Homo* such as *H. habilis* (2.3–1.6 Ma) or *H. rudolfensis* (2.4–1.8 Ma) by a complex of skeletal and dental features reflecting a lifestyle that was more similar to that of modern humans than that inferred for earlier and contemporaneous hominins. These skeletal and dental features include a larger body mass, more human-like body proportions, relatively long legs, obligate bipedalism coupled with a limited facility for climbing, relatively small teeth and jaws suggesting major dietary change, and a tendency towards an extended period of growth and development. Although not all anthropologists agree that *Homo ergaster* is the first member of the genus *Homo* (e.g., McHenry & Coffing 2000), this review follows Wood & Collard (1999) and focuses on the energetic consequences of the human-like complex of features that distinguishes *Homo ergaster*.

Increased Body Mass

One of the most obvious and energetically important features of *Homo ergaster* is its significantly larger body mass in comparison to earlier and contemporaneous hominins. The body mass estimates (Table 1) that are commonly accepted in the literature are derived largely from the work of McHenry (1992a,b; 1994) and are determined on the basis of hindlimb joint size (but see Aiello & Wood 1994 and Kappelman 1996 for cranially determined body mass estimates). It is clear from these estimates that *Homo ergaster* is considerably heavier than any of the australopithecines or paranthropines and that females have increased in mass more than males. This means that *Homo ergaster* is not only characterized by a significant size increase but also by a marked reduction in sexual dimorphism (Leonard & Robertson 1997, Aiello & Key 2002).

There is increasing evidence that *Homo ergaster* was occupying a more open (xeric) environment than were the australopithecines and paranthropines (de Menocal 1995, Reed 1997, Sikes 1999). Large body size has a number of advantages in a more open environment including the capacity to exploit broader dietary niches in larger foraging areas, greater mobility and prey size, and increased sociality (Foley 1987). Large body size also permits females to efficiently carry their children to an older age and increased mass (Kramer 1998). Coupled with the taller and more linear physique of *Homo ergaster*, there are also physiological advantages in relation to thermoregulation and water budgets (Ruff 1991; Wheeler 1992, 1993). These physiological advantages may have been particularly important to pregnant females because of their increased susceptibility to heat stress as the result of their increased weight for height as the pregnancy developed (J. C. K. Wells, submitted). A recent analysis found that 10% of the between population variability in modern human birth weight could be attributed to thermal load, after taking confounding factors into account (Wells & Cole 2002). It would benefit both mothers and their unborn children to maximize their thermoregulatory advantage. In modern humans, hot weather mothers are smaller, gain less weight, and are less fat than cold weather mothers. Further modeling is needed to demonstrate the net thermoregulatory advantage of the larger body mass coupled with the more linear physique of *Homo ergaster* in comparison to the lighter but squatter australopithecines. It is, however, highly probable that the *Homo ergaster* body form provided a net thermoregulatory advantage in the relatively xeric conditions of the African Plio-Pleistocene.

TABLE 1 Inferred body mass and daily energy requirements for the hominins

	Sex	Body mass[a]	MR[b]	DEE[C]	DEE[C] + gestation[d]	DEE[C] + lactation[e]	DEE[f]	DEE[f] + gestation[d]	DEE[f] + lactation[e]
A. afarensis	f	29.3	881.6	1175.3	1469.1	1633.7	1248.1	1560.2	1734.9
	m	44.6	1208.1	1610.6			1740.9		
A. africanus	f	30.2	901.8	1202.3	1502.8	1671.2	1278.4	1598.0	1777.0
	m	40.8	1130.0	1506.6			1622.3		
A. robustus	f	31.9	939.6	1252.7	1565.9	1741.2	1335.1	1668.8	1855.7
	m	40.2	1117.6	1489.9			1603.4		
A. boisei	f	34.0	985.6	1314.0	1642.6	1826.5	1404.2	1755.3	1951.8
	m	48.6	1288.5	1717.8			1863.4		
H. ergaster	f	52.0	1355.5	1807.2	2259.0	2475.8	1966.0	2457.4	2732.7
	m	63.0	1565.3	2086.9			2288.6		
H. sapiens	f	56.8	1448.3	1930.9	2413.6	2664.7	2108.3	2635.4	2930.6
	m	70.0	1694.0	2258.5			2487.8		

[a]Body mass (kg) after McHenry (1992).

[b]RMR (resting metabolic rate) is computed according to the Kleiber equation (Kleiber 1932, 1961) RMR = 70 $W^{0.75}$, where W = body mass (kg).

[c]Daily energy requirements (kcal d^{-1}) = 93.3 $W^{0.75}$(Key & Ross 1999).

[d]Daily energy requirements during gestation = DEE* 1.25 (Aiello & Key 2002).

[e]Daily energy requirements during lactation = DEE* 1.39 for the australopithecines and paranthropines, = DEE* 1.37 for *Homo ergaster*, and = DEE* 1.38 for *Homo sapiens* (Aiello & Key 2002).

[f]Daily energy requirements (DEE) = 86.0 $W^{0.792}$ (Leonard & Robertson 1997). Note that this equation produces daily energy requirements that are between 6%–10% higher than those produced by the Aiello & Key (2002) equation (DEE^{3}). The daily energy requirements during gestation and lactation are correspondingly elevated. See text for explanation.

One major disadvantage of larger body size in *Homo ergaster* is the increased energetic burden it represents and the correspondingly increased dietary requirements necessary to fuel the increased energy demands. The extra maintenance metabolic requirements of this weight gain can be calculated using Kleiber's standard formula for the relationship between body mass and resting metabolic rate (RMR). RMR is the amount of energy utilized by an inactive organism under thermal neutral conditions (Durnin & Passmore 1967), and in the following formula W = body mass (kg) and RMR = kcal/d^{-1} (Kleiber 1932, 1961):

$$RMR = 70\ W^{0.75}.$$

The resting metabolic requirements of *Homo ergaster* would have been 39% higher than for *Australopithecus afarensis* (30% higher for males and 54% higher for females) (Table 1).

Dietary Implications of Increased Energy Expenditure

The larger body size in *Homo* implies a corresponding increase in either the daily amount of food or the quality of the food eaten in order to satisfy the increased energy needs. If *Homo ergaster* ate the same type of diet as the smaller bodied australopithecines, this would imply a significant alteration in the activity budget where feeding time would have to be increased in proportion to the extra calories required by the larger body mass. Even if this had been possible and *Homo ergaster* could have balanced time needed for traveling, socializing, and resting against the necessarily increased feeding time, it is unlikely that they adopted this strategy. *Homo ergaster* jaws and teeth are reduced in size, which suggests a major dietary shift away from more fibrous and more difficult to masticate foods (Walker & Leakey 1993, Wood & Aiello 1998). Equally, the trunk proportions in *Homo ergaster* suggest a relatively small gut that is compatible with a higher quality and more easily digested diet (Aiello & Wheeler 1995). The more open xeric habitat occupied by *Homo ergaster* would also offer different dietary opportunities.

It is probable that meat comprised a greater proportion of the *Homo ergaster* diet than it did for the earlier and contemporaneous australopithecines and paranthropines (Aiello & Wheeler 1995). However, it is unlikely that meat by itself would have met the increased energy requirements of *Homo ergaster*. It is clear from analyses of modern people that humans are incapable of metabolizing sufficient protein to meet more than 50% of their energy needs (Speth & Spielmann 1983, Speth 1989). Those modern people who rely more heavily on animal-based resources also rely heavily on fat for the remainder of their energy requirements.

For a number of reasons such a diet would have been unlikely for *Homo ergaster*. The specific dynamic action, the rise in metabolism or heat production resulting from ingestion of food, is very high for protein. If modern people such as the Eskimos for whom 90% of caloric needs are met by meat and fat are anything to go by, such a diet would elevate RMR by 13%–33%, with significant implications for thermoregulation in a hot open country environment. This also means that they would have had to eat correspondingly more meat to satisfy their basic energy requirements. A high meat diet also demands increased water intake, and this is an unlikely strategy to adopt in a hot open environment (Speth & Spielmann 1983). Furthermore, wild African ungulates have a relatively low fat content (Speth & Spielmann 1983, Speth 1989), and modern African hunters and gatherers such as the San or Hadza who rely heavily on meat during the dry season also rely on cultural means to recover maximum fat from the carcasses—a strategy that would not have been available to the early hominins.

Meat protein is easier to digest than plant protein and even with a limited amount of fat would still have been a valuable source of essential amino and fatty acids, fat soluble vitamins, and minerals (Milton 1999). It would satisfy nutritional requirements with a lower dietary bulk. This would allow increased reliance on plants of lower overall nutritive quality but high carbohydrate content, such as underground storage organs, to provide the majority of the energy to fuel their larger bodies. Carbohydrates also have a protein sparing advantage over dietary supplementation with fat. In situations of calorie restriction such as might be expected during the dry season on the African savanna, a diet supplemented with carbohydrates is more efficient than one supplemented by fat in sparing limited protein from being metabolized for energy and thereby restricts the availability of the limited essential nutrients and amino acids derived from that protein (Speth & Spielmann 1983).

An added advantage of including meat in the diet is the high methionine content of animal protein (Milton 1999). This would provide an adequate supply of sulfur-containing amino acids that are necessary for the detoxification of toxic (cyanogenetic) plant foods. Milton (1999) also points out that infants need dietary protein consisting of 37% of its weight in essential amino acids (compared to 15% in adults) and that animal protein would have been a valuable component of weaning foods.

Homo ergaster would undoubtedly have made use of a variety of other food resources such as invertebrates (e.g., termites) or nuts, seeds, honey, etc. However, increased reliance on mammalian meat and fat would have altered the basic balance between dietary quality and dietary bulk and would be consistent with the assumptions of the expensive tissue hypothesis (ETH) (Aiello & Wheeler 1995) and also the work of Barton (1992), which suggests that for our body sizes, humans eat less bulk than nonhuman primates. The diet of *Homo ergaster* was therefore not an australopithecine diet with added meat, but involved a change in the proportions and type of both animal and vegetable foods (Leonard & Robertson 1992, 1994).

What RMR is Actually Measuring—The Role of Expensive Tissues and Adipose Tissue

Overall RMR is the sum total of the RMR of the tissues that compose the body. Organ tissues tend to be of high metabolic rate per unit mass whereas muscle and adipose tissue is of substantially lower metabolic cost. There is considerable variation across species and during ontogeny. For example, in adult humans the brain takes up approximately 20% of the total RMR of the individual, whereas in other primates it takes up 8%–9% (Holliday 1986, Mink et al. 1981). There is also considerable variation in the size of other organ masses across species (Stahl 1965).

The differential contribution of tissues to total body RMR is the basis of the ETH for the co-evolution of brain size, gut size, and diet in human evolution (Aiello & Wheeler 1995,

Aiello 1997, Aiello et al. 2001). Prior to the publication of the ETH, there was considerable puzzlement over the apparent lack of correlation between relative brain size and relative RMR across mammals (e.g., Leonard & Robertson 1994). Humans have a RMR predicted by the Kleiber equation, but have a significantly larger brain size that would be expected to considerably elevate human RMR (Leonard & Robertson 1994, Aiello & Wheeler 1995). Aiello & Wheeler (1995) demonstrated that the metabolic costs of the relatively large and energy-expensive human brain were balanced by a corresponding reduction of the size of the equally expensive human gut. Diet quality in primates is significantly correlated with relative brain size (Leonard & Robertson 1994) but also determines the relative size of the gut. The higher the quality of the diet the smaller and simpler is the gut. It is probable that the well-known relationship between diet quality and relative brain size is explained, at least in part, by the energy sparing consequences of the relatively smaller gut. Aiello & Wheeler (1995) also suggest that the change in the size and shape of the thorax and pelvis between australopithecines and *Homo ergaster* reflects a reduction in the size of the gut in *Homo ergaster*.

It is important to remember that this does not negate other possible relationships between diet quality and brain size such as the importance of essential fatty and amino acids, vitamins, and minerals (Broadhurst et al. 1998, Horrobin 1998, Milton 1999) or the role of a high quality diet in supporting maternal nutrition during gestation and especially lactation (Martin 1996, Leonard & Robertson 1994). It is also important to remember that the hypothesis is not necessarily weakened by the fact that there is no universal correlation between relative brain size and relative gut size across mammals. Brain size does not make up a significant component of total body RMR in many other animals as it does in humans and therefore is not a limiting factor. The emerging field of ecophysiology also clearly demonstrates that animals as varied as snakes, birds, and mammals manipulate their RMRs through differential size of other expensive tissues to meet varying environmental or life-history challenges (Aiello et al. 2001).

Changes in the expensive tissues are also not the only potential source of changes in the constituents of the human RMR. A further hypothesis, to our knowledge not considered previously, is that the increased adiposity of later *Homo* species has partially concealed an increase in RMR of *Homo sapiens*. Reconstruction of hominin energy stores is well nigh impossible due to the poor preservation of soft tissue in the fossil record. Data on body fatness of nonhuman apes is sparse, and body composition is rarely considered when addressing the relationship between body size and metabolic rate. Although orangutans, like humans, appear to have the capacity to store fat in the abdomen (Zihlman & McFarland 2000), wild-living individuals from most contemporary primate species have percentage body fat lower than the 26%–28% of a well nourished woman or than the 14% of a man

(Forbes 1987, Rutenberg et al. 1987, McFarland 1997). Even in populations inhabiting harsh environments, body fatness in women is around 20% (Lawrence et al. 1987).

In modern humans, both fat mass and fat-free mass contribute to total RMR. Based on 104 normal women, the relative contribution of fat mass (FM) and fat-free mass (FFM) is:

$$RMR = k_1 FM + k_2 FFM,$$

where values for k_1 and k_2 are 0.31 and 1.35 Joules $s^{-1} kg^{-1}$, respectively (Garby et al. 1988). These values increase to 0.96 and 2.14 Joules $s^{-1} kg^{-1}$ at moderate activity levels, indicating that the relative metabolic cost of fat stores rises with the level of activity. The contribution of FM to RMR is attributed to the energy requirements of adipose tissue (Simonsen et al. 1994).

A change in the relative contributions of fat mass and fat-free mass to body mass confounds between-species energetic comparisons on a per kg body weight basis. In this instance, the greater fatness of humans suggests that, relative to nonhuman primates, RMR per unit fat-free mass of *Homo sapiens* has increased. Such an increase would suggest that rather than increased brain costs being fully offset by reduced gut costs, they may in part remain, concealed by the low-cost requirements of increased adipose tissue.

A higher maintenance expenditure of energy than expected on the basis of body size implies that humans must either compensate on expenditure energy on non-basal functions such as physical activity or obtain increased food resources. In general, higher resting energy requirements are predicted to be favored when food supply is abundant (Mueller & Diamond 2001). This may not be the case in hominin evolution; however, an alternative strategy for supporting high maintenance expenditure is the preservation of energy as fat in order to overcome fluctuations in food availability.

We do not know when hominins began to become fat, although Pond (1997) demonstrates that the distribution of fat deposits is similar in many mammals, including humans. In her opinion, bipedal posture is important in the distribution of human fat and, for example, the groin deposits in other mammals are extended in humans to form a continuous layer from pelvis to knee. Because the details of the anatomy and distribution of adipose tissue in living apes remain largely unknown, it is not possible to say when the unique features of human adipose tissue evolved (Pond 1991, 1997).

The ability to accumulate fat would be of enormous value in the more seasonal open environments occupied by *Homo ergaster*. Horrobin (2001) notes a kilogram of fat provides around 9000 calories, enough to survive reasonably well for 4–6 days (assuming consumption of 1500–2500 kcal d^{-1}). Although famine conditions may have been relatively rare in hominin evolution, less extreme fluctuations in food availability may have been relatively common. Contemporary Gambian farmers experience successive hunger and harvest seasons in which the highest energy expenditure on subsistence is required in the season of lowest food availability (Lawrence et al. 1987). Gambian women accommodate these seasonal stresses through highly flexible fat stores, and may gain or lose up to 4 kg of fat depending on the ability of energy intake to satisfy requirements (Lawrence et al. 1987). The ability to accommodate seasonal variation in food supply through physiological adaptation contrasts with the alterations of group size and structure that characterize closely related species such as chimpanzees, although orangutans also store fat to buffer against seasonal food supply fluctuations (Knott 1997).

Accumulation of fat to buffer seasonal stresses may therefore have been a crucial factor in the survival of *Homo ergaster* as compared to other hominin lines, and may have influenced group structure and sociality as well as energy balance per se. This hypothesis is particularly interesting given the faster reproductive turnover of human versus ape females and the proposed role of grandmothers in feeding older dependent offspring, implying a greater need to preserve group structure over time (see below).

The significance of energy stores for female reproductive fitness is also supported by observations of a reduced ability to conceive (Frisch & Macarthur 1974) and a higher rate of miscarriage in thin women, consistent with the life history theory prediction that unpredictable environments should favor maintaining parental survival probability at the expense of reproductive investment (Hirschfield & Tinkle 1975).

More on the Energetic Costs of the Brain

There is more in relation to the energetic costs of the brain than the relationship between relatively large brain and the energy balance of the adult individual. The increased brain costs of later hominin species are particularly significant in early life, when brain weight is a higher proportion of total body mass and takes up to 60%–70% of total energy requirements in the individual (Holliday 1986). Modern human infants and children have an elevated RMR throughout ontogeny that undoubtedly supports the higher energy demands of the proportionally large brain as well as the costs of growth (see below). Foley & Lee (1991) have calculated the human brain to increase energy requirements by 8.7% relative to *Pan* during the first 18 months postpartum.

Aiello and colleagues (2001) have suggested that the payoff between the size of the brain and gut may be particularly important to the child's energy balance after it is weaned and before it has acquired the necessary skills to acquire food for itself. However, increased energy intake is not the only strategy for meeting the costs of a larger brain, and during childhood the alternative strategy of reduced growth is observed.

A comparison of modern humans and *Pan* indicates that whereas growth in weight up to 2 years is relatively similar, for the ensuing 10 years *Pan* grows at a significantly faster rate (Ulijaszek 1995). Subsequently, this pattern is reversed, with growth in *Pan* slowing and mature size attained by about 12 years, whereas humans maintain and even increase their childhood growth rate during an adolescent growth spurt that continues to about 18 years.

The total energy cost of tissue growth is relatively constant between primate species, regardless of whether the weight gain comprises fat or lean tissue (Roberts & Young 1988). Further, given that much of the weight gain represents water, it is possible to ascribe a final cost of 4.5 kcal g^{-1} of tissue gain (FAO/WHO/UNU 1985). Growth costs, averaged over the first 10 years can therefore be calculated as 57 kcal d^{-1} and 44 kcal d^{-1} in male and female *Pan*, but only 27 kcal d^{-1} in both sexes in modern humans. In the following 8 years, the contrast is reversed, with *Pan* costs averaging 11 kcal d^{-1} in both sexes, and human costs being 42 kcal d^{-1} in both sexes.

This comparison indicates that the energy costs of growth are divided into three periods, with the most vulnerable childhood period protected by a slower growth rate. The initial growth period is funded directly through maternal metabolism (see also Martin 1996), whereas the final period is funded by the independent offspring when the ability to compete against adult conspecifics is improved (Jansen & van Schaik 1993).

Foley & Lee (1991) use the increased costs of brain growth to infer the likely evolution of slowed growth rate across hominin taxa. They suggest that with the evolution of *Homo* the burden becomes sufficiently severe to benefit from slower growth. Consistent with this prediction of the importance of brain size for growth rate, growth in *Homo ergaster*, with a brain size two-thirds of that of average modern humans, appears not to be slowed to the degree present in *Homo sapiens* (Dean et al. 2001).

Furthermore, slowed growth is a general feature of highly social species such as primates and carnivores (Bogin & Smith 1996). However, the association between slowed growth and sociality need not necessarily be attributed only to increased costs of brain growth. In social species, weaned offspring may remain partially dependent on the mother for food during the juvenile period, and selection may have favored slowed childhood growth in humans in order to protect maternal total fitness at the expense of fitness of individual offspring (Wells 2002). Thus parent–offspring conflict as well as increased energy requirements for brain growth may have favored slower growth during human childhood.

The Energetic Costs of Locomotion

Homo ergaster was not only significantly larger than the australopithecines and paranthropines, but also had significantly longer legs in relation to its body mass. This has further ramifications for energy turnover. The majority of the literature on bipedalism and energetics has been concerned with the energetic advantage of human bipedalism over primate quadrupedalism. It has been well established that, at maximum running speed, human bipedalism is twice as expensive energetically than estimated for a quadrupedal mammal of the same body mass (Taylor et al. 1970, Fedak & Seeherman 1979) and that human walking is energetically much more efficient that human running (Fedak et al. 1974). At an average walking speed of 4.5 km h^{-1}, human bipedalism is slightly more efficient than is quadrupedalism in the average mammal (Rodman & McHenry 1980). Both bipedalism and quadrupedalism are equally as expensive in chimpanzees (Taylor & Rowntree 1973), and at average walking speeds the chimpanzee consumes 150% more energy (g^{-1} km^{-1}) than does a similarly sized quadruped (Rodman & McHenry 1980).

This means that if the proto-hominin was energetically equivalent to a modern chimpanzee there would have been considerable energy savings through adoption of bipedalism, particularly if a large proportion of time was spent moving on the ground (Foley & Elton 1998). Foley (1992) calculated that at the same body mass a bipedal hominin would have been able to travel up to 11 km for the same level of energy expenditure as a chimpanzee would use over a 4-km distance. At a larger body size, bipedal hominins were likely to have been more energy efficient than chimpanzees, to the extent that a 53-kg hominin would have been able to travel 14 km, while a 57-kg hominin would have been able to travel 13 km. This would have allowed a greater foraging area. Similarly, using data on the energetics of modern human locomotion, Leonard & Robertson (1995) calculate that the energy savings for females would have been considerably greater than that for males, an important conclusion in relation to the high-energy demand of gestation and lactation (see below).

These estimates assume that bipedalism in hominins was as efficient as that in modern humans. However, it has generally been assumed that the relatively long legs in *Homo ergaster* gave it an advantage over the shorter-legged australopithecines and paranthropines (e.g., Jungers 1982, 1991; McHenry 1991; Webb 1996). Kramer (1999) and Kramer & Eck (2000) convincingly demonstrates that although long legs allow an individual to take fewer steps to cover a given distance and thereby reduce energy, long legs also are heavier and require more energy to move. The mass-specific mechanical power (W kg^{-1}) required to move australopithecine lower limbs (specifically AL 288-1, *Australopithecus afarensis*) is considerably less than in modern humans, whereas the cost of transport (J kg^{-1} m^{-1}) is virtually identical (Kramer 1999). The main disadvantage of australopithecine short legs would be a reduced walking speed, and on this basis Kramer & Eck (2000) calculate that the daily range of AL 288-1 would have been between 20%–40% smaller than for a modern human.

The advantage of bipedalism appears to be energy savings at walking speeds, whereas the advantage of relatively long *Homo* legs would have been the potential for a significantly increased daily range. Put simply, *Homo* could have moved faster at an energetically advantageous walking speed than would have been possible for the australopithecines. The cost of locomotion, however, is still proportional to body mass and distance covered. This brings up the issue of the daily energy expenditure (DEE) of the hominins.

Daily Energy Expenditure (DEE)

In spite of the fact that bipedalism is more efficient than primate quadrupedalism, Leonard & Robertson (1997) have established that human hunter–gatherers have substantially higher daily energy requirements than would be expected for a primate of our body mass. Their analysis is based on time-budget data from the literature, and DEE was computed by summing the caloric needs for maintenance (i.e., sleeping) and daily activities. Data for nonhuman primates were converted to caloric costs using the energetic models derived from Coelho (Coelho 1974, Coelho et al. 1979) and those for humans (!Kung and Ache) using models from the World Health Organization (FAO/WHO/UNU 1985). Their analysis results in a positive relationship between DEE and body mass ($DEE = 86.0\ W^{0.793}$, where W = body mass in kilograms), although the relationship is isometric when humans are excluded from the analysis (Key & Ross 1999, Aiello & Key 2002). Based on the inferred body mass of *Homo ergaster*, Leonard & Robertson suggest that its DEE would be between 40% and 85% greater than that of the australopithecines (see also Table 1). The higher percentage increase (80%–85%) is based on the assumption that *Homo ergaster* had human-like and not chimpanzee-like ranging behavior.

Leonard & Robertson (1997) also demonstrate that relative energy expenditure and day ranges are positively correlated with diet quality across primates, including humans. The relationship between diet quality and increased energy levels is also consistent with the observation that primates with higher diet quality have higher levels of social activity (Milton 1999).

Speculations on the Relationship Between Energetics and the Evolution of Human Social Organization

A further effect of the increased size of *Homo ergaster* mothers and hence offspring would have been the greater energy requirements during gestation and lactation. Gestation increases DEE by 20%–30% in mammals (Gittleman & Thompson 1988) and lactation by at least 37%–39% in primates (Oftedal 1984, Aiello & Key 2002). Aiello & Key (2002) demonstrate that the DEE for a lactating *Homo ergaster* female is about 45% higher than for a lactating australopithecine or paranthropine and almost 100% higher than for a non-lactating and nongestating smaller-bodied hominin (Table 1). They argue that the resulting high per offspring energy costs could have been considerably reduced by decreasing the interbirth interval, with the additional benefit of increasing the number of offspring per mother. A faster reproductive schedule reduces the most expensive part of reproduction, lactation, although the benefit would be countered by a smaller increase in the energy required to support dependent offspring. Interbirth intervals have been estimated at around 4 years in gorillas, 5.5 years in wild chimpanzees, and 8 years in orangutans (Galdikas & Wood 1990), considerably longer than in most contemporary hunter–gatherer societies (Sear et al. 2000, Aiello & Key 2002).

Even taking into account this improved efficiency of reproduction in *Homo*, Aiello & Key (2002) argue that the increased requirements could only have been attained through a radical shift in foraging strategy involving the dietary changes highlighted earlier in this paper including increased exploitation of both animal products and underground storage organs (O'Connell et al. 1999, Wrangham et al. 1999).

An important aspect of this is that the energetic costs of feeding dependent offspring need not be met only by the mother. Hawkes and colleagues (1997a,b; 1998) have proposed the grandmother hypothesis, whereby postmenopausal women contribute to the parenting of their daughter's offspring. An increased level of paternal care, possibly mediated by changes in the stability of the parental pair bond, represents another potential source of energy for parental investment (Key 1998, 1999; Key & Aiello 1999, 2000; Kaplan et al. 2000). A recent analysis of data from the Gambia provided support for the grandmother hypothesis, showing that maternal grandmothers had a significant effect on offspring height (Sear et al. 2000). In contrast, the effect of paternal grandfathers and male kin on child height was negligible. An alternative and simpler hypothesis is that the cost of supporting offspring is reduced when there are several dependent offspring simultaneously (Peccei 2001), although the principal energetic costs of growth and maintenance are predicted to be minimally affected by such a strategy (Aiello & Key 2002).

Summary

In summary, the emergence of *Homo* is characterized by three changes in maintenance energy requirements: (*a*) an absolute increase, due to greater body size; (*b*) a shift in the relative requirements of different organs, with increased energy diverted to brain metabolism at the expense of gut tissue, possibly mediated by changes in the proportion of weight comprised of fat; and (*c*) a slower rate of childhood growth, offset by higher growth costs during infancy and adolescence when faster growth rates are more viable. These direct changes then impose significant knock-on costs, including increased costs of reproduction, and also must be viewed in the context of the inferred changes in foraging strategy for *Homo ergaster*, which would have involved larger daily ranges and correspondingly elevated locomotor costs. Collectively, these increased costs are predicted to have been met by adaptations in energy stores, reproductive schedule, social interaction, changes in body form and leg length, and in foraging strategies that were modified by some form of economic division of labor. Of particular interest, given the contemporary increase in obesity, is the increased tendency to store fat as a buffer between high energy turnover and variable food supply.

Acknowledgments

We would like to thank Tim Cole, Cathy Key, Kristin Hawkes, and Peter Wheeler for numerous and invaluable discussions during the development of the ideas presented in this paper.

The *Annual Review of Anthropology* is online at http://anthro.annualreviews.org

Literature Cited

Aiello LC. 1997. Brains and guts in human evolution: the expensive tissue hypothesis. *Braz. J. Genet.* 20:141–48

Aiello LC, Bates N, Joffe T. 2001. In defense of the expensive tissue hypothesis. In *Evolutionary Anatomy of the Primate Cerebral Cortex*, ed. D Falk, K Gibson, pp. 57–78. Cambridge: Cambridge Univ. Press

Aiello LC, Key C. 2002. The energetic consequences of being a *Homo erectus* female. *Am. J. Hum. Biol.* 14:In press

Aiello LC, Wheeler P. 1995. The expensive tissue hypothesis: the brain and digestive system in human and primate evolution. *Curr. Anthropol.* 36:199–221

Aiello LC, Wood BA. 1994. Cranial variables as predictors of hominine body mass. *Am. J. Phys. Anthropol.* 95:409–26

Barton RA. 1992. Allometry of food intake in free-ranging anthropoid primates. *Folia Primatol.* 58:56–59

Bogin B, Smith BH. 1996. Evolution of the human life cycle. *Am. J. Hum. Biol.* 8:703–16

Broadhurst CL, Cunnane SC, Crawford MA. 1998. Rift Valley lake fish and shellfish provided brain-specific nutrition for early *Homo. Br. J. Nutr.* 7:3–21

Coelho AM. 1974. Socio-bioenergetics and sexual dimorphism in primates. *Primates* 15:263–69

Coelho AM, Bramblett CA, Quick LB. 1979. Activity patterns in howler and spider monkeys: an application of socio-bioenergetic methods. In *Primate Ecology and Human Origins*, ed. IS Bernstein, EO Smith, pp. 175–200. New York/London: Garland STPM

Dean C, Leakey MG, Reid D, Schrenk F, Schwartz GT, et al. 2001. Growth processes in teeth distinguish modern humans from *Homo erectus* and earlier hominins. *Nature* 414:628–31

de Menocal PB. 1995. Plio-Pleistocene African climate. *Science* 270:53–59

Durnin JVGA, Passmore R. 1967. *Energy, Work and Leisure.* London: Heinemann. 166 pp.

FAO/WHO/UNU. 1985. Energy and protein requirements. *WHO Tech. Rep. Ser.* 724. Geneva: WHO

Fedak MA, Pinshow B, Schmidt-Nielsen K. 1974. Energetic cost of bipedal running. *Am. J. Physiol.* 227:1038–44

Fedak MA, Seeherman AJ. 1979. Reappraisal of energetics of locomotion shows identical costs in bipeds and quadrupeds including ostrich and horse. *Nature* 282:713–16

Foley RA. 1987. *Another Unique Species: Patterns in Human Evolutionary Ecology.* Harlow: Longman Sci. Tech.

Foley RA. 1992. Evolutionary ecology of fossil hominids. In *Evolutionary Ecology and Human Behavior*, ed. EA Smith, B Winterhalder, pp. 131–64. Chicago: Aldine de Gruyter

Foley RA, Elton S. 1998. Time and energy: the ecological context for the evolution of bipedalism. In *Primate Locomotion*, ed. E Strasser, J Fleagle, A Rosenberger, H McHenry, pp. 419–33. New York/London: Plenum

Foley RA, Lee PC. 1991. Ecology and energetics of encephalisation in hominid evolution. *Philos. Trans. R. Soc. London Ser. B* 334:223–32

Forbes GB. 1987. *Human Body Composition: Growth, Aging, Nutrition and Activity*. New York: Springer-Verlag. 350 pp.

Frisch RE, McArthur JW. 1974. Menstrual cycles; fatness as a determinant of minimum weight for height necessary for their maintenance or onset. *Science* 185:949–51

Galdikas BMF, Wood JW. 1990. Birth spacing patterns in humans and apes. *Am. J. Phys. Anthropol.* 83:185–91

Garby L, Garrow JS, Jørgensen B, Lammert O, Madsen K, et al. 1988. Relation between energy expenditure and body composition in man: specific energy expenditure in vivo of fat and fat-free tissue. *Eur. J. Clin. Nutr.* 42:301–5

Gittleman JL, Thompson DS. 1988. Energy allocation in mammalian reproduction. *Am. Zool.* 28:863–75

Hawkes K, O'Connell JF, Blurton Jones NG. 1997a. Menopause: evolutionary causes, fossil and archaeological consequences. *J. Hum. Evol.* 32:A8–9 (Abstr.)

Hawkes K, O'Connell JF, Blurton Jones NG. 1997b. Hadza women's time allocation, offspring provisioning, and the evolution of long postmenopausal lifespans. *Curr. Anthropol.* 38:551–77

Hawkes K, O'Connell JF, Blurton-Jones NG, Alvarez H, Charnov EL. 1998. Grandmothering, menopause, and the evolution of human life histories. *Proc. Natl. Acad. Sci. USA* 95:1336–39

Hirschfield MF, Tinkle DW. 1975. Natural selection and the evolution of reproductive effort. *Proc. Natl. Acad. Sci. USA* 72:2227–31

Holliday MA. 1986. Body composition and energy needs during growth. In *Human Growth: A Comprehensive Treatise*, ed. F Falkner, JM Tanner, 2:101–7. New York: Plenum. 2nd ed.

Horrobin DF. 1998. Schizophrenia: the illness that made us human. *Med. Hypotheses* 50: 269–88

Horrobin DF. 2001. *The Madness of Adam and Eve*. London: Bantam. 275 pp.

Janson CH, van Schaik CP. 1993. Ecological risk aversion in juvenile primates: slow and steady wins the race. In *Juvenile Primates: Life History, Development and Behaviour*, ed. ME Pereira, LA Fairbanks, pp. 57–74. Oxford: Oxford Univ. Press

Jungers WL. 1982. Lucy's limbs, skeletal allometry and locomotion in *Australopithecus africanus. Nature* 297:676–78

Jungers WL. 1991. A pygmy perspective on body size and shape in *Australopithecus afarensis* (AL 288-1, 'Lucy'). In *Origines de la Bipedie chez les Hominides*, ed. Y Coppens, B Senut, pp. 215–24. Paris: Editions Centre Natl. Rech. Sci.

Kaplan H, Hill K, Lancaster J, Hurtado AM. 2000. A theory of human life history evolution: diet, intelligence, and longevity. *Evol. Anthropol.* 9:156–85

Kappelman J. 1996. The evolution of body mass and relative brain size in fossil hominids. *J. Hum. Evol.* 30:243–76

Key CA. 1998. *Cooperation, paternal care and the evolution of hominid social groups.* Doctoral diss. Dep. Anthropol., Univ. Coll. London/Univ. London

Key CA. 1999. Non-reciprocal altruism and the evolution of paternal care. In *Proceedings of Genetic Algorithms and Evolutionary Computation Conference* (*GECCO-99*), ed. W Banzhaf, J Daida, AE Eiben, MH Garzon, V Honavar, M Jakiela, RE Smith, 2:1313–20. San Francisco: Morgan-Kaufman

Key CA, Aiello LC. 1999. The evolution of social organization. In *The Evolution of Culture*, ed. RIM Dunbar, C Knight, C Power, pp. 15–33. Edinburgh: Edinburgh Univ. Press

Key CA, Aiello LC. 2000. A prisoner's dilemma model of the evolution of paternal care. *Folia Primatol.* 71:77–92

Key CA, Ross C. 1999. Sex differences in energy expenditure in non-human primates. *Proc. R. Soc. London Ser. B* 266:2479–85

Kleiber M. 1932. Body size and metabolism. *Hilgardia* 6:315–53

Kleiber M. 1961. *The Fire of Life: An Introduction to Animal Energetics.* Huntington, NY: Krieger

Knott CD. 1997. The effects of changes in food availability on diet, activity and hormonal patterns in wild Bornean orangutans. *Am. J. Phys. Anthropol.* (*Suppl.*) 24:145

Kramer PA. 1998. The costs of human locomotion: maternal investment in child transport. *Am. J. Phys. Anthropol.* 107:71–85

Kramer PA. 1999. Modelling the locomotor energetics of extinct hominids. *J. Exp. Biol.* 202:2807–18

Kramer PA, Eck GG. 2000. Locomotor energetics and leg length in hominid bipedality. *J. Hum. Evol.* 38:651–66

Lawrence M, Coward WA, Lawrence F, Cole TJ, Whitehead RG. 1987. Fat gain during pregnancy in rural African women: the effect of season and dietary status. *Am. J. Clin. Nutr.* 45:1442–50

Leonard WR, Robertson ML. 1992. Nutritional requirements and human evolution: a bioenergetics model. *Am. J. Hum. Biol.* 4:179–95

Leonard WR, Robertson ML. 1994. Evolutionary perspectives on human nutrition: the influence of brain and body size on diet and metabolism. *Am. J. Hum. Biol.* 6:77–88

Leonard WR, Robertson ML. 1995. Energetic efficiency of human bipedality. *Am. J. Phys. Anthropol.* 97:335–38

Leonard WR, Robertson ML. 1997. Comparative primate energetics and hominid evolution. *Am. J. Phys. Anthropol.* 102:265–81

Martin RD. 1996. Scaling of the mammalian brain: the maternal energy hypothesis. *News Physiol. Sci.* 11:149–56

McFarland R. 1997. Female primates: fat or fit? In *The Evolving Female*, ed. ME Morbeck, A Galloway, AL Zihlman, pp. 163–75. Princeton: Princeton Univ. Press

McHenry HM. 1991. Femoral lengths and stature in Plio-Pleistocene hominids. *Am. J. Phys. Anthropol.* 85:149–58

McHenry HM. 1992a. Body size and proportions in early hominids. *Am. J. Phys. Anthropol.* 87:407–31

McHenry HM. 1992b. How big were early homnids? *Evol. Anthropol.* 1:15–19

McHenry HM. 1994. Behavioral ecological implications of early hominid body size. *J. Hum. Evol.* 27:77–87

McHenry HM, Coffing K. 2000. *Australopithecus* to *Homo*: transformations in body and mind. *Annu. Rev. Anthropol.* 29:125–46

Milton K. 1999. A hypothesis to explain the role of meat-eating in human evolution. *Evol. Anthropol.* 8:11–21

Mink JW, Blumenschine RJ, Adams DB. 1981. Ratio of central nervous system to body metabolism in vertebrates: its constancy and functional basis. *Am. J. Physiol. Regul. Integr. Comp. Physiol.* 241:R203–12

Mueller P, Diamond J. 2001. Metabolic rate and environmental productivity: well-provisioned animals evolved to run and idle fast. *Proc. Natl. Acad. Sci. USA* 98:12550–54

O'Connell JF, Hawkes K, Blurton Jones NGB. 1999. Grandmothering and the evolution of *Homo erectus*. *J. Hum. Evol.* 36:461–85

Oftedal TO. 1984. Milk composition, milk yield and energy output at peak lactation: a comparative review. *Symp. Zool. Soc. London* 51:33–85

Peccei JS. 2001. Menopause: adaptation or epiphenomenona? *Evol. Anthropol.* 10:43–57

Pond C. 1991. Adipose tissue in human evolution. In *The Aquatic Ape: Fact or Fiction?*, ed. M Roede, J Wind, JM Patrick, V Reynolds, pp. 193–220. London: Souvenir

Pond C. 1997. The biological origins of adipose tissue in humans. In *The Evolving Female*, ed. ME Morbeck, A Galloway, AL Zihlman, pp. 147–62. Princeton: Princeton Univ. Press

Reed KE. 1997. Early hominid evolution and ecological change through the African Plio-Pleistocene. *J. Hum. Evol.* 32:289–322

Roberts SB, Young VR. 1988. Energy costs of fat and protein deposition in the human infant. *Am. J. Clin. Nutr.* 48:951–55

Rodman PS, McHenry HM. 1980. Bioenergetics and the origin of hominid bipedalism. *Am. J. Phys. Anthropol.* 52:103–6

Ruff CB. 1991. Climate and body shape in hominid evolution. *J. Hum. Evol.* 21:81–105

Rutenberg GW, Coehlo AM Jr, Lewis DS, Carey KD, Gill HC Jr. 1987. Body composition in baboons: evaluating a morphometric method. *Am. J. Primatol.* 12:275–85

Sear R, Mace R, McGregor IA. 2000. Maternal grandmothers improve nutritional status and survival of children in rural Gambia. *Proc. R. Soc. London Ser. B* 267:1641–47

Sikes NE. 1999. Plio-Pleistocene floral context and habitat preferences of sympatric hominid species in East Africa. In *African Biogeography, Climate Change, and Human Evolution*, ed. T Bromage, F Schrenk, pp. 301–15. Oxford: Oxford Univ. Press

Simonsen L, Bulow J, Madsen J. 1994. Adipose tissue metabolism in humans determined by vein catheterization and microdialysis techniques. *Am. J. Physiol. Endocrinol. Metab.* 266:E357–65

Speth JD. 1989. Early hominid hunting and scavenging: the role of meat as an energy source. *J. Hum. Evol.* 18:329–13

Speth JD, Spielmann KA. 1983. Energy source, protein metabolism, and hunter–gatherer subsistence strategies. *J. Anthropol. Archaeol.* 2:1–31

Stahl WR. 1965. Organ weights in primates and other mammals. *Science* 150:1039–42

Stearns SC. 1992. *The Evolution of Life Histories.* Oxford: Oxford Univ. Press

Taylor CR, Rowntree VJ. 1973. Running on two or four legs: which consumes more energy? *Science* 179:186–87

Taylor CR, Schmidt-Nielsen K, Raab JL. 1970. Scaling of energetic cost of running to body size in mammals. *Am. J. Physiol.* 219:1104–7

Ulijaszek SJ. 1995. Energetics and human evolution. In *Human Energetics in Biological Anthropology*, ed. SJ Ulijaszek, pp. 166–75. Cambridge: Cambridge Univ. Press

Walker A, Leakey R, eds. 1993. *The Nariokotome Homo erectus Skeleton.* Cambridge, MA: Harvard Univ. Press

Webb D. 1996. Maximum walking speed and lower limb length in hominids. *Am. J. Phys. Anthropol.* 101:515–25

Wells JCK. 2002. Thermal environment and human birth weight. *J. Theor. Biol.* 214:413–25

Wells JCK, Cole TJ. 2002. Birth weight and environmental heat load: a between-population analysis. *Am. J. Phys. Anthropol.* In press

Wheeler PE. 1992. The thermoregulatory advantages of large body size for hominids foraging in savanna environments. *J. Hum. Evol.* 23:351–62

Wheeler PE. 1993. The influence of stature and body form on hominid energy and water budgets: a comparison of *Australopithecus* and early *Homo*. *J. Hum. Evol.* 24:13–28

Wood B. 1992. Origin and evolution of the genus *Homo*. *Nature* 355:783–90

Wood B, Aiello LC. 1998. Taxonomic and functional implications of mandibular scaling in early hominins. *Am. J. Phys. Anthropol.* 105:523–38

Wood B, Collard M. 1999. The human genus. *Science* 284:65–71

Wrangham RW, Jones JH, Laden G, Pilbeam D, Conklin-Brittain N. 1999. The raw and the stolen: cooling and the ecology of human origins. *Curr. Anthropol.* 5:567–94

Zihlman AL, McFarland RK. 2000. Body mass in lowland gorillas: a quantitative analysis. *Am. J. Phys. Anthropol.* 113:61–78

SECTION 11

ECOLOGY AND DIET

Introduction to Chapter 13

As our ancestors moved out of the forest, they began to exploit new food sources, including underground roots and tubers and large animal prey. These dietary shifts triggered a greater reliance on technology and more mutual dependence among various members of the social group. The mastery of fire may also have been a key catalyst in human evolution.

In Chapter 12, Aiello and Wells argued that early hominins traded off one costly organ system against another; they suggested that hominins reduced expenditures on digestion to pay for calorically expensive brains. Another way to address brain costs—not an alternative to a reduction in gut size but useful along with it—is to improve the quality of the diet. Only briefly discussed by Aiello and Wells, hominin dietary strategies are a main focus of Sonia Ragir's chapter.

How do we study human diets from an evolutionary perspective? The problem may seem overwhelming because human diet is so variable: People eat different foods in China or in Morocco than you do. But those cultural differences are relatively superficial and recent; we want to know what kinds of diets predominated over the big sweep of human evolution. Anthropologists have several ways of reconstructing what our ancestors ate. One is to sift the fossil and archaeological records for food remains or for indications of how foods were processed. Another is to study existing hunter-gatherer populations. Hunter-gatherers do not have any domesticated animals or crops. Domestication is less than 10,000 years old, so, for several million years before that, humans had to get all their food from naturally occurring plants and animals. Thus, existing hunter-gatherers provide a glimpse into the pre-agricultural past that prevailed for 99.9% of the time our lineage has been on the planet.

By studying existing hunter-gatherers, we have learned that human diets are very different from those of our close primate relatives—chimpanzees, gorillas or orangutans. Each of these ape cousins has a unique diet, to be sure, but they are all heavily based on *collected* foods. Collected foods are ones that you just pick up and eat. If you have ever eaten blackberries on a hike, then you have made use of a collected food. But collected foods are not the mainstay of hunter-gatherer diets. Humans rely instead on *extracted* foods. Extracted foods cannot simply be plucked and eaten. They need at least some additional processing or handling. A soft fruit can be collected, but a nut, surrounded by a hard shell, must be extracted. Likewise, tubers or roots must be dug up, and large animals must be pursued, killed and butchered, so these are all extracted food. Chimpanzees, our closest living relatives, have diets that are about 95% collected and about 5% extracted. In contrast, human hunter-gatherers rely more than 90% on extracted foods. This is the key difference between ape and human feeding niches.

With the exception of nectar "bribes" paid to pollinators and fruit rewards for seed dispersers, being eaten by animals does not generally boost a plant's reproductive success. Selection thus favors any plant mutation that provides protection from would-be munchers, and many different kinds of plant defenses have evolved. Some are obvious, such as irritating spines and hairs. Others are chemical toxins—allelochemicals—that work by interfering with the digestive processes of the consumer. Alleolochemicals differ in strength (toxicity). Some can be eaten in small quantities at sufficiently spaced intervals, but others must be diluted or eliminated before the plant can be eaten. Thus, beyond the basic harvesting tool kit, other kinds of soaking, leeching, fermenting and drying techniques may be necessary. In addition, clay can absorb these allelochemicals, so some humans and other animals eat soil (called geophagy) in order to reduce the harmful effects of these toxins. These kinds of strategies had to evolve in parallel with any reliance on wild tubers and bulbs—and probably were taught to kin and other foraging partners (see Chapter 18).

Evidence both from chimpanzees and from human hunter-gatherers suggests that meat and tubers may have entered the hominin diet because ancestral males and females were employing somewhat separate foraging strategies. In all known hunter-gatherer populations there is a very strong sexual division of labor: Men hunt larger animal prey and women forage for immobile plant foods. Interestingly, this same difference is found among chimpanzees. Chimps only derive about 1% of their total food intake from animal prey—most of it being monkeys. But this hunting is almost exclusively done by males, who cooperate with each other to close off the escape routes of their intended prey. When chimps are successful in capturing a monkey, the resulting meat is shared among the males who cooperated in the hunt and with females who happen to be ovulating at the time—and thus able to conceive. Yes, chimps regularly trade meat for sex, but in general, males get more of the meat, and thus female chimps spend considerably more time fishing for termites and cracking nuts (two good alternative sources of protein) than males do.

Among human hunter-gatherers, food distribution patterns vary in a predictable way. Vegetable foods collected by women and small animal prey tend to be kept within the family, shared by a woman and her mate and their children. On the other hand, large animal prey are divided by the hunter and distributed widely across the social group, mostly based on closeness of genetic kinship to the hunter. You should notice that this corresponds to the predictions of kin-selection theory. It also exemplifies the idea that windfalls too large to be consumed before they spoil can be converted to future benefits by creating bonds of reciprocity (see Chapter 7).

A related and very interesting question in human evolution is, whether enduring male-female bonds—families—grew out of a mutual dependence on the fruits of each other's hunting and gathering efforts. In other words, did ancestral men and women pair up so she could provide the calories and he could provide the protein? Does the fact that males share their foraging gains more widely argue against this view? Or is it just a consequence of the need to insure against an uncertain foraging future? Some detailed research on the *Ache*—a South American hunter-gatherer tribe—has suggested that the best hunters have more offspring with other men's wives. Meat-for-sex may be a retained primitive trait in the human-chimp clade!

A final idea that deserves attention is the role of fire in human evolution. Because time destroys everything, early fossil evidence—of anything—tends to be scarcer than recent fossil evidence. There is good evidence for the use of fire by humans 300,000 years ago, but poorer evidence before that. Richard Wrangham, a Harvard-based anthropologist, acknowledges that, because fire occurs naturally (e.g., lightening-caused fires), the earlier we look, the more difficult it is to tell natural fires from human-built hearths. But he suggests in a recent book, *Catching Fire*, that the hearths are there, dating back two million years. In other words, members of the genus *Homo* may have been using fire since their origins. The benefits of fire are many. It decontaminates food. It makes more of the nutrients in plant foods available for digestion by breaking down their tough cell walls. And it makes it possible to consume much more meat by rendering it chewable. If you have ever eaten raw meat—steak tartar for example—I guarantee that it had been heavily processed by grinding or pounding. This is because raw unprocessed muscle meat is almost impossible to chew (large carnivores such as lions do not chew it; they swallow it in large unchewed chunks). Aiello and Wells argued that a higher-quality, more nutrient-dense diet was essential to supporting the expanding human brain. Wrangham argues that fire is what made enough of those nutrients accessible.

Chapter 13 Glossary

allelochemicals: Toxic compounds that do not enter the metabolic pathways of the plant but inflict costs on animals that consume them; also sometimes called secondary compounds because they are secondary to the plant's metabolism.

Plio-Pleistocene: The period straddling the boundary between the Pliocene and the Pleistocene.

rhizome: Underground storage organ of a plant; a rootstock from which the plant can send up new green shoots after lying dormant during a cold or dry season; usually grows horizontally.

tuber: Underground storage organ of a plant; similar to rhizome (some tubers are thickened rhizomes).

Chapter 13
Diet and Food Preparation: Rethinking Early Hominid Behavior (2000)

Sonia Ragir

At least four innovations in nutrient sources, preparation, and distribution underlie the transformation of our evolutionary ancestors into modern humans: the digging, preparation, and consumption of tubers and rhizomes; the technological mediation of hunting and butchering of animal prey; the socially mediated redistribution of animal prey; and the control of fire for cooking. The emergence of technologies for processing hard-to-obtain or difficult-to-digest foods such as animal protein, savanna tubers, rhizomes, and perennial bulbs probably precipitated changes in energy availability and expenditure that directly affected gut proportion and indirectly affected sexual dimorphism, fetal weight, and brain size.[1,2] The indigestibility or toxicity of several potential food items, including rootstocks and carrion, could be extremely important for understanding hominid adaptations to the mosaic ecology of late Plio-Pleistocene South and East Africa.[3–5] Primate consumption of rootstocks, seeds, and meat, which is often assumed to be essential for hominid adaptation to the savanna-woodland, is constrained by digestion-inhibiting agents in underground storage organs and by the rapid bacterial contamination of carrion. These potential restrictions on hominid food choice have led me to argue that hunting rather than scavenging, together with technologically assisted extractive foraging and food preparation, was an essential part of the earliest hominid behavioral repertoire.[4,6]

The archeological and fossil record and studies of comparative gut morphology demonstrate that major technological innovations and relatively minor adaptations in digestive physiology often accompanied new sources of nutrition.[1,7,8] Because plant toxins and

Sonia Ragir, "Diet and Food Preparation: Rethinking Early Hominid Behavior," from *Evolutionary Anthropology: Issues, News, and Reviews*; Vol. 9 Issue 4, pp. 153–155.

digestion-inhibiting compounds constrain primates' dietary choices,[5] their presence in a majority of savanna rootstocks and mature leaves must have had an impact on food choices and motivated hominid food preparation.[9,10] With the exception of wooden digging sticks, technologically assisted foraging is not usually attributed to Australopithecines. Yet some simple extractive techniques such as crushing, soaking, and termite fishing can be found among chimpanzee and other primate communities, which suggests that, at the very least, these techniques would have been within the capacity of the earliest hominids.[11–13]

Tubers, rhizomes, and perennial bulbs are rich in carbohydrates but low in protein, and may have been important sources of energy for early hominids.[7,10] The edible wild tubers of the rainforest and savanna are mostly yams (*Dioscorea* spp.); when cooked, they become a staple food for extant populations of hunter–gatherers.[10] Because their large size made feeding among the small ends of branches difficult, hominids frequently would have foraged on the ground where the vegetation from edible tubers and rhizomes grows out of the moist soil of a rainforest. Aboveground visual cues to the presence of edible roots would have been part of the knowledge that hominids carried from the tropical forest to riparian woods and out onto the baked ground of the grasslands.[14] The pattern of wear on australopithecine incisor and molar surfaces and on the polished ends of long bone and antler tools at Swartkrans in South Africa has been interpreted as evidence of the extraction and consumption of rootstocks by *Australopithecus* and *Paranthropus*.[15,16]

The exploitation of mosaic, semi-arid, and seasonal habitats by early hominids would have required either physiological or technological adaptations in order to include wild tubers and bulbs as staple items in their diets. Most apes cannot digest large quantities of toxic plant compounds. In contrast, herbivores have specialized chambers of the digestive tract in which a symbiotic intestinal flora deactivates plant allelo-chemicals through the process of fermentation. Chimpanzees and other large primates rarely exploit the underground storage organs that are the staple of many tropical hunter–gather populations. Outside the rainforest, in the savanna-woodlands of subtropical Africa, fewer varieties of tubers and bulbs are present.[9] And most tuberous species in these drier areas have increased amounts of digestion-inhibiting compounds such as invertase, amylase, and proteinase inhibitors, which prevent the enzyme decomposition of fat, sugar, starch, and protein.[3,5,17]

Before the use of fire for cooking, hominids would have had to remove or deactivate the digestion inhibitors in rhizomes and rootstocks mechanically by crushing, soaking, fermenting, or drying them, or by eating them with clay.[4,6,10] Crushing and soaking leaches out allelo-chemicals in roots, while fermentation allows wild yeast to break down the remaining toxins. Pharmacological research has demonstrated how alkaloids and other toxic compounds in roots and rhizomes are effectively bound by clay. Humans deliberately use the adsorptive properties of clays and, occasionally, other substances such as charcoal and lime to bind toxins in food in ways that appear to be an elaboration of the geophagy that is observed in animals.

The most common and reliable subsistence strategy in tropical and midlatitude modern hunter–gatherer population is based on a high daily consumption of roots, fruit, flowers, and young leaves that are gathered primarily by women and children. These are supplemented with animal protein from both small, slow-moving animals, also collected by women and children, and larger mammals that are hunted by men. The proportion of animal protein in diets increases as hunters move to higher latitudes: meat constitutes 5% to 20% of the tropical hunter–gather diet but more than 70% of the winter diet of subArctic and Arctic hunters.[18]

As is true among most primates, there is a significant difference in foraging range and diet between females and males in contemporary hunter–gatherers. It seems likely that this traditional asymmetry in the distribution of animal protein was also to be found among female Australopithecines and early *Homo*. Female chimpanzees tend to eat more low-nutrient foods than do adult males. Females also have to spend more time foraging than males do. Among chimpanzees, it has been observed that the use of tools for the exploitation of insects and hard-to-process oily nuts is primarily a female and juvenile activity.[11–13,16] Because rootstocks are hard to obtain and require time-consuming preparation in order for humans to absorb their nutrients, they most likely were gathered, prepared, and eaten by early hominid females and juveniles.[18,19] It seems reasonable to assume that hominid adult males would have had relatively little need to exchange meat for plant food with females. Because of their larger size, they, like chimpanzee males, would have had preferential access to easily obtained and digested ripe or dried fruit, nuts, and meat during the wet and dry seasons.

Because digging, as well as crushing and soaking, was necessary to obtain and detoxify rootstocks, female hominids may have played a central role in the emergence of tool use and manufacture.[20] Until tools became necessary for processing foods in male-dominated domains such as hunting, australopithecine and early *Homo* food preparation and tool-making may have been largely female activities to gather hard-to-obtain foods.[12,13,20,21]

Because of maternal provisioning during their relatively long period of semi-dependency, male juveniles would have been familiar with tool use and could have transferred this knowledge to male activities such as skinning and butchering. However, adult males probably did not enter into the systematic manufacture of tools until early *Homo erectus* began killing and butchering larger herbivores.[1,20] Killing large animals required implements for holding, battering, and piercing, while cutting and chopping implements were needed for skinning, defleshing, and dismembering. Males might have adapted the female tool kit. For example, they may have used sharpened digging sticks to pierce and hold prey, pounding and crushing stones to dismember carcasses and extract marrow, and root peelers and scrapers to skin and deflesh carcasses. Among ethnographic hunters, hunting and affiliative exchanges are time-consuming and leave the men with little time or motivation for other foraging activity.[21] As early *Homo erectus* males engaged in hunting larger prey and extended sharing of meat, they too would have had less motivation for foraging or preparing plant foods. The larger herbivores found butchered in East African Acheulian sites suggests that more meat was available than the hunters could consume in one sitting.[1,8,13]

An institutionalized exchange of meat and prepared plant food between males and females may have commenced and intensified among *Homo erectus*. Demand sharing rather than formal reciprocal exchange could have provided the foundation for alliances among the males. These male alliances and female provisioning of semi-dependent juveniles could have created strong enough extended-family and community ties to support closer birth intervals and larger groups. The existence of this year-round supply of protein that is essential for the growth of a large brain and body not only supported changes in fetal and postnatal development, but also fueled population expansion and the dispersal of *H. erectus* out of Africa. On the other hand, the long-term reciprocal exchanges that underlie regional intergroup networks could hardly have emerged on the basis of demand-sharing of an episodically available and rapidly spoiling resource like meat.[2] Intergroup alliances such as marriage, regional-networks for exchanging raw material and finished products, and social stratification, which depend on long-term reciprocity, would require food preservation, storage technologies, and a more elaborate division of labor—that is, a specialization in the distribution of knowledge and production skills.[2]

The transition from late presapiens to archaic *H. sapiens* some 300,000 to 250,000 years ago was accompanied by the abundant evidence of the use of fire for cooking.[22] A revolution in food preparation, storage technology, and food distribution was precipitated by the use of fire. Because hominid females probably were the main participants in technologically assisted food extraction and preparation, and rarely strayed far from the safety of the social group, they were also available to maintain fires once a home base had been established. The sexual differentiation of gathering and hunting activity and the tendency of nonhuman and human females to forage close to the main group or camp put hominid females in a position to control the use of fire. Thus, it is likely that women were responsible for cooking and the innovations in human culture that followed from it.[4,13]

Cooking also gave females access to meat above and beyond those portions that they received after the hunters had shared with other males. In the process of cooking, females could informally appropriate pieces of meat for themselves and their infants before the formal redistribution of choice foods, which probably was still dominated by hunters and male-male affiliation. The enormous cranial volumes found in archaic *Homo sapiens* and the reduction of size dimorphism to modern proportions in late *Homo erectus* may be explained in part by an animal protein component in the female and juvenile diet comparable to that of modern high-latitude hunters.[18] This last significant episode of encephalization, the one that catapulted presapiens to *Homo sapiens*, may best be understood as the result of intensive hunting of large game and a cultural revolution that intensified with the use of fire for cooking.[1,4,22]

Female hominids were likely to have been the innovators of the early plant processing technology that males transferred to hunting. Hunting larger animals may have initiated demand sharing of meat and a greater year-round dietary stability. Nutritional stability in females then led to shorter birth spacing, and changes in the number of dependent juveniles in communities. This shift in the age composition of the group paved the way for group responsibility for the socialization of semi-dependent juveniles. The growth in population probably initiated hominid expansion into the vast temperate plains and forests of Europe and Asia. Concurrently, the increasing density of late *Homo erectus* and early *Homo sapiens* populations may have been the impetus for long-term reciprocal exchanges, insuring more balanced, hierarchical relationships within communities and stable relationships between them.

Because of their inherent advantages over females in size, strength, and access to preferred foods, as well as their lower expenditures of reproductive energy, hominid males were likely to have been behaviorally conservative. They did not have the motivation to invent nor would they have readily adopted energy-expensive technological innovations. Why should they? Preferential access to the high-nutrient foods that were easy to obtain, process, and digest did not require technological mediation of male foraging or hunting except, perhaps, in times of severe ecological crisis or population growth.

A conservative interpretation of the evidence from primate behavior leads to the assumption that, as among chimpanzees and baboons, female Australopithecines rarely profited from male hunting activity. Australopithecine females, who were meeting the protein and energy requirements of encephalization in fetuses and semi-dependent juveniles, were not only capable of but also motivated to develop the technology for digging, crushing, and detoxifying rootstocks. The association of early hominid tools and early Pleistocene African kill sites suggests that hominid males clung to opportunistic hunting without elaborating its technology for more than two million years. Finally, about one-and-a-half to two million years ago, male hominids probably borrowed and adapted the "female" foraging technology to satisfy an increased demand for animal protein that arose as the brain enlarged, the birth interval decreased, and the proportion of semi-dependent juveniles increased. The requirement of affiliative exchange between adult males and an increase in the number of semi-dependent juveniles probably motivated males to practice more intensive cooperative hunting of large prey, and permitted females access to a relatively stable supply of protein and amino acids essential for reproduction and growth.

Acknowledgments

I thank Nancy Bogen, Department of English, Sandra Brandler, Department of Sociology, Anthropology, Social Work, and Martin Rosenberg, New York University Medical Center, for their criticism and comments.

References

1. Aiello LC, Wheeler P. 1995. The expensive-tissue hypothesis: the brain and the digestive system in human and primate evolution. Curr Anthropol 36:199–221.
2. Deacon TW. 1997. The symbolic species. The co-evolution of language and the brain. New York: W.W. Norton.
3. Buonocore V, Silano V. 1986. Biochemical, nutritional and toxicological aspects of alpha-amylase inhibitors from plant foods. In Friedman M, editor. Nutritional and toxicological significance of enzyme inhibitors in foods. Advances in experimental medicine and biology vol. 199:483–507.
4. Stahl AB. 1984. Hominid dietary selection before fire. Curr Anthropol 25:151–168.
5. Waterman PG. 1984. Food acquisition and processing as a function of plant chemistry. In Chivers DJ, Wood BA, Bilsborough A, editors. Food acquisition and processing in primates. New York: Plenum. p 177–211.
6. Gordon KD. 1987. Evolutionary perspectives on human diet. In Johnson FE, editor. Nutritional anthropology. New York: Alan R. Liss. p 3–39.
7. Lee-Thorp JA, van der Merwe NJ, Brain CK. 1994. Diet of *Australopithecus robustus* at Swartkrans from stable carbon isotopic analysis. J Hum Evol 27:361–372.
8. McHenry H. 1994. Behavioral ecological implications of early hominid body size. J Hum Evol 27:77–87.
9. Peters CR, O'Brien EM. 1994. Potential hominid plant foods from woody species in semi-arid versus sub-humid sub-tropical Africa. In Chivers DJ, Langer P, editors. The digestive system in mammals. Food, form and function. Cambridge: Cambridge University. p 166–192.
10. Johns T. 1996. The origins of human diet and medicine: chemical ecology. Tucson: University of Arizona Press.
11. Boesch C. 1993. Aspects of transmission of tool-use in wild chimpanzees. In: Gibson KR, Ingold T, editors. Tools, language and cognition in human evolution. Cambridge: Cambridge University Press. p 171–184.
12. McGrew WC. 1977. Evolutionary implications of sex differences in chimpanzee predation and tool use. In: Hamburg DA, McCown ER, editors. The great apes. Menlo Park: Benjamin/Cummings. p 441–463.
13. Boesch C, Boesch H. 1984. Possible causes of sex differences in the use of natural hammers by wild Chimpanzees. J Hum Evol 13:415–440.
14. Hunt KD, Nishida T, Wrangham RW. (n.d.) Sex differences in chimpanzee positional behavior, activity budget and diet: relative contributions of rank, reproductive-demands and body size, and implications for tool-use. Am J Phys Anthropol.

15. Schoeninger MF. 1996. Stable isotope studies in human evolution. Evol Anthropol 4:83–98.
16. Kay RF. 1985. Dental evidence for the diet of Australopithecus. Ann Rev Anthropol 14:315–341.
17. Prathibha S, Nambisan B, Leelamma S. 1995. Enzyme inhibitors in tuber crops and their thermal stability. Plant Foods Hum Nutr 48:247–257.
18. Hayden B. 1981. Subsistence and ecological adaptations of modern hunter–gatherers. In: Harding RSO, Teleki G, editors. Omnivorous primates. New York: Columbia University Press. p 344–421.
19. Hawkes K, O'Connell JF, Blurton Jones NG. 1997. Hadza women's time allocation, offspring provisioning, and the evolution of long post-menopausal life spans: with CA comment. Curr Anthropol 38:551–578.
20. Zihlman A. 1997. The Palaeolithic glass ceiling: women in human evolution. In: Hager LD, editor. Women in human evolution. New York: Routledge. p 91–113.
21. O'Connell JF, Hawkes K, Blurton Jones NG. 1999. Grandmothering and the evolution of *Homo erectus*. J Human Evol 36:461–486.
22. James SR. 1989. Hominid use of fire in the Lower and Middle Pleistocene: a review of the evidence. Curr Anthropol 30:1–26.

SECTION 12

TOOLS

Introduction to Chapter 14

The manufacture and use of tools is not restricted to humans; our closest relatives also have some basic technology. In both early humans and chimpanzees, tool use is strongly associated with food acquisition, and knowledge of it seems to be culturally transmitted.

Chimpanzees and humans are sister taxa—species that share a common ancestor. In this case both fossil and genetic evidence suggest that our common ancestor lived approximately seven million years ago. There are presently two species of chimpanzee whose lineages separated approximately two million years ago. Both chimpanzee species have been studied in their natural habitats and both are known to spontaneously make and use tools, though both species are much less reliant on technology than humans are.

As discussed previously, human diets rely much more on extracted foods than chimpanzees' diets do. Extractive foraging generally requires some kind of tool use, for example, a hammer stone and an anvil stone in the case of nut extraction, digging implements for roots and tubers, and sharp implements for killing and butchering animals. This difference also probably explains why chimpanzees are less reliant on tools, because they use tools only when engaging in extractive foraging such as nut cracking or "termite fishing." However, chimpanzees seldom use tools in the context of killing or dismembering animals. So chimpanzees' tool use is generally restricted to extractive foraging, but not all of their extractive foraging depends on it.

Humans have been making tools for at least 2.6 million years, and the archaeological record offers evidence in the form of use scars suggesting they were used for digging tubers and for butchering animals—two kinds of extractive foraging. Remember that 2.6 million years ago, there were apparently no members of the genus *Homo*, so the tool makers and users must have been some kind of relatively small-brained *Australopithecus*. If a large brain is not required (chimps have roughly *Australopithecus*-sized brains), perhaps hominins used tools even earlier than 2.6 MYA, but tools that were made from more perishable materials than stone. One of the main points of Chapter 14 is that this earlier tool use is very likely, because some basic tool-making and tool-using abilities seem to be primitive in the chimp-human clade. In other words, because humans and chimps both possess these abilities to some degree, the simplest explanation is that our common ancestor did as well.

The chapter carefully points out the features that are similar, as well as the features that differ, between chimpanzee tool use and what we can reconstruct of hominin tool use. Pay close attention to the cognitive implications of these similarities and differences: What kinds of planning skills and communicative abilities are required to support the tool making and use that we see in each taxon?

Chapter 14
The Oldowan: The Tool Making of Early Hominins and Chimpanzees Compared (2009)

Nicholas Toth and Kathy Schick

Abstract

The Oldowan was the term first coined by Louis Leakey to describe the world's earliest stone industries, named after the famous site of Olduvai (formerly Oldoway) Gorge in Tanzania. The Oldowan Industrial Complex documents the first definitive evidence of early hominin culture as well as the earliest known archaeological record. This review examines our state of knowledge about the Oldowan and the hominin tool makers who produced this archaeological record and compares and contrasts these patterns with the technological and cultural patterns of modern apes, especially chimpanzees and bonobos. Of special interest are methodological approaches that can attempt to make direct comparisons between the early archaeological record and modern ape material culture, including a long-term collaborative experimental program in teaching modern apes to make and use stone tools.

Key Words: bonobo, hominid, human evolution, stone technology, Palaeolithic

Department of Anthropology, Indiana University, Bloomington, and Stone Age Institute, Gosport, Indiana 47433; email: toth@indiana.edu, kaschick@indiana.edu

Introduction

The Oldowan Industrial Complex is the first definitive evidence for early hominin tool making and culture and marks the beginning of the archaeological record. Palaeolithic research into aspects of early stone tools has now been carried out for well over 150 years (research into the Oldowan for more than 50 years), including excavation and documentation of early sites and stone artifact assemblages in Africa, Europe, and Asia, as well as a variety of laboratory and experimental studies exploring their significance. Awareness of chimpanzee tool use in the wild began to emerge approximately 50 years ago, after Goodall's (1964) initial documentation of such behaviors, and field and laboratory studies of chimpanzee tool-making and tool-using abilities have grown dramatically over the past few decades. After such concerted research and the development of a fairly extensive literature in each of these areas, it would seem an appropriate time and stage in the discipline to undertake a comparison of tool-related behaviors evident among early hominin tool makers and that now documented among our closest living relatives, the chimpanzees and bonobos.

Why Compare Oldowan and Chimpanzee Tool Makers?

The makers and users of Oldowan tools are now extinct, with no modern representatives of their mental and physical abilities and behaviors. The very earliest Oldowan sites emerge, in fact, prior to definitive evidence of any significant increase in brain size in early hominins and are contemporary with a small-brained, bipedal hominin form, *Australopithecus garhi* (Asfaw et al. 1999), whose cranial capacity (~450 cc) is within the range of modern apes.

Thus, we are devoid of modern representatives of the ancient species of tool makers, but we do have relatives, other living ape species, that show considerable tool-making and tool-using abilities, namely members of the genus *Pan* (the chimpanzees and the bonobos). It can be safely argued that chimpanzees exhibit the most elaborate set of tool-related behaviors of any existing nonhuman species. Because the chimpanzee's cranial capacity is roughly equivalent to that of a potential candidate for the earliest tool maker, and in consideration of the chimpanzee's documented propensity to make and use tools, it can be extremely useful to examine the similarities and differences between chimpanzee and early hominin tool-related behaviors.

Such comparisons can help inform the fields of paleoanthropology and primatology as well as anthropology as a whole. These may help provide models for other possible tool behaviors of early hominins, which may be archaeologically invisible in the material record; they may highlight behavioral adaptations among early hominins that go beyond behavior patterns observed among other apes and which may have had significance in our species' evolutionary success; they can likewise highlight aspects of modern primate behavior that show parallels with the behavioral transformations in the evolutionary lineage that led to

Homo sapiens, or conversely, provide insight into important differences in the evolutionary trajectory of apes; and overall they may help provide a more refined view of how well, and in what ways, modern apes might serve as models for early hominin tool makers.

The Oldowan: An Overview

The earliest known assemblages of definite stone tools, consisting of stone artifacts that have been deliberately flaked through percussive blows, appear in the archaeological record at 2.6 Mya at Oldowan localities at Gona in Ethiopia (Semaw 2006), and numerous sites bearing such tools have been found over the ensuing 1.5 My, first in Africa, then also in Europe and Asia. For other discussions of the Oldowan, see Isaac (1981, 1982, 1984, 1989), Harris (1983), Toth (1985), Toth & Schick (1986, 2005, 2006), Schick (1986, 1987), Potts (1991), Harris & Capaldo (1993), Schick & Toth (1993, 1994, 2001, 2006, 2009), Klein (1999), Martínez et al. (2003), de Beaune (2004), Lewin & Foley (2004), Plummer (2004), Roche (2005), Pickering et al. (2007), Barsky (2009), Braun & Hovers (2009), Carbonell et al. (2009), de la Torre & Mora (2009), and Hovers & Braun (2009). Here we outline the hominin candidates for early tool makers, summarize the nature of Oldowan sites and their stone tool industries, and discuss possible behavioral and cognitive implications of these industries.

Who Were the Tool Makers? The Fossil Hominins

From the current evidence, the earliest stone tool-making hominins of the Oldowan were likely australopithecine-grade with smallish brains and large dentition. The discovery of *A. garhi* at approximately the same time as the Gona sites in Ethiopia and only 60 km to the south would suggest this species as a candidate for the maker of the very early tool industries at 2.6 Mya. This taxon is also roughly contemporaneous with *A. aethiopicus* in East Africa and *A. africanus* in South Africa.

Starting ~2.3 Mya, hominin remains have been assigned to the genus *Homo*, although good evidence for the beginning of the cranial expansion generally associated with this genus has not been documented until ~2 Mya. During the time span from 2.0 Mya to 1.0 Mya, the hominin taxa that have been identified that coexisted with stone tool assemblages include the robust australopithecines *A. boisei* in East Africa and *A. robustus* in South Africa and early members of the genus *Homo*: *H. rudolfensis*, *H. habilis*, and *H. erectus*.

It cannot be ruled out that more than one of these hominin forms could have had some involvement in stone tool manufacture and use, but it is apparent that members of the genus *Homo* (*a*) demonstrate a significant brain expansion during this period, between 2.0 and 1.0 Mya, likely correlated with a tool-making emphasis in their evolution; (*b*) also apparently carry this tool-making tradition out of Africa into Eurasia (Bar-Yosef & Goren-Inbar 1993, de Lumley et al. 2005, Diez-Martín 2006); and (*c*) continue this tradition beyond the time of the extinction of the robust australopithecines by 1 Mya. Thus, the *Homo* lineage would represent the major progenitors of Oldowan tools and, subsequently, the Acheulean tools (hand axes, cleavers, picks) that also appear on the paleolandscape starting ~1.6–1.7 Mya (about the time of the emergence of *H. erectus*) and is contemporaneous with these simpler industries.

The Nature of Oldowan Sites and Stone Industries

Stone artifacts constitute nearly the entirety of the record of early hominin tool making and tool using because these are nearly impervious to the many destructive forces at work since these sites were occupied. If early hominins also had a tool repertoire involving organic materials such as wood, hide, or other materials, direct evidence of these is, for the most part, invisible in the archaeological record. A small number of polished and striated bones that may have served as digging tools have been reported, however, and may give valuable hints about some of the missing elements of the Oldowan hominins' tool kits (Brain 1981, 2007; d'Errico et al. 2001; d'Errico & Backwell 2003).

Fundamentally, early Oldowan stone artifacts are primarily products of hand-held percussive flaking, i.e., holding a stone hammer in one hand and hitting another stone cobble or chunk held in the other hand with a strong percussive blow to detach flakes (a procedure called knapping). Another technique seen in the Oldowan is bipolar technique, in which a core is placed on an anvil and struck from the top with a hammer. Although this is ostensibly a relatively simple activity, experiments have shown this is not such an easy task to master, particularly with regard to the placement, angle, and power of the percussive blow (discussed further below).

Early Oldowan archaeological sites consist, at a minimum, of quantities of stone artifacts and often also contain fossil animal bones, mostly from medium-to-large-size animals. A number of these bones bear evidence of cut marks made with stone tools as well as evidence of deliberate percussive pitting and fracture (e.g., Blumenschine & Peters 1998, Bunn 1983, Pickering & Domínguez-Rodrigo 2006), presumably to access marrow. A lively debate has centered on whether such butchery traces represent earlier, more primary access to animal remains through hunting and/or confrontational scavenging (Bunn 1983, Bunn & Kroll 1986, Domínguez-Rodrigo 2009, Domínguez-Rodrigo et al. 2007, Pickering et al. 2007, Pickering & Domínguez-Rodrigo 2006) or whether hominins had later, secondary access to carcasses by scavenging the remains of carnivore kills (e.g., Blumenschine 1986, 1989).

Concentrations of hundreds or sometimes thousands of stone artifacts are typically found at many Oldowan sites, and sometimes these sites are clustered in major basins occupied by hominins and that were accumulating layers of sediment during the Plio-Pleistocene. Many of these sites are located in the Rift Valley of Eastern Africa, in karstic caves in South Africa, and in sedimentary basins in North Africa. Major localities include Gona (Semaw 2000, 2006; Semaw et al. 1997, 2003), Hadar (Kimbel et al. 1996), Middle Awash (de Heinzelin et al. 1999), Melka-Kunture (Chavaillon et al. 1979), Konso Gardula (Asfaw et al. 1992), Omo (Howell et al. 1987), and Fejej (Asfaw et al. 1991, de Lumley & Beyene 2004) in Ethiopia; East Turkana (Isaac & Isaac 1997), West Turkana (Delagnes & Roche 2005, Roche 2005, Roche et al. 1999), and Kanjera (Plummer et al. 2009) in Kenya; Olduvai Gorge in Tanzania (Blumenschine & Peters 1998; Leakey 1971, 1994; Peters & Blumenschine 1995, 1996; Potts 1988); Nyambusosi in Uganda (Texier 1995); Sterkfontein and Swartkrans in South Africa (Field 1999; Kuman 1998, 2005); Ain Hanech and El Kherba in Algeria in North Africa (Sahnouni 1998, 2006; Sahnouni et al. 1997, 2002); and Dmanisi in the Republic of Georgia (de Lumley et al. 2005).

A typical Oldowan stone tool assemblage generally includes percussors (hammerstones, spheroids), simple core forms (choppers, discoids, polyhedrons, heavy-duty scrapers), retouched elements (scrapers, awls), and debitage (flakes and fragments). After ~2 My, some sites exhibited higher proportions of artifact classes such as retouched forms and battered spheroids, which Mary Leakey called "Developed Oldowan" (Leakey 1971, pp. 1–8).

Oldowan artifacts, particularly the larger pieces or cores (so-called core tools), have often been categorized by various researchers according to their shapes and placed into inferred functional groupings such as choppers or scrapers. Experimental studies, however, have called into question whether such categories represent intentional end-products on the part of the hominin tool makers and also question the functional inferences often implied (Toth 1982, 1985). These experiments in manufacturing Oldowan artifact forms have demonstrated that the full range of typical core forms found at early sites can result as by-products of percussive flaking to produce a set of sharp flakes, although sharp-edged core forms could also be used for a range of chopping and scraping activities.

Raw materials used for stone artifacts tended to be found in the form of rounded cobbles from river gravels or angular chunks from primary rock outcrops. Depending on a given region, typical rock types included volcanic lavas (basalts, trachytes, rhyolites, phonolite, occasionally obsidians, etc.), ignimbrites ("welded tuffs"), quartzes, quartzites, limestones, and cherts.

A recurrent pattern at many Oldowan sites is evidence for transport of stone resources, including quantities of flaked materials, from place to place on the paleolandscape, as well as selectivity in choices of rock types and quality for tools (see Blumenschine et al. 2008; Braun et al. 2008, 2009a,b; Goldman-Neuman & Hovers 2009; Harmand 2009; Hay 1976; Negash et al. 2006; Piperno et al. 2009; Schick 1987; Stout et al. 2005; Toth 1982). At some sites, these transport distances were more than ten kilometers. At Olduvai Gorge, Tanzania, for instance, raw materials are quite often found several kilometers and sometimes 8–20 km from their sources, and at Kanjera, Kenya transport distances were up to 13 km.

Longer distance transport does not, of course, necessarily imply that hominins accomplished this in one event because raw materials may well have been moved on separate occasions from one site to another, and such movement of stone was likely embedded in their foraging patterns rather than special long-distance trips just for stone. From analysis of reconstructed cores and from technological analysis of the artifact assemblages, it is evident that hominins were often flaking cores prior to transporting them to a particular site, conducting further flaking at the site, and then subsequently transporting some of the artifacts away from the site. This indicates a level of behavioral complexity that has only recently begun to be appreciated.

One of the long-standing challenges of Palaeolithic archaeology is the determination of artifact function. For the Oldowan, most of the evidence is indirect—based on ethnographic analogy, experimental feasibility studies, and archaeological context (e.g., the association of stone artifacts with animal bones). We know that battered hammers and spheroids served as percussors for flaking stone, and roughly pitted stone hammers and anvils testify to their use in bipolar flaking. And, as previously mentioned, the processing of animal carcasses can leave diagnostic cut-mark traces from the stone knives used to skin, deflesh, and dismember, as well as produce diagnostic fracture patterns from breaking bones for marrow and brains. This evidence is particularly clear at the FLK Zinj site in Bed I at Olduvai (the "Woodstock" of Oldowan studies), but it should be noted that a number of Oldowan sites with associated stone artifacts and animal bones bear little or no evidence of hominin modification (e.g., Domínguez-Rodrigo 2009) and leave the probable function of these artifacts an open question.

Experiments in the use of a range of Oldowan artifact forms for a variety of possible tasks substantiate the effectiveness of simple flake edges in cutting tasks, particularly in animal butchery (Jones 1994; Toth 1982, 1985). Microscopic usewear analysis on a sample of Oldowan artifacts from East Turkana has indicated use of a number of flakes for cutting meat as well as use of some others for cutting soft plants (perhaps grasses for bedding) and for scraping wood (Keeley & Toth 1981). This latter evidence may suggest the use of stone tools to produce tools in other materials, e.g., perhaps the shaping of wood into spears or digging sticks, but such direct evidence is so far absent in the Oldowan.

The Oldowan documents one of the major phases of hominin brain evolution, with cranial capacities increasing from ~450 cc in *A. garhi* to up to 900 cc in early *Homo erectus*. Holloway et al. (2004) suggests that this period of brain evolution is correlated with increased language abilities, social complexity, tool standardization, hunting, and the development of home bases. Recently, brain-imaging studies (Stout et al. 2009) have shown that brain activity during the manufacture of Oldowan (and Acheulean) tools partially overlaps with areas associated with language, suggesting a possible coevolution of these two systems. For overviews and further discussions of the possible cognitive implications of early stone tools, see Parker & Gibson (1979), Isaac (1986), Wynn (1989, 2002), Gibson (1986), Dunbar (1993), Gibson & Ingold (1993), Toth & Schick (1993), Aiello & Wheeler (1995), Gowlett (1996), Joulian (1996), Mellars & Gibson (1996), Mithen (1996), Noble & Davidson (1996), Deacon (1997), Parker & McKinney (1999), Ambrose (2001), de la Torre et al. (2003), Holloway et al. (2004), de la Torre & Mora (2005), Pelegrin (2005), Roux & Bril (2005), Stout (2006), Stout & Semaw (2006), Stout et al. (2006, 2009), and Renfrew et al. (2009).

Summary: Implications of Oldowan Sites

Some important inferences that bear on possible cognitive abilities of the early hominin tool makers can be drawn from the Oldowan patterns:

1. Stone tool manufacturing skill: Even very early stone artifacts at the earliest sites at Gona demonstrate remarkable skill and control in flaking stone;
2. Forethought and transport: Hominin tool makers showed considerable forethought in multiple aspects of their tool manufacture and use, including transport of raw materials and tools to and from different site locales;
3. Selectivity in use of raw materials: Hominin tool makers were aware of and responsive to signs of raw material quality that would affect ease and control of fracture as well as tool effectiveness;
4. Concentrating artifacts: Hominin behaviors tended to concentrate substantial amounts of tool materials at certain locations, possibly indicating repeated use or large social group use of these locales;
5. Acquisition of animal resources: Evidence indicates that hominins were often engaged in accessing meat resources from fairly sizeable animals using stone tools to deflesh carcasses and to fracture bones to access marrow. They may also have been actively involved in transporting these animal parts and concentrating them at some site locations, presumably for amenities such as shade, shelter, or protection or water. Consistent acquisition of such food sources would have placed them in more direct competition with active predators and scavengers and likely increased their risk factors from predation as well.

Chimpanzee Tools and Technology

Studies of Wild Chimpanzee Tools

The range and instances of documented wild chimpanzee technology have increased dramatically during the past few decades of research. This increase likely is largely the result of the growing number of habituated chimpanzee populations combined with the number of long-term, committed projects investigating chimpanzee populations in different parts of Africa. The number of articles and chapters discussing chimpanzee technology and cultural traits far exceeds the citation limit of this review, so here we focus on the references that attempt a synthesis of our state of knowledge. A number of researchers from different backgrounds and perspectives have addressed the relevance of chimpanzee technology to human evolutionary studies, including Beck (1980) (animal tools), Bonner (1980) (animal culture), Goodall (1986) (general), Foley (1987) (tool phylogeny), Wynn & McGrew (1989) (primate and hominin tool use), Sept (1992, 1998) (nesting patterns), McGrew (1992, 1993, 2004) (general), Berthelet & Chavaillon (1993) (primate and hominin tool use), Wrangham (1996) (general), Whiten et al. (1999, 2009) (chimpanzee cultural traits), Stanford (2001) (general), Panger et al. (2002) (evolutionary history of technology), Matsuzawa (2002) (general), van Schaik et al. (2003) (ape cultural traits), Hunt (2006) (sex differences in tool use), Lycett et al. (2007) (cladistics of chimpanzee cultural traits), and Carvalho et al. (2008) (chaînes opératoires).

Studies of chimpanzee tool use afford us much more fully textured insight into the range of material culture employed by these populations than is possible for Oldowan tools (e.g., Goodall 1986; McGrew 1992, 1993). McGrew (1993) has argued effectively for an intelligent, flexible, problem-solving use of tools among chimpanzees and, moreover, that tool use is the norm among wild chimpanzee populations. The range of tools used may differ among populations, but tool use is observed daily in any well-habituated population. Chimpanzee tool use involves a variety of organic materials that do not tend to be preserved in the archaeological record, and furthermore, it is possible to observe directly a wealth of detail regarding many aspects of tool use.

The variety of details that can be obtained from studies of chimpanzee tool use among wild populations can include preparation or processing of the tool, specifics regarding how it was used and on what sort of material(s), potential reuse of a tool, the use of tool sets combining a sequence of tools for a specific purpose, the frequency of observed uses of a tool, possible age or sex differences in tool use, the process of learning tool use, fine-grained information regarding transport of tools and other materials, seasonal or ecological factors affecting tool use, contemporary regional or population similarities and differences, possible details regarding the locale of tool use (shade or protection, food or other resources, etc.), and potentially other activities also conducted at the site. These data can provide a wealth of information not directly available to the Palaeolithic archaeologist.

McGrew (1992, 2004) has provided broad overviews of material culture as well as culture writ large among chimpanzee populations, particularly among wild chimpanzees. As he has noted, most observations of habitual chimpanzee tool use are oriented toward subsistence activities, obtaining or processing materials for consumption, especially social insects such as termites or ants and nuts. Typical tool use for subsistence would include fishing for termites with twigs or grasses, using leaf sponges to scoop brains from a cranium or fruit from a husk, or using stone or wood hammers and anvils to crack open hard-shelled nuts. One report (Mercader et al. 2007) has suggested that a locality in the rainforest of Côte d'Ivoire dated to 4300 years ago may be a chimpanzee nut-cracking site, which would indicate some longevity for this practice if chimpanzees were responsible for the apparent activities here. In addition, in Senegal, chimpanzees appear to have used stone anvils to smash open baobab fruits (Marchant & McGrew 2005).

Another category of tools consists of materials used as weapons, such as sticks and stones thrown at other chimpanzees or at baboons competing for the same food, behaviors that are well known but not systematically studied. Although chimpanzee males are known to prey on smaller animals such as monkeys and small antelope, they generally have been observed to carry out the hunt and the consumption of the animal without the use of tools. An exception to this pattern with regard to hunting has recently been documented in Senegal by Pruetz & Bertolani (2007), who observed a number of chimpanzees, particularly females and including immature individuals, on several occasions shape wooden branches into pointed tools to try to jab and extract prosimians from tree cavities; they observed one successful kill in 22 bouts of observations.

Besides such use of stone hammers and anvils, another chimpanzee activity that could have archaeological visibility is their consumption of prey animals, which can leave tooth-marks on bones, including tooth scoring, canine punctures, and damage to bone ends. This practice has been observed in the wild (Plummer & Stanford 2000) as well as in an experimental setting (Pickering & Wallis 1997). [Toothmarks on bones from Oldowan sites are often assumed to be produced by carnivores, although there is a growing appreciation that Oldowan hominins could also be responsible for some of these (White & Toth 2007)].

Some sex differences have been noted among chimpanzees in terms of tool-related behaviors. Notably, fishing for termites and dipping for ants are important subsistence activities conducted with tools that are preferentially associated with females, who have been observed to pursue these activities much more often than do males. McGrew (1992) has observed that these activities require prolonged and systematic persistence using a tool to extract predictable resources and that they are, in a sense, akin to gathering. Hunt (2006)

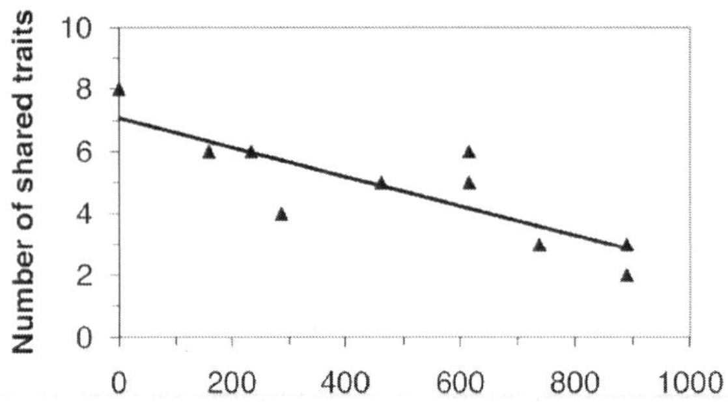

Figure 1. The relation between the number of shared chimpanzee cultural traits (habitual or customary, from the Whiten et al.1999 paper) and distances between pairs of chimpanzee groups of the same subspecies. Note that groups in closer proximity tend to share more traits and that the number of shared traits drops by more than half (to fewer than four) at a distance of ~700 km. A Pearson r^2 value of 0.702 was derived for the 11 pairs of 7 groups; among the East African chimpanzee groups (10 pairs), Pearson $r = -0.829$, $r^2 = 0.687$, $p = 0.003$; Mantel test $p = 0.014$.

has observed that not only do female chimpanzees use tools more frequently than do males, but they do so especially for lower-return food items requiring significant processing. Hunt further notes that females also use tools during arboreal feeding, whereas males use technology to harvest terrestrial resources. Among the nut-cracking chimpanzee populations in West Africa, investigators have observed that females are more apt and efficient than are males in opening the harder-shelled varieties. As mentioned above, hunting of smaller mammals is a predominantly male activity, albeit without the use of tools.

A number of researchers have compiled evidence and analyses from a number of chimpanzee study areas and discerned that chimpanzee material culture and nonmaterial culture show some regional patterning, indicating the potential role of cultural transmission in spreading and maintaining regional patterns of behavior (Whiten et al. 1999, 2001). Such a pattern might be expected because many shared behaviors among chimpanzees appear to be learned, often transmitted through observation and a trial-and-error learning curve. Much of this transmission seems to be from mother to offspring, sometimes with a prolonged period of apprenticeship (Boesch & Boesch-Achermann 2000, Goodall 1986, McGrew 2004).

To investigate large-scale chimpanzee cultural patterning, Toth & Schick (2007) examined the relationships between geographical proximity of different chimpanzee populations in West and East Africa and the number of shared cultural traits reported in the Whiten et al. (1999) study. At the species level, there was no significant pattern, but at the subspecies level (comparing West African groups to other West African groups of *Pan troglodytes verus* and comparing East African groups to other East African groups of *Pan troglodytes schwein-furthii*), a highly significant pattern appeared to emerge (Figure 1). The number of shared cultural traits between groups dropped by more than half (from eight shared traits to fewer than four) at a distance of ~700 km (about 450 miles).

At the species level, with West African and East African populations separated by more than 4000 kilometers (more than 2700 miles), and perhaps two million years of time based on some genetic estimates, the results would appear to indicate some degree of convergence (independent invention) of cultural traits among disparate populations, without any clear evolutionary history. At the subspecies level, with a much more recent evolutionary history, there appeared to be some geographic patterning to the number of shared cultural traits by proximity to other chimpanzee groups. The drop-off of more than half the number of cultural traits in ~700 kilometers was used as a model for early hominin groups on the basis of known Oldowan archaeological sites (Toth & Schick 2007, Whiten et al. 2009). Such a subspecies patterning has also been independently suggested by Lycett et al. (2007) on the basis of a cladistic/phylogenetic analysis of chimpanzee cultural traits.

Thus, there is no universal chimpanzee culture in terms of tools but rather different clusters of tool-use behaviors in differing populations. One major difference noted between East African and West African populations is the prevalent (though not universal) use of hammers and anvils of stone or wood to crack open hard-shelled nuts in West African chimpanzee populations, a behavior that has not yet been documented among East African populations. Whiten et al. (2001) found that 39 behavior patterns, many of which involved tool use, variably observed among a group of 9 long-term chimpanzee study sites across Africa, showed patterning consistent with social transmission.

As might be expected, as quadrupedal, knuckle-walking animals, chimpanzees are not proficient at transporting materials. They do transport tools to tool-use sites, though generally over fairly short distances. Interesting patterns are observed in the tool transport behaviors for nutting activities in West Africa (Boesch & Boesch 1983, 1984, 1990; Boesch & Boesch-Achermann 2000; Boesch-Achermann & Boesch 1994). For the softer-shelled *Coula* nuts, wooden hammers are sometimes chosen and taken up into a *Coula* tree to crack open nuts on a tree branch. For the harder, *Panda* nuts, however, stone hammers are sometimes carried short distances to the base of the *Panda* tree. The distance a stone or wooden hammer is transported may be relatively low in a single instance, but cumulative trips could accomplish greater distances.

Boesch & Boesch (1984) documented transport of wooden or stone hammers primarily over distances of less than 20 meters but with many transports evident over a distance of up to 500 m and, in very rare instances, more than 500 m. Their study indicated the chimpanzees could develop mental maps of resource locations and follow a least-distance rule in choosing stones to transport to nut tree locations, likely in response to the difficulty chimpanzees face in transporting heavier materials over longer distances. Chimpanzees also generally do not transport vegetable foods or invertebrates any great distance away from the food source. After a hunt, males may transport the kill (e.g., in the mouth or around the neck) to a safe or comfortable place for consumption, but with some difficulty in any case. Under such constraints, it is not surprising that, as McGrew has observed (1992), containers are not part of the tool equipment employed by chimpanzees.

Chimpanzees in the wild have not been observed to flake stone deliberately and thus do not produce materials that may be directly compared with Oldowan technology. Although Mercader et al. (2002) suggested that a West African nut-cracking locality presumably used by chimpanzees contained materials comparable to artifacts at early Oldowan sites, this material does not appear to represent the products of deliberate percussive flaking (unlike most Oldowan artifacts) but instead is only the by-product of nut-cracking (Schick & Toth 2006, pp. 24–26). Interestingly, no food-getting or other activity conducted by modern chimpanzees appears to require a reliance on cutting activities, and this may be the primary reason that a culture of flaked stone technology has apparently not developed among chimpanzees.

To explore the ability of this closely related ape to manufacture Oldowan-type artifacts, then by knapping, we conducted an experimental study.

An Experimental Study of Bonobo Stone Tool Manufacture

One major obstacle in attempts to compare and contrast Oldowan technology with the material culture of chimpanzees is that modern apes in the wild are not known to flake stones intentionally in the wild. Beginning in 1990, we embarked on a long-term experimental project to teach bonobos (*Pan paniscus*) to make and use flaked stone tools. In collaboration with cognitive psychologists Sue Savage-Rumbaugh and Duane Rumbaugh and their colleagues at the Language Research Laboratory of Atlanta and then the Great Ape Trust of Iowa, we began to investigate the tool-making and tool-using capabilities of bonobos in an experimental setting.

Pioneering work by Wright (1972) with a young orangutan demonstrated that a great ape could be taught to make and use a stone tool. Although this experiment used a flint core strapped to a stable board and did not continue beyond the first flake produced and used, it was nonetheless one of the inspirations behind this project. We produced a more naturalistic environment for the bonobos, where freehand, hard-hammer percussion was used to flake cobbles of quartzite, lava, and chert, and the sharp flakes produced were then used to cut a cord to open a box (or cut through the membrane of a drum) and retrieve a food reward. Our first bonobo subject, Kanzi, learned both the flaking and the cutting tasks through observing a human tool maker, began using flakes the first day of the experiment, and made his first tool within a month of the onset of the experiment. He has now been flaking stone for 18 years, and his sister Panbanisha is now also a practiced stone tool maker (Savage-Rumbaugh & Fields 2006; Schick et al. 1999; Toth & Schick 1993, 2006).

Recently we undertook a three-way comparison of stone tools manufactured (*a*) by very early tool makers at Gona, Ethiopia (possibly *A. garhi*); (*b*) by bonobo (*Pan paniscus*) tool makers with several years experience in stone tool making; and (*c*) by modern *H. sapiens* very experienced in Oldowan tool manufacture (Toth et al. 2006), all using the same raw materials. These three populations of stone artifacts were then analyzed in detail and compared in terms of dozens of assemblage characteristics, particularly those that would indicate a level of tool-making skill.

For most of the traits attributed to skill, the bonobos tended to be the outgroup, with characteristics of the Gona artifacts either clustering with the modern human sample or intermediate between the bonobo and human samples. The bonobo cores tended to be heavier (the bonobos tended to select larger cobbles, probably because their hands were larger), less heavily reduced, and with fewer scars and a great deal of hammerstone battering on core edges from unsuccessful blows. The morphology of the bonobo cores and flakes appears to have been a function of less impact velocity (a probable biomechanical constraint) as well as less control as to where exactly to detach flakes from a cobble core (a possible cognitive constraint).

The Gona artifacts, however, show much better skill in cobble reduction than the bonobo artifacts do. Cores are more heavily reduced, with almost twice the number of flake scars, and exhibit significantly less battering from misplaced hammerstone blows. Biomechanical studies (Dapena et al. 2006, Harlacker 2009) of the arm swing during Oldowan flaking indicate that manufacture by modern humans produces a very rapid speed of the hammerstone, reaching a final velocity of up to 20 mph. The bonobo arm swing during tool making is considerably less, which may help account for the lower skill evident in their flaking and the considerable battering on the bonobo cores relative to the Gona artifacts and those produced by modern humans.

This study has demonstrated that our closest living relatives among the apes are definitely capable of stone tool manufacture. The apes in this study, however, are not as proficient in stone tool making, even after many years of experience, as were the early hominin tool makers. As noted above, this difference in skill may be attributed both to cognitive processing and to the biomechanical constraints of the ape.

Discussion and Conclusions

In view of the significant technological repertoire of chimpanzees, there are valid arguments for using their behaviors as models for aspects of early hominin activities that are elusive or largely invisible to us. There are, however, also significant differences in chimpanzee biology, behavior patterns, and ecology that should temper us from basing our models of hominid behavior on modern chimpanzees too strictly or uniformly.

This overview has highlighted a number of elements of chimpanzee technology and behavior that appear to have, or may be likely to have, some counterpart in early hominin behavior and technology. These would include the concentrating of tools at sites of use, consumption of meat involving hunting activities and even group cooperation, carrying and transport of tools including stone, battering and bashing activities with stone, their use of probing sticks (which may have some counterpart in early bone tools), and even their tendency to gather together in groups on a daily basis (in nesting trees at night).

We could also infer that the cultural transmission of tool use within a group and between groups would have parallels between the chimpanzee mode (especially from mother to offspring) and early Oldowan hominins. We do not know if the sexual differences observed in chimpanzee tool use and behaviors had counterparts in early hominins, but the ape model does raise this question. Hunt (2006) suggests, based on chimpanzee analogies, that female Oldowan hominins were more frequent tool users than males. The use by chimpanzees of a great variety of tools in perishable, organic materials highlights the probability that early hominins likewise had a much richer, more diverse, and varied tool kit than is visible in the archaeological record. Bipedal hominins would have had a considerable advantage in terms of transporting tools and foodstuffs around the landscape, and this practice could have been greatly enhanced with the use of containers.

The emergence of the Oldowan around 2.6 Mya, at our present state of knowledge, appears to occur during an evolutionary stage involving relatively small-brained, bipedal australopithecines. The following one million years documents a period of dramatic encephalization with the rise and evolution of the genus *Homo*, a reduction in the size of hominin jaws and teeth, the first spread of hominins out of Africa and into Eurasia, and the earliest appearance of Acheulean industries.

Wild chimpanzees and Oldowan hominins, considering their material culture, would appear to share the following characteristics. First, stone is transported to and used at activity areas, making spatial concentrations of material culture. Second, stone tools become modified (battered and pitted) from their use as hammers and anvils.

As previously mentioned, it is likely that Oldowan hominins had a rich suite of cultural traits that leave little prehistoric visibility. Similarly, the majority of chimpanzee cultural traits and tool-related behaviors would leave little long-term archaeological record.

Although their tool use is intelligent and flexible, chimpanzees tend to modify their tools with their bodies, e.g., stripping branches or pulling off bark with their hands or feet or even sharpening tips of branches with their teeth. Early hominins may well have accomplished some tasks in a similar fashion, but the human paleontological evidence suggests that a decrease in size of jaws and teeth over time may be correlated with the rise in extrasomatic tool use, with technology creating "synthetic organs" and gradually allowing hominins to move into niches traditionally occupied by other animals, such as the carnivore guild. We have called this phenomenon "techno-organic" evolution (Schick & Toth 1993).

Major differences in material culture between wild chimpanzees and Oldowan hominins would include the following traits observed in the Oldowan:

1. Skilled, forceful stone knapping by direct percussion with stone hammers, or bipolar flaking with stone hammers and anvils to create sharp edges that could be used for cutting, chopping, and scraping.
2. More selectivity and long-distance transport of lithic raw materials from their geological sources to activity areas ("sites"); concentrations of flaked and battered stone artifacts can number into the hundreds or thousands at a given locality, and transport distances can range from tens of meters to more than 10 kilometers.
3. The acquisition, processing, and consumption of large mammal carcasses (or parts of carcasses), assisted with technology (stone knives and percussors) to exploit meat, marrow, and organ foods, leaving recognizable traces on the bones in the form of stone tool cut marks and hammerstone-induced fracture.
4. Longer-term curational behavior of material culture over longer distances and probably longer time periods, suggesting a higher level of planning and anticipatory behavior.

It is likely, but less demonstrable, that during this period hominid populations developed more human-like characteristics, including the emergence of containers and carrying devices (e.g., of skin, shell, or bark); digging tools such as sharpened digging sticks to process underground plant resources; simple spears, throwing sticks or stone missiles, and clubs for predation; larger average group sizes and home ranges; food-sharing behavior; more sexual division of labor; more emphasis on central foraging places (home bases); more complex communicative skills; and the beginnings of symbolic behavior.

Future research into Oldowan archaeology will almost certainly continue to stress the role of technology in its ecological context and explore new ways to study and test the significance and patterning of this technology during the course of human evolution. As new sites are discovered, our sample sizes of well-excavated stone artifact assemblages, associated animal bones and other materials, and associated hominin tool makers will allow more rigorous methodologies and more robust scientific results. Studies of our ape relatives in the wild will become increasingly crucial and urgent as their habitats dwindle and their populations become endangered, and our disciplines will also gain a great deal of understanding from well-constructed studies of captive apes, who may become the surviving guardians of their genetic and behavioral legacy. Chimpanzees and bonobos are our closest living relatives. Each of our lineages has managed to survive for millions of years since we separated from a last common ancestor; we still have much to learn about them, and they still have much to teach us about ourselves.

Disclosure Statement

The authors are not aware of any affiliations, memberships, funding, or financial holdings that might be perceived as affecting the objectivity of this review.

Literature Cited

Aiello L, Wheeler P. 1995. The expensive tissue hypothesis. *Curr. Anthropol.* 36(2): 199–221

Ambrose S. 2001. Palaeolithic technology and human evolution. *Science* 291:1748–53

Asfaw B, Beyene Y, Semaw S, Suwa G, White T, Wolde Gabriel G. 1991. Fejej: a new palaeontological research area in Ethiopia. *J. Hum. Evol.* 21:137–43

Asfaw B, Beyene Y, Suwa G, Walter RC, White TD, et al. 1992. The earliest Acheulean from Konso-Gardula. *Nature* 360:732–35

Asfaw B, White T, Lovejoy O, Latimer B, Simpson S. 1999. *Australopithecus garhi*: a new species of early hominid from Ethiopia. *Science* 284(5414):629–34

Barsky D. 2009. An overview of some African and Eurasian Oldowan sites: evaluation of hominin cognition levels, technological advancement and adaptive skills. See Hovers & Braun 2009, pp. 39–47

Bar-Yosef O, Goren-Inbar N. 1993. The lithic assemblages of 'Ubeidiya: a Lower Palaeolithic site in the Jordan Valley. *Oedem* 45:1–266

Beck BB. 1980. *Animal Tool Behavior*. New York: Garland

Berthelet A, Chavaillon J, eds. 1993. *The Use of Tools by Human and Non-Human Primates*. Oxford: Oxford Univ. Press

Blumenschine RJ. 1986. *Early Hominid Scavenging Opportunities: Implications of Carcass Availability in the Serengeti and Ngorongoro Ecosystems*. Oxford: Br. Archaeol. Rep.

Blumenschine RJ. 1989. A landscape taphonomic model of the scale of prehistoric scavenging opportunities. *J. Hum. Evol.* 18:345–71

Blumenschine RJ, Masao FT, Tactikos JC, Ebert J. 2008. Effects of distance from stone source on landscape-scale variation in Oldowan artifact assemblages in the Paleo-Olduvai Basin, Tanzania. *J. Archaeol. Sci.* 35:76–86

Blumenschine RJ, Peters CR. 1998. Archaeological predictions for hominid land use in the paleo-Olduvai basin, Tanzania. *J. Hum. Evol.* 34:565–607

Boesch C, Boesch H. 1983. Optimization of nut-cracking with natural hammers by wild chimpanzees. *Behavior* 83:265–86

Boesch C, Boesch H. 1984. Mental maps in wild chimpanzees: an analysis of hammer transports for nut cracking. *Primates* 25(2): 160–70

Boesch C, Boesch H. 1990. Tool use and tool making in wild chimpanzees. *Folia Primatol.* 54:86–99

Boesch C, Boesch-Achermann H. 2000. *The Chimpanzees of the Tai Forest: Behavioral Ecology and Evolution*. Oxford: Oxford Univ. Press

Boesch-Achermann H, Boesch C. 1994. Hominization in the rainforest: the chimpanzee's piece of the puzzle. *Evol. Anthropol.* 3:9–16

Bonner JT. 1980. *The Evolution of Culture in Animals.* Princeton, NJ: Princeton Univ. Press Brain CK. 1981. *The Hunters or the Hunted? An Introduction to African Cave Taphonomy.* Chicago: Univ. Chicago Press

Brain CK. 2007. Fifty years of fun with fossils: some cave taphonomy-related ideas and concepts that emerged between 1953 and 2003. See Pickering et al. 2007, pp. 1–24

Braun DR, Harris JWK, Mania DN. 2009. Oldowan raw material procurement and use: evidence from the Koobi Fora Formation. *Archaeometry* 51:26–42

Braun DR, Hovers E. 2009. Current issues in Oldowan research. See Hovers & Braun 2009, pp. 1–14

Braun DR, Plummer T, Ditchfield P, Ferraro JV, Mania D, et al. 2008. Oldowan behavior and raw material transport: perspectives on the Kanjera Formation. *J. Archaeol. Sci.* 35:2329–45

Braun DR, Plummer TW, Ditchfield PW, Bishop LC, Ferraro JV. 2009. Oldowan technology and raw material variability at Kanjera South. See Hovers & Braun 2009, pp. 99–110.

Bunn H. 1983. Evidence of the diet and subsistence patterns of Plio-Pleistocene hominids at Koobi Fora, Kenya, and Olduvai Gorge, Tanzania. In *Animals and Archaeology,* Vol. 1: *Hunters and Their Prey,* ed. J Clutton-Brock, C Grigson, pp. 21–30. Oxford: Br. Archaeol. Rep.

Bunn H, Kroll E. 1986. Systematic butchery by Plio-Pleistocene hominids at Olduvai Gorge, Tanzania. *Curr. Anthropol.* 27(5):431–52

Carbonell E, Sala R, Barsky D, Celiberti V. 2009. From homogeneity to multiplicity: a new approach to the study of archaic stone tools. See Hovers & Braun 2009, pp. 25–37

Carvalho S, Cunha E, Sousa C, Matsuzawa T. 2008. Chaînes opératoires and resource-exploitation strategies in chimpanzee (*Pan troglodytes*) nut cracking. *J. Hum. Evol.* 55:148–63

Chavaillon J, Chavaillon N, Hours F, Piperno M. 1979. From the Oldowan to the Middle Stone Age at Melka-Kunturé (Ethiopia): understanding cultural change. *Quaternaria* 21:87–114

Dapena J, Anderst W, Toth N. 2006. The biomechanics of the arm swing in Oldowan stone flaking. See Toth & Schick 2006, pp. 333–38

Deacon T. 1997. *The Symbolic Species: The Co-Evolution of Language and the Brain.* New York: Norton

de Beaune SA. 2004. The invention of technology: prehistory and cognition. *Curr. Anthropol.* 45:139–62

de Heinzelin J, Clark JD, White TD, Hart WK, Renne PR, et al. 1999. Environment and behavior of 2.5-million-year-old Bouri hominids. *Science* 284:625–29

Delagnes A, Roche H. 2005. Late Pliocene hominid knapping skills: the case of Lokalalei 2C, West Turkana, Kenya. *J. Hum. Evol.* 48:435–72

de la Torre I, Mora R. 2 005. *Technological Strategies in the Lower Pleistocene at Olduvai Beds I & II.* Liege: ERAUL

de la Torre I, Mora R. 2009. Remarks on the current theoretical and methodological approaches to the study of early technological strategies in East Africa. See Hovers & Braun 2009, pp. 15–24

de la Torre I, Mora R, Domínguez-Rodrigo M, Luque L, Alcala L. 2003. The Oldowan industry of Peninj and its bearing on the reconstruction of the technological skills of Lower Pleistocene hominids. *J. Hum. Evol.* 44:203–24

de Lumley H, Beyene J, eds. 2004. *Les Sites Préhistoriques de la Région de Fejej, Sud-Omo, Éthiopie, dans Leurs Contexte Stratigraphique et Paléontologique.* Paris: Éd. Rech. Civiliz.

de Lumley H, Nioradze M, Barsky D, Cauche D, Celiberti V, et al. 2005. Les industries lithiques préoldowayennes du début du Pléistocène inférieur du site de Dmanissi en Géorgie. *Anthropologie* 109:1–182

d'Errico F, Backwell LR. 2003. Possible evidence of bone tool shaping by Swartkrans early hominids. *J. Archaeol. Sci.* 30:1559–76

d'Errico F, Backwell LR, Berger LR. 2001. Bone tool use in termite foraging by early hominids and its impact on our understading of early hominid behaviour. *S. Afr. J. Sci.* 97:71–75

Diez-Martín F. 2006. After the African Oldowan: the earliest technologies of Europe. See Toth & Schick 2006, pp. 129–51

Domínguez-Rodrigo M. 2009. Are all Oldowan sites palimpsests? If so, what can they tell us about hominid carnivory? See Hovers & Braun 2009, pp. 129–47

Domínguez-Rodrigo M, Egeland CP, Barba R. 2007. *Deconstructing Olduvai.* New York: Springer

Dunbar RI. 1993. Coevolution of neocortical size, group size and language in humans. *Behav. Brain Sci.* 16:681–735

Field AS. 1999. *An analytical and comparative study of the earlier Stone Age archaeology of the Sterkfontein Valley.* MSc thesis, Univ. Witwatersrand

Foley R. 1987. Hominid species and stone tool assemblages: How are they related? *Antiquity* 61:380–92

Gibson KR. 1986. Cognition, brain size and the extraction of embedded food resources. In *Primate Ontogeny, Cognition and Social Behavior*, ed. JG Else, PC Lee, pp. 93–103. Cambridge, UK: Cambridge Univ. Press

Gibson KR, Ingold T, eds. 1993. *Tools, Language and Cognition in Human Evolution*. Cambridge, UK: Cambridge Univ. Press

Goldman-Neuman T, Hovers E. 2009. Methodological considerations in the study of Oldowan raw material selectivity: insights from A. L. 894 (Hadar, Ethiopia). See Hovers & Braun 2009, pp. 71–84

Goodall J. 1964. Tool-using and aimed throwing in a community of free-living chimpanzees. *Nature* 201:1264–66

Goodall J. 1986. *The Chimpanzees of Gombe*. Cambridge, MA: Harvard Univ. Press

Gowlett JAJ. 1996. Mental abilities of early *Homo*: elements of constraint and choice in rule systems. See Mellars & Gibson 1996, pp. 191–215

Harlacker L. 2009. *The biomechanics of stone tool-making: kinematic and kinetic perspectives on Oldowan Lithic technology*. PhD thesis, Anthropol. Dept., Indiana Univ., Bloomington

Harmand S. 2009. Variability in raw material selectivity at the late Pliocene sites of Lokalalei, West Turkana, Kenya. See Hovers & Braun 2009, pp. 85–97

Harris JWK. 1983. Cultural beginnings: Plio-Pleistocene archaeological occurrences from the Afar, Ethiopia. *Afr Archaeol. Rev.* 1:1–31

Harris JWK, Capaldo SD. 1993. The earliest stone tools. In *The Use of Tools by Human and Non-Human Primates*, ed. A Berthelet, J. Chavaillon, pp. 196–220. Oxford: Clarendon

Hay RL. 1976. *Geology of the Olduvai Gorge*. Berkeley: Univ. Calif. Press

Holloway RH, Broadfield DC, Yuan MS. 2004. *The Human Fossil Record*, Vol. 3: *Brain Endocasts, The Paleoneurological Evidence*. Hoboken: Wiley

Hovers E, Braun DR, eds. 2009. *Interdisciplinary Approaches to the Oldowan*. Dordrecht: Springer

Howell FC, Haesaerts P, de Heinzelin J. 1987. Depositional environments, archaeological occurrences and hominids from Members E and F of the Shungura Formation (Omo basin, Ethiopia). *J. Hum. Evol.* 16:665–700

Hunt K. 2006. Sex differences in chimpanzee foraging behavior and tool use: implications for the Oldowan. See Toth & Schick 2006, pp. 243–66

Isaac G. 1981. Stone age visiting cards: approaches to the study of early land-use patterns. In *Patterns of the Past*, ed. I Hodder, G Isaac, N Hammond, pp. 131–55. Cambridge, UK: Cambridge Univ. Press

Isaac G. 1982. The earliest archaeological traces. In *Cambridge History of Africa*, Vol. 1: *From the Earliest Times to c. 500 BC*. Cambridge, UK: Cambridge Univ. Press

Isaac G. 1984. The archaeology of human origins: studies of the Lower Pleistocene in East Africa. *In Advances in World Archaeology*, ed. F Wendorf, A Close, pp. 1–87. New York: Acad. Press

Isaac G. 1986. Foundation stones: early artifacts as indicators of activities and abilities. In *Stone Age Prehistory*, ed. GN Bailey, P Callow, pp. 221–41. Cambridge, UK: Cambridge Univ. Press

Isaac G. 1989. *The Archaeology of Human Origins: Papers by Glynn Isaac*. Cambridge, UK: Cambridge Univ. Press

Isaac G, Isaac B, eds. 1997. *Koobi Fora Research Project*, Vol. 5: *Plio-Pleistocene Archaeology*. Oxford: Clarendon

Jones PR. 1994. Results of experimental work in relation to the stone industries of Olduvai Gorge. See Leakey 1994, pp. 254–98

Joulian F. 1996. Comparing chimpanzee and early hominid techniques: some contributions to cultural and cognitive questions. See Mellars & Gibson 1996, pp. 173–89

Keeley L, Toth N. 1981. Microwear polishes on early stone tools from Koobi Fora, Kenya. *Nature* 293:464–66

Kimbel WH, Walter RC, Johanson DC, Reed KE, Aronson JL, et al. 1996. Late Pliocene *Homo* and Oldowan tools from the Hadar Formation (Kada Hadar Member), Ethiopia. *J. Hum. Evol.* 31:549–61

Klein RG. 1999. *The Human Career: Human Biological and Cultural Origins*. Chicago: Univ. Chicago Press Kuman K. 1998. The earliest South African industries. In *Early Hominid Behavior In Global Context: The Rise and Diversity of the Lower Palaeolithic Record*, ed. MD Petraglia, R Korisettar, pp. 151–86. London: Routledge

Kuman K. 2005. La préhistoire ancienne de l'Afrique méridonale: contribution des sites à hominids d'Afrique du Sud. In *Le Paléolithique en Afrique: L'Histoire la Plus Longue*, ed. M Sahnouni, pp. 53–82. Paris: Éd. Artcom'

Leakey MD. 1971. *Olduvai Gorge*, Vol. 3: *Excavations in Beds I and II, 1960–1963*. Cambridge, UK: Cambridge Univ. Press

Leakey MD, with D Roe. 1994. *Olduvai Gorge*, Vol. 5: *Excavation in Beds III, IV, and the Masek Beds, 1968–1971*. Cambridge, UK: Cambridge Univ. Press

Lewin R, Foley RA, 2004. *Principles of Human Evolution*. Oxford: Blackwell

Lycett SJ, Collard M, McGrew WC. 2007. Phylogenetic analyses of behavior support existence of culture among wild chimpanzees. *Proc. Natl. Acad. Sci. USA* 104:17588–93

Marchant LF, McGrew WC. 2005. Percussive technology: chimpanzee baobab smashing and the evolutionary modeling of hominin knapping. See Roux & Bril 2005, pp. 341–50

Martínez J, Mora R, de la Torre I, eds. 2003. *Oldowan: Rather More Than Smashing Stones*. Bellaterra: Univ. Autonom. Barc.

Matsuzawa T, ed. 2002. *Primate Origins of Human Cognition and Behavior*. Tokyo: Springer

McGrew WC. 1992. *Chimpanzee Material Culture*. Cambridge, UK: Cambridge Univ. Press

McGrew WC. 1993. The intelligent use of tools: twenty propositions. See Gibson & Ingold 1993, pp. 151–70 McGrew WC. 2004. *The Cultured Chimpanzee: Reflections on Cultural Primatology*. Cambridge, UK: Cambridge Univ. Press

Mellars P, Gibson K, eds. 1996. *Modelling the Early Human Mind*. Cambridge, UK: McDonald Inst.

Mercader J, Barton H, Gillespie J, Harris J, Kuhn S, et al. 2007. 4,300-year-old chimpanzee sites and the origins of percussive stone technology. *Proc. Natl. Acad. Sci. USA* 104:3043–48

Mercader J, Panger M, Boesch C. 2002. Excavation of a chimpanzee stone tool site in the African rainforest. *Science* 296:1452–55

Minthen S. 1996. *The Prehistory of the Mind*. London: Thames and Hudson

Negash A, Shackley MS, Alene M. 2006. Source provenance of obsidian artifacts from the Early Stone Age (ESA) site of Melka Konturé, Ethiopia. *J. Archaeol. Sci.* 33:1647–50

Noble W, Davidson I. 1996. *Human Evolution, Language and Mind: A Psychological and Archaeological Inquiry*. Cambridge, UK: Cambridge Univ. Press

Panger MA, Brooks AS, Richmond BG, Wood B. 2002. Older than the Oldowan? Rethinking the emergence of hominin tool use. *Evol. Anthropol.* 11:2 3 5–45

Parker ST, Gibson KR. 1979. A developmental model for the evolution of language and intelligence in early hominids. *Behav. Brain Sci.* 2:367–408

Parker ST, McKinney ML. 1999. *Origins of Intelligence: The Evolution of Cognitive Development in Monkeys, Apes, and Humans*. Baltimore: Johns Hopkins Univ. Press

Pelegrin J. 2005. Remarks about archaeological techniques and methods of knapping: elements of a cognitive approach to stone knapping. See Roux & Bril 2005, pp. 23–33

Peters CR, Blumenschine RJ. 1995. Landscape perspectives on possible land use patterns for Early Pleistocene hominids in the Olduvai Basin, Tanzania. *J. Hum. Evol.* 29:321–62

Peters CR, Blumenschine RJ. 1996. Landscape perspectives on possible land use patterns for Early Pleistocene hominids in the Olduvai Basin, Tanzania: Part II, expanding the landscape model. *Kapuia* 6:175–221

Pickering TR, Domínguez-Rodrigo M. 2006. The acquisition and use of large mammal carcasses by Oldowan hominins in eastern and southern Africa: a selected review and assessment. See Toth & Schick 2006, pp. 113–28

Pickering TR, Domínguez-Rodrigo M, Egeland C, Brain CK. 2007. Carcass foraging by early hominids at Swartkrans Cave (South Africa): a new investigation of the zooarchaeology and taphonomy of Member 3. See Pickering et al. 2007, pp. 233–53

Pickering TR, Schick K, Toth N, eds. 2007. *Breathing Life into Fossils: Taphonomic Studies in Honor of C.K. (Bob) Brain.* Gosport, IN: Stone Age Inst. Press

Pickering TR, Wallis J. 1997. Bone modification resulting from captive chimpanzee mastication: implications for the interpretation of Pliocene archaeological faunas. *J. Archaeol. Sci.* 24:1115–27

Piperno M, Collina C, Gallotti R, Raynal J, Kieffer G, et al. 2009. Obsidian exploitation and utilization during the Oldowan at Melka Kunturé (Ethiopia). See Hovers & Braun 2009, pp. 111–28

Plummer T. 2004. Flaked stones and old bones: biological and cultural evolution at the dawn of technology. *Yearb. Phys. Anthropol.* 47:118–64

Plummer TW, Bishop LC, Ditchfield PW, Ferraro JV, Kingston JD, et al. 2009. The environmental context of Oldowan hominin activities at Kanjera South, Kenya. See Hovers & Braun, pp. 149–60

Plummer TW, Stanford CB. 2000. Analysis of a bone assemblage made by chimpanzees at Gombe National Park, Tanzania. *J. Hum. Evol.* 39:345–65

Potts R. 1988. *Early Hominid Activities at Olduvai.* New York: Aldine

Potts R. 1991. Why the Oldowan? Plio-Pleistocene toolmaking and transport of resources. *J. Anthropol. Res.* 47:153–76

Pruetz JD, Bertolani P. 2007. Savanna chimpanzees, *Pan troglodytes verus*, hunt with tools. *Curr. Biol.* 17:1–6

Renfrew C, Frith C, Malafouris L, eds. 2009. *The Sapient Mind: Archaeology Meets Neuroscience.* Oxford: Oxford Univ. Press

Roche H. 2005. From simple flaking to shaping: stone knapping evolution among early hominins. See Roux & Bril 2005, pp. 35–48

Roche H, Delagnes A, Brugal J, Feibel C, Kibunjia M, et al. 1999. Early hominid stone tool production and technical skill 2.34 Myr ago in West Turkana, Kenya. *Nature* 399:57–60

Roux V, Bril B, ed. 2005. *Stone Knapping: The Necessary Conditions for a Uniquely Hominin Behaviour*. Cambridge, UK: McDonald Inst.

Sahnouni M. 1998. *The Lower Palaeolithic of the Magreb: Excavations and Analyses at Ain Hanech, Algeria*. Oxford: Br. Archaeol. Rep.

Sahnouni M. 2006. The North African Early Stone Age and the sites at Ain Hanech, Algeria. See Toth & Schick 2006, pp. 77–111

Sahnouni M, Hadjouis D, Van Der Made J, Derradji A, Canals A, et al. 2002. Further research at the Oldowan site of Ain Hanech, North-east Algeria. *J. Hum. Evol.* 43:925–37

Sahnouni M, Schick K, Toth N. 1997. An experimental investigation into the nature of faceted limestone "spheroids" in the Early Paleolithic. *J. Archaeol. Sci.* 24:701–13

Savage-Rumbaugh S, Fields WM. 2006. Rules and tools: beyond anthropomorphism. See Toth & Schick 2006, pp. 223–41

Schick K. 1986. *Stone Age Sites in the Making: Experiments in the Formation and Transformation of Archaeological Occurrences*. Oxford: Br. Archaeol. Rep.

Schick K. 1987. Modelling the formation of Early Stone Age artifact concentrations. *J. Hum. Evol.* 16:789–807

Schick K, Toth N. 1993. *Making Silent Stones Speak: Human Evolution and the Dawn of Technology*. New York: Simon and Schuster

Schick K, Toth N. 1994. Early Stone Age Technology in Africa: a review and case study into the nature and function of spheroids and subspheroids. In *Integrative Paths to the Past: Palaeoanthropological Advances in Honor of F. Clark Howell*, ed. R Corruccini, R Ciochon, pp. 429–49. Englewood Cliffs: Prentice-Hall

Schick K, Toth N. 2001. Palaeoanthropology at the millennium. In *Archaeology at the Millenium: A Sourcebook*, ed. D Feinman, G Price, pp. 30–108. New York: Kluwer

Schick K, Toth N. 2006. An overview of the Oldowan Industrial Complex: the sites and the nature of their evidence. See Toth & Schick 2006, pp. 3–42

Schick K, Toth N, eds. 2009. *The Cutting Edge: New Approaches to the Archaeology of Human Origins*. Gosport, IN: Stone Age Inst. Press

Schick K, Toth N, Garufi GS, Savage-Rumbaugh ES, Rumbaugh D, Sevcik R. 1999. Continuing investigations into the stone tool-making and tool-using capabilities of a bonobo (*Pan paniscus*). *J. Archaeol. Sci.* 26:821–32

Semaw S. 2000. The world's oldest stone artifacts from Gona, Ethiopia; their implications for understanding stone technology and patterns of human evolution between 2.6–1.5 million years ago. *J. Archaeol. Sci.* 27:1197–214

Semaw S. 2006. The oldest stone artifacts from Gona (2.6–2.5 Ma), Afar, Ethiopia: implications for understanding the earliest stages of stone knapping. See Toth & Schick 2006, pp. 43–75

Semaw S, Renne P, Harris JWK, Feibel CS, Bernor RL, et al. 1997. 2.5-million-year-old stone tools from Gona, Ethiopia. *Nature* 385:333–36

Semaw S, Rogers MJ, Quade J, Renne PR, Butler RF, et al. 2003. 2.6-million-year-old stone tools and associated bones from OGS-6 and OGS-7, Gona, Ethiopia. *J. Hum. Evol.* 45:169–77

Sept JM. 1992. Was there no place like home? A new perspective on early hominid archaeological sites from mapping of chimpanzee nests. *Curr. Anthropol.* 33(2):187–207

Sept JM. 1998. Shadows on a changing landscape: comparing nesting habits of hominids and chimpanzees since their last common ancestor. *Am. J. Prim.* 46:85–101

Stanford C. 2001. *Significant Others: The Ape-Human Continuum and the Quest for Human Nature.* New York: Basic Books

Stout D. 2006. Oldowan toolmaking and hominin brain evolution: theory and research using positron emission tomography (PET). See Toth & Schick 2006, pp. 267–305

Stout D, Quade J, Semaw S, Rogers MJ, Levin NE. 2005. Raw material selectivity of the earliest stone toolmakers at Gona, Afar, Ethiopia. *J. Hum. Evol.* 48:365–80

Stout D, Semaw S. 2006. Knapping skill of the earliest stone toolmakers: insights from the study of modern human novices. See Toth & Schick 2006, pp. 307–20

Stout D, Toth N, Schick K. 2006. Comparing the neural foundations of Oldowan and Acheulean toolmaking: a pilot study using positron emission tomography. See Toth & Schick 2006, pp. 321–31

Stout D, Toth N, Schick K, Chaminade T. 2009. Neural correlates of Early Stone Age toolmaking: technology, language, and cognition in human evolution. See Renfrew et al. 2009, pp. 1–19

Texier PJ. 1995. The Oldowan assemblage from NY 18 site at Nyabusosi (Toro-Uganda). *Comptes Rendus Acad. Sci., Paris* 320:647–53

Toth N. 1982. *The stone technologies of early hominids at Koobi Fora, Kenya: an experimental approach.* PhD thesis, Univ. Calif., Berkeley

Toth N. 1985. The Oldowan reassessed: a close look at early stone artifacts. *J. Archaeol. Sci.* 12:101–20

Toth N, Schick KD. 1986. The first million years: the archaeology of protohuman culture. *Adv. Archaeol. Methods Theory* 9:1–96

Toth N, Schick KD. 1993. Early stone industries and inferences regarding language and cognition. See Gibson & Ingold, pp. 346–62

Toth N, Schick K. 2005. African origins. In *The Human Past: World Prehistory and the Development of Human Societies*, ed. C Scarre, pp. 46–83. London: Thames and Hudson

Toth N, Schick K, eds. 2006. *The Oldowan: Case Studies into the Earliest Stone Age*. Gosport, IN: Stone Age Inst. Press

Toth N, Schick K. 2007. *An archaeological view of chimpanzee cultural traits*. Presented at the "Palaeoanthropology meets Primatology" conference, March, Leverhume Center, Cambridge Univ.

Toth N, Schick K, Semaw S. 2006. A comparative study of the stone tool-making skills of *Pan*, *Australopithecus*, and *Homo sapiens*. See Toth & Schick 2006, pp. 155–222

van Schaik CP, Ancrenaz M, Borgen G, Galdikas BF, Knott CD, et al. 2003. Orangutan cultures and the evolution of material culture. *Science* 299:102–5

White TD, Toth N. 2007. Carnivora and carnivory: assessing hominid toothmarks in zooarchaeology. See Pickering et al. 2007, pp. 281–96

Whiten A, Goodall J, McGrew WC, Nishida T, Reynolds V, et al. 1999. Cultures in chimpanzees. *Nature* 399:682–85

Whiten A, Goodall J, McGrew WC, Nishida T, Reynolds V, et al. 2001. Charting cultural variation in chimpanzees. *Behaviour* 138:1481–516

Whiten A, Schick K, Toth N. 2009. The evolution and cultural transmission of percussive technology: integrating evidence from palaeoanthropology and primatology. *J. Hum. Evol.* In press

Wrangham R. 1996. *Demonic Males: Apes and the Origins of Human Violence*. Boston: Houghton Mifflin

Wright RV. 1972. Imitative learning of a flaked tool technology—the case of an orangutan. *Mankind* 8:296–306

Wynn T. 1989. *The Evolution of Spatial Competence*. Champaign-Urbana: Univ. Ill. Press

Wynn T. 2002. Archaeology and cognitive evolution. *Behav. Brain Sci.* 25:389–438

Wynn T, McGrew WC. 1989. An ape's view of the Oldowan. *Man* 24:383–98

SECTION 13

ORIGIN AND SPREAD OF *HOMO SAPIENS*

Introduction to Chapter 15

One hundred thousand years ago, there were at least three species of Homo—including our own—thriving on planet Earth, but now there is just one. When and why did the others disappear?

There are many twists and turns to the hominin story. One theme, predicted by Darwin himself on the basis of our close cousinship with the African apes, is that much of that story unfolded in Africa. The chimpanzee and human (panin and hominin) lineages diverged there some 7 million years ago. Moreover, as you saw in Chapters 9 and 10, between 2 and 2.5 million years ago the genus *Homo* also evolved in Africa. In the current chapter, Richard Klein argues that the species to which all living humans belong, *Homo sapiens*, has it roots in Africa as well.

In Chapter 15, Klein argues that *Homo sapiens* evolved in Africa and only later spread from there to populate the rest of the planet. There are a few paleoanthropologists who still disagree with this perspective, but a large majority accepts it. The alternative (and minority) view is that several geographically distinct populations of ancient hominins—some in Europe, some in Asia and some in Africa—*all* crossed the threshold to *H. sapiens*. I will lay the background for Klein's argument and outline the kinds of evidence he offers. Figure F summarizes the relevant cast of characters and places them along a time line.

In Chapters 9 and 10, we examined the emergence of the genus *Homo* from it roots in *Australopithecus*. In Chapter 15, we are focusing on a more recent time period during which the genus *Homo* diversified. Notice that Klein briefly mentions three "out of Africa" events. As a way of logically positioning our discussion, let's begin with the first.

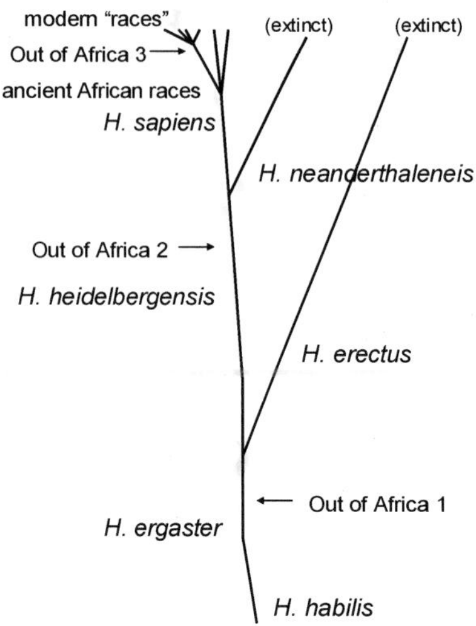

Figure F: The family tree of *Homo*, beginning about 2 MYA. Three separate dispersals from Africa are shown, by *H. ergaster*, *H. heidelbergensis* and *H. sapiens*, respectively.

You will remember from Chapter 10 that *Homo ergaster* was the first member of our genus to show both a significantly enlarged brain and significantly modern body proportions. The fossil record suggests that it was also the first hominin to leave Africa. Remember also that the earliest specimens placed in the taxon *H. ergaster* come from East African sites that date to about 1.9 MYA. We know that some populations of this species spread quite quickly out of Africa because their remains are found in the Caucus Mountains of central Eurasia by roughly 1.7 MYA; this spread of *H. ergaster* was Out of Africa 1. East Asian (Javan and Chinese) populations of *H. ergaster* seem to have subsequently evolved into a distinct species, *H. erectus*. This Asian species is not as well known as we would like, partly because of geopolitical issues that have impeded relevant research. But the sparse record we do have suggests that *H. erectus* persisted for roughly a million and a half years, at least until 30 KYA (thousand years ago), and perhaps even closer to the present.

Meanwhile, African populations of *H. ergaster* gave rise to a more modern-looking species known as *H. heidelbergensis*. As you might expect from its name, some populations of *H. heidelbergensis* spread to western Eurasia; this was Out of Africa 2. In Europe, during a period of glacial (cold climate) pulses, *H. heidelbergensis* gave rise to *H. neanderthalensis*. Somewhat later, some populations of *H. heidelbergensis* that remained in Africa gave rise to *H. sapiens*.

Notice that, because dispersal events reduce the amount of gene flow between populations, dispersal is typically followed by phenotypic divergence. This happened after each out-of-Africa migration. After *H. ergaster* arrived in Asia it became specifically distinct from its African lineage. Likewise, European *H. heidelbergensis* diverged to become *H. neanderthalensis*. Even the most recent dispersal (of *H. sapiens*) happened long enough ago to have produced some phenotypic divergence among its far-flung descendant populations.

There is a table on the next page to help you integrate the various species and tool traditions along a time line. Note the three out-of-Africa dispersals.

	Africa	Europe	Asia
Out of Africa 1			
1.7 MYA			
hominins	*H. ergaster*	*H. ergaster*	
industries	Oldowan	Oldowan	
Out of Africa 2			
0.5 MYA			
hominins	*H. heidelbegensis*	*H. heidelbegensis*	*H. erectus*
period	Early Stone Age	Lower Paloelothic	Lower Paloelothic
industries	Acheulean	Acheulean	Acheulean/Oldowan
200 KYA			
hominins	*H. sapiens*	*H. neanderthalensis*	*H. erectus*
period	Middle Stone Age	Middle Paleolithic	Lower Paloelothic
industries	Late Acheulean	Mousterian	Acheulean/Oldowan
Out of Africa 3			
25 KYA			
hominins	*H. sapiens*	*H. sapiens*	*H. sapiens*
industries	Late Stone Age	Upper Paleolithic	Upper Paleolithic
	Aurignacian-like	Aurignacian	Aurignacian-like

These patterns of dispersal and subsequent speciation mean that, between 100 and 200 KYA, there were three species of *Homo* on the planet: *H. erectus* in East Asia, *H. neanderthalensis* in western Eurasia, and *H. sapiens* in Africa. Beginning about 50–60 KYA, some of these *H. sapiens* populations launched Out of Africa 3, setting themselves on a collision course with the other two *Homo* species. Genetic, anatomical and cultural evidence suggest that *H. sapiens* replaced both of them, with little or no interbreeding. Let's outline the nature of that evidence, beginning with the cultural.

Just as there are styles of art or music today, there are styles of ancient tools that can be distinguished by their size, their shape, how they are made, and the materials used to make them. One important kind of evidence for the out-of-Africa theory is that there is a big change in tools styles all around the world that occurs between 40 and 30 KYA. Maybe resident people all over the planet just changed their style; or maybe new people—with different tool-making traditions—arrived and replaced them. The second kind of evidence is anatomical, and it supports the replacement theory. Modern *Homo sapiens* are physically different in an array of traits from both *H. erectus* and *H. neanderthalensis*. That is why they were originally put into different taxa. Between 40 and 30 KYA—at the very same time the tool styles changed in each world area—we see an abrupt change to *H. sapiens* with essentially no intermediate phenotypes.

In two separate ways, the genetic evidence tells the same story. You might be surprised to learn that it is possible to extract DNA from old bone. Neanderthals disappeared about 30 KYA, but their remains still yield analyzable DNA. In fact the entire *H. neanderthalensis* genome has now been preliminarily sequenced, making it possible to directly compare it to the *H. sapiens* genome. Of course, not all modern humans are genetically identical, but that variation is actually scientifically useful and informative. For purposes of the present discussion, it allows us to say how much genetic variability our species contains and to ask whether Neanderthals fall inside or outside that range of variation. The answer is that they are very far outside. We can calibrate how far by comparing the amount of genetic difference we see between Neanderthals and ourselves to the amount of difference we see between chimpanzees and ourselves. Using the chimpanzee-human diverge time, or 6.5 MYA (the date when the last common ancestor between humans and chimpanzees died), as a yardstick, we can estimate the divergence time between humans and Neanderthals. That divergence dates to just over 500 KYA (0.5 MYA). This date accords well with the hypothesized spread and subsequent separation of the *H. heidelbergensis* populations that gave rise to *H. sapiens* in Africa and *H. neaderthalensis* in Europe.

Genetic evidence can also be used to investigate the relationships among living human populations. This also amounts to a matter of divergence dates, but of course the dates are more recent. When we look at the patterns of human genetic variation around the planet, we find something interesting: There is considerably more genetic variation within Africa than there is across the entire rest of the planet. Moreover, all the non-Africans seem to be most similar to a single African population. This information suggests that *H. sapiens* arose in Africa (from southern populations of *H. heidelbergensis*) roughly 190 KYA. Over the next 130 thousand years, *H. sapiens* evolved into (at least) three fairly distinct geographic African races. Then, beginning between somewhere between 60 and 50 KYA, members of one—and only one—of those races began expanding out of Africa. Over a span of roughly 40 thousand years, that single African race populated the entire rest of the planet: Europe, Asia, Australia and the New World, reaching the southern tip of South America by 14 KYA. The cultural, phenotypic and genetic discontinuities mentioned above suggest that this wave of *H. sapiens* replaced whatever other hominins they encountered along the way. Many of these conclusions are summarized in Figure F; now would be a good time to reexamine it.

Klein places a lot of material in his Box 1. The main point of that box is to support the idea that Late Stone Age (LSA) human populations were larger than Middle Stone Age (MSA) populations. The way Klein attempts to show this is by presenting evidence about the contents of shell middens. A midden is a refuse heap (people always made trash!) associated with an ancient human habitation. Klein's relatively simple point is that, in these middens, the shells of edible mollusks are smaller in the LSA than they are in the MSA. He argues that people always prefer the largest mollusks they can find. But when there are more people foraging, they will have to begin to accept smaller mollusks to find enough food, and this acceptance will bring down the average size shells in the middens. Of course, he presents evidence that the size change is not merely a result of other environmental factors directly affecting the mollusks.

Chapter 15 Glossary

Acheulean: Lower and Middle Paleolithic stone tools that are more sophisticated than Oldowan tools; Acheulean tools first appear about 1.4 million years ago (MYA) and persist for more than a million years. They had rather slow product cycles back then; no new ipod this year!

Aurignacian: The name attached to an Upper Paleolithic culture known from its material remains; the culture first appears in Europe roughly 40 KYA and is believed to have been brought by *H. sapiens*. The culture is characterized by ornamental items (rock paintings, carved figurines) as well as very finely worked stone and bone implements.

Châtelperronian: The name attached to an Upper Paleolithic culture known from its material remains; the culture first appears in Europe roughly 35 KYA. In its styles of manufacture and choice of materials it is significantly intermediate between Mousterian and Aurignacian. It thus gives some support to the possibility that *H. sapiens* and *H. neanderthalensis* mixed; on the other hand, it is know from very few sites, and there is argument that these sites may have been disturbed, thus mixing older and younger occupation levels.

Late Stone Age: A term used by students of African prehistory to refer to a period when stone tools begin to be supplemented with other materials such as bone, and when ornamental objects begin to be produced; begins roughly 50 KYA.

Middle Stone Age: A term used by students of African prehistory to refer to the same time period as the Middle Paleolithic; 300KYA to 50 KYA.

Middle Paleolithic: A term used by students of European prehistory to refer to the same time period as the Middle Stone Age; 300KYA to 50 KYA.

Mousterian: The name attached to a Middle Paleolithic culture known from its material remains; the culture that held sway in Europe from roughly 300 KYA to 35 KYA. The industry seems to have been based entirely on stone tools, mostly flint. It is a "prepared-core" technology requiring considerable skill and foresight.

Upper Paleolithic: A term used by students of European prehistory to refer to refer to a period when stone tools begin to be supplemented with other materials such as bone, and when ornamental objects begin to be produced; begins roughly 40 KYA, about 10 KY after such items appear in Africa.

Chapter 15
Out of Africa and the Evolution of Human Behavior (2008)

Richard G. Klein

Twenty-one years ago, a landmark exploration of mitochondrial DNA diversity popularized the idea of a recent African origin for all living humans.[1] The ancestral African population was estimated to have existed 200 ka (thousands of years ago) plus or minus a few tens of thousands of years. A corollary was that at some later date the fully modern African descendants of that population expanded to swamp or replace the Neanderthals and other nonmodern Eurasians. The basic concept soon became known as "Out of Africa," after the Academy Award winning film (1985) that took its title, in turn, from Isak Dinesen's classic autobiography (1937). Many subsequent genetic analyses, including those of Ingman and coworkers[2] and Underhill and coworkers,[3] have reaffirmed the fundamental Out of Africa model. The fossil and archeological records also support it strongly. The fossil record implies that anatomically modern or near-modern humans were present in Africa by 150 ka; the fossil and archeological records together indicate that modern Africans expanded to Eurasia beginning about 50 ka.

Most paleoanthropologists now accept Out of Africa and argue mainly about the extent to which nonmodern Eurasians and modern African immigrants may have interbred. Most authorities further agree that a behavioral transformation underlay the modern African expansion, but they presently divide between a majority who believe that advanced behaviors accumulated gradually between perhaps 120 and 50 ka and a minority who believe they appeared abruptly about 50 ka. Those who favor gradual development usually attribute

Key Words: Out of Africa; behavioral evolution; modern human origins; Neanderthal extinction

it to long-term social, demographic, or economic shifts, while those who perceive abrupt development, mainly the present writer, suggest that it was prompted by genetic change. My main purpose here is to summarize the evidence for the sociodemographic and genetic alternatives and to explain why I prefer the genetic explanation. Its principal failing has long been that it could not be evaluated independently of the archeology that suggests it, but modern and ancient DNA now promise a direct test.

This summary is abstracted from a much longer monographic treatment in press,[4] which supplies many additional details. Both the summary and the monograph emphasize the genetic explanation for Out of Africa because I think it fits the available evidence better. However, I'm not dedicated to it, and if someone could show me evidence that supports the sociodemographic alternative more strongly, I'd switch without looking back. I want to be right, but I care much more that someone can be. My main concern is that we approach closure on what underlies Out of Africa, just as we have on its occurrence.

Background to Out of Africa

The Out of Africa hypothesis might be better called "Out of Africa 3," since it concerns the pattern of human evolution after "Out of Africa 1," the widely accepted initial human dispersal from Africa before 1 Ma and "Out of Africa 2," the less widely celebrated dispersal of late Acheulean people from Africa at roughly 600 ka. However, for simplicity's sake, in keeping with present convention, Out of Africa 3 will be known here simply as Out of Africa. Genetics have played the leading role in its acceptance but, at base, it is grounded in the fossil record, which shows that human populations diverged morphologically between Africa, Europe, and the Far East, especially after 500 ka. From this time onward, there were at least three evolving human lineages or species (Fig. 1): *Homo sapiens* in Africa, *H. neanderthalensis* in Europe, and *H. erectus* in the Far East.

The European lineage is the best documented. It is marked by the accretion of Neanderthal features, culminating in the classic Neanderthals between 190 and 130 ka.[5] Glacial climates dominated the long interval when the Neanderthals were evolving in Europe and physiological adaptation to cold probably explains their principal postcranial specializations, including, above all, their broad trunks and short distal limbs.[6–10] Neanderthal craniofacial features are less obviously adaptive and could have been fixed mainly by random drift (chance) in populations that were always small and that were periodically further reduced and isolated by harsh climatic swings.[11] Statistical tests founded on explicit predictions from quantitative and population genetic theory show that drift alone could explain the craniometric difference between Neanderthals and modern humans.[1]

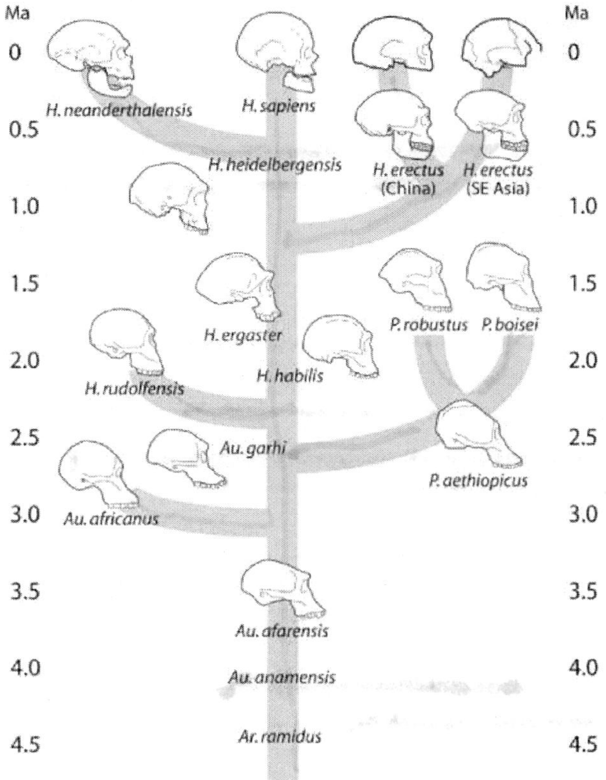

Figure 1. A working phylogeny of the hominins after 4.5 Ma. (***Ar. = Ardipithecus; Au. = Australopithecus; P. = Paranthropus; H. = Homo)***.

The pertinent African fossil record is much less complete than the European one, but it contains no specimens that anticipate the Neanderthals.[13] The African fossils suggest that modern craniofacial features accumulated in Africa between 250 ka or before and perhaps 50 ka.[14,15] The pattern recalls the mosaic accretion of Neanderthal features in Europe; in both Africa and Europe, the process may owe more to drift than to natural selection.

The Far Eastern record is the most sketchy. It may actually comprise two distinct evolutionary trajectories: one in southeastern Asia that suggests continuity within Javan *Homo erectus* from perhaps 1 Ma until 50 ka,[16,17] and a second one in China, which may indicate evolution from classic Chinese *H. erectus* between 1 Ma and 500 ka to populations that, by 200–100 ka, combined classic *H. erectus* cranial features with ones that recall the more ancient Afro-European species, *H. heidelbergensis*.[18] *H. heidelbergensis* is based on fossils that probably or provisionally date between 600 and 400 ka; its advocates commonly regard it as the last shared ancestor of *H. sapiens* and *H. neanderthalensis*.[19,20] It was presumably members of *H. heidelbergensis* who brought late Acheulean artifacts from Africa to Europe about 600 ka. The artifacts provide strong circumstantial support for a common African-European species at this time.

As presently revealed, the Chinese fossil record is perhaps the biggest impediment to unqualified acceptance of Out of Africa, but it is actually not so much contradictory as it is poorly known. China has provided only a handful of fossils, most notably those from Dali, Jinniushan, and Maba, that probably postdate classic *Homo erectus*, and none of these is precisely dated. In this light, the real problem with the Chinese fossil record is that its bearing on Out of Africa is uncertain. A fuller record may show that, like European *H. neanderthalensis*, contemporaneous archaic Chinese populations (advanced *H. erectus*?) were replaced by immigrant African *H. sapiens* 50–40 ka. Alternatively, that record might suggest that local populations and African immigrants interbred. In the latter instance, it might even reveal a dispersal from Africa to the Far East long before 50 ka. If significant interbreeding (gene flow) were demonstrated, the species distinction between invaders and locals could not be maintained. It is the growing genetic evidence against interbreeding in Europe and the abrupt replacement of the Neanderthals there that most strongly support separate species labels for the Neanderthals and modern humans.

The skeletal remains of early modern Europeans sometimes exhibit features that could imply interbreeding with Neanderthals. The strongest recent claims concern an early modern individual from Portugal[21] and three from Romania.[22–25] In each case, however, the supposed Neanderthal traits are swamped by others that are indisputably modern, and the indications for hybridization are problematic. The occurrence of a diagnostic Neanderthal feature, the suprainiac fossa, on one of the Romanian fossils has been contested,[26] but the more general problem is the muted expression of the supposed Neanderthal characters and their unknown heritability. It is especially unclear whether these characters could be expected in individuals that lived long after the putative hybridization event. The fossils for which they have been proposed mainly postdate this event by at least 100 generations.

The heritability of genes is unproblematic, and ancient DNA now joins the genetics of living humans to argue that Neanderthals and early modern Europeans rarely, if ever, interbred. Since Neanderthal mitochondrial (mt) DNA was first reported in 1997,[27] it has been extracted from 15 additional Neanderthal bones, representing at least 13 different individuals, scattered throughout the Neanderthal range, from Spain on the west to south-central Siberia on the east.[28–38] The fossil mtDNA underscores the divergent evolution of the Neanderthals. In addition, like modern human mtDNA, it is roughly 5 times less variable than is the mtDNA of the African great apes.[39] The providing Neanderthals died mainly, if not entirely, in the middle of the last glaciation (early OIS 3), between roughly 59 and 40–35 ka. The limited diversity of their mtDNA thus suggests a recent climatically forced bottleneck of the kind whose occurence earlier on could help explain the mosaic accumulation of Neanderthal craniofacial features. A more important point from the perspective of this article is that the absence of Neanderthal mtDNA from the living human gene pool implies that Neanderthal females either did not participate in interbreeding or participated so rarely that their mtDNA was lost by chance long ago.

The recent recovery of the Y-chromosome from two Neanderthal bones suggests a parallel situation with regard to males[40]: Neanderthal males either did not mate with modern human females or did so infrequently enough that Neanderthal Y-chromosomes failed to survive to the present. The DNA of the earliest modern Europeans might yet reveal occasional interbreeding, but testing so far, involving well-preserved bones from seven individuals who lived in western and central Europe mostly between 35 and 22 ka, has produced no Neanderthal mtDNA.[31,39,41]

TABLE 1. Features That Distinguish the Archeological Record Beginning 50–40 ka*

- Substantial growth in the diversity and standardization of artifact types.
- Rapid increase in the rate of artifactual change through time and in the degree of artifact diversity through space.
- Oldest indications for widespread shaping of bone, ivory, shell, and related materials into formal artifacts ("points," "awls," "needles," "pins," and others).
- Earliest appearance of indisputable art and personal ornamentation.
- Oldest undeniable evidence of spatial organization of camp floors, including elaborate hearths and the oldest indisputable structural "ruins."
- Oldest evidence of the transport of large quantities of highly desirable stone raw material over scores or even hundreds of kilometers.
- Earliest secure evidence of ceremony or ritual, expressed both in art and in relatively elaborate graves.
- First evidence of human ability to live in the coldest, most continental parts of Eurasia (northeastern Europe and northern Asia).
- First evidence of human population densities approaching those of historic hunter-gatherers in similar environments.
- First evidence of fishing and other significant advances in human ability to extract energy from nature.

*In the view that this article espouses, these are not isolated traits that define "modern" behavior, but related outcomes of the innovative burst behind the Out of Africa expansion.

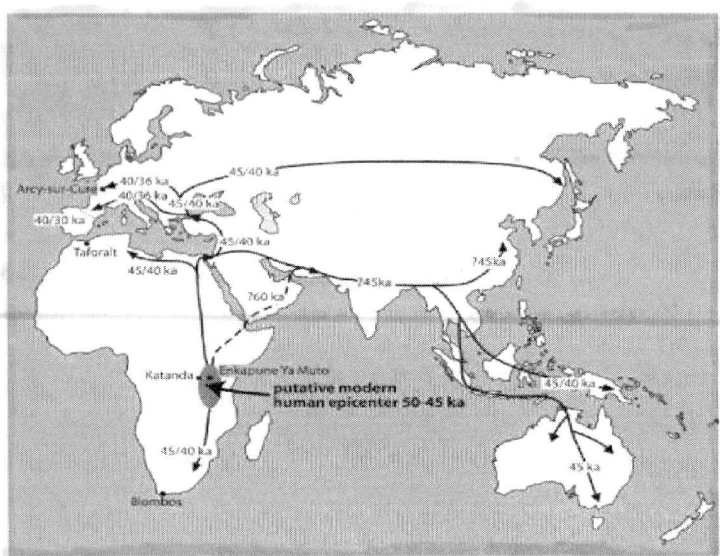

Figure 2. Hypothetical routes of modern human dispersal from Africa beginning roughly 50 ka (partly after Bar-Yosef,[137] Fig. 1). The attached dates must be imprecise because the dispersal occurred beyond the effective range of the radiocarbon dating method. The available alternative methods are currently less reliable.

Recent advances in DNA extraction and sequencing promise to yield the entire Neanderthal genome.[42] If the same procedures can be applied to fossils of "late *Homo erectus*," they could provide the most compelling check on Out of Africa. Admittedly, however, even if fresh fossil DNA confirms what known fossil DNA implies, it would not demonstrate the species distinctions proposed here. In fact, given the relatively short interval over which the proposed species diverged, they are likely to have remained genetically compatible. According to the model that this article advocates, behavioral separation would account for the rarity or absence of interbreeding when modern African invaders contacted nonmodern Eurasians.

An obvious objection to Out of Africa is the failure of modern or near-modern humans to expand from Africa immediately after they appeared, by 100 ka or before. Instead they seem to have been confined to Africa until roughly 50 ka, and it is even possible that they were replaced by Neanderthals on the southwest Asian margin of Africa, in what is now Israel around 80 ka.[43,44] Archeology provides a partial answer to the apparent conundrum. The people who inhabited Africa between 100 and 60–50 ka may have been physically modern or near-modern, but they were behaviorally similar to the Neanderthals and other nonmodern humans. The relatively full African and European archeological records show a distinct rupture only at 50–40 ka, when the Middle Stone Age (MSA) in Africa and the broadly similar Middle Paleolithic in Europe gave way, respectively, to the Later Stone Age (LSA) and Upper Paleolithic. It is only LSA and Upper Paleolithic sites, postdating 50–40 ka, that have commonly provided material residues that are indistinguishable from those of many later Prehistoric and historic hunter–gatherers. Table 1 lists some features that distinguish the archeological record after 50–40 ka from what came before.

The most significant behavioral novelty is often taken to be the burgeoning of unequivocal art and personal ornamentation because it suggests a capacity for abstract or "symbolic" thought. However, it is impossible to demonstrate that this capacity did not exist tens of thousands of years earlier, when it was expressed only occasionally, as, for example, at Blombos Cave, as discussed below. The difference at 50–40 ka is that unequivocal art, ornamentation, and other advanced behaviors were closely tied to a dramatic increase in human numbers, notably including the Out of Africa expansion. In short, these behaviors appear to have been part of a package that significantly enhanced human fitness—the ability to survive and reproduce. It is in this sense that they signal true evolutionary change as opposed to mere historical change. After the initial flowering of advanced behavioral markers, local historical and environmental conditions and the vagaries of preservation influenced their presence or expression. Many sites lack them and there are even places, perhaps above all Tasmania,[45,46] where they were more conspicuous prehistorically than they were ethnohistorically. The fundamental point, however, is that their variable occurrence after 50–40 ka contrasts sharply with their almost uniform absence before. It is this difference that signals something special.

The beginnings of the LSA and the Upper Paleolithic lie beyond the practical lower boundary of the radiocarbon dating method. Moreover, methods that can provide older ages are often more reliable in theory than in practice. This is particularly true of optically stimulated luminescence,[47] thermoluminescence,[48] and electron spin resonance,[49] in large part because they require an accurate estimate of the radiation dose to which buried items were subjected and must either assume a constant rate, when sediments often imply otherwise,[50] or make unverifiable site-specific assumptions about how the rate may have varied through time. The calculated ages are most compelling when they closely match results from radiocarbon or other methods that do not require site-specific assumptions. In the instances that matter most to this paper, such matches are not possible. There is the additional complication that the earliest LSA is still poorly known and thus weakly dated. Still, with these caveats in mind, the available dates suggest that the archeological markers of advanced behavior appeared first in eastern Africa, probably between 50 and 45 ka,[51] that they spread to western Asia and eastern Europe between 45 and 40 ka,[52,53] and that they reached western Europe only between 40 and 36 ka[54,55] (Fig. 2). The geographic sequence is plainly what Out of Africa would predict.

The advanced human behavioral traits that blossom after 50 ka imply the fully modern capacity for innovation that underlies culture in the narrow anthropological sense. In the next section, I will briefly explore the thorny problem of explaining why modern innovative ability developed when it did, but the most fundamental point is that it provided the competitive advantage that allowed fully modern humans to replace their nonmodern contemporaries. The time when advanced behavioral markers appeared in China and adjacent southeastern Asia remains unsettled, with most artifact assemblages that are thought to date between 50 and 10 ka differing little from older, even much older, assemblages.[56,57] In fact, however, the relevant archeological record is slim and poorly dated. Conspicuous archeological change occurred 50–40 ka in neighboring regions, especially Siberia[58] and Sahul (= the glacial supercontinent that included Australia, New Guinea, and Tasmania).[59] Much fresh research will be necessary to determine whether the pattern in China and southeastern Asia was truly different.

Some Problems with Out of Africa

Out of Africa is the most reasonable and parsimonious explanation of the available fossil and archeological data, but some opposing observations remain and cannot simply be ignored. Some specialists also believe that proponents of Out of Africa have unwittingly imposed their intellectual preconceptions on contrary or ambiguous data.[60] This leads them to reject Out of Africa in advance. Carried to its logical extreme, however, this perspective precludes any decision on Out of Africa, barring the unlikely development of data collection procedures that do not require advance assumptions or expectations. New intellectual frameworks or paradigms may yet prove helpful, but my aim here is to reiterate some problems with Out of Africa that are more evidentiary than epistemological.

What Explains the Relatively Abrupt Florescence of Advanced Human Behavior (The Modern Capacity for Culture) at 50 ka?

The most popular answer is probably that it was driven by social, economic, or demographic change.[59,61–64] Social change, for example, could have involved the initial development of the nuclear family as the fundamental productive unit and, together with this, the division of labor by sex and age that characterized all historic hunter–gatherer societies.[65] Nuclear family organization and a newly invented division of labor could, in turn, have led to the modern notions of kinship and descent that promote economic and political cooperation among individuals and groups. Population growth could have followed and larger, denser populations could explain the accelerated innovation that marks the archeological record after 50 ka. This kind of explanation is logically coherent, but it fails in at least one crucial respect: It does not explain why social relations changed when they did or why they changed at all.

Population growth could underlie the timing, if it is assumed that growth came first and that behavior changed about 50 ka when population density crossed a critical threshold that forced social reorganization. However, even if we ignore the need to explain what drove population growth, an explanation rooted in it must confront the problem that the advanced behavior presumably arose in Africa, while archeology suggests that African populations were shrinking, not growing, when the advance occurred. In southern Africa, the large average size of humanly collected intertidal shells and tortoises in MSA sites implies that by more recent Prehistoric standards human population density was low and that it was more or less constant between 120 and 70 ka (Box 1). Shortly after 60 ka, people became archeologically all but invisible, probably because hyperaridity in the middle of the last glaciation sharply reduced their numbers.[66,67] A similar pattern appears to have characterized northern Africa.[68–71] Eastern Africa was more mesic at 60–50 ka,[72] and people may have remained more numerous there. However, even when this is considered, the archeological indicators for African population size about 50 ka are consistent with genetic analyses, which suggest that the African population from which all living humans derive included no more than 10,000 breeding adults and that population growth mainly followed Out of Africa.[73,74]

Given what we know or don't know about demographic and social change, it then becomes at least as plausible to tie the basic behavioral shift at 50 ka to a fortuitous mutation that promoted the fully modern brain. This proposal follows on two widely accepted observations: that natural selection for more effective brains largely drove the earlier phases of human evolution and that the relationship between morphological and behavioral change shifted abruptly about 50 ka. Before this time, morphology and behavior appear to have evolved relatively slowly and more or less in tandem. After this time, however, morphology remained relatively stable while behavioral (cultural) change accelerated rapidly. What could explain this better than a neural change that promoted the extraordinary modern human ability to innovate? This is not to say that the Neanderthals and their nonmodern contemporaries had apelike brains or that they were as biologically and behaviorally primitive as yet earlier humans were. It is only to suggest that an acknowledged genetic link between morphology and behavior in even earlier people persisted until the emergence of fully modern ones and that the postulated genetic change at 50 ka fostered the uniquely modern ability to adapt to a wide range of natural and social circumstances with little or no physiological change.

Many archeologists dismiss the neural hypothesis out of hand, perhaps because they have been trained to distrust biological explanations for behavioral change. In addition, some specialists seem to feel that a biological explanation reflects unthinking bias against the Neanderthals and other nonmodern humans.[75,76] Ideological positions aside, however, the main problem with a neural explanation has long been that it cannot be tested with fossils. Earlier in human evolution, a link between behavioral and neural change can be inferred from conspicuous increases in average brain size, but humans virtually everywhere had achieved modern or near-modern brain size by 200 ka. Any neural change that occurred around 50 ka must thus have been in organization, and fossil skulls provide only speculative evidence regarding brain structure. Neanderthal skulls, for example, differ dramatically in shape from modern ones, but they were as large or larger. Furthermore, based on present evidence it is not clear that the difference in form implies a significant difference in function. A link between form and function becomes especially unlikely if, as I suggested earlier, random genetic drift was primarily responsible for the difference in form.

Fossils may never allow an independent test of the neural hypothesis, but there is now the possibility that genetics could do so. Clinically oriented investigations have identified numerous genes that probably bear on cognition and communication.[77,78] If the functions of these genes can be more precisely determined, it may be possible to determine if one or more experienced strong selection at roughly the time that modern humans spread from Africa. In addition, once the Neanderthal nuclear genome is available, it will become possible to assess the extent to which Neanderthals and modern humans shared behaviorally relevant genes. If differences are found, they would indirectly support the neural explanation, for they would suggest that behaviorally relevant genetic change occurred even after the modern human lineage had emerged. An expectation to the contrary is implicit in hypotheses that link the modern human expansion to strictly social or demographic factors.

Is It True That Modern Behavioral Markers Appear Widely Only at About 50–40 ka?

With regard to art and ornamentation, for example, virtually all specialists agree that they become commonplace only after 50 ka and that older examples are both rare and crude. The most widely cited older examples are abstract engravings and perforated shells, which occur in only a small fraction of the sites where they might be expected. Representational (figurative) art objects and intentionally shaped ornaments (beads or pendants) appear only at sites that postdate 50 ka. However, even if authorities agree that 50 ka marks an inflection point, they disagree sharply on what the inflection means. To some, the rarity and simplicity of supposed art before 50 ka implies that modern cognitive abilities were present but were weakly or infrequently expressed before 50 ka, while to others (including

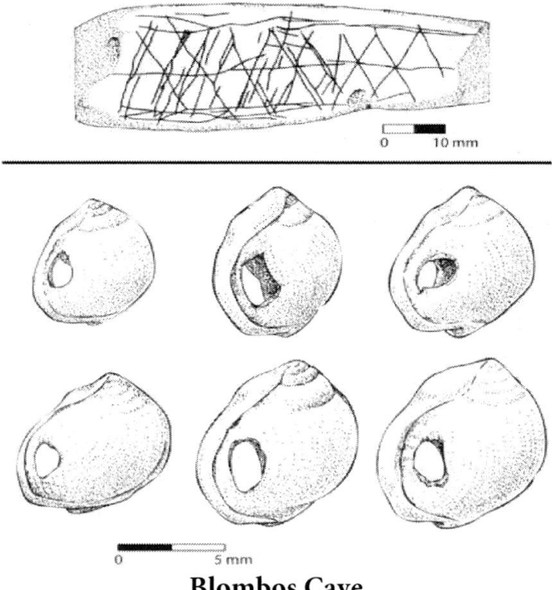

Figure 3. Top: A red ochre fragment with an incised, cross-hatched patter from the MSA deposits of Blombos Cave, South Africa. (Drawn from a photo in Henshilwood and coworkers,[79] p. 1279). Bottom: Proposed tick-shell beads from the same deposits. (Drawn from a photo in Henshilwood and coworkers,[80] p. 404).

me), it suggests that the fully modern capacity for culture may have appeared only about this time.

Some of the rare art objects that antedate 50 ka are probably younger intrusions that even the most careful excavation cannot detect, while others are probably the result of human or natural actions that will inevitably, on rare occasions, mimic crude human attempts at art. In this regard, credible claims for art or other modern human behavioral markers before 50 ka must involve sizable numbers of conspicuously patterned objects from carefully documented contexts. With this criterion in mind, two MSA sites, Blombos Cave, South Africa, and the Katanda open-air (riverside) site cluster, D. R. Congo, probably present the most serious obstacles to the neural explanation for Out of Africa favored here. At Blombos, the objects include a pigment (ochre) lump on which an abstract pattern has been incised,[79] 41 perforated tick-shells interpreted as beads,[80] and 29 indisputable bone artifacts,[81] all fixed by luminescence dating of sand grains and heated stone artifacts between 84 and 74 ka.[82,83] At Katanda, the objects comprise eight whole or partial barbed bone points and four other well-made bone artifacts[84,85] dated to between 90 and 60–70 ka by luminescence on the sandy matrix and by electron spin resonance on associated mammal teeth.

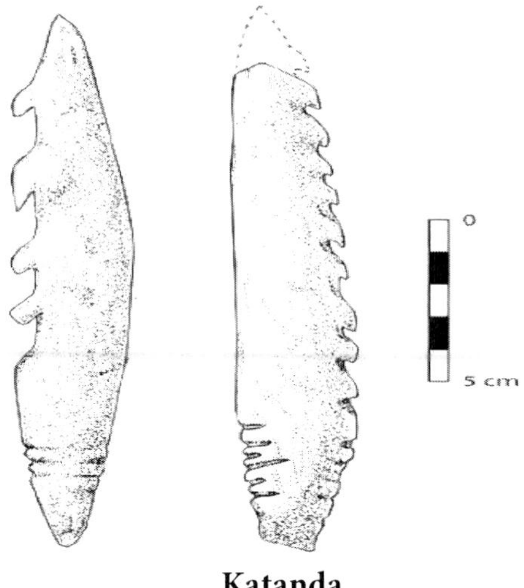

Figure 4. Two of eight barbed bone points excavated at Katanda, Democratic Republic of the Congo (redrawn after Yellen, 85 p. 189).

The incised pattern on the Blombos pigment lump comprises a series of 6 or 7 crude X marks framed by additional incised lines (Fig. 3, top). Many observers accept the sum as abstract art. Some of the other 8,000-plus pigment lumps from Blombos exhibit incised lines that could represent incomplete or less successful stabs at similar abstract expression. Scored lines also occur on lumps from other broadly contemporaneous MSA sites. A lump from Klein Kliphuis Rockshelter, roughly 400 km northwest of Blombos, exhibits eight intersecting lines that arguably form a simpler version of the Blombos pattern.[86] Everywhere, however, MSA people ground or scraped pigment to obtain powder and they may have scored it to test its quality or roughen its surface before grinding. Conceivably, MSA people used the powder for paint, perhaps for application to human skin. However, the disposition of powder on ancient stone artifacts and modern experimentation with it indicate that powder was an important ingredient in the glue used to attach stone bits to wooden handles or shafts.[87–90] Because this is the only function that archeological and experimental observations confirm, it is reasonable to ask, given the large number of pigment lumps at Blombos, Klein Kliphuis, and other sites, whether scoring for practical purposes might not occasionally produce crisscrossing marks that appear to be deliberately patterned. The Blombos engraving would be more persuasively artistic if it were widely replicated or, of course, if it were less abstract and suggested a human or animal figure. In addition, whatever its meaning, it cannot bear specially on the evolution of modern behavior or on Out of Africa, since the Neanderthals who occupied Pech de l'Azé Cave 1, France, also incised abstract patterns on pigment lumps.[91]

The perforated Blombos tick shells may be beads, but the case depends mainly on the need to explain why people would bring home such tiny shells. The perforations are less conspicuously artificial than they are on much later LSA shell beads. Also, the basic shape of the tick shells remained unaltered (Fig. 3, bottom). The same is true of thirteen putative tick shell beads at Pigeon Cave (Taforalt), Morocco, dated by luminescence to roughly 82 ka.[92] Unlike the proposed Blombos beads, some of the Pigeon Cave specimens were abraded and initially choked with beach sediment; and the circumstances of their excavation have been only weakly described. They are less compelling than their Blombos counterparts and might have been ignored if the Blombos finds had not already been publicized. The key point is that neither the Blombos nor Pigeon Cave beads are deliberately shaped. So far, the earliest unequivocally shaped beads postdate 50 ka. The oldest are ostrich eggshell beads, dated to beyond 40 ka at Enkapune Ya Muto and, perhaps, other early LSA sites in eastern Africa.[51] Shaped beads are also well known from European Upper Paleolithic sites that postdate 40 ka.[93]

The Blombos bone artifacts may be divided between two groups, twenty-six that were shaped mainly by use and three that were more conspicuously fashioned in advance and closely resemble polished LSA bone projectile points. The pieces that were shaped by use recall the smoothed and pointed antelope horncores and bone splinters dated to more than 1 Ma at the Swartkrans, Sterkfontein, and Drimolen Caves, South Africa.[94,95] Their cognitive implications need be no greater. The three artifacts that resemble polished LSA projectile points are another matter because they could imply LSA-like hunting proficiency. One was initially associated with three radiocarbon readings on charcoal near 2 ka,[81] but if these dates are discounted and the MSA associations of all three are accepted, the Blombos mammalian assemblage might be expected to exhibit the same elevated proportion of more dangerous ungulates that distinguish LSA assemblages from MSA assemblages elsewhere in the region. It does not[96] and, in this connection, the large average size of the associated shells and tortoise bones suggests that the Blombos people were much less numerous than LSA people living under similar conditions (Box 1). The bottom line is that whatever the cognitive or cultural implications of the Blombos artifacts, they do not appear to have conferred an LSA-like fitness (reproductive and survival) advantage. This may explain why they did not spread from Blombos and why they did not prompt an Out of Africa expansion.

The Katanda barbed points may be seen to parallel the Blombos polished points, but they are far more elaborate (Fig. 4). If they are genuinely older than 60 ka, they would more surely imply modern cognition long before the Out-of-Africa expansion. This would raise the question again, however, of why they remained geographically isolated and why their use did not promote human population increase. The answer may be that they are actually much younger than proposed, which might be checked by direct radiocarbon dating. They are much fresher looking than the heavily abraded mammalian teeth that have been partly used to date them. The next oldest similar points in eastern Africa date from 25 ka or less.[84,97] Most postdate 10 ka.

Were Neanderthals Fundamentally Incapable of Fully Modern Behavior?

As outlined here, Out of Africa postulates that the Neanderthals were replaced because they could not compete culturally with their modern human "Cro-Magnon" successors. If cognitive limitations explain this inability, they might have created a behavioral barrier to interbreeding between Neanderthals and modern humans. The idea that the Neanderthals were not competitive is bolstered over most of Europe by the relatively abrupt nature of their replacement. At most sites where Cro-Magnon/Upper Paleolithic occupations directly overlie Neanderthal/Middle Paleolithic layers, there is no indication of a substantial break in time or of any transition between the two. It is therefore reasonable to infer that in any given region the replacement took a relatively short time, a few centuries or perhaps even a few decades.

However, there is the occasional discovery of artifact assemblages that include subequal numbers of Neanderthal/Middle Paleolithic and Cro-Magnon/Upper Paleolithic artifact types. The most compelling examples come from western France and northern Spain, where they have been assigned to the Châtelperronian culture.[98–100] The Châtelperronian probably began around 45 ka and persisted until perhaps 37–36 ka, when it was truncated by the early Upper Paleolithic Aurignacian culture. Human fossils from La Roche á Pierrot Rockshelter, Saint-Césaire[101] and the Grotte du Renne, Arcy-sur-Cure,[102,103] indicate that Châtelperronian people were Neanderthals. In contrast, early Aurignacians were anatomically modern people whose biological roots almost certainly lay in Africa.

If only stone tools were involved, the Châtelperronian might be regarded as the final stage of the local Mousterian of Acheulean Tradition Type B (with numerous backed knives) that converged on the Upper Paleolithic. Indeed, the early Châtelperronian may have been just that. In support, the Châtelperronian and the Mousterian of Acheulean Tradition B have almost identical geographic distributions.[104] However, at Arcy-sur-Cure, late Châtelperronians produced not only a mix of typical Middle and Upper Paleolithic stone artifacts, but also typical Upper Paleolithic bone tools and personal ornaments and modified their living spaces in a characteristically Upper Paleolithic fashion.[105–107] This might mean that they borrowed Upper Paleolithic cultural traits from Aurignacian neighbors, but even if this is accepted it begs one fundamental question: If Upper Paleolithic culture was clearly superior and Châtelperronian Neanderthals could imitate it (that is, they were not biologically precluded from behaving in an Upper Paleolithic way), why didn't the Neanderthals acculturate more widely, with the result that they or their genes would have persisted much more conspicuously into Upper Paleolithic times (after 40–35 ka)?

Box 1. South African MSA and LSA Shell Middens

Middle Paleolithic sites in the Mediterranean region that antedate 50 ka sometimes contain small numbers of intertidal shells and remains of marine vertebrates.[117–119] So far, however, only contemporaneous South African MSA coastal sites have provided true shell middens. The principal MSA sites are Die Kelders Cave 1,[120,121] Blombos Cave,[96,122] Herolds Bay Cave,[123] the Pinnacle Point Caves,[124] and the Klasies River Cave complex[66,125]

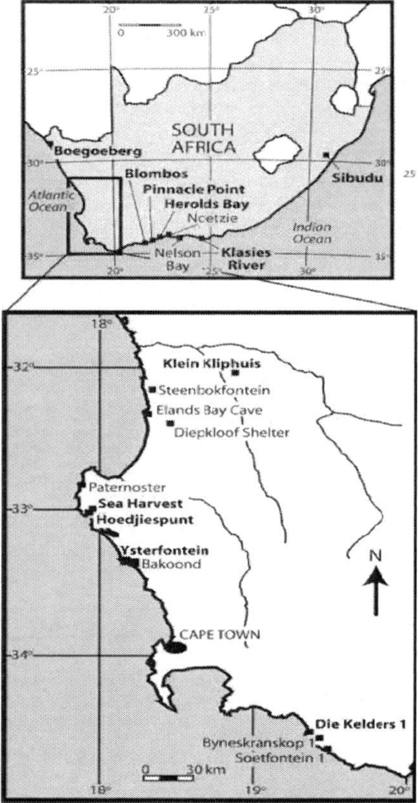

Box 1, Figure 1. The approximate locations of the South African MSA and LSA sites in the text and in Box 1, Figures 2 and 3. MSA sites are boldfaced.

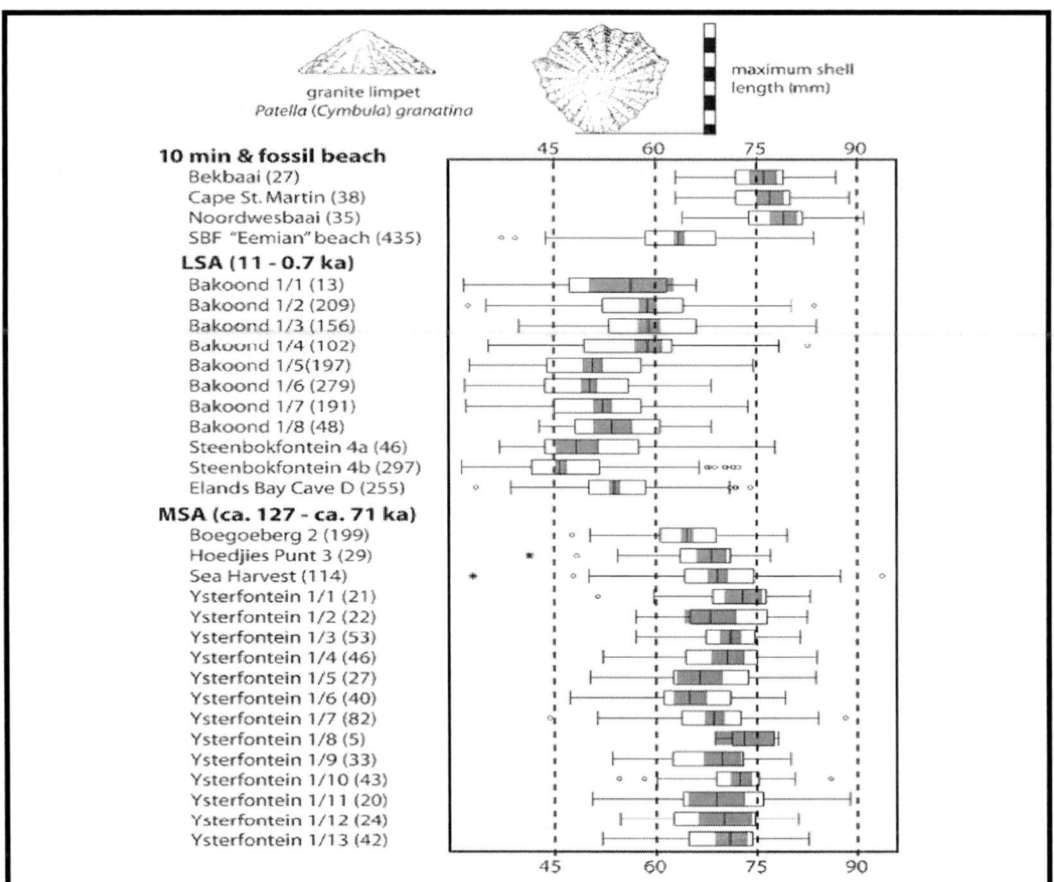

Box 1, Figure 2. Box plots summarizing the maximum length of granite limpets from the MSA deposits at Boegoeberg 2,[126] Hoedjiespunt 3,[127] Sea Harvest,[128] and Ysterfontein 1[129,130]; LSA deposits at Elands Bay Cave,[127] Steenbokfontein,[138] and Bakoond[139]; modern "10-minute samples" at Bekbaai, Cape St. Martin, and Noordwesbaai near the town of Paternoster[134]; and a probable last interglacial beach near Steenbokfontein (SBF "Eemian" beach) (R. Yates, unpublished). The number in parentheses after each site is the number of shells in the sample. Box 1, Figure 1 locates the sites. Following Volleman,[140] the key elements in each box plot are the median, represented by the line near the center; the open rectangle enclosing the middle half of the data (between the 25th and 75th percentiles); the shaded rectangle indicating the 95% confidence limits for the median; and the bisecting line, which signifies the range of more or less continuous data. Starbursts and open circles mark outliers (values that are especially far from the median). Chance is unlikely to explain the difference between medians having 95% confidence limits that do not overlap.

on the southern coast of South Africa, and Boegoeberg 2,[126] Hoedjies Punt 1 and 3,[127] Sea Harvest,128 and Ysterfontein 1[129,130] on the western coast (Box 1, Fig. 1). Both coasts also have rich LSA shell middens with which the MSA examples can be fruitfully compared.

The MSA sites all lie beyond the range of the radiocarbon method, but luminescence dating and other geochronological indicators imply that they formed mainly during the last interglacial (= Oxygen Isotope Stage 5) between roughly 127 and 71 ka. Their precise placement within the last interglacial and with respect to each other is often uncertain, but luminescence ages, supported now by stratigraphic observations at Diepkloof Rockshelter[131] and Sibubu Cave,[132] indicate that the well-documented Still Bay (MSA 1) occupation at Blombos Cave antedates the equally well-known Howieson's Poort occupation at Klasies River. Radiocarbon dating shows that the LSA middens all date from the Present Interglacial (OIS 1), between 12 ka and the historic present. Middens that formed during the Last Glaciation (OIS 4-2), between 71 and 12 ka, are rare or lacking, because sea level rise has drowned the coastlines on which they formed. In their absence, however, the last and present interglacial examples still provide an opportunity to investigate aspects of coastal foraging before and after the Out of Africa expansion 50 ka. In addition, since the MSA and LSA middens formed under broadly similar climatic conditions, any highly conspicuous, consistent differences between them are most likely to reflect a change in culture as opposed to a change in environment. An environmental explanation for particularly obvious, consistent differences is further improbable, because the two coasts on which the middens lie differ environmentally today. The MSA and LSA faunas indicate that they differed in broadly the same way throughout the last and present interglacials.

Two features strongly differentiate the MSA and LSA faunas, regardless of coast. First, compared to mammal bones or shells, fish bones are rare at MSA sites. They are far more abundant in LSA sites, where they often outnumber mammal bones by an order of magnitude. Only the LSA sites have provided artifacts that anticipate ethnohistorically observed fishing implements,[133] and the sum suggests that only LSA people fished routinely. The importance of this cannot be exaggerated, because fish abound offshore on both coasts. All other things being equal, people with fishing technology would surely outnumber people who lacked it.

The second striking MSA/LSA contrast, again independent of coast, is that the shells of major intertidal species tend to be significantly larger in MSA sites. Box 1, Figures 2 and 3 use box plots to illustrate this for the granite limpet [*Patella (Cymbula) granatina*], which is endemic to the west coast, and for the Cape turban shell (*Turbo sarmaticus*), which is endemic to the southern coast. The legend for Box 1, Figure 2 details the box plot format. The key elements in each plot are the median, represented by the vertical line

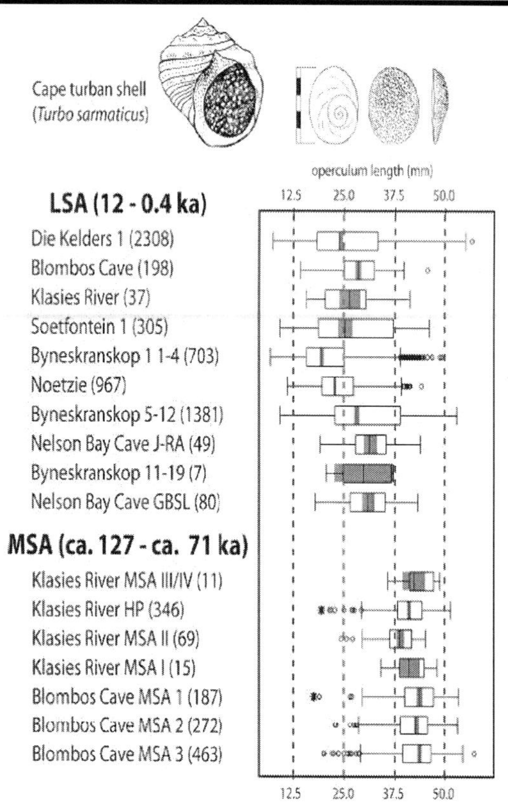

Box 1, Figure 3. Box plots summarizing the length (maximum dimension) of Cape turban shell opercula from the MSA deposits at Blombos Cave[96,122] and Klasies River,[66,125] and from LSA deposits at Nelson Bay Cave,[133] Byneskranskop,[141] Noetzie,[142] Soetfontein 1,[143] Klasies River,[125] Blombos Cave,[96] and Die Kelders Cave 1.[144] The number in parentheses after each site is the number of opercula in the sample. Figure 5 locates the sites; the caption to Figure 6 explains the box-plot format.

near the middle, and the 95% confidence limits for the median, represented by the gray bar around the median. Medians whose 95% confidence limits that do not overlap differ significantly in the conventional statistical sense. The figures include only those MSA samples that are large enough for numeric analysis. They could include many additional LSA samples, but these would not affect the basic pattern and would impede legibility.

The figures show that median size in both shellfish species varies within the MSA and the LSA, but the ranges of variation do not overlap. The MSA shells are consistently larger. Since shellfish collection requires no special tools or risk and both MSA and LSA people probably collected the largest available specimens first, large differences in median shell size probably reflect differences in collection intensity. The most plausible reason for a difference in intensity is a difference in the number of person hours devoted to collection; the most likely reason for a difference in person hours is a change in the number of collectors. A shift in either environment or culture (technology) could affect the number of collectors. Also, environmental variation might explain size variation within the MSA and LSA. However, it is unlikely to explain the large and consistent MSA/LSA size contrasts, if only because many of the MSA and LSA samples probably accumulated under similar environmental conditions. In short, the larger median size of MSA granite limpets, turban shells, and other shellfish species on both coasts almost certainly means that MSA culture supported smaller, less dense human populations.

Box 1, Figure 2 includes four control samples that illustrate the potential for collection intensity to affect average granite limpet size. Modern collectors accumulated three of the samples (Bekbaai, Cape St. Martin, and Noordwesbaai) near the town of Paternoster from intertidal rocks that no one else had recently visited.[134] In each instance, the collectors were given 10 minutes and, like Prehistoric people, tended to collect the largest, most visible specimens first. The shells in the three samples show how large granite limpets can become when they are not exploited. The fourth sample (labeled SBF "Eemian" beach) came from a last interglacial fossil beach at Steenbokfontein. It documents average (as opposed to maximum) granite limpet size long before the LSA. The granite limpets in all four control samples are remarkably large, but they are particularly large relative to LSA specimens and imply that LSA limpet collection was especially intense.

Box 1, Figure 3 includes turban shells from both the Still Bay (MSA 1) occupation at Blombos Cave and the Howieson's Poort (HP) occupation at Klasies River. The Klasies River samples came from relatively unsystematic excavations in 1967–1968, but subsequent, more meticulous excavations provided specimens that are closely similar in average size.135 At Blombos, the Still Bay layers and the immediately underlying (MSA 2) layers provided the engraved ocher fragment, proposed tick shells, and bone tools discussed in the text. The large average size of the turban shells at both Blombos Cave and Klasies River implies that whatever the cognitive implications of Still Bay and Howieson's Poort artifacts, the associated human populations remained small by LSA standards. The addition of fishing alone could explain why LSA people appear to have been so much more numerous than MSA people living under similar circumstances.

Many of the coastal sites that provided the shell samples in Box 1, Figures 2 and 3, as well as nearby inland sites, have also provided large numbers of bones from the angulate tortoise (Chersina angulata). Like shellfish collection, tortoise collection involves no special expertise or technology, and both MSA and LSA people probably took the largest tortoises first, since these were the meatiest and most visible. Just as for shellfish then, more intensive collection pressure, reflecting a larger number of collectors, should reduce average tortoise size. The available observations in fact reveal the same basic pattern: tortoise size varies within both the MSA and the LSA, but MSA tortoises tend to be significantly larger than are their LSA counterparts.[96,130,136] This is important not only because any other outcome would undermine the interpretation of the shellfish results, but also because tortoises and shellfish occupy independent ecosystems. This enhances the likelihood that culture, rather than environment, explains the large size of both shellfish and tortoises in MSA sites.

The shellfish and tortoise observations bear on the theme of this article, arguing that human population size varied around a relatively low mean during the later part of the MSA. It follows that MSA population growth is unlikely to have prompted the behavioral changes that prompted the Out of Africa expansion.

The Arcy Châtelperronian contradicts more abundant evidence of a behavioral difference between Neanderthals and Cro-Magnons. It is reasonable to ask whether excavation could be responsible. The excavations were conducted between 1948 and 1963, and the methods were excellent for their time. However, hindsight suggests that they would not meet present standards, particularly in a deposit that was stratigraphically complex.[108,109] It is possible that the excavators inadvertently failed to separate a typical Châtelperronian occupation without ornaments and well-made bone tools from an overlying early Aurignacian occupation that had both. It has been argued that the Arcy Châtelperronians employed distinctive methods to manufacture ornaments and other special pieces,[110] but a comprehensive comparative analysis shows that both the manufacturing methods and the final products fit comfortably within the early Aurignacian range.[111]

The Arcy example underscores the extent to which archeological interpretation depends on excavation quality. Outsiders must usually take quality for granted, but even the most careful, experienced excavators may fail to detect mixture between occupations in a complex cave like the Grotte du Renne. This reinforces what should be an archeological maxim: The first discovery of a unique or unexpected assemblage should be regarded as a possible accident; even the second discovery could be a coincidence. In general, only repeated, independent discoveries establish a pattern that merits serious behavioral interpretation. Nearly 50 years after the Arcy Châtelperronian was first reported, it nearly remains unique. Only the Châtelperronian layers at Quinçay Cave, southwestern France, provide meager corroboration, in the form of four pierced animal teeth.[112,113] Well-excavated Châtelperronian layers elsewhere, for example, at Grotte XVI,[114–116] also in southwestern

France, lack Upper Paleolithic-like ornaments and bone tools. Among the 18 or so commonly accepted Châtelperronian sites, Grotte XVI illustrates the rule. At least until the Arcy Châtelperronian is independently replicated, it need not imply fundamental similarity in behavioral capability between Neanderthals and Cro-Magnons.

Conclusion

Since the 1910s, fossil and archeological discoveries have suggested that fully modern (Cro-Magnon) immigrants replaced the Neanderthals in Europe. Fossil and archeological support for an abrupt replacement grew stronger in succeeding decades, but became particularly compelling from the late 1980s onwards. During that period, new dates and fresh fossils demonstrated that near-modern or modern humans had appeared in Africa by 100 ka; new fossils demonstrated the accretional evolution of the Neanderthal lineage in Europe; genes showed that all living humans share a common African ancestor that existed after the Neanderthal and modern human lineages had differentiated; and DNA extracted from the bones of Neanderthals simultaneously underscored their divergent evolutionary history and suggested that they rarely, if ever, interbred with modern humans. Some of the new (and old) evidence is ambiguous, circumstantial, or even contradictory, but if the study of human origins were a jury trial, the verdict would surely be that modern humans, originating in Africa, swamped or extinguished the Neanderthals. The jury would probably also accept that a behavioral transformation accounted for modern human success, but they might deadlock on whether sociodemographic or genetic change underlay the transformation.

In fact, of course, research on human origins differs from a jury trial in that no verdict need ever be final; new evidence and new jury members are always welcome. I doubt that a future jury will reverse the verdict on Neanderthal extinction, but fresh evidence from the modern human and Neanderthal genomes may permit closure on whether sociodemographic or genetic change underlies modern human success.

Acknowledgments

I thank the National Science Foundation for research support, Kathryn Cruz-Uribe for help with the illustrations, and Curtis Marean, James O'Connell, John Shea, Teresa Steele, and Tim Weaver for thoughtful comments on a draft.

About the Author

Richard G. Klein is Professor of Anthropology and Biology at Stanford University. The University of Chicago Press will publish the third edition of his book, *The Human Career: Human Biological and Cultural Origins*, in April 2009. Program in Human Biology, Bldg 20, Inner Quad, Stanford University, Stanford, CA 94305, Phone: (650) 725-9819, Fax: (650) 725-0605. E-mail: rklein@stanford.edu

References

1. Cann RL, Stoneking M, Wilson AC. 1987. Mitochondrial DNA and human evolution. Nature 329:31–36.
2. Ingman M, Kaessmann H, Pääbo S, Gyllensten U. 2000. Mitochondrial genome variation and the origin of modern humans. Nature 408:708–713.
3. Underhill PA, Passarino G, Lin AA, Shen P, Lahr MM, Foley RA, Oefner PJ, Cavalli-Sforza LL. 2001. The phylogeography of Y chromosome binary haplotypes and the origins of modern human populations. Am J Hum Genet 65:43–62.
4. Klein RG. 2009. The human career: human biological and cultural origins, 3rd ed. Chicago: University of Chicago Press.
5. Hublin J-J. 1998. Climatic changes, paleogeography, and the evolution of the Neandertals. In: Akazawa T, Aoki K, Bar-Yosef O, editors. Neandertals and modern humans in Western Asia. New York: Plenum Press. p 291–310.
6. Trinkaus E. 1981. Neanderthal limb proportions and cold adaptation. In: Stringer CB, editor. Aspects of human evolution. London: Taylor and Francis. p 187–224.
7. Ruff CB. 1993. Climatic adaptation and hominid evolution: the thermoregulatory imperative. Evol Anthropol 2:53–60.
8. Holliday TW. 1997. Body proportions in late Pleistocene Europe and modern human origins. J Hum Evol 32:423–447.
9. Pearson OM. 2000. Postcranial remains and the origin of modern humans. Evol Anthropol 9:229–247.
10. Weaver TD. 2003. The shape of the Neanderthal femur is primarily a consequence of hyper-polar body form. Proc Nat Acad Sci 100:6926–6929.

11. Howell FC. 1952. Pleistocene glacial ecology and the evolution of "classic" Neanderthal man. Southwest J Anthropol 8:377–410.
12. Weaver TD, Roseman CC, Stringer CB. 2007. Were neandertal and modern human cranial differences produced by natural selection or genetic drift? J Hum Evol 53:135–145.
13. Stringer CB. 2002. Modern human origins: progress and prospects. Philas Trans R Soc Lond B 357:563–579.
14. Brauer G. 2008. The origin of modern anatomy: by speciation or intraspecific evolution? Evol Anthropol 17:22–37.
15. Pearson OM. 2008. Statistical and biological definitions of "anatomically modern" humans: suggestions for a unified approach to modern morphology. Evol Anthropol 17:38–48.
16. Rightmire GP. 1992. *Homo erectus*: ancestor or evolutionary side branch? Evol Anthropol 1:43–49.
17. Antón S. 2003. Natural history of *Homo erectus*. Yrbk Phys Anthropol 46:126–170.
18. Rightmire GP. 1998. Human evolution in the Middle Pleistocene: the role of *Homo heidelbergensis*. Evol Anthropol 6:218–227.
19. Rightmire GP. 2008. *Homo* in the Middle Pleistocene: hypodigms, variation, and species recognition. Evol Anthropol 17:6–21.
20. Stringer CB. 2006. *Homo britannicus*: the incredible story of human life in Britain. London: Penguin Books.
21. Duarte C, Maurício J, Pettitt PB, Souto P, Trinkaus E, van der Plicht H, Zilhão J. 1999. The early Upper Paleolithic human skeleton from the Abrigo do Lagar Velho (Portugal) and modern human emergence in Iberia. Proc Nat Acad Sci 96:7604–7609.
22. Trinkaus E. 2005. Early modern humans. Ann Rev Anthropol 34:207–230.
23. Soficaru A, Doboş A, Trinkaus E. 2006. Early modern humans from the Peştera Muierii, Baia de Fier, Romania. Proc Nat Acad Sci 103:17196–17201.
24. Trinkaus E. 2007. European early modern humans and the fate of the Neandertals. Proc Nat Acad Sci 104:7367–7372.
25. Soficaru A, Petrea C, Doboş A, Trinkaus E. 2007. The human cranium from the Peştera Cioclovina Uscată, Romania. Curr Anthropol 48:611–619.
26. Harvati K, Gunz P, Grigorescu D. 2007. Cioclovina (Romania): affinities of an early modern European. J Hum Evol 53:732–746.
27. Krings M, Stone A, Schmitz RW, Krainitzki H, Stoneking M, Pääbo S. 1997. Neanderthal DNA sequences and the origin of modern humans. Cell 90:19–30.

28. Krings M, Geisert H, Schmitz RW, Krainitzki H, Pääbo S. 1999. DNA sequence of the mitochondrial hypervariable region II from the Neandertal type specimen. Proc Nat Acad Sci 96:5581–5585.
29. Ovchinnikov IV, Götherström A, Romanova GP, Kharitonov VM, Lidén K, Goodwin W. 2000. Molecular analysis of Neanderthal DNA from the northern Caucasus. Nature 404:490– 493.
30. Schmitz RW, Serre D, Bonani G, Feine S, Hillgruber F, Krainitzki H, Pääbo S, Smith FH. 2002. The Neanderthal type site revisited: interdisciplinary investigations of skeletal remains from the Neander Valley, Germany. Proc Nat Acad Sci 99:13342–13347.
31. Serre D, Langaney A, Chech M, Teschler-Nicola M, Paunovic M, Mennecier P, Hofreiter M, Possnert G, Pääbo S. 2004. No evidence of Neandertal mtDNA contribution to early modern humans. PLoS Biol 2:313–317.
32. Beauval C, Maureille B, Lacrampe-Cuyaubère F, Serre D, Peressinotto D, Bordes J-G, Cochard D, Chouchoud I, Dubrasquet D, Laroulandie W, Lehoble A, Mallge JB, Pasty S, Primault J, Rohland Paabos, Trinkaus. 2005. A late Neandertal femur from Les Rochers-de-Villeneuve, France. Proc Nat Acad Sci 102:7085–7090.
33. Lalueza-Fox C, Lourdes Sampietro M, Caramelli D, Puder Y, Lari M, Calafell F, Martínez-Maza C, Bastir M, Fortea J, de la Rasilla M, Bertranpetit J, Rosas A. 2005. Neandertal evolutionary genetics: mitochondrial DNA data from the Iberian peninsula. Mol Biol Evol 22:1077–1081.
34. Rosas A, Martínez-Maza C, Bastir M, Garcia-Tabernero A, Lalueza-Fox C, Huguet R, Ortiz JE, Julià R, Soler V, de Torres T, Martinez E, Canaveras JC, Sanchez-Moral S, Cuezva S, Lario J, Santamaria D, de la Rasilla M, Fortea J. 2006. Paleobiology and comparative morphology of a late Neandertal sample from El Sidrón, Asturias, Spain. Proc Nat Acad Sci 103:15266–15271.
35. Lalueza-Fox C, Krause J, Caramelli D, Catalano G, Milini L, Sampietro ML, Calafell F, Martínez-Maza C, Bastir M, Garcia-Tabernero A, de la Rasilla M, Fortea J, Pääbo S, Bertranpetit J, Rosas A. 2006. Mitochondrial DNA of an Iberian Neandertal suggests a population affinity with other European Neandertals. Curr Biol 16:R629–R630.
36. Orlando L, Darlu P, Toussaint M, Bonjean D, Otte M, Hänni C. 2006. Revisiting Neandertal diversity with a 100,000 year old mtDNA sequence. Curr Biol 16:R400–R402.
37. Caramelli D, Lalueza-Fox C, Condemi S, Longo L, Milani L, Manfredini A, de Saint Pierre M, Adoni F, Lari M, Giunti P, Ricci S, Casoli A, Calafell F, Malleghi F,

Bertranpetit Stanyon R, Bertorelle G, Barvjani G. 2006. A highly divergent mtDNA sequence in a Neandertal individual from Italy. Curr Biol 16:R630–R632.

38. Krause J, Orlando L, Serre D, Viola B, Prüfer K, Richards MP, Hublin J-J, Hänni C, Derevianko AP, Pääbo S. 2007. Neanderthals in central Asia and Siberia. Nature 449:902–904.
39. Serre D, Pääbo S. 2006. The fate of European Neanderthals: results and perspectives from ancient DNA analyses. In: Harvati K, Harrison T, editors. Neanderthals revisited: new approaches and perspectives. Dordrecht: Springer. p 211–220.
40. Krause J, Lalueza-Fox C, Orlando L, Enard W, Green RE, Burbano HA, Hublin J-J, Bertranpetit J, Hänni C, Fotea J, de la Rasilla M, Bertranpetit J, Rosas A, Pääbo S. 2007. The derived FOXP2 variant of modern humans was shared with Neandertals. Curr Biol 17:1–5.
41. Caramelli D, Lalueza-Fox C, Vernesi C, Lari M, Casoli A, Mallegni F, Chiarelli B, Dupanloup I, Bertranpetit J, Barbujani G, Bertorelle G. 2003. Evidence for a genetic discontinuity between Neandertals and 24,000-year-old anatomically modern humans. Proc Nat Acad Sci 100:6593–6597.
42. Green RE, Krause J, Ptak SE, Briggs AW, Ronan MT, Simons JF, Du L, Egholm M, Rothberg JM, Paunovic M, Pääbo S. 2006. Analysis of one million base pairs of Neanderthal DNA. Nature 444:330–336.
43. Tchernov E. 1992. Biochronology, paleoecology, and dispersal events of hominids in the southern Levant. In: Akazawa T, Aoki K, Kimura T, editors. The evolution and dispersal of modern humans in Asia. Tokyo: Hokusen-Sha. p 149–188.
44. Bar-Yosef O. 1995. The Lower and Middle Paleolithic in the Mediterranean Levant: chronology, and cultural entities. In: Ullrich H, editor. Man and environment in the Palaeolithic. Liège: Université de Liège, p 246–263.
45. Jones R. 1990. From Kakadu to Kutikina: the southern continent at 18,000 years ago. In: Gamble C, Soffer O, editors. The world at 18 000 BP, Vol 2. Low latitudes. London: Unwin Hyman. p 264–295.
46. Cosgrove R. 1999. Forty-two degrees south: the archaeology of Late Pleistocene Tasmania. J World Prehist 13:357–402.
47. Jacobs Z, Roberts RG. 2007. Advances in optically stimulated luminescence dating of individual grains of quartz from archeological deposits. Evol Anthropol 16:210–223.
48. Richter D. 2007. Advantages and limitations of thermoluminescence dating of heated flint from Paleolithic sites. Geoarchaeology 22:671–683.
49. Grün R. 2006. Direct dating of human fossils. Yrbk Phys Anthropol 49:2–48.

50. Feathers JK. 2002. Luminescence dating in less than ideal conditions: case studies from Klasies River Mouth and Duinefontein, South Africa. J Archaeol Sci 29:177–194.
51. Ambrose SH. 1998. Chronology of the Later Stone Age and food production in East Africa. J Archaeol Sci 25:377–392.
52. Bar-Yosef O. 2000. The Middle and early Upper Paleolithic in Southwest Asia and neigh boring regions. Bull Peabody Mus Archaeol Ethnol 8:107–156.
53. Kuhn SL, Stiner MC, Reese DS, Güleç E. 2001. Ornaments of the earliest Upper Paleolithic: new insights from the Levant. Proc Nat Acad Sci 98:7641–7646.
54. Zilhão J. 2006. Neandertals and modern humans mixed, and it matters. Evol Anthropol 16:183–195.
55. Mellars PA. 2006. A new radiocarbon revolution and the dispersal of modern humans in Eurasia. Nature 439:931–935.
56. Pope GG. 1988. Recent advances in Far Eastern paleoanthropology. Ann Rev Anthropol 17:43–77.
57. Gao X, Norton CJ. 2002. A critique of the Chinese "Middle Palaeolithic." Antiquity 76:397–412.
58. Hoffecker JF, Elias SA. 2007. Human ecology in Beringia. New York: Columbia University Press.
59. O'Connell JF, Allen J. 2007. Pre-LGM Sahul (Pleistocene Australia-New Guinea) and the archaeology of early modern humans. In: Mellars P, Boyle K, Bar-Yosef O, Stringer CB, editors. Rethinking the human revolution. Cambridge: McDonald Institute for Archaeological Research. p 395–410.
60. Clark GA. 2006. Observations on systematics in Paleolithic archaeology. In: Hovers E, Kuhn SL, editors. Transitions before the transition: evolution and stability in the Middle Paleolithic and Middle Stone Age. New York: Springer. p 29–56.
61. Hayden B. 1993. The cultural capacities of the Neandertals: a review and re-evaluation. J Hum Evol 24:113–146.
62. Soffer O. 1994. Ancestral lifeways in Eurasia: the Middle and Upper Paleolithic records. In: Nitecki MH, Nitecki DV, editors. Origins of anatomically modern humans. New York: Plenum Press. p101–119.
63. McBrearty S, Brooks AS. 2000. The revolution that wasn't: a new interpretation of the origin of modern human behavior. J Hum Evol 39:453–563.
64. Henshilwood CS, Marean CW. 2003. The origin of modern human behavior: critique of the models and their test implications. Curr Anthropol 44:627–651.
65. Kuhn SL, Stiner MC. 2006. What's a mother to do? The division of labor among Neandertals and modern humans in Eurasia. Curr Anthropol 47:953–980.

66. Deacon HJ. 1995. Two late Pleistocene-Holocene archaeological depositories from the southern Cape, South Africa. S Afr Archaeol Bull 50:121–131.
67. Beaumont PB, Vogel JC. 2006. On a timescale for the past million years of human history in central South Africa. S Afr J Sci 102: 217–228.
68. Camps G. 1975. The Prehistoric cultures of North Africa: radiocarbon chronology. In: Wendorf F, Marks AE, editors. Problems in Prehistory: North Africa and the Levant. Dallas: Southern Methodist University Press. p 181–192.
69. Wendorf F, Schild R. 1992. The Middle Paleolithic of North Africa: a status report. In: Klees F, Kuper R, editors. New light on the Northeast African past. Köln: Heinrich-Barth Institut. p 41–78.
70. Cremaschi M, Di Lernia S, Garcea EAA. 1998. Some insights on the Aterian in the Libyan Sahara: chronology, environment, and archaeology. Afr Archaeol Rev 15:261–286.
71. Close AE. 2002. Backed bladelets are a foreign country. Archeol Papers Am Anthropol Assoc 12:31–44.
72. Scholz CA, Johnson TC, Cohen AS, King JW, Peck JA, Overpeck JT, Talbot MR, Brown ET, Kalindekafe L, Amoako PYO, Lyons RP, Shanahan TM, Castaneda IS, Heil CW, Forman SL, McHargue LR, Beuning KR, Gomez J, Pierson J. 2007. East African megadroughts between 135 and 75 thousand years ago and bearing on early-modern human origins. Proc Nat Acad Sci 104:16416–16421.
73. Harpending HC, Batzer MA, Gurven M, Jorde LB, Rogers AR, Sherry ST. 1998. Genetic traces of ancient demography. Proc Nat Acad Sci 95:1961–1967.
74. Zhivotovsky LA, Rosenberg NA, Feldman MW. 2003. Features of evolution and expansion of modern humans, inferred from genomewide microsatellite markers. Am J Hum Genet 72:1171–1186.
75. Bahn P. 1998. Archaeology: Neanderthals emancipated. Nature 394:719–721.
76. Speth JD. 2004. News flash: negative evidence convicts Neanderthals of gross mental incompetence. World Archaeol 36:519–526.
77. Dorus S, Vallender EJ, Evans PD, Anderson JR, Gilbert SL, Mahowald M, Wyckoff GJ, Malcolm C, Lahn BT. 2004. Accelerated evolution of nervous system genes in the origin of *Homo sapiens*. Cell 19:1027–1040.
78. Fisher SE. 2006. Tangled webs: tracing the connections between genes and cognition. Cognition 101:270–297.
79. Henshilwood CS, d'Errico F, Yates RJ, Jacobs Z, Tribola C, Duller GAT, Mercier N, Sealy JC, Valladas H, Watts I, Wintle AG. 2002. Emergence of modern human behavior: Middle Stone Age engravings from South Africa. Science 295:1278–1280.

80. Henshilwood CS, d'Errico F, Vanhaeren M, van Niekerk KL, Jacobs Z. 2004. Middle Stone Age shell beads from South Africa. Science 304:404.
81. Henshilwood CS, d'Errico F, Marean CW, Milo RG, Yates RJ. 2001. An early bone tool industry from the Middle Stone Age of Blombos Cave, South Africa: implications for the origins of modern human behaviour, symbolism and language. J Hum Evol 41:631–678.
82. Jacobs Z, Duller GAT, Wintle AG, Henshilwood CS. 2006. Extending the chronology of deposits at Blombos Cave, South Africa, back to 140 ka using optical dating of single and multiple grains of quartz. J Hum Evol 51:255–273.
83. Tribolo C, Mercier N, Selo M, Valladas H, Joron J-L, Reyss JL, Henshilwood CS, Sealy J, Yates R. 2006. TL dating of burnt lithics from Blombos Cave (South Africa): further evidence for the antiquity of modern human behaviour. Archaeometry 48:341–357.
84. Brooks AS, Helgren DM, Cramer JS, Franklin A, Hornyak W, Keating JM, Klein RG, Rink WJ, Schwarcz HP, Leith Smith JN, Stewart K, Todd NE, Verniers J, Yellen JE. 1995. Dating and context of three Middle Stone Age sites with bone points in the Upper Semliki Valley, Zaire. Science 268:548–553.
85. Yellen JE. 1998. Barbed bone points: tradition and continuity in Saharan and sub-Saharan Africa. Afr Archaeol Rev 15:173–198.
86. Mackay A, Welz A. n.d. Engraved ochre from a Middle Stone Age context at Klein Kliphuis in the Western Cape of South Africa. J Archaeol Sci 35. In press.
87. Wadley L, Williamson BS, Lombard M. 2004. Ochre in hafting in Middle Stone Age southern Africa. Antiquity 78:661–675.
88. Wadley L. 2005. Putting ochre to the test: replication studies of adhesives that may have been used for hafting tools in the Middle Stone Age. J Hum Evol 49:587–601.
89. Lombard M. 2005. Evidence of hunting and hafting during the Middle Stone Age at Sibudu Cave, KwaZulu-Natal, South Africa: a multianalytical approach. J Hum Evol 48:279–300.
90. Lombard M. 2007. The gripping nature of ochre: the association of ochre with Howiesons Poort adhesives and Later Stone Age mastics from South Africa. J Hum Evol 53:406–419.
91. d'Errico F, Henshilwood CS, Lawson G, Vanhaeren M, Tillier A-M, Soressi M, Bresson F, Maureille B, Nowell A, Lakarra J, Backwell L, Julienlo M. 2003. Archaeological evidence for the emergence of language, symbolism, and music: an alternative multidisciplinary perspective. J World Prehist 17:1–70.
92. Bouzouggar A, Barton N, Vanhaeren M, d'Errico F, Collcutt S, Higham TFG, Hodge E, Parfitt S, Rhodes E, Schwenninger J-L, Stringer C, Turner E, Ward S,

Moutmir A, Stambouli A. 2007. 82,000-year-old shell beads from North Africa and implications for the origins of modern human behavior. Proc Nat Acad Sci 104:9964–9969.

93. White R. 2003. Prehistoric art: the symbolic journey of humankind. New York: Harry N. Abrams.
94. Brain CK, Shipman P. 1993. The Swartkrans bone tools. In: Brain CK, editor. Swartkrans: a cave's chronicle of early man. Pretoria: Transvaal Museum. p 195–215.
95. d'Errico F, Backwell L. 2003. Possible evidence of bone tool shaping by Swartkrans early hominids. J Archaeol Sci 30:1559–1576.
96. Henshilwood CS, Sealy JC, Yates RJ, Cruz-Uribe K, Goldberg P, Grine FE, Klein RG, Poggenpoel C, Van Niekerk KL, Watts I. 2001. Blombos Cave, southern Cape, South Africa: preliminary report on the 1992–1999 excavations of the Middle Stone Age levels. J Archaeol Sci 28:421–448.
97. Phillipson DW. 2005. African archaeology. Cambridge: Cambridge University Press.
98. Harrold FB. 1989. Mousterian, Chatelperronian and Early Aurignacian in Western Europe: continuity or discontinuity? In: Mellars PA, Stringer CB, editors. The human revolution: behavioural and biological perspectives on the origins of modern humans. Edinburgh: Edinburgh University Press. p 677–713.
99. Lévêque F, Miskovsky J-C. 1983. Le Castelperronien dans son environnement géologique. L'Anthropologie 87:369–391.
100. Zilhão J, d'Errico F. 1999. The chronology and taphonomy of the earliest Aurignacian and its implications for the understanding of Neandertal extinction. J World Préhist 13:1–68.
101. Lévêque F, Backer AM, Guilbaud M, editors. 1993. Context of a Late Neandertal: implications of multidisciplinary research for the transition to Upper Paleolithic adaptations at Saint-Césaire, Charente-Maritime, France. Madison: Prehistory Press.
102. Hublin J-J, Spoor F, Braun M, Zonneveld F. 1996. A late Neanderthal associated with Upper Paleolithic artifacts. Nature 381:224–226.
103. Bailey SE, Hublin J-J. 2006. Dental remains from the Grotte du Renne at Arcy-sur-Cure (Yonne). J Hum Evol 50:485–508.
104. Mellars PA. 1996. The Neanderthal legacy: an archaeological perspective from Western Europe. Princeton: Princeton University Press.
105. Leroi-Gourhan A. 1965. Le Châtelperronien: problème ethnologique. In: Ripoll Perello E, editor. Miscelanea en Homenaje al Abate Henri Breuil, vol 2. Barcelona:

Diputacion Provincial de Barcelona, Instituto de Prehistória y Arqueológia. p 75–81.

106. Movius HL. 1969. The Châtelperronian in French archaeology: the evidence of Arcy-sur-Cure. Antiquity 43:111–123.
107. Farizy C. 1994. Behavioral and cultural changes at the Middle to Upper Paleolithic transition in Western Europe. In: Nitecki MH, Nitecki DV, editors. Origins of anatomically modern humans. New York: Plenum Press, p 93–100.
108. White RK. 2001. Personal ornaments from the Grotte du Renne at Arcy-sur-Cure. Athena Rev 2:41–46.
109. Schmider B. 2002. Avant-propos. Gallia Préhist XXXIV supplément:7–13.
110. d'Errico F, Zilhão J, Julien M, Baffier D, Pelegrin J. 1998. Neanderthal acculturation in Western Europe? A critical review of the evidence and its interpretation. Curr Anthropol 39:S1–S44.
111. Taborin Y. 2002. Les objets de parure. Gallia Préhist XXXIV supplément:253–256.
112. Granger J-M, Lévêque F. 1997. Parure castelperronienne et aurignacienne: étude de trois séries inédites de dents percées et comparaisons. CR Acad Sci Paris 325:537–543.
113. White RK. 1998. Comment on "Neanderthal acculturation in western Europe? A critical review." Curr Anthropol 39:S30–S32.
114. Rigaud J-P, Simek JF, Ge T. 1995. Mousterian fires from Grotte XVI (Dordogne, France). Antiquity 69:902–912.
115. Karkanas P, Rigaud J-P, Simek JF, Albert RM, Weiner S. 2002. Ash, bones and guano: a study of the minerals and phytoliths in the sediments of Grotte XVI, Dordogne, France. J Archaeol Sci 29:721–732.
116. Grayson DK, Delpech F. 2003. Ungulates and the Middle-to-Upper Paleolithic transition at Grotte XVI (Dordogne, France). J Archaeol Sci 30:1633–1648.
117. Barton RNE. 2000. Mousterian hearths and shellfish: late Neanderthal activities on Gibraltar. In: Stringer CB, Barton RNE, Finlayson JC, editors. Neanderthals on the edge. Oxford: Oxbow Books. p 211–220.
118. Stiner MC. 1994. Honor among thieves: a zooarchaeological study of Neandertal ecology. Princeton: Princeton University Press.
119. Bouzouggar A, Kozlowski JK, Otte M. 2002. Étude des ensembles lithiques atériens de la grotte d'El Aliya à Tanger (Maroc). L'Anthropologie 106:207–248.
120. Grine FE, Klein RG, Volman TP. 1991. Dating, archaeology, and human fossils from the Middle Stone Age levels of Die Kelders, South Africa. J Hum Evol 21:363–395.

121. Marean CW, Goldberg P, Avery G, Grine FE, Klein RG. 2000. Middle Stone Age stratigraphy and excavations at Die Kelders Cave 1 (Western Cape Province, South Africa): the 1992, 1993, and 1995 field seasons. J Hum Evol 38:7–42.
122. Henshilwood CS. 2005. Stratigraphic integrity of the Middle Stone Age at Blombos Cave. In: d'Errico F, Backwell L, editors. From tools to symbols: from early hominids to modern humans. Johannesburg: Witwatersrand University Press. p 441–458.
123. Brink JS, Deacon HJ. 1982. A study of a last interglacial shell midden and bone accumulation at Herolds Bay, Cape Province, South Africa. Palaeoecol Afr 15:31–40.
124. Marean CW, Bar-Matthews M, Bernatchez J, Fisher E, Goldberg P, Herries ALR, Jacobs Z, Jerardino A, Karakanas P, Minichillo T, Nilssen PJ, Thompson E, Watts I, Williams HM. 2007. Early human use of marine resources and pigment in South Africa during the Middle Pleistocene. Nature 449:905–908.
125. Singer R, Wymer JJ. 1982. The Middle Stone Age at Klasies River Mouth in South Africa. Chicago: University of Chicago Press.
126. Klein RG, Cruz-Uribe K, Halkett D, Hart T, Parkington JE. 1999. Paleoenvironmental and human behavioral implications of the Boegoeberg 1 late Pleistocene hyena den, Northern Cape Province, South Africa. Quatern Res 52:393–403.
127. Parkington JE. 2006. Shorelines, strandlopers and shell middens. Cape Town: Creda Communications.
128. Volman TP. 1978. Early archaeological evidence for shellfish collecting. Science 201: 911–913.
129. Klein RG, Avery G, Cruz-Uribe K, Halkett D, Parkington JE, Steele T, Volman TP, Yates RJ. 2004. The Ysterfontein 1 Middle Stone Age site, South Africa, and early human exploitation of coastal resources. Proc Nat Acad Sci 101:5708–5715.
130. Avery G, Halkett D, Orton J, Steele TE, Tusenius M, Klein RG. n.d. 2008. The Ysterfontein 1 Middle Stone Age rockshelter and the evolution of coastal foraging. S Afr Archaeol Soc Goodwin Ser. In press.
131. Rigaud J-P, Texier P-J, Parkington JE, Poggenpoel C. 2006. Le mobilier Stillbay et Howiesons Poort de l'abri Diepkloof: La chronologie du Middle Stone Age sud-africain et ses implications. CR Palevol 5:839–849.
132. Wadley L. 2007. Announcing a Still Bay industry at Sibudu Cave, South Africa. J Hum Evol 52:681–689.
133. Deacon J. 1984. Later Stone Age people and their descendants in Southern Africa. In: Klein RG, editor. Southern African Prehistory and paleoenvironments. Rotterdam: A. A. Balkema. p 221–328.

134. Buchanan WF, Hall SL, Henderson J, Olivier A, Pettigrew JM, Parkington JE, Robertshaw PT. 1978. Coastal shell middens in the Paternoster area, southwestern Cape. S Afr Archaeol Bull 33:89–93.
135. Thackeray JF. 1988. Molluscan fauna from Klasies River, South Africa. S Afr Archaeol Bull 43:27–32.
136. Klein RG, Cruz-Uribe K. 1983. Stone age population numbers and average tortoise size at Byneskranskop Cave 1 and Die Kelders Cave 1, southern Cape Province, South Africa. S Afr Archaeol Bull 38:26–30.
137. Bar-Yosef O. 2002. The Upper Paleolithic revolution. Ann Rev Anthropol 31:363–393.
138. Jerardino A, Yates R. 1996. Preliminary results from excavations at Steenbokfontein Cave: implications for past and future research. S Afr Archaeol Bull 51:7–16.
139. Orton J. 2007. Final report on excavations at Erven 2149, 2157 and 2158 (Bakoond), Yzerfontein, Malmesbury Magisterial District, Western Cape Province. Cape Town: Archaeology Contracts Office, University of Cape Town.
140. Velleman PF. 1997. Data desk version 6.0: statistics guide. Ithaca, NY: Data Description.
141. Schweitzer FR, Wilson ML. 1982. Byneskranskop 1, a late Quaternary living site in the southern Cape Province, South Africa. Ann S Afr Mus 88:1–203.
142. Orton J, Halkett D. 2007. Excavations at Noetzie Midden, an open site on the Cape south coast. The digging stick 24:5–7.
143. Avery G. 1976. A systematic investigation of open station shell middens along the southwestern Cape Coast. M. A. Thesis. Cape Town: University of Cape Town.
144. Schweitzer FR. 1979. Excavations at Die Kelders, Cape Province, South Africa: the Holocene deposits. Ann S Afr Mus 78:101–233.

SECTION 14

MATING

Introduction to Chapter 16

Long-term, relatively stable bonds between a breeding male and a breeding female are unusual in mammals but quite typical of humans. Thus, some evolutionary explanation is required to explain our derived mating system. The answer seems to involve a mix of selection pressures, though their relative intensity may vary from one situation to another.

From Chapter 8 you learned that the force of sexual selection is driven by the relative reproductive rates of males and females. At the end of my introduction to that Chapter I asked you to try to place our own species in the framework of their reproductive-rate model. If you do that you will see that, because men do not gestate or lactate, they could have much higher reproductive rates than women. In fact, we know that some men have had thousands of offspring—something a woman could not possibly do. So men are the fast sex, and how fast they can be will depend on just how many partners they can recruit to produce offspring for them. That leads to the puzzle that Robert Quinlan is trying to unravel: Why should a man pair up with one woman when there are so many other options for increasing his reproductive success?

Students sometimes answer, "Because he loves her." Sweet as this answer might be, it is not convincing because it starts in the middle of the problem and dodges the difficult part. Love—the capacity to feel love and be motivated by it—is part of the pair-bonding adaptation. Saying he's in love is just highlighting the emotional component of pair bonding. Why are humans the kind of creatures that are susceptible to falling in love and thus truncating their mating opportunities? If love were not good for fitness, selection would not have created the neural and hormonal circuitry that permits it!

Pair-bonding is not very common in mammals; about 4% of mammal species form durable bonds between a single male and female. Virtually all the rest have mating systems that are either promiscuous (where there are no stable mating relationships) or polygynous (where successful males have harems and unsuccessful males are excluded from mating). Among our close relatives, chimpanzees are promiscuous and gorillas have harems. For comparison, you might be interested to know that birds show the reverse pattern: about 90% of bird species form monogamous breeding units; most of the remaining 10% are polygynous or promiscuous, but about 0.5% are polyandrous (where a successful female will have a "harem" of males who mate with her and rear her young; really!).

So, to return to the question at hand, why are humans such odd mammals in terms of their mating relationships? Why do males hang around with one female instead of trying to fertilize as many as they can? Do you see why I'm phrasing the question from the male point of view? It should be obvious that a male's reproductive success will be proportionate to the number of females he can fertilize—because many females can be producing offspring for him simultaneously. This statement is not obviously reversible by sex. In other words, how would having more mates increase a *female's* reproductive success? I wouldn't want to claim that she would get no advantage; in fact I can think of three potential evolutionary advantages (and Quinlan mentions them), but none of them seem to be as large as the advantage a male might get by summing the reproductive output of a large harem of females. A man with 100 mates could have pretty close to 100 times the reproductive success of a man with one mate. Could a woman with 100 mates reap such a large reproductive advantage? In fact, could she reap *any* reproductive advantage? Normally, a woman can only carry one infant at a time—regardless of how many mates she has.

So, why do men forego the large advantages they might get from promiscuity, and for completeness, why do females forego the small advantages they might realize from having multiple partners? Quinlan offers a few ideas about the benefits of pair bonding.

The first is that human infants are relatively helpless (see Chapter 11 and its Introduction). They might survive better with multiple care-takers. A male who stays with one female does give up additional mating opportunities, but he gets an evolutionary benefit by increasing the chances that his current offspring will survive to reproduce. Data from a wide array of sources indicate that this benefit is real and non-trivial. Loss of these benefits is what Quinlan is referring to when he mentions the "costs of abandonment." Quinlan argues that the biggest benefits of this type occur while the mother is nursing. In fact, he argues that comparisons with the other large apes suggest that human nursing has been accelerated: Women do not have to nurse their infants as long as chimpanzees and gorillas because men's provisioning improves their milk quality.

The second possible benefit of pair bonding is mate defense. A male who abandons one mate in search of another not only hurts his offspring's survival chances; he also loses exclusive access to the first mate's reproductive potential. Right; it is a trade-off. You cannot simultaneously guard one mate and search for another. So what kinds of circumstances make it better to stay with the prospects you have, rather than shopping around? Particularly in this context, Quinlan notes that pair bonding can also occur in the context of stable *polygynous* matings. Picture a man with two wives. Each woman is pair bonded to him, and he is pair bonded to each of them. Taking the point of view of the man or either women, he or she has a stable bond—involving various responsibilities and expectations about ongoing benefits—with the opposite-sex partner.

Let me make explicit one of Quinlan's key analytical stances. It works this way: if X is the function of pair bonds, then pair bonds should be more stable where that function is critical and less stable where it is less important. He uses this logic to generate various predictions and uses cross-cultural comparison to test these predictions. Cross-cultural analysis is logically parallel to cross-species comparison (see Chapter 5), but the units being compared are different cultures rather than different species. The goal is the same: to see if certain traits are associated with certain conditions/environments/needs.

Based on these kinds of analyses, Quinlan believes that human pair bonds may serve different functions in different environments. He argues this by showing that different factors predict pair-bond stability (see above) in different environments. The final section of his chapter is devoted to child development. Here he suggests that, because pairing is facultatively dependent on environmental circumstances, offspring must receive inputs during their development that tell them what kind of pairing environment to prepare for. This is consistent with the logic of facultative adaptation developed in Chapter 1.

Another key issue that runs through Chapter 16 concerns the *form* or *mode* of sexual selection. Until now we have only considered the *intensity* of sexual selection; our conclusion was that it was more intense in the fast sex—the sex with the higher potential reproductive rate. On that score we have agreed that, because of gestation and lactation, males are usually the fast sex in mammals. So we know that males will probably be forced to compete for access to females more than females are forced to compete for access to males. But the question we have not addressed is, what *form* will that competition take? There are multiple possibilities, and each will produce somewhat different evolutionary outcomes.

Males might compete by displaying traits that females desire (females should evolve to desire traits that augment their own reproductive success). In this domain there are two broad categories of male traits that might benefit females: good genes and good paternal investment. Alternatively, males might forego display and compete physically to monopolize mating access to females. Finally, they might not be able to gain privileged access to females by any of these routes, but their sperm might compete within the female reproductive tract with the sperm of the other males they could not exclude. The following table lays out these possible modes of sexual selection and the likely evolutionary outcomes.

Mode of Sexual Selection	Favored Traits
1. Female choice	
A. For good genes	Flamboyant coloration or structures
B. For good paternal investment	Flamboyant displays of resources, skills
2. Male contests	Large body size, muscle mass, weapons
3. Sperm competition	Large testes size compared to body size

Mode 1 dominates when females decide which males get to father offspring and males accept the outcomes of female choice. Whether females should choose based on a male's genes or his parenting abilities would depend on which would contribute most to the eventual reproductive success of her offspring. In mode 2, aggressive interactions among males exclude some males from mating, and females accept the winners of this competition. In mode 3, females are relatively unselective and males are not able to exclude each other from mating, so fatherhood is decided through competition among the sperm of different males competing to fertilize the female's egg. Mode 3 favors anything that gives a male an advantage in such competition, for example large testes that allow him to produce lots of sperm.

When laid out this way, sexual selection in humans reveals itself to be a complex mix. There is not much phenotypic evidence for mode 1A, female choice for good genes, because men are not very gaudy; for example, they do not have the kinds of adornments that peacocks have. But all the other modes seem to have been operating to some degree. With respect to mode 1B, males do flamboyantly display their resource-acquisition skills (for example, Quinlan's discussion of men's show-off work, or men's penchant for expensive cars). Skipping ahead to mode 3 for the moment, men have relatively larger testes than is typical of monogamous or harem-polygynous primates. (Note that in a harem-polygynous situation, a male mates with several females, but each of "his" females mate only with him. Thus, he faces no sperm competition). So men's relatively large testes suggest that ancestral women sometimes mated with several males during their monthly fertile phase. Finally, sex differences in muscle mass suggest that mode 2 competition also occurred; in other words, men fought significantly over reproductive access to women. Quinlan misses this to some degree. He is fooled by the fact that, overall, men are not much heavier than women. This is true, but women have much more fat than men, and men have much more muscle than women. Sumo wrestlers notwithstanding, muscle is much more useful in aggressive competition than is fat. Men have excess muscle because of a history of selection for success in physical contests over mates. Why do women have excess fat? If you cannot answer this question you should revisit Chapter 12 and its Introduction.

Chapter 16 Glossary

alloparents: Caretakers other than the mother or father; may include older siblings, aunts, uncles, grandparents; typically are genetically related to the individual being cared for; why?

conjugal union/conjugal relationship: marriage. All human societies recognize a special relationship between husband and wife and that this relationship carries certain rights and responsibilities.

fecundity: The physiological capacity to conceive and bear an offspring. Poor nutritional status could reduce a woman's fecundity and good nutritional status could increase it.

lactation: Nursing; milk production. This is the defining characteristic of mammals and carries significant physiological costs for women—roughly 500 calories per day!

maternal avuncular: Relating to the mother's brother, the maternal uncle. In about 10% of described societies the mother's brother (rather than the father!) has important obligations to children.

matrilineal: A cultural system for kinship reckoning in which individuals belong to their mother's (but not their father's) kin group; as if you took your mother's family name and did not acknowledge any kinship relationships with your aunts, uncles and cousins on your father's side.

matrilocal: A cultural system for making residence decisions in which individuals live near their mother and her matrilineal (see above) kin.

opportunity cost: An important concept from economics that has been borrowed by evolutionists. Opportunity costs are the (possible) benefits of alternative strategies that you forego when you pursue a given course of action. For example, additional matings are opportunity costs when a male stays with one partner. Likewise, delayed ovulation (see below) is an opportunity cost of extended lactation.

perennial female breast: Quinlan uses this phrase to refer to the permanently enlarged nature of the human female breast; other primates would only show such enlargement if they were nursing. The derived condition of the human breast requires explanation. One idea is that it is a sexually selected signal that communicates maternal investment abilities to potential mates.

phenotypic plasticity: The ability of an organism to respond facultatively to different circumstances (see chapter 1).

philopatry: Remaining to live as an adult near where you were born; failing to disperse from you natal area. Male philopatry means men do not disperse; female philopatry means that females do not.

postpartum ovulation: Ovulating after giving birth. In mammals, lactation generally postpones ovulation.

Chapter 16
Human Pair-Bonds: Evolutionary Functions, Ecological Variation, and Adaptive Development (2008)

Robert J. Quinlan

Stable mating relationships are widespread in our species, with important economic, social, and reproductive implications.[1] Pair-bonds are part of the unique human mosaic, including very large brains, childhood, concealed ovulation, sexual intercourse in private, cultural symbols, and complex social groups. Yet we understand relatively little about the evolution of human pairing, its functions, and consequences for human diversity. We can define pair-bonds as the long-term affiliation, including a sexual relationship, between two individuals. The important point is that the union, whether monogamous or polygamous, is relatively enduring. Recent debate about human pair-bonds highlights apparently conflicting hypotheses: Are pair-bonds the evolutionary consequence of male mating competition[2,3] or are they an adaptation for paternal provisioning?[4,5] Unfortunately, a simple answer seems unlikely. The evidence indicates selective pressures from both mating competition and provisioning needs, suggesting different benefits of pair-bonds in different contexts. Whether a bond emphasizes mating or parenting effort may depend on environmental cues. Childhood experience

Key Words: reproductive strategies; parental investment; mating effort; life history; conjugal union

---

Department of Anthropology, Washington State University, Pullman, WA 99164-4910.
E-mail: rquinlan@wsu.edu

Robert. J. Quinlan, "Human Pair Bonds: Evolutionary Functions, Ecological Variation and Adaptive Development," from *Evolutionary Anthropology: Issues, News, and Reviews*; Vol. 17 Issue 5, pp. 227–238.

evidently affects pair-bond development, suggesting further adaptive design for flexible life-history strategies.

Functional and developmental accounts of pair-bonds rarely converge, but cross-fertilization could stimulate advances. Here I review theory and data for pair-bond functions before turning to the development of human pairing behavior in a life-history perspective. My approach is to examine primate comparisons, cross-cultural analyses, and ethnographic case studies. The goal is to develop refined hypotheses for human pair-bonding through the convergence of existing data.

Pair-Bonds and Provisioning

In 1966, Washburn and Lancaster suggested that during human evolution increasing need for biparental care created selective pressure for pair-bonds.[4,5] Children have a long and expensive developmental period during which they are dependent on others for sustenance and protection. Child rearing, hence, can be difficult for one person. A father shares fifty percent of his genes with his child, giving him more genetic interest in the child than other relatives have, making him a more motivated care-giver.[6] Fathers can care for children in at least two ways. They can provide direct care or they can help the mother, who is then freed to give direct care.

Men's fitness depends in part on parental investment decisions about pair-bonding. Parental investment is defined as expenditures benefiting one offspring at a cost to parents' ability to invest in other components of fitness.[7] Theoretically, a man's willingness to care for children depends on his options for fitness enhancement. From a parental investment perspective, abandonment by a father is predicted in environments where paternal care does not benefit men's fitness as much as do alternative behaviors, such as seeking additional mating opportunities. A comparative study of birds and mammals indicated that pair-bonding "may be selectively favored in humans and other animals when mothers' feeding requirements interfere with their baby-tending," increasing benefits of paternal provisioning and costs of abandonment.[8:48] Subsequent comparative analyses suggest that mammalian pair-bonds may not have evolved in response to parenting pressures,[3] although biparental care appears to be important in avian bonds.[9] Among humans, however, there is not a simple linear relationship between men's provisioning and pair-bond stability (Fig. 1).[10] Some parental investment predictions for pair-bonding have empirical support, but the question requires attention to alloparenting, subsistence cooperation, and paternal provisioning before weaning.

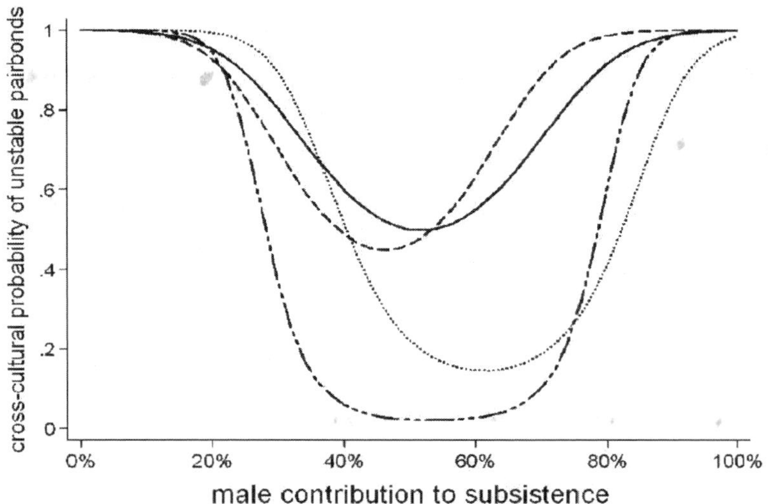

Figure 1. Pair-bond instability is a curvilinear function of men's contribution to subsistence across traditional societies. Pair-bond stability is greatest in societies where men and women contribute equally to subsistence. The graph shows predicted probabilities based on five logistic models in Quinlan and Quinlan.[10] The dash-dot line has multiple controls.

Breastfeeding May Be a Critical Period for Male Provisioning

Breastfeeding appears to be an important element of human pair-bonds because male provisioning seems to be particularly important during lactation.[6,11] Evidence from industrial populations, socioecological case studies of hunter-gather groups, and cross-cultural analysis of traditional societies converge on one conclusion: Stable conjugal relationships support breastfeeding in ways that other kin relations do not.[6] Lactation, which appears to be a universal "critical period" for paternal investment, may have created strong selective pressure for human pair-bonds.[11,12]

Breastfeeding is a primary mechanism among mammals for provisioning dependent offspring. It is also a key component of parental investment. Human female breasts and breastfeeding have unusual features compared with other apes and mammals in general. In fact the "perennial" human female breast is an evolutionary mystery probably tied to female sexual signaling.[13] These unusual features of human parental investment deserve more attention.

For mothers, lactation entails energetic and opportunity costs, and suppresses fertility.[14] Human lactation requires 670 kcal/day during exclusive breastfeeding.[15] Increased energy demand presents costs to household production and may delay future reproduction through reduced fecundity.[16] Breastfeeding may suppress postpartum ovulation through effects on gonadotrophin-releasing hormone.[17] The costs of breastfeeding for future reproduction or "residual reproductive value" indicate life-history trade-offs. Reduced future reproduction due to lactation suggests that to enhance fitness most mammals should wean their offspring as soon as possible. However, the effects of lactation on human fecundity diminish as breastfeeding continues. For example, in one study 50% of well-nourished nursing women returned to reproductive cycling within 10 months of giving birth. One-hundred percent of lactating women returned to cycling within 20 months,[18] which is 10 months earlier than the cross-cultural average age at weaning at 30 months.[19] Resumption of cycling while lactating might account for shorter interbirth intervals among humans than among great apes.[20] The comparatively low reproductive cost of lactation among humans may suggest that energetic costs can be reduced by provisioning. The opportunity costs of breastfeeding also can be substantial.[21] Nursing often interferes with women's work, which may benefit other children or kin. Opportunity costs rather than delays in reproductive cycling may be the major force driving human weaning decisions.

Human weaning shows comparatively unusual features. Other great ape species wean when offspring are about 5 to 7 years old.[19,20] Based on allometric relationships between adult size,[22] molar eruption,[23] and weaning age among primates, humans are predicted to wean at about 6 years.[19] Despite predictions for late weaning among humans, cross-culturally the average and median age at weaning is around 2.5 years.[19,20,23] These data indicate that the average age for human weaning may be at an adaptive minimum. One challenge in many human environments is not to find ways to hasten weaning, but rather to delay it. Maternal social support provides a solution for the unusual challenge of human lactation.

Provisioning infants with energy is not the only or perhaps the most important function of human breastfeeding. Availability of weaning foods is not associated with age at weaning cross-culturally,[24] suggesting that considerations other than feeding are in play. The evolution of cooking, however, may have played a role in the uniqueness of human weaning. In fact, because of expensive brain growth, breastfeeding alone does not support infant nutritional needs much beyond 6 months.[20,25] Many other health benefits of breastfeeding, such as giving infants resistance to infections and allergies, are well known.[26,27] Prolonged nursing is associated with improved long-term psychomotor and neural development in well nourished populations.[28–30] Nursing can be important to the mother-child bond, associated with positive emotions and attachment linked to maternal hormones, including prolactin and oxytocin.[31] Maternal responsiveness, which is related to nursing, appears to influence the development of children's attachment styles and adult conjugal relations.[32] Hence, breastfeeding and its underlying hormonal correlates may play a role in attachment organization.[33] These findings suggest fitness benefits beyond mere energy provisioning, in which alloparental care cannot substitute for nursing.

Support mothers receive from potential alloparents may affect their work and breastfeeding patterns. Kinswomen appear to be more willing to help each other with childcare than with other work.[34] Breastfeeding, however, is usually beyond the scope of alloparenting. Leaving a baby with a kinswoman prolongs periods of mother-child separation and reduces milk production, which may hasten weaning in households with coresident alloparents.[21] This is similar to early weaning by working women in developed countries.[35,36] Analysis of traditional cultures showed earlier weaning by 5.5 months in groups with high levels of alloparenting compared with groups in which mothers were primarily responsible for child care.[6] Given unusual features of human lactation, including nonnutritional benefits, earlier weaning is probably associated with reduced offspring fitness. Hence, the father of a woman's child seems well situated to enhance her fitness by supporting breastfeeding.

Evidence from foraging groups indicates that biparental care may be especially important during lactation. Foraging men "provide a considerable portion of the energy consumed by juveniles and reproductive-aged women …".[37:173] Among foragers, men increase their time spent in subsistence when their mate is nursing and a woman's subsistence work is inversely related to her mate's when the couple has a nursing child.[11,38] Among the Hadza foragers of Tanzania, husbands apparently compensate for their wives' diminished foraging return when they have young children.[11] Hadza women had significantly lower foraging return rates when they had nurslings; conversely, Hadza men increased foraging return and provisioning of mates with nursing children. Similarly, among the Ache and Hiwi foragers, women's time spent foraging and in child care were inversely related; nursing women spent less time foraging than did women who were not nursing. Also, women's foraging time was inversely related to their husbands' foraging.[38] Based on these findings, Marlowe suggests that pair-bonds in human evolution function to provision a mate and offspring during a "critical period" coinciding with lactation.[11] In sum, evidence of the origin of human pairing is incomplete, but male provisioning during lactation offers a promising lead.

If pair-bonds support lactation, then divorce may impair a woman's ability to nurse her child. Among foragers, "divorce or paternal death leads to high rates of child mortality among the Ache, the Hiwi, and the Kung, but not the Hadza."[37:173] Similarly, in the world's large-scale "industrial" populations, public health studies consistently find that single mothers tend to wean their children earlier than do women living with a mate,[39] and that this has short- and long-term child health and developmental effects.[26–30] This association is probably related to the trade-off between breastfeeding and women's work, which can be particularly pressing among single mothers.[35,36] If pair-bonds evolved to support lactation, then pair-bond stability should be associated with breastfeeding duration. In a comparison of 74 traditional societies including hunter-gathers, horticulturalists, and pastoralists, the frequency of divorce and age at weaning were inversely associated: Children tended to be weaned about 5 months earlier in societies where divorce was common.[6] Although there are multiple potential payoffs to paternal care, those benefits are not as consistently experienced cross-culturally as is lactation. Moreover, strong selective pressures for provisioning during lactation suggest that perennial female breast swelling in humans mimicking lactation may function to attract male attention and provisioning.[13]

Alloparenting Is Associated with Unstable Pair-Bonds

Parental investment theory predicts stable conjugal unions in societies where parenting effort is more beneficial for men's fitness than is mating effort. When nonparental caregivers (alloparents) are important, paternal care is less important because of reduced costs of male abandonment; hence, pair-bonds may be unstable. A cross-cultural analysis shows that when alloparents are involved in childrearing, pair-bonds are less stable,[10] which is consistent with other findings. Whether alloparenting "causes" conjugal instability or is a consequence of it is not clear, but a study of intracultural variation among the matrilocal, matrilineal Khasi of Northeast India suggests that alloparenting frees fathers to expend their effort elsewhere. Among the Khasi, the presence in the household of the wife's mother was associated with smaller economic contributions from husbands[11] and increased probability of divorce.[40] Similarly, classic kinship studies show that where maternal avuncular relationships are salient, pair-bonds often are unstable and unimportant,[41] presumably because paternal care is less crucial and people are free to pursue other avenues to enhance fitness. For example, in "avunculate" societies both sexes may invest more heavily in mating effort. For some men there may be a substantial payoff in fertility; for many women there may be an advantage to increasing the genetic diversity in their offspring by having children with several men. Increased genetic diversity in offspring could be beneficial in response to high pathogens loads[42] or other environmental risks.[43]

Relations between pair-bonding and alloparenting are complicated because the availability of alloparents often improves child well-being and survival,[44] as does father-presence.[45] From a child's perspective, the ideal family environment should include two parents and alloparents. Yet alloparenting can reduce men's costs of abandoning a pair-bond. Fathers, mothers, kin, and children have conflicting interests in paternal care, suggesting a delicate balance of factors influencing the range of human family configurations. More detailed research into family composition effects, such as the Khasi case study,[34,40] will improve our understanding of human pair-bonds and the evolution of the family.

Male-Female Subsistence Complementarity Is Associated with Stable Pair-Bonds

Subsistence complementarity between men and women may lead to conjugal stability. "It is the partnership between men and women that allows long-term juvenile dependence and learning and high rates of survival".[37:173] Following parental investment predictions, conjugal unions should be least stable when women do the majority of subsistence work because paternal provisioning is unnecessary. Conversely, pair-bonds should be most stable when men do the majority of subsistence work because women and children are particularly dependent. One cross-cultural study, however, found no association between conjugal stability and the division of subsistence work.[46] However, that finding was probably due to analysis that could not detect curvilinear effects. A more recent cross-cultural analysis found that pair-bonds tend to be unstable when either men or women contribute the majority to subsistence. Conjugal unions tended to be most stable in cultures where men and women are about equally responsible for subsistence (Fig. 1).[10] This general pattern of conjugal stability holds across all subsistence types; there are no significant interactions between subsistence strategy and sexual division of subsistence labor.

Conclusions about the effects of sexual division of subsistence labor on pair-bond stability await further study. At present, the clearest evidence of associations between pair-bond stability and division of labor comes from analysis of Murdock and White's Standard Cross-Cultural Sample (SCCS).[47] The SCCS is a sample of traditional societies chosen to give a balanced representation of the range of human cultural variation. SCCS data are coded from ethnographies. Often the coded data are crude ordinal and categorical variables. Many of the approximately 2,000 existing variables have demonstrable reliability, but the reliability of most coded variables is unknown. Low reliability is a bigger problem for rejecting null results than for failing to reject positive results reported here. There are other important considerations for assessing the adequacy of cross-cultural analyses. Cross-cultural data aggregate groups of various subsistence styles, population densities, and levels of acculturation. One approach is to limit analyses to societies of one subsistence type, such as foragers. This is a crude solution likely to result in unstable statistical analyses by excluding as much as 90% of the SCCS data. A more sophisticated, sensible, and robust approach is to use appropriate statistical controls for various factors related to the agglomeration of cross-cultural data.[6] The cross-cultural analyses discussed here used careful multivariate analyses controlling for many possible confounds. Finally, for any findings, we can only draw firm conclusions with replication from a variety of data sources. Findings regarding associations between human pair-bonds and weaning, for example, are on firm ground, given convergent results from detailed case studies, multivariate cross-cultural analysis, and large-scale public health studies. Initial associations between division of subsistence labor and pair-bonding are less conclusive. We can increase our confidence in initial cross-cultural findings through close examination of the ethnographic record. The !Kung (Ju/'hoansi) foragers offer an example of conjugal complementarity in the division of subsistence labor.

Among the Dobe !Kung hunter-gatherers, divorce is common early in marriage, but ethnographic and demographic accounts both indicate that marriages are quite stable after an initial "stormy" period.[48,49] Among the !Kung, 65% of first marriages precede menarche, 30% follow shortly thereafter, "and typically there is still a wait of some years before first conception".[49:177] The average age of first birth among !Kung women is about 19 years, at least 3 years after the average age of menarche.[49] These data suggest that many, if not most failed marriages occur before childbirth.

There is important food sharing between !Kung husbands and wives.[49] In the SCCS, !Kung men contribute about 40% of the diet. Meat from men contributes about 30% of calories consumed.[48] Because meat is often shared broadly beyond the nuclear family, male provisioning may not account for human pair-bonds.[50] Among the !Kung, there appear to be multiple benefits to sharing meat broadly among the camp.[51] Although established !Kung marriages are quite stable, !Kung camps may not be stable as they fission in the face of intra-group conflict. Lee describes a life-cycle of !Kung camps centered around a core group of siblings and spouses with peripheral members that may come and go.[48] In the context of this fission-fusion social organization, subsistence complementarity may allow a conjugal family to be self-sufficient for extended periods.[52] Living in a cooperative conjugal family allows humans the flexibility to respond to fluctuations in resource availability and social conflict. Such flexibility means that we are not locked into larger social groups that may spawn important conflicts of interest. Finally, the !Kung themselves suggest that subsistence complementarity may be at the heart of stable unions, because stinginess is often reported as cause for divorce.[49]

Pair-Bonds and Mating Competition

Male-male competition can also create selective pressures for pairing and conjugal stability. Thus, pair-bonds could support mate guarding rather than parenting effort.[2,53] Sexual dimorphism in body size reflects the evolutionary history of male-male competition in a species.[53] As compared with other great apes, humans show moderate to low levels of sexual dimorphism, suggesting low levels of intrasexual *physical* competition.[55] However, competition can take on economic, social, and symbolic dimensions that are not reflected in body size. Such competition could have influenced pairing in the Pleistocene at least as far back as 40,000 years ago with the appearance of the first unequivocal symbolic artifacts.

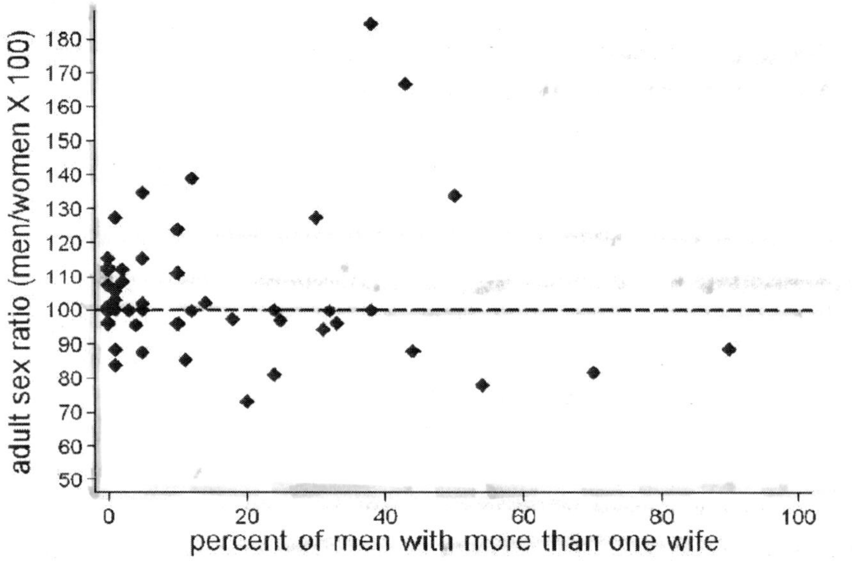

Figure 2. Sex ratio by polygyny level in the SCCS. The horizontal line at 100 on the Y-axis indicates an equal number of men and women. Values less than 100 indicate female-biased sex ratios. Few populations have a sex ratio low enough to support polygyny without creating male mating competition.

There are at least two possibilities for effects of intrasexual competition on pair-bonds. In a comparative analysis of nonhuman mammals, the spatial distribution of females rather than male provisioning predicted monogamy.[3] Monogamy, however, is not synonymous with long-term pairing. Gorillas for example, are "pair-bonded" in the context of "harem-defense" polygyny.[56] But gorillas show no male provisioning. Pair-bond stability in harem-defense polygyny[57] and monogamy when females are spatially dispersed[3] may share a common evolutionary logic: Males defend long-term mating relationships when there is low probability of finding another available mate. The density of females across the landscape is associated with the likelihood of encountering a potential new mate. The spatial distribution of women probably has little relevance to human pair-bonds, though there might be some special circumstances, such as low-density foragers, in which groups fission into small dispersed clusters for several months of the year. The distribution of women across the Pleistocene landscape might have created selective pressures for pairing when populations were small and dispersed.

The intensity of male mating competition can increase costs of abandoning a current bond in favor of seeking a new bond. If relatively few females are available, then males should defend their current relationship and pair-bonds should be stable. Male-biased operational sex ratio, hence, is predicted to lead to stable pair-bonds, whereas female-bias is predicted to lead to less stable bonds.[58] Cross-national studies have found that promiscuity was more acceptable in populations with female-biased sex ratios and less acceptable in populations with male-biased sex ratios,[59] while a female-biased sex ratio was associated with a greater degree of single parenthood.[60]

Level of polygyny may be associated with conjugal stability because polygyny creates a shortage of women, increasing male costs of abandoning a relationship. This prediction might seem problematic because in polygynous societies some men have multiple mates and some polygynous species do not have pair-bonds. Human polygyny, however, is somewhat unusual because it occurs in multi-level, multi-male groups with alliances among adult males[61] in a species with a generally balanced sex-ratio (though there is significant cross-cultural variation in human sex ratios). Figure 2 shows that most human populations have a relatively balanced sex ratio (dashed horizontal line), making high levels of polygyny difficult; few populations have a sex ratio low enough to support polygyny without creating male mating competition. Polygyny within multi-male groups with relatively balanced sex ratios creates a shortage of marriageable women, which increases pressure for mate guarding that could support pairbond stability.

Not all polygynyous species are pair-bonded.[62] There are other factors that promote bonding in some polygynyous systems. The spatial distribution of one-male-units (OMUs) in the population may be an important factor. Where OMUs are clustered in multi-level communities, pair-bonding can occur with polygyny. Comparison of hamadryas and anubis baboons illustrates this point.[63] Anubis baboons exhibit female philopatry, no pair-bonds, and promiscuous mating. In contrast, hamadryas baboons, which are closely related to anubis, exhibit male philopatry, polygyny, and pair-bonds based on a combination of coercion and attraction. A particularly noteworthy point is that hamadryas and gelada OMUs exist in close association in locally dense multi-level populations with long-term associations between mates.[64] Similarly, human polygyny occurs in relatively densely clustered polygynous households within larger communities. Relatively close spatial association among OMUs or polygynous households may be the primary factor leading to pair-bonding in polygynous mating systems.

Polygyny levels are low among human groups[65] (Table 1), but they are high enough to create shortages of marriageable women. Figure 3 shows that polygyny limited to two wives can create a shortage of women even in populations with substantially female-biased sex ratios. (The portion of the graph below the zero line indicates a shortage of women for the remaining marriageable men.) Comparing Figures 2 and 3 shows that few societies have sex ratios low enough to avoid male mating competition generated by relatively low levels

Table 1. Prevalence of Polygyny in the Standard Cross-Cultural Sample[α]

Level of polygyny: % men with plural wives	N	% of SCCS societies	Cumulative % of SCCS societies
0–10	86	59.3	59.3
11–20	13	9.0	68.3
21–50	37	25.5	93.8
>50	9	6.2	100
Total societies	145	100	

[α] 80% of forager societies have <10% polygyny rates.[7]

of polygyny. Hence, most men compete to establish and maintain a single union. This reasoning suggests a somewhat counterintuitive prediction: In societies with higher levels of polygyny, pair-bonds should be relatively stable. In a recent study, human polygyny level was inversely associated with frequency of divorce, which may indicate that males maintain pair-bonds when there are fewer available women.[10] Similarly, a comparative analysis could not exclude mate guarding as a selective pressure favoring pair-bonds among nonhuman primates.[53] In short, pair-bonds could have evolved in response to male mating competition. However, an additional unpublished analysis indicates a somewhat more complex cross-cultural relationship between polygyny and conjugal stability, with divorce appearing to become less common as the proportion of polygynous unions increases to about 50%. Beyond 50%, which is a high level of polygyny among humans, conjugal unions become unstable cross-culturally. More attention to interactions among demographic factors such as spatial distribution, sex ratio, and frequency of polygyny in mating systems can improve our understanding of sexual selection in hominins,[66] which thus far is based largely on simplified models from evolutionary psychology.

A plausible alternative interpretation suggests that the association between conjugal stability and polygyny is not due to mating competition, but rather to marriage alliances between kin groups. Conjugal stability associated with polygyny may result from pressure from kinsmen who fear the economic and political consequences of divorce. There is no empirical support for this interpretation: In the SCCS, the association between the presence of corporate kin groups and frequent divorce is not significant ($p = 0.22$) and is in the opposite direction predicted (odds ratio for frequent divorce = 1.7), as is the association between patriliny and frequent divorce (odds ratio = 1.3, $p = 0.61$). However, as mentioned earlier, null results from the SCCS must be interpreted with caution.

Even low levels of polygyny during the course of human evolution could have created substantial selective pressure for increased pair-bond stability through mate guarding. But the role of polygyny in human evolution is unresolved. Some scenarios for early hominin social structure envision a chimp-like promiscuous mating system.[2] Other equally plausible arguments suggest a gorilla-like polygynous mating system.[61] Sexual dimorphism in fossils could indicate early hominin mating behavior because sexual dimorphism is associated with primate mating systems.[54] Polygynous species, like gorillas, tend to have high levels of dimorphism, while promiscuous species, like chimpanzees, tend toward moderate dimorphism. Unfortunately, paleoanthropologists, using the same data, come to different conclusions about the degree of early hominin sexual dimorphism. Many studies indicate substantial sexual dimorphism, similar to gorillas,[67] but one analysis has concluded that early hominins had a level of sexual dimorphism similar to that among chimpanzees.[68]

Human reproductive anatomy may shed additional light: Testes size, reflecting sperm competition, is correlated with mating behavior in primates.[69] Primates with large testes tend to experience intense sperm competition in promiscuous multi-male groups. Primates with small testes tend to experience male-male competition through physical force in defending resources or mates in the context of harem polygyny. Human testes, which are proportional to body size, are larger than those of gorillas with harem polygyny and smaller than those of chimpanzees with promiscuous multi-male groups.[69] Human testes size suggests an evolutionary history of modest sperm competition, while cross-cultural and fossil evidence suggest the presence of at least moderate rates of polygyny. This further evidence of the unique human mosaic could complicate cross-species analysis. In sum, the cross-cultural association between polygyny and pair-bond stability suggests that polygyny and associated male mating competition may have been important selective pressures during hominin evolution. The polygyny-pair-bond hypothesis may be controversial, but the evidence is promising. These limited findings suggest that more detailed analysis of husband-wife and male-female relations across the range of human mating systems will clarify the adaptive functions of human pair-bonding.

Human pair-bonds may be a form of male mating effort through mate guarding,[2] but how do women benefit from pair-bonds? Polygyny levels might reflect male coercion; men may coerce women to stay in conjugal relationships even when there is little benefit for women in doing so.[70-73] But in many societies women often initiate divorce. One solution is for women to tolerate pair-bonds if men provision them and their offspring. Thus, male provisioning could be mating and parenting effort simultaneously (see Hewlett[74] for a similar interpretation of paternal care). The inverse relation between polygyny and men's contribution to subsistence suggests, however, that coercion occurs.[75] If men do not work to provision mates, and if fathers are not involved in direct parental care, why do women have any interest in long-term conjugal unions, monogamous and otherwise? Men may improve their mates' fitness by protecting them.

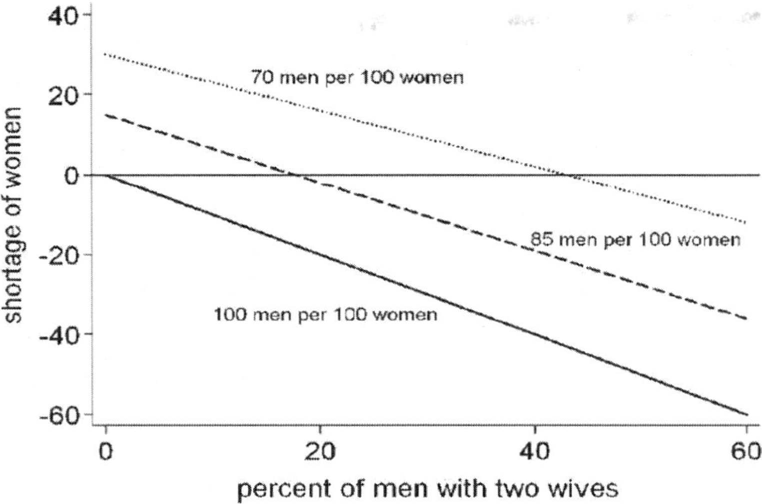

Figure 3. Shortage of women created by polygyny at three population sex ratios. Y-axis values less than 0 indicate a shortage of marriageable women for the remaining marriageable men; values greater than 0 indicate a surplus of marriageable women.

Male Aggression and Infanticide Apparently Do Not Account for Human Pair Bonds

Male-male competition can increase selective pressure for pair-bonds through infanticide and violence toward women. In some foraging societies, women contribute significantly more dietary calories than men do.[2] Often, meat from men's hunting is shared broadly; hence, women do not need a mate for provisioning.[50] Women might have entered conjugal unions to protect offspring from infanticide by aggressive males, following the suggested trend for pair-bonds among primates.[2,76–78] Men's cost of abandoning a bond could be substantial because male aggression is more dangerous for dependent offspring when they are not defended by their father. Among the Ache forager-horticulturalists, infanticide and homicide are important causes of infant and child mortality, and a co-resident father reduces the likelihood of infanticide.[79] Even among baboons that are not pair-bonded, fathers tend to protect their probable offspring.[80] Direct evidence of the role of infanticide in the evolution of monogamous pair-bonds across species, however, is lacking.[81] In a comparative analysis of nonhuman primates, 5 of 6 predictions from the infanticide hypothesis were not supported in two-adult groups.[53] Whether pair-bonds among polygynous primates function to reduce infanticide is not clear.

In societies where male aggression is frequent and intense, pair-bonds are predicted to be more stable, following the infanticide hypothesis.[2,76] This prediction, however, was not supported in recent cross-cultural tests.[10] Contrary to predictions, divorce was significantly more frequent where males were more aggressive. Again, ethnographic cases fill important gaps in comparative data: The Ache of Paraguay, for example, have remarkably high rates of infanticide, while the average Ache adult has about 10 marriages during his or her life.[79] In addition, a comparative study of nonhuman primates shows "no support for significant levels of male-male aggression related to male protection of females."[53:965] These findings suggest that human pair-bonds probably did not evolve to protect women and offspring from aggressive males. Cross-cultural findings are consistent with female strategies among other primates that avoid infanticide through promiscuous mating, which confuses paternity.[82,83] That, in turn, undoubtedly destabilizes pair-bonds.

Alternatively, it is possible that pair-bonds offer women protection from aggressive men, but that male combat results in realignment of mates when a winner claims the loser's mate for himself. This alternative interpretation makes the male aggression/infanticide hypothesis difficult, if not impossible, to test.

It is possible that protection from infanticide provided the initial evolutionary "kick" for human pair-bonds in our ancestors. The significant positive association between human male aggression and conjugal *instability* among contemporary populations may not reflect the adaptive function of human pair-bonds. Mismatch between current conditions and "environments of evolutionary adaptation" is possible,[84] but evolved mechanisms for human pair-bonding are unlikely to behave in ways diametrically opposed to their evolved function. The mechanics of that mismatch are not evident. If adaptations motivating human pairing evolved in response to male aggression, then the bizarre association among contemporary societies demands empirically testable explanations. Otherwise, the mismatch claim is more dogma than science.

Men's Show-off Work May Be Associated with Unstable Pair-Bonds

As mentioned earlier, male contribution to subsistence shows a nonlinear association with pair-bonds among traditional societies. At low levels of male "provisioning," pair-bonds were least stable. Conjugal stability increased up to a maximum at about 50% male-female contribution, but conjugal stability decreased beyond the 50% point. At 100% male contribution to subsistence, pair-bonds tended to be unstable cross-culturally (Fig. 1).[10] This finding suggests that men's work is not always geared to paternal provisioning. The signal value of men's work could be particularly strong in societies where men are primarily responsible for subsistence. At high levels of male contribution to subsistence, males might use subsistence resources to seek mating opportunities that conflict with stable pair-bonds.

Men's subsistence work can be geared toward "showing off" their genetic quality through the strength and skills necessary for economic success.[85] If so, male work may not support paternal provisioning.[50] Men's time allocation to work in different modes of production over the life course is consistent with showing off. Among Machagenka and Piro forager-horticulturalists in lowland South America, for example, young men (20 to 35 years old) spend the majority of their subsistence time in hunting. Time spent hunting dramatically tapers off in middle age (35 to 55 years) even though hunting return rates are highest during middle age after the peak in hunting time allocation.[86] This pattern is consistent with men's interest in showing off during a mating effort life phase. (Among lowland South American hunter-horticulturalists, men could focus on the signaling benefits of hunting in early adulthood, then shift to the political benefits of gardening later in life when horticultural produce is used for food sharing or making large quantities of beer for hosting fetes for allies.[87]) If conjugal relations are fluid, then payoffs to men's subsistence work may be greater for mating effort than for paternal investment.

Conjugal instability under male-dominated subsistence suggests some predictions for when men's work is showing off versus paternal provisioning: Whether men's work is showing off rather than provisioning depends on patterns of cooperation within the household or camp. When alloparents are present, then male provisioning is less important and women could choose genetically high-quality mates instead of good providers. This should, in turn, enhance the benefit of costly signaling and destabilize conjugal relations.

The nature of risk in the environment[43,83] can also influence women's mate choice criteria and the benefits of showing off. Extrinsic mortality is the risk of dying, which is equally shared by all members of a population. More specifically, extrinsic mortality is "not sensitive to changes in reproductive decisions."[89:182] When offspring survival and fitness is less dependent on parental care,[43] pair-bonds may be unstable and women are predicted to concentrate on men's genetic quality.[75] Conversely, when extrinsic mortality is low and fitness depends on parental care, then fathers' provisioning could be important. In this situation, women are predicted to concentrate on men's parenting quality and showing off is predicted to be less salient. Furthermore, the positive association between aggression and conjugal instability cross culturally indicates other channels for costly signaling; that is, men may signal genetic quality through aggressive behavior.[10] Possible associations between extrinsic mortality and the value of "showing off" puts mate choice and pairing behavior squarely in the realm of life-history theory.

The ethnography of unacculturated Marshall Islanders[90] helps make sense of men's work and pair-bond instability. Among the Marshallese, fishing and horticulture are almost exclusively men's work; women contribute little to subsistence. Conjugal bonds are fluid, unstable, and informal. A Marshallese proverb characterizes conjugal relations thus: "The woman does as she likes, the man does as he likes."[91] The Marshallese, therefore offer one model for men's subsistence contribution and conjugal instability.

Men's returns from fishing are distributed in ways that enhance their status and are consistent with showing off. Gifts of food are the main means of establishing and maintaining personal relationships.[90] Costly signaling theory suggests that to maximize signal strength, large, difficult-to-obtain game should be shared widely and in public, whereas smaller, easier-to-obtain packages should be consumed in private and not widely shared.[92–94] A small sample of Marshallese fish-distribution events are consistent with these predictions: Large game fish (marlin, shark, and tuna) were widely shared on Majuro in the Marshall Islands, whereas smaller fish were retained for household consumption.[90] In some cases, a fisherman did not keep any of the catch because he "did not need any fish, and wished none."[90:329] Distribution of fish occurred in public on the beach in ways that might be characterized as "demand sharing."[91] Men's marine foraging may be an honest signal of individual qualities that are important in mating competition, alliance building, and status attainment.[91–94] Marshallese culture also includes imposed norms that could increase costly signal strength: Women are prohibited from fishing and "fishing techniques belong essentially to the men."[90:139]

Pair-Bonds, Socioecological Variation, and Child Development

There appears to be predictable variation in pair-bond stability among societies and individuals. In some social environments, like that on the Marshall Islands, pair-bonds have little influence on fitness, whereas in others, like that among the !Kung, pair-bonds may be essential for survival. Recent theory and research suggest that predictable variation influences the development of life-history strategies. Because children can easily observe their parents' relationship and associated parenting behavior, pair-bonding is well situated to serve important regulatory functions in child development.[88,95–97]

Life history reflects two basic "decisions": whether to reproduce now or later and the amount of care to invest in each offspring.[89] These two decisions are associated with a broad suite of behaviors involving pair-bonds, interpersonal relations, and risk-taking. "Choosing" a strategy, whether consciously or not, depends on the costs and benefits of alternatives. When local success depends on high levels of skill and social competence, people are predicted to delay reproduction and invest a lot in a few offspring. When local success depends on stochastic factors more than personal competence, then people are predicted to reproduce early and invest relatively little in many offspring in hopes of beating the odds. If knowledge, skill, and social competence lead to success,[37,98] then low fertility and higher levels of parental investment are predicted to enhance parents' long-term fitness.[57,99]

In an early influential work, Draper and Harpending[96] proposed that humans have psychological mechanisms that use cues in the childhood family environment to shape the development of reproductive behavior. Fathers' involvement during children's development was predicted to affect behavioral "strategies" later in life. Draper and Harpending argued that pair-bond stability and father involvement are reliable indicators of local resource stability and the long-term benefits of parental care. Their model is based in parental investment theory predicting father abandonment in environments where paternal care does not benefit men's fitness as much as do alternative behaviors related to mating effort.[7]

Draper and Harpending also drew inspiration from the Whitings' classic cross-cultural study of the aloofness and intimacy of husbands and wives.[100] "Aloofness" between women and their mates may influence socialization practices that shape adult behavior. Hence, an aloof relationship between parents acts as a cue for a child to develop a mating-effort strategy. Conversely, an intimate relationship between parents cues the development of a parental-effort strategy. If childhood environment reliably predicts the demands of the adult environment, then developmental "canalization" is adaptive.

Belsky, Steinberg, and Draper[95] and Chisholm[101] refined the Draper-Harpending model and human life-history theory by suggesting that parent-child attachment mediates between early father involvement and adult behavior. Generally, attachment style refers to relatively stable "internal working models of social relationships."[102] An insecure internal model views social relationships as unstable, exploitative, and based in mistrust. Conversely, secure attachment includes stable relationships that are supportive and based in trust. Parenting behavior is associated with cultural variation likely reflecting developmental effects.[88] Cross-culturally,[88] father involvement in early childhood is one of the most consistent predictors of the adult reproductive phenotype.

Father absence may create a family environment in which mothers are less responsive to their offspring because child care is more taxing and maternal attention is more focused on mating effort.[95,101] Maternal unresponsiveness during a sensitive period (birth to 7 years of age) results in insecure internal models, a mating-effort strategy, and unstable conjugal (and other) relationships. Conversely, secure attachment leads to secure internal representations, conjugal unions that are likely to be stable, and a parental-effort strategy.[95]

It has also been suggested that parental unresponsiveness related to single parenthood promotes the development of "externalizing behaviors" that often involve delinquency, violence, and other antisocial acts, as well as risky behaviors geared toward exploiting social and material resources in unstable and unpredictable environments.[95,101,103] Externalizing and lack of inhibition in early childhood may establish a developmental path toward risk-taking later in life. Such differences in development apparently shape cross-cultural trends in adult behavior reflecting evolutionary design for developmental plasticity.[88] In sum, there is substantial socioecological variation in pair-bond stability that may influence cultural models of social cognition and risk taking.

A sizeable body of research supports many predicted relations between pair-bond stability and life-history development.[97] Stressful family environments and low levels of parental care are associated with development emphasizing mating-effort behaviors; stable families and higher levels of parental care are associated with the development of greater emphasis on parental-effort behaviors.[97,104,105] Quality of parental care during childhood may indicate appropriate adult strategies and affect developmental pathways tuned to socio-environmental risk.

Conclusion

There may be several adaptive functions for human pair-bonds in different environments. Recent debate about the function of human pair-bonds focuses on mutually exclusive views of men's work. Thus, men's work is either for provisioning or for mating effort. This polemic neglects phenotypic plasticity as the key feature of human adaptation to a range of environments. There is solid evidence of paternal provisioning during lactation, indicating selective pressure for pair-bonds. Parental investment factors are further apparent in associations between alloparenting and pair-bond stability: When alloparents are more available, biparental care is less crucial and men might increase their fitness through other behaviors. Cross-cultural analyses and comparisons with other mammals suggest, however, that male mating competition also plays a part in pair-bonds. Where there is a shortage of women, conjugal unions tend to be more stable. Moreover, the inverse relation between polygyny and male provisioning[75] and the positive association between polygyny and conjugal stability[10] hints that there may be two different types of human pair-bond: a "biparental bond" geared toward child rearing and a "mate-defense" pair-bond geared toward male reproductive success. If men in pair-bonds do not protect women against aggression nor provision offspring, then men must coerce women into accepting a conjugal union.[71] This is similar to the kind of coercion suggested for some polygynyous unions.[72] Hence, women's motivation for entering pair-bonds may range from provisioning to coercion, which has important implications for behavior and well-being.

There is little evidence indicating that infanticide risk and male-male aggression promote pair-bonds in humans or nonhuman primates. It is possible that protection from infanticide provided the initial evolutionary "kick" for human pair-bonds. Among traditional human societies, however, male aggression is positively associated with conjugal instability. Mismatch between current and evolutionary environments is possible, but it seems unlikely that adaptive mechanisms would behave in ways completely inconsistent with evolved function.

Fathers' presence may serve as a cue for developing reproductive strategies. Yet many studies demonstrate that fathers' presence alone is not the only predictor of developmental outcomes.[101] It is possible that families based on "biparental" versus "mate-defense" pair-bonds provide substantially different developmental environments for children. The quality of pair-bonds may guide offspring reproductive and sexual development toward locally "expected" conditions. Better understanding of the nature and variety of human pair-bonds could open new avenues for life-history research. For example, we might expect mate defense bonds to exist even when high extrinsic mortality, which is independent of parental care, creates rapidly diminishing returns for parental effort, including paternal provisioning.[43] If we view pair-bonds as exclusively adapted for paternal provisioning, then some otherwise promising models for human reproductive behavior may be neglected.

The analysis is further complicated because the relationship between men's production and conjugal stability is not linear. Relationships among showing off, high levels of male subsistence contribution, and pair-bond instability are not clear. There may be some configuration of domestic cooperation that occurs in male-dominated subsistence economies that permits conjugal instability and "show-off" effort. It seems likely that male maternal kinsmen fill the provisioning role in such economies, but the socio-ecological underpinnings of that complex are not readily apparent. Relations among pair-bond stability, division of labor, domestic cooperation, mate competition, and showing off require further study.

In sum, human pair-bond behavior appears to be considerably more complex than Washburn and Lancaster envisioned in 1966. This complexity suggests important ecological variation in human mating and parenting decisions. The human adaptive complex, including culture, may well have evolved to exploit predictable environmental variation. Flexible conjugal behavior and associated developmental effects could provide important insights into this evolutionary process.

References

1. Chapais B. 2008. Primeval kinship: how pair-bonding gave birth to human society. Cambridge: Harvard University Press.
2. Hawkes K. 2004. Mating, parenting and the evolution of human pair bonds. In: Chapais B, Berman C, editors. In: Kinship and Behavior in Primates. Oxford; Oxford University Press, p 443–473.
3. Komers PE, Brotherton PNM. 1997. Female space use is the best predictor of monogamy in mammals. Proc R Soc B: Biol Sci 264:1261– 1270.
4. Washburn SL, Lancaster CS. 1966. The evolution of human hunting. In: Lee R, DeVore L, editors. Man the Hunter. Chicago: Aldine de Gruyter. p 293–320.
5. Lancaster JB, Lancaster C. 1987. The water shed: change in parental-investment and family-formation strategies in the course of human evolution. In: Lancaster JB, Altmann J, Rossi AS, Sherrod LR, editors. Parenting across the life span: biosocial dimensions New York: Aldine de Gruyter. p 187–205.
6. Quinlan R, Quinlan M. 2008. Human lactation, pairbonds & alloparents: a cross-cultural analysis. Hum Nat 19:87–102.
7. Clutton-Brock TH. 1991. The evolution of parental care. Princeton: Princeton University Press.
8. Ember M, Ember CR. 1979. Male-female bonding: a cross-species study of mammals and birds. Behav Sci Res 14:37–56.
9. Burely NT, Johnson K. 2002. The evolution of avian parental care. Philos Trans R Soc London, Series B: Biol Sci 357:241–250.
10. Quinlan RJ, Quinlan MB. 2007. Evolutionary ecology of human pair-bonds: cross-cultural tests of alternative hypotheses. Cross-Cultural Res 41:149–69.
11. Marlowe FW. 2003. A critical period for provisioning by Hadza men: implications for pair bonding. Evol Hum Behav 24:217–229.
12. Fisher HE. 1987. The four year itch. Nat Hist 96:22–28.
13. Low BS, Alexander RD, Noonan KM. 1987. Human hips, breasts and buttocks: is fat deceptive. Ethol Sociobiol 8:249–257.
14. Valeggia CR, Ellison PT. 2001. Lactation, energetics and postpartum fecundity. In: Ellison PT, editor. Reproductive ecology and human evolution. Hawthorne, NY: Aldine de Gruyter. p 85–105.
15. Tracer DP. 1996. Lactation, nutrition, and post-partum amenorrhea in lowland Papua, New Guinea. Hum Biol 6:277–292.
16. Dewey KG. 1997. Energy and protein requirements during lactation. Annu Rev Nutrition. 17:19–36.

17. Jasienska G. 2001. Why energy expenditure causes reproductive suppression in women: an evolutionary and bioenergetic perspective. In: Ellison PT, editor. Reproductive ecology and human evolution. Hawthorne, NY: Aldine de Gruyter. p 59–84.
18. Vitzthum VJ. 1997. Flexibility and paradox: the nature of adaptation in human reproduction. The evolving female: a life history perspective. In: Morbeck ME, Gallowya A, Zihlman AL, editors. Princeton: Princeton University Press. p 242–259.
19. Dettwyler KA. 1995. A time to wean: the hominid blueprint for the natural age of weaning in modern human populations. In: Stuart-Macadam P, Detwyler KA, editors. Breastfeeding: biocultural perspectives. New York: Aldine de Guyter. p 39–73.
20. Valeggia CR, Ellison PT. 2004. Lactational amenorrhoea in well-nourished Toba women of Fromosa, Argentina. J Biosoc Sci 36:573–595.
21. Kennedy GE. 2005. From ape's dilemma to weanling's dilemma: early weaning and its evolutionary context. J Hum Evol 48:123–145.
22. Quinlan RJ, Quinlan MB, Flinn MV. 2003. Parental investment and age at weaning in a Caribbean village. Evol Hum Behav 24:1–16.
23. Charnov EL, Berrigan D. 1993. Why do female primates have such long lifespans and so few babies? Or life in the slow lane. Evol Anthropol 1:191–194.
24. Smith BH. 1992. Life history and the evolution of human maturation. Evol Anthropol 1:134–142.
25. Sellen DW, Smay DB. 2001. Relationship between subsistence and age at weaning in "preindustrial" societies. Hum Nat 12:47–87.
26. McDade T, Worthman C. 1998. The weanling's dilemma reconsidered: a biocultural analysis of breastfeeding ecology. Dev Behav Pediatr 19:286–299.
27. Oddy WH. 2001. Breastfeeding protects against illness and infection in infants and children: a review of the evidence. Breastfeeding Rev 9:11–18.
28. Leon-Cava N, Lutter C, Ross J, Martin L. 2002. Quantifying the benefits of breastfeeding: a summary of the evidence. Washington, DC: Pan American Health Organization.
29. Horwood LJ, Darlow BA, Mogridge N. 2001. Breast milk feeding and cognitive ability at 7–8 years. Arch Dis Childh 84:F23–27.
30. Pollock JI. 1994. Long-term associations with infant feeding in a clinically advantaged population of babies. Dev Med Child Neurol 36:429–440.

31. Vestergaard M, Obel C, Henriksen TB, Sorensen HT, Skajaa E, Ostergaard J. 1999. Duration of breastfeeding and developmental milestones during the latter half of infancy. Acta Paediatr 88:1327–1332.
32. Ellison PT. 2001. On fertile ground: a natural history of human reproduction. Cambridge: Harvard University Press.
33. Belsky J. 1997. Attachment, mating, and parenting: an evolutionary interpretation. Hum Nat 8:361–381.
34. Insel TR. 2000. Toward a neurobiology of attachment. Rev Gen Psychol 4:176–185.
35. Leonetti DL, Nath DC, Hemam NS, Neill DB. 2004. Do women really need marital partners to support their reproductive success? The case of the matrilineal Khasi of N.E. India. In: Alvard M, editor. Socioeconomic aspects of human behavioral ecology: research in economic anthropology, Oxford: Elsevier. p 151–174.
36. Fein SB, Roe B. 1998. The effect of work status on the initiation and duration of breast feeding. Am J Public Health 88:1042–1046.
37. Visness CM, Kennedy KJ. 1997. Maternal employment and breast-feeding. Am J Public Health 87:945–950.
38. Kaplan HS, Hill KR, Lancaster JB, Hurtado AM. 2000. A theory of human life history evolution: diet, intelligence, and longevity. Evol Anthropol 9:156–185.
39. Hurtado AM, Hill K, Kaplan H, Hurtado I. 1992. Trade-offs between female food acquisition and child care among Hiwi and Ache foragers. Hum Nat 3:185–216.
40. Bar-Yam NB, Darby L. 1997. Fathers and breastfeeding: a review of the literature. J Hum Lact 13:45–50.
41. Leonetti DL, Nath D, Hemam N. 2008. In-law conflict: women's reproductive lives and the respective roles of grandmothers and husbands among the matrilineal Khasi. Curr Anthropol 49:861–890.
42. Gough EK. 1959. The Nayars and the definition of marriage. J R Anthropol Inst 89:23–34.
43. Low B. 1988. Pathogen stress and polygyny in humans. In: Betzig L, Borgerhoff Mulder M, Turke P, editors. Human reproductive behavior: a Darwinian perspective. Cambridge: Cambridge University Press. p 115–127.
44. Quinlan RJ. 2007. Human parental effort and environmental risk. Proc R Soc B: Biol Sci 274:121–125.

45. Sear R, Mace R, McGregor IA. 2000. Maternal grandmothers improve nutritional status and survival of children in rural Gambia. Proc R Soc Series B. Biol Sci 267:1641–1647.
46. Hurtado AM, Hill KR. 1992. Paternal effect on offspring survivorship among the Ache and Hiwi hunter-gatherers. In: Hewlett B, editors. Father-child relations. New York: Aldine de Gruyter. p 31–56.
47. Hendrix I, Pearson W. 1995. Spousal interdependence, female power, and divorce: a cross-cultural examination. J Comp Fam Stud 26:217–232.
48. Murdock GP, White DR. 1969. Standard cross-cultural sample. Ethnology 8:329–369.
49. Lee RB. 1993. The Dobe Ju/'hoansi, 2nd ed New York: Harcourt.
50. Howell N. 2000. Demography of the Dobe !Kung, 2nd ed. New York: Aldine de Gruyter.
51. Hawkes K, O'Connell JF, Blurton Jones NG. 2001. Hunting and nuclear families. Curr Anthropol 42:681–709.
52. Wiessner P. 2002. Hunting, healing and *hxaro* exchange: a long-term perspective on !Kung Ju/'hoansi large-game hunting. Evol Hum Behav 23:407–436.
53. Bell D. 2001. Comment on Hawkes et al.: hunting and nuclear families. Curr Anthropol 42:695.
54. Fuentes A. 2002. Patterns and trends in primate pair bonds. Int J Primatol 23:953–978.
55. Andersson M. 1994. Sexual selection. Monographs in behavior and ecology. Princeton: Princeton University Press.
56. Alexander RD, Hooglan JL, Howard RD, Noonan KM, Sherman PW. 1979. Sexual dimorphisms and breeding systems in Pinnipeds, Ungulates, Primates and Humans. In: Chagnon NA, Irons W, editors. Evolutionary biology and human social behavior: an anthropological perspective. North Scituate, MA: Duxbury Press. p 402–435.
57. Harcourt AH, Stewart KJ. 2007. Gorilla society: what we know and don't know. Evol Anthropol 16:147–158.
58. Low B. 2000. Why sex matters: a Darwinian look at human behavior. Princeton: Princeton University Press.
59. Pedersen FA. 1991. Secular trends in human sex ratios: their influence on individual and family behavior. Hum Nat 2:271–291.
60. Schmitt DP. 2005. Sociosexuality from Argentina to Zimbabwe: a 48 nation study of sex, culture and strategies of human mating. Behav Brain Sci 28:247–311.

61. Barber N. 2003. Paternal investment prospects and cross-national differences in single parenthood. Cross-Cultural Res 37:163–177.
62. Flinn MV, Geary DC, Ward CV. 2005. Ecological dominance, social competition, and coalitionary arms races. Evol Hum Behav 26:10– 46.
63. Kappeler PM, van Schaik CP. 2002. Primate social systems. Int J Primatol 23:707–740.
64. Jolly CJ, Phillips-Conroy JE. 2003. Testicular size, mating system, and maturation schedules in wild anubis and hamadryas baboons. Int J Primatol 24:126–142.
65. Stammbach D. 1987. Desert, forest and montane baboons: multilevel societies. In: Smuts BB, Cheney DL, Seyfarth RS, Wrangham FW, Struhsaker TT editors. Primate societies Chicago: University of Chicago Press. p 112–120.
66. White DR. 1988. Rethinking polygyny. Curr Anthropol 29:529–572.
67. Wiegmann DD, Nguyen T. 2006. Mating system and demographic constraints on the opportunity for sexual selection. Theor Popul Biol 69:34–47.
68. McHenry HM, Coffing K. 2000. Australopithecus to Homo: transformations in body and mind. Annu Rev Anthropol 29:125–146.
69. Reno PL, Meindl RS, McCollum MA, Lovejoy CO. 2003. Sexual dimorphism in *Australopithecus afarensis* was similar to that of humans. Proc Natl Acad Sci USA 100:9404–9409.
70. Møller AP. 1988. Ejaculate quality, testes size and sperm competition in primates. J Hum Evol 17:479–488.
71. Marlowe FW. 2003. Mating system of foragers in the Standard Cross-Cultural Sample. Cross-Cultural Res 37:282–306.
72. Smuts BB, Smuts RW. 1993. Male aggression and sexual coercion in females in non-human primates. In: Slater PJB, Rosenblatt JS, Snowdown CT, Milinski M, editors. Advances in the Study of Behavior. 22:1–63 New York: Academic Press.
73. Strassmann BI. 2000. Polygyny, family structure and child mortality: a prospective study among the Dogon of Mali. In: Cronk L, Chagnon N, Irons W, editors. Adaptation and human behavior: an anthropological perspective. Hawthorne, NY: Aldine de Gruyter. p 49–68.
74. Chisholm JS, Burbank SV. 1991. Monogamy and polygyny in Southeast Arnhem Land: male coercion and female choice. Ethol Sociobiol 12:291–313.
75. Hewlett BS. 1992. Husband-wife reciprocity and the father-infant relationship among the Aka pygmies. In: Hewlett BS, editor. Father-child relations: cultural and biosocial contexts. New York: Aldine de Gruyter. p 153–176.

76. Marlowe FW. 2000. Paternal investment and the human mating system. Behav Processes, 51:45–61.
77. Mesnick SL. 1997. Sexual alliances: evidence and evolutionary implications. In: Gowaty PA, editor. Feminism and evolutionary biology: boundaries, intersections and frontiers. New York: Chapman & Hall. p 207–257.
78. Palombit RA. 1999. Infanticide and the evolution of pair bonds in nonhuman primates. Evol Anthropol 7:117–129.
79. van Schaik CP, Kappeler PM. 1997. Infanticide risk and the evolution of male-female associations in primates. Proc R Soc London: Series B 264:1687–1694.
80. Hill K, Hurtado AM. 1996. Ache life history: the ecology and demography of a foraging people. New York: Aldine de Gruyter.
81. Buchan JC, Alberts SC, Silk JB, Altmann J. 2003. True paternal care in a multi-male primate society. Nature 425:179–181.
82. Reichard UH. 2003. Monogamy: past and present. In: Reichard UH, Boesch C, editors. Monogamy: mating strategies and partnerships in birds, humans and other mammals. Cambridge: Cambridge University Press. p 3–25.
83. van Schaik CP, Pradhan GR, van Noordwijk MA. 2004. Mating conflict in primates: infanticide, sexual harassment and female sexuality. In: Kappeler PM, van Schaik CP, editors. Sexual selection in primates. Cambridge: Cambridge University Press. p 131–150.
84. Pradhan GR, van Schaik CP. 2008. Infanticide-driven intersexual conflict over matings in primates and its effects on social organization. Behaviour 145:251–275.
85. Tooby J, Cosmides L. 1992. The psychological foundations of culture. In: Barkow JH, Cosmides L, Tooby J, editors. The adapted mind. Oxford: Oxford University Press. p 19–136.
86. Hawkes K, Bliege Bird R. 2002. Showing off, handicap signaling, and the evolution of men's work. Evol Anthropol 11:58–67.
87. Gurven M, Kaplan H. 2006. Determinants of time allocation to production across the life-span among the Machiguenga and Piro indians of Peru. Hum Nat 17:1–49.
88. Johnson A. 2003. Families of the forest: the Matsigenka indians of the Peruvian Amazon. Berkeley: University of California Press.
89. Quinlan RJ, Quinlan MB. 2007. Parenting and cultures of risk: a comparative analysis of infidelity, aggression and witchcraft. Am Anthropol 109:164–179.
90. Stearns SC. 1992. The evolution of life histories. Oxford: Oxford University Press.

91. Spoehr A. 1949. Majuro: a village in the Marshall Islands. Fieldiana: Anthropology vol. 39. Chicago: Chicago Natural History Museum.
92. Erdland A. 1914. Die Marshall-Insulaner: ethnological monograph. Miinster, Germany: Ethnologische Anthropos Bibliothek.
93. Bliege Bird R, Smith EA, Bird DW. 2001. The hunting handicap: costly signaling in human foraging strategies. Behav Ecol Sociobiol 50:9–19.
94. Smith EA, Bliege Bird R 2000. Turtle hunting and tombstone opening: public generosity and costly signaling. Evol Hum Behav 21:245–261.
95. Smith EA, Bliege Bird R, Bird DW. 2003. The benefits of costly signaling: Meriam turtle hunters. Behav Ecol 14:116–126.
96. Belsky J, Steinberg L, Draper P. 1991. Childhood experience, interpersonal development, and reproductive strategy: an evolutionary theory of socialization. Child Dev 62:647–670.
97. Draper P, Harpending H. 1982. Father absence and reproductive strategy: an evolutionary perspective. J Anthropol Res 38:255–279.
98. Quinlan RJ. 2003. Father-absence, parental care and female reproductive development. Evol Hum Behav 24:376–390.
99. Flinn MV. 2004. Culture and developmental plasticity: evolution of the social brain. In: MacDonald K, Burgess RL, editors. Evolutionary perspectives on child development. Thousand Oaks, CA: Sage. p 73–98.
100. Mace R. 2000. An adaptive model of human reproductive rate where wealth is inherited: why people have small families. In: Cronk L, Chagnon N, Irons W, editors. Adaptation and human behavior: an anthropological perspective. New York: Aldine de Gruyter. p 261–282.
101. Whiting JWM, Whiting BB. 1975. Aloofness and intimacy of husbands and wives: a cross-cultural study. Ethos 3:183–207.
102. Chisholm J. 1999. Death, hope and sex: steps to an evolutionary ecology of mind and morality. New York: Cambridge.
103. Pietromonaco PR, Barrett IF. 2000. The internal working models concept: what do we really know about the self in relation to others? Rev Gen Psychol 4:155–175.
104. Belsky J. 1998. Paternal influence and children's well-being: limits of, and new directions for, understanding. In: Booth A, Crouter AC, editors. Men in families: when do they get involved? What difference does it make? Mahwah, NJ: Lawrence Erlbaum. p 279–290.

105. Chisholm JS, Quinlivan JA, Petersen RW, Coall DA. 2005. Early stress predicts age at menarche and first birth, adult attachment, and expected lifespan. Hum Nat 16:233–265.

106. Ellis B, McFadyen-Ketchum S, Dodge K, Pettit G, Bates J. 1999. Quality of early family relationships and individual differences in the timing of pubertal maturation in girls: a longitudinal test of an evolutionary model. J Personality Soc Psychol 77:387–401.

Introduction to Chapter 17

There are consistent genetic and neurobiological differences among rodent species that differ in their pair-bonding behavior, suggesting that these genes have been naturally selected for their effects on mating behavior. Recent research suggests that very similar genes affect pair bonding behavior in men.

As we approach the end of the course, you should notice that your knowledge about human evolution becomes more unified, and that you are better able to connect theories, data and methods from different areas of study. Chapter 17 offers a nice platform for that kind of integration. Here, Hasse Walum and his coauthors unite ideas from genetics with theories about pair bonding and with a sophisticated use of the comparative method. The paper is one of the most interesting we will read. It is also fairly technical, so this introduction will parallel it closely. Get ready for an interesting tour.

As you learned in Chapter 1, when a gene is expressed, the result is a protein. These proteins interact with other proteins (specified by other genes), and with the environment, in shaping our phenotypes. Note that we have not drawn a strict line between anatomical aspects of the phenotype, like the shape of the pelvis or the size of the brain, and behavioral aspects of the phenotype such as tool using abilities, or pair bonding inclinations, or language abilities (see the next chapter). We have not drawn a line because there isn't one. In both cases, genes are favored if and only if they build adaptive phenotypes—phenotypes that work well in the prevailing environment. Toth and Schick's arguments about selection shaping hominin tool use and Quinlan's arguments about selection for hominin pair bonds assume that selection works on behavior as well as anatomy. This is not as big a leap as it seems on the surface, because selection for behavior *is* selection for anatomy—for example, for the neuroanatomy that produces the behavior. In Chapter 17, the authors explore both the neurobiology and the genetics underlying pair bonding.

The story starts with voles (rodents) of the genus *Microtus*. I have a special fondness for voles because I also studied them for more than a decade, for essentially the same reason they are discussed in this chapter. The reason is that, in a single genus, different species of *Microtus* exhibit a wide range of mating systems. For example, *M. pennsylvanicus* (meadow voles) and *M. montanus* (montane voles) are highly promiscuous, whereas *M. ochrogaster* (prairie voles) and *M. pinetorum* (pine voles) are quite monogamous. The promiscuous species show little or no pair-bonding behavior, but the monogamous ones form strong pair bonds. That is very handy for researchers: It gives us a clear case of evolutionary divergence among closely related species (members of a single genus). We could use that divergence to test theories about the functions of pair-bonds (and some researchers have), but Walum and company want to understand the genetic and neurobiological differences between the monogamous and promiscuous vole species. They want to do so to find out if there are parallel differences within our own species—but I am getting ahead of the story.

There are just two genes we need to discuss. One of these genes codes for a neuropeptide that allows certain kinds of neurons (brain cells) to communicate with each other. This neuropeptide is called arginine vasopressin (AVP is its nickname); you should think of it as a message carrier. The other gene, *avpr1a*, codes for a receptor protein called V1aR. (Genes generally have logically abbreviated names; "AVP receptor one-a" is shortened to *avpr1a*.) Gene products cannot do their work unless they have a way to be "heard." Just as you need a radio to receive radio waves and a television to receive TV waves, the body needs many specific kinds of receptors to interpret the messages carried by specific gene products. You can think of the V1aR protein as a specialized catcher's mitt for AVP. If a neuron lacks V1aR (for example, if its *avpr1a* gene is turned off or missing), that neuron will not be able to receive the AVP message.

What do the proteins AVP and V1aR have to do with pair bonding? Experiments show that if you increase the amount of AVP in their brains, voles will more readily form pair bonds. Conversely, if you give them a substance that interferes with the ability of V1aR to catch the AVP message, they will be less likely to pair bond. Thus, these two proteins have important effects on key aspects of mating behavior.

Now, remember that monogamous vole species spontaneously form pair bonds, whereas promiscuous vole species do not. As would be expected if these differences had been shaped by natural selection, they seem to have a genetic basis: The promiscuous vole species naturally have less V1aR in their brains, because they have fewer neurons that express the *avpr1a* gene. If you use a specially designed virus to increase the density of cells that express the *avpr1a* gene in the brains of promiscuous vole species, they pair bond more than they do otherwise. Not only do the monogamous species have more brain cells that express the *avpr1a* gene, they also have a different version of the gene, with an extra

428-base "tail." If you transfer this elongated version of the *avpr1a* gene from the monogamous species to the promiscuous species, the behavior of the promiscuous voles changes, becoming more like that of the monogamous voles. Finally, there is some allelic variation in the *avpr1a* gene in monogamous vole species (for example, not all prairie voles have the same *avpr1a* genotype); and the strength of their pair bonds correlates with which *avpr1a* genes they have.

Cool stuff. We can think of the loci that code for the AVP and V1aR proteins as genes that shape pair bonding. In other words, when selection is building stronger (or weaker) pair bonds, perhaps it is accomplishing that by favoring certain mutations in these genes that affect how much they are expressed. At this point, you probably want to know if humans have these same genes. Given your understanding of evolution, do you think that would be likely or unlikely? Remember that evolution is a tinkerer. Much is conserved and reused; for example, whales have a forelimb (a flipper) that has most of the same bones as your arm.

The answer is yes. Humans have the gene that codes for AVP, as do most mammals. Humans also have several genes that code for receptors of AVP, including a 1A type receptor, the *AVPR1A* gene, which is homologous to the *avpr1a* vole gene (note that the gene names are the same except that the human gene is capitalized). In the case of genes, "homologous" means that the base sequences are similar enough that they seem likely to be derived from the same ancestral sequence—which would have to be at least 65 million years old in this case. Not only does human *AVPR1A* share a common ancestor with vole *avpr1a*, but the human gene also has a "tail," as do the monogamous vole species. The tails of the human *AVPR1A* come in three major types that differ in their genetic sequences. The types and their basic sequences are shown below.

Tail type	Basic sequence
GT_{25}	$(GT)_{25}$
RS1	$(GATA)_{14}$
RS3	$(CT)_4$-TT-$(CT)_8$-GT_{24}

These are easy to read. For example, $(GT)_{25}$ means that there is a 50-base sequence that simply repeats G, T 25 times. The RS3 type is the longest: 12 C, T units, separated between the 4th and 5th by one T, T unit, and finishing up with 24 G, T units. That is the basic or ancestral RS3 tail, but there are actually 11 different variants of it (listed in Table 2 of the chapter), and each has a slight variation of this sequence. Right; each variant needs to be regarded as a different allele. The question is, do people who have certain *AVPR1A* tail types form stronger (or weaker) pair bonds than individuals with other tail types? The answer is yes.

To discover this, the researchers had to determine two things: They had to figure out which tail type each person had, and they also had to measure how well each person pair bonded. The tail typing was done using standard tools of molecular genetics. That kind of task is technical but so well worked out that a lot of it is now done by machines. You do not need to bother about it; we are just going to assume that they did it correctly. The second part—measuring people's pair-bonding tendencies—is pretty straight forward, too. I suspect that if you were planning this study, you would have devised something similar to what the authors did. First, there are some simple, objective measures of a person's pair bonding tendencies, such as whether they are married versus merely cohabiting. (The researchers did not study single people, but comparing single people with married people might have been a useful approach as well; why?). Another objective measure is whether the person had experienced a marital crisis or begun divorce proceedings. The authors made these simple determinations for each of their study participants. Second, as in many other areas (such as political views, interests and aptitudes), you can measure where people fall along a continuum by asking them a series of relevant questions. So the authors constructed a "Pair Bonding Scale" (PBS) consisting of 13 questions and statements. Here are examples of some they used:

"How often do you kiss your mate?"
"How often are you and your partner involved in common interests outside the family?"
"I don't like when other people come too close to me."

Participants in the study were asked to respond to each statement or question on a numerical 1–7 scale where 1 was labeled "not at all" or "never" and 7 was labeled "very much" or "all the time." The other values (2, 3, 4, 5, and 6) labeled steps along the continuum such as "seldom" or "often." The authors then just added up each participant's responses to these 13 items as a measure of his or her pair-bonding tendency. Higher scores indicate a person who tends to form stronger, more enduring pair bonds. Lower scores indicate the reverse.

Once you know what *AVPR1A* tail type each person has, and what their pair-bonding tendencies are, the answer is just a matter of statistics. As shown in Table 1, the GT_{25} and RS1 alleles were not correlated with the participants' PBS scores, but for men the RS3 alleles were. Table 2 gives a finer-grained analysis of the same thing, showing which RS3 alleles were associated with PBS scores. Men who have at least one copy of the allele called "334" have significantly lower PBS scores than men who have no 334 alleles.

How much lower? The right way to measure that is in terms of what researchers call the standard deviation. The standard deviation tells how much variability there is in a population—in this case the population of people's PBS scores. Measuring the effect of something in terms of standard deviations tells how much of a difference it makes in terms of the range of variability we have observed. The "effect size" (or *d* as it is labeled in statistics) for the 334 allele is 0.27 of a standard deviation (just a bit more than one quarter of a standard deviation). You would have to be looking at statistical tables to make the following translation, but a drop of 0.27 standard deviations moves a score about 11% of the way along the total range of actual values. We can now simplify this one more step. Let's pretend that the lowest PBS score observed in this study is 0, that the highest is 100 and that the average is 50, just half way between the two extremes. On this scale, compared to people who do not have the 334 allele, having at least one copy of it lowers the average PBS score from 50 to 39 (11% of the way along the 0–100 scale). The authors' point is that this effect size is similar to other known genetic influences on personality.

But there is more to the results. Table 3 shows two additional findings. First, it shows that the 334 allele is not just correlated with PBS scores. It is also associated with the other two measures of pair bonding: Being married versus cohabiting and experiencing a marital crisis. And it also shows that the effects of the 334 allele are "dose-dependent," meaning that being homozygous for the 334 allele weakens pair bonding more than having just one copy of it does.

Shall we review? Humans and voles share a very similar pair of genes, one coding for a neurotransmitter and the other coding for a receptor of that neurotransmitter. In voles, different versions of those genes are associated with different degrees of pair bonding. In men, the very same genes also seem to affect pair-bonding tendencies. Based on what you have learned in this chapter, can you suggest at least one new study that would be interesting to do?

Chapter 17 Glossary

5' flanking region: (Pronounced "five-prime flanking region.") DNA has a head end and a tail end based on its molecular structure and the direction that it is transcribed into messenger RNA. The 5' flanking region often contains "promoters" or "enhancers" that affect the activity level of an adjacent gene.

antagonist: A chemical that interferes with biochemical activity of a gene product.

Hardy-Weinberg equilibrium: An equation that gives the expected genotype frequencies in a population based on the allele frequencies. A lot could be written about this, but the most important implication of the authors' statement that, "The allele and genotype distributions of … RS1, RS3 and GT_{25} … did not deviate from Hardy-Weinberg equilibrium" is that directional selection is not presently operating on these alleles. In other words, whatever selection has previously done to increase the frequency of genes for pair bonding in humans, that selection has stopped—at least in the Swedish population studied by Walum and his buddies.

neuropeptide: A protein that brain cells use to communicate with each other.

viral vector gene transfer: Some viruses can insert genes into the genotypes of other organisms. Biologists have harnessed that ability to use viruses to transplant genes either for medical or experimental purposes.

CHAPTER 17
Genetic Variation in the Vasopressin Receptor 1a Gene (*AVPR1A*) Associates with Pair-Bonding Behavior in Humans (2008)

Hasse Walum[*†‡], *Lars Westberg*[†§], *Susanne Henningsson*[§], *Jenae M. Neiderhiser*[¶], *David Reiss*, *Wilmar Igl*[*], *Jody M. Ganiban*[**], *Erica L. Spotts*[††], *Nancy L. Pedersen*[*], *Elias Eriksson*[§], *and Paul Lichtenstein*[*]

Pair-bonding has been suggested to be a critical factor in the evolutionary development of the social brain. The brain neuropeptide arginine vasopressin (AVP) exerts an important influence on pair-bonding behavior in voles. There is a strong association between a polymorphic repeat sequence in the 5' flanking region of the gene (*avpr1a*) encoding one of the AVP receptor subtypes (V1aR), and proneness

* Department of Medical Epidemiology and Biostatistics, Karolinska Institutet, Box 281, S-171 77 Stockholm, Sweden;

§ Department of Pharmacology, Institute of Neuroscience and Physiology, University of Gothenburg, Box 431, S 405 30 Gothenburg, Sweden;

¶ Department of Psychology, Pennsylvania State University, University Park, PA 16802; Yale Child Study Center, Yale University, New Haven, CT 06520;

** Department of Psychology, The George Washington University, Building GG 2125 G St NW, Washington, DC 20052; and ††Behavioral and Social Research Program, National Institute on Aging, Bethesda, MD 20892-9205

† H.W. and L.W. contributed equally to this work.

‡ To whom correspondence should be addressed. E-mail: hasse.walum@ki.se.

for monogamous behavior in males of this species. It is not yet known whether similar mechanisms are important also for human pair-bonding. Here, we report an association between one of the human *AVPR1A* repeat polymorphisms (RS3) and traits reflecting pair-bonding behavior in men, including partner bonding, perceived marital problems, and marital status, and show that the RS3 genotype of the males also affects marital quality as perceived by their spouses. These results suggest an association between a single gene and pair-bonding behavior in humans, and indicate that the well characterized influence of AVP on pair-bonding in voles may be of relevance also for humans.

Primate social organization is often characterized by bonded relationships, and recent analyses suggest that it may have been the particular demands for pair-bonding behavior that triggered the evolutionary development of the primate social brain (1). The brain neuropeptide arginine vasopressin (AVP), acting through the receptor subtype V1aR, plays a key role in the regulation of pair-bonding behavior in male rodents, as revealed by a series of elegant studies on closely related vole species, i.e., montane voles (*Microtus montanus*), meadow voles (*Microtus pennsylvanicus*), and prairie voles (*Microtus ochrogaster*) (2). In prairie voles, which in contrast to montane and meadow voles are socially monogamous and highly social, pair-bond formation and related behaviors are facilitated by AVP and prevented by a V1aR antagonist (3). Supporting the theory that the striking difference in pair-bonding between monogamous and nonmonogamous voles is related to the influence of AVP on this behavior, the neuroanatomical distribution of V1aR differs considerably between these vole species (4) and is associated with sexual and social fidelity among prairie voles (5). Moreover, partner preference is enhanced in the nonmonogamous meadow vole when the V1aR density is increased in relevant brain areas by using viral vector gene transfer (6). Although there are no major differences in the coding sequence of the gene encoding V1aR (*avpr1a*) between prairie, montane or meadow voles, the former species displays a 428-base pair sequence in the 5' flanking region that is not found in the latter two species. When the *avpr1a* of the prairie vole, including the sequence in the 5' region, is transgenically inserted into the nonmonogamous species mouse (7), more pronounced social behavior, similar to that displayed by prairie voles, is generated. Furthermore, variation in the 5' flanking region of prairie vole *avpr1a* affects brain expression of the gene and alters intraspecific variation in partner preference (8).

Human *AVPR1A* is situated on chromosome 12q14–15 (9). Whereas there is no sequence in the human *AVPR1A* 5' flanking region homologous to the one found in prairie voles, humans do have three repetitive sequences in this region that are polymorphic: A $(GT)_{25}$ dinucleotide repeat, a complex $(CT)_4$-TT-$(CT)_8$-$(GT)_{24}$ repeat (RS3), and a $(GATA)_{14}$ tetranucleotide repeat (RS1) (10). Although as yet not consistently replicated, previous studies have revealed associations between *AVPR1A* repeat polymorphisms and autism (11–13), age at first sexual intercourse (14), and altruism (15), suggesting that these repetitive sequences may have an impact on human social behavior.

The aim of this study was to investigate whether variability in the 5' flanking region of *AVPR1A* affects pair-bonding behavior in humans as it does in prairie voles. To this end, the three repeat polymorphisms of the *AVPR1A* were genotyped in adult men and women from the Twin and Offspring Study in Sweden (TOSS), comprised of 552 same-sex twin-pairs and their spouses/partners (16). All subjects were assessed with respect to various indices of the quality of the marital relationship, including a new scale—the Partner Bonding Scale (PBS)—which is comprised of items that correspond to the behavioral patterns observed when measuring features of pair-bonds among nonhuman primates.

Results

The allele and genotype distributions of the three repeat polymorphisms (RS1, RS3, and GT_{25}) were similar to what has been reported in previous studies (10, 11, 17) and did not deviate from Hardy-Weinberg equilibrium. After correction for multiple tests, there was a significant global *P* value for an association between the RS3-repeat polymorphism and the outcome of the PBS for men ($P < 0.01$ after a Bonferroni correction of the six tests), but not for women (Table 1). No associations were found for the other *AVPR1A* polymorphisms. When comparing the mean scores of the PBS for each RS3 allele (Table 2), this value was found to be significantly lower for men carrying allele 334 than for those not carrying this allele ($F_{1,130} = 16.35$, $P < 0.0001$, $d = 0.27$; $P < 0.001$ after correction for the 11 tests). In addition, a dose-dependent effect of the number of 334 alleles on the PBS score (Table 3) was found, with carriers of two alleles showing the lowest scores. The size of these effects were $d = 0.27$ between men not carrying any 334 allele and 334 heterozygotes, and $d = 0.38$ between men not carrying any 334 allele and 334 homozygotes. After Bonferroni correction, no RS3 allele other than the 334 allele displayed a significant association with scores on the PBS.

The association between the RS3 polymorphism and the scores of the PBS prompted us to examine to what extent an influence of this polymorphism on marital quality could be detected when using other measures than the PBS. To this end, we first assessed whether carriers of allele 334 reported more marital problems than men without it, by using an item collected from a life event questionnaire based on the Social Readjustment Rating Scale (18), asking whether the male subjects had experienced marital crisis or threat of divorce during the last year. In line with our assumption, carriers of the RS3 allele 334 responded affirmatively more often to this question (Table 3). Fifteen percent of the men carrying no

Table 1. Association between the different microsatellite polymorphisms in the AVPR1A 5' flanking region and the Partner Bonding Scale

Men				Women			
Repeat	*df*	*F*	*P*	Repeat	*df*	*F*	*P*
GT_{25}	21, 148	0.39	0.99	GT_{25}	18, 138	1.05	0.41
RS1	16, 187	1.03	0.43	RS1	15, 197	0.99	0.46
RS3	19, 157	2.48	0.001	RS3	21, 166	1.19	0.27

Only genotypes for which n > 10 were included in the analyses.

Table 2. Association between different RS3 alleles and the Partner Bonding Scale in men

Allele	Freq	Percent	Mean	*df*	*F*	*P*
320	21	2.3	48.8 (6.21)	1, 12	1.52	0.24
330	92	9.9	47.6 (7.18)	1,37	0.21	0.65
332	128	13.8	47.5 (6.45)	1, 50	0.06	0.81
334	371	40.0	46.2 (6.23)	1, 130	16.35	<0.0001
336	359	38.7	47.6 (6.35)	1, 133	1.51	0.22
338	170	18.3	48.3 (6.21)	1,77	4.73	0.03
340	263	28.4	47.5 (6.56)	1, 106	0.40	0.53
342	30	3.2	47.0 (4.49)	1, 12	0.05	0.82
344	23	2.5	45.6 (6.43)	1,8	1.64	0.24
346	126	13.6	46.7 (6.87)	1, 60	1.30	0.26
348	37	4.0	47.9 (8.47)	1, 16	0.36	0.55

Analyses were performed by comparing individuals carrying one or two of an allele with individuals not carrying this allele. Freq, Frequency, denoting number of individuals carrying one or two of the given allele. Mean, Mean value for the Partner Bonding Scale (standard deviation within brackets). Only alleles for which *n* > 10 were included in the analyses. Six alleles were thereby excluded.

334 allele reported marital crisis, whereas 34% of the men carrying two copies of this allele reported marital crisis, suggesting that being homozygous for the 334 allele doubles the risk of marital crisis compared with having no 334 allele.

The validity analysis, reported in the *Materials and Methods* section, showed that unmarried individuals scored significantly lower than married subjects on the PBS. Thus, we hypothesized that men carrying the RS3 allele 334 more often were involved in a relationship without being married. The allele 334 was indeed associated with marital status (Table 3); the frequency of nonmarried men being higher among 334 homozygotes (32%) than among men with no 334 alleles (17%).

Next we investigated whether the genotype of the men influenced marital quality as perceived by their spouses. For this purpose, we used the Dyadic Consensus, Dyadic Satisfaction, Dyadic Cohesion, and Affectional Expression subscales from the Dyadic Adjustment Scale (DAS) (19), measures frequently used to evaluate the quality of marital relationships. As hypothesized, the marital quality, as perceived by the wives, was significantly associated with the RS3 genotype of their husbands. Women married to men with one or two 334 alleles scored significantly lower on the Affection Expression, Dyadic Consensus, and Dyadic Cohesion subscales than did women married to men without the 334 allele (Table 4), and effect sizes ranged from $d = 0.14–0.20$. However, the difference between carriers of one or two 334 alleles that was observed when analyzing the outcome of the PBS for the men was not found for the rating conducted by their spouses. When the women's ratings were adjusted for the husbands' scores on the PBS, a considerable change of regression estimates (β) was obtained; suggesting that the behaviors assessed by the PBS mediate the association of the 334 allele with the wives' reported quality of the marital relationship.

Discussion

The results from the current study suggest an association between a *AVPR1A* polymorphism and human pair-bonding behavior possibly analogous to that reported for voles (8). One of the most common RS3 alleles, the allele 334, was associated with perceived partner bonding in men as assessed by using the PBS. This association could be detected also by assessing marital problems and marital status in men, and the perception of the quality of the marital relationship expressed by their spouses. That an association between the studied gene and items reflecting pair-bonding was found only in men is consistent with the fact that the influence of vasopressin on social behavior is more prominent in male than in female voles (20).

Although the functional importance of the RS3 polymorphism of the *AVPR1A* remains to be clarified, an association between the length of the RS3 repeat and the amount of hippocampal mRNA in human postmortem tissue has been reported (15). Moreover, a recent study in healthy subjects suggests that the 334 allele is associated with increased activation of amygdala, a brain region known to be of importance for pair-bonding behavior (17). The conclusion of our study (that the 334 allele of the RS3 polymorphism influences brain function) is well in line with previous observations.

The possible influence of AVP on social interactions has led researchers to suggest an involvement of this transmitter in conditions characterized by social deficits, for example, autism and autism-related conditions. This theory has gained support from studies assessing the possible association between *AVPR1A* and risk for autism (11–13) and other traits related to interpersonal relationships (15). Although it is difficult to compare the results of these studies to those of our study, it is of interest to note that one of these studies suggests the 334 allele to be over-transmitted to subjects with autism (11). The observation that a gene variant, which according to our data, is negatively associated with the ability to interact within a relationship, may enhance the risk for a condition characterized by impaired social impairments of social relatedness and communication is obviously noteworthy.

The effect size (d) for the influence of the studied allele on PBS scores when comparing men who carry one or two 334 alleles with those who do not carry any was 0.27. This is comparable with what has been reported in large metaanalyses of the association between a DRD4 polymorphism and the personality trait novelty seeking ($d = 0.32$) (19) and that between a serotonin transporter polymorphism and neuroticism ($d = 0.23$) (20), despite the fact that the outcome of the PBS, unlike novelty seeking and neuroticism to some extent is influenced not only by the informant but also by his/her partner.

It is notable that an association was found between the RS3 repeat of the *AVPR1A* and indices of pair-bonding behavior in a cohort in which all subjects had been married or cohabiting for at least five years. Tentatively, such an association would be even stronger in a population also comprising subjects not involved in any long-term romantic relationships. It would also be of importance to assess the possible influence of this polymorphism on measures of pair-bonding that are more objective than self-report, such as proneness for cohabiting versus living alone, marriage, and divorce. However, of some interest in this context is our observation that men that were homozygous for the 334 allele were more likely to be unmarried than other men, despite the fact that the cohabiting individuals in our sample had been in a relationship persisting for at least five years and that in the vast majority of all of these couples, both individuals were biological parents to a adolescent child, ranging in age from 11- to 22-years-old. This finding is in line with the observation

Table 3. Effect of 0, 1 or 2 334 alleles on male reports on the Partner Bonding Scale, marital crisis, and marital status

	Number of 334 alleles					
Measure	0	1	2	*df*	*F*	*P*
Mean score for the Partner Bonding Scale in the three groups						
Partner Bonding Scale	48.0 (6.50)	46.3 (6.16)	45.5 (6.71)	2, 143	0.0	0.0004
Frequency and column-wise percentage of subjects reporting marital crisis/threat of divorce in the three groups						
Have you experienced marital crisis or threat of divorce during the last year?						
No	469 (85%)	277 (84%)	27 (66%)	2, 143	5.00	0.008
Yes	81(15%)	51(16%)	14 (34%)			
Frequency and column-wise percentage of subjects being married or cohabiting in the three groups						
Marital status						
Married	457 (83%)	275 (84%)	28 (68%)	2, 143	4.36	0.01
Cohabiting	96 (17%)	52(16%)	13 (32%)			

Values for the Partner Bonding Scale are means with standard deviation in brackets.

that unmarried men displayed lower scores on the PBS (see *Materials and Methods*) and may tentatively reflect a lower degree of commitment in those being unmarried.

The relatively small effect size of the *AVPR1A* polymorphism on traits tentatively reflecting pair-bonding in males observed in this study clearly does not mean that this polymorphism may serve as a predictor of human pair-bonding behavior on the individual level. However, by demonstrating a modest but significant influence of this gene on the studied behavior on the group level, we have provided support for the assumption that previous studies on the influence of the gene coding for V1aR on pair-bonding in voles are probably of relevance also for humans.

Materials and Methods

Subjects

The study consisted of 552 twin pairs and their spouses from the second cohort of the Twin and Offspring Study in Sweden (TOSS), a two-cohort study of twin parents, one adolescent child, and the spouse/partner, for which detailed measures of parent-child relationships, marital relationships, personality, attachment style, and the mental health of all study participants were collected (16). Participants were mostly middle class and born between 1944 and 1971. Consistent with the population of Sweden, the vast majority were Caucasian. A more detailed description of the sample is available in a previous article by Neiderhiser and coworkers (16). The same-sex twins included in the study were required to

Table 4. Association between 334 alleles in men and their wives' reports of marital qualities

Quality		No 334 (mean)	One or two 334 (mean)	β	*df*	*F*	*P*
Affectional expression	Unadjusted	18.0 (2.99)	17.4 (2.92)	−0.64	1, 113	10.08	0.002
	Adjusted	—	—	−0.39	1, 111	4.30	0.04
Dyadic consensus	Unadjusted	65.4 (8.11)	63.9 (8.57)	−1.46	1, 117	6.92	0.01
	Adjusted	—	—	−0.82	1, 115	2.46	0.12
Dyadic cohesion	Unadjusted	19.5 (4.34)	18.9 (4.10)	−0.60	1, 116	4.27	0.04
	Adjusted	—	—	−0.20	1, 114	0.53	0.47
Dyadic satisfaction	Unadjusted	43.3 (3.14)	43.2 (2.92)	−0.12	1, 111	0.49	0.49

Mean, Mean value on the outcome for the different DAS Scales for wives with standard deviation within brackets. Adjusted, Analysis with the Partner Bonding Scale included as a covariate. The category of subjects not carrying any 334 allele was used as reference group when constructing the regression estimates (β). Analyses of adjusted values were only performed for the scales that were significantly associated with the 334 allele in the unadjusted analysis.

have a relationship of at least five years with their partner; whereas 82% were married, 18% were cohabiting but unmarried. For simplicity, both married and unmarried cohabiting individuals are referred to as "husband," "wife," or "spouse." The twins and their spouses were first sent a questionnaire that was followed by a home visit, during which additional questionnaires were administered. DNA was extracted from mouthwash samples that were collected by using a DNA self-collection kit. Zygosity was determined primarily by genotyping. There were 238 monozygotic (MZ) pairs and 314 dizygotic (DZ) pairs. In total, 2,186 adult individuals were included in the study, of which 1,899 provided usable DNA samples.

Partner Bonding Scale

The pair bond is a critical element in the study of the evolution of primate social organization (21). Pair bonds among nonhuman primates are generally assessed by measures of partner specific affiliative interaction, proximity, and reciprocity between two individuals (22–24). Furthermore, the strength and stability of the bond is related to its persistence through time (25). In accordance with the behavioral domains observed when studying pair-bonding among nonhuman primates, items were collected from the DAS (19), a frequently used assessment of the quality of marital relationships and similar dyads, the Support Seeking and Giving (SSG) (26) assessment measuring subjects' engagement with other people, and the Marital Instability Scale (MIS) (27). Partner specific affiliative interaction was measured by the occurrence of partner exclusive actions (for example, "How often do you kiss your mate?"). Proximity measures, which in nonhuman primates are measured as the amount of spatial closeness between two individuals, were assessed by two types of items: The proband's experiences of closeness to other people (for example, "I don't like when other people come too close to me") and items concerning the proband's motivation to spend time together with their spouse (for example, "How often are you and your partner involved in common interests outside the family?"). Because one requirement for inclusion in the TOSS dataset was that the adult individuals were part of a dyadic relationship that had persisted for at least five years, no information about the final length of the pair-bonds were available. Instead the proband's reports of their attitudes toward the stability of the relationship (for example, "Have you discussed a divorce or separation with a close friend?") were used as individual indicators of future persistence of the relationship. No relevant measures of reciprocity could be found in the TOSS dataset. Thus, of a total of 49 items, 18 questions (7 DAS, 10 SSG, and 1 MIS) were considered relevant measures of human pair-bonding. A factor analysis was performed, and items with loadings <0.4 on the first principal component were excluded [see supporting information (SI) Table S1] resulting in the final PBS, which were created as the sum of 13 items (7 DAS, 5 SSG, and 1 MIS), with scores ranging from 5 to 66. The reliability, as measured with Cronbach's alpha, was 0.79. Validity estimates of the PBS and the original subscales of the validated questionnaires showed plausible patterns of moderate to high correlation coefficients ($r = .40–.75$). These results were confirmed by our findings on known-groups validity, which showed significant differences between married and nonmarried subjects ($F1{,}105 = 28.28$, $P < 0.0001$), with nonmarried subjects scoring lower on the PBS. We also observed that subjects that had experienced during the last year marital crisis/threat of divorce scored significantly lower on the PBS than those who had not ($F1{,}162 = 186.22$, $P < 0.0001$). By using the fact that the studied population comprised twin pairs, we finally made an assessment of the heritability of this parameter in the studied cohort. The intraclass correlation for the scale was 0.27 for monozygotic (MZ) and 0.03 for dizygotic (DZ) males. The corresponding figures were 0.47 and 0.33 for females. Heritability according to Falconer's formula ($h^2 = 2(r_{MZ} - r_{DZ})$) (28) was 0.27 for men and 0.28 for women, similar to what has been observed for marital satisfaction (29) and divorce (30).

Microsatellite Genotyping

The GT_{25} repeat polymorphism was amplified with primers 5'-TGTCAGACAAAACGCTGTTC-3' (forward) and 5'-TGTGGCTTTA-AAAGTTATCCAG-3' (reverse), the RS3 repeat polymorphism was amplified with primers 5'-TCCTGTAGAGATGTAAGTGC-3' (forward) and 5'-gtttcttTCT-GGAAGAGACTTAGATGG-3' (reverse) (11, 12, 17), and the RS1 repeat polymorphism was amplified with primers 5'-AGGGACTGGTTCTACAATCTGC-3' (forward) and 5'-ACCTCTCAAGTTATGTTGGTGG-3' (reverse) (11,12). The fluorescently labeled DNA fragments were analyzed by size with automated capillary electrophoresis by using an ABI PRISM 3730 Genetic Analyzer (Applied Biosystems).

Statistical Analysis

Statistical associations between the continuous and categorical predictors on the one hand and continuous and binary criteria on the other were estimated by using Generalized Linear Mixed Effects Models (GLMM). As earlier studies have shown that the effects of vasopressin on pair-bonding behavior differ between sexes (20), all analyses were performed for men and women separately.

To take the correlated data structure into account and to avoid estimation problems, different variance-covariance matrices were modeled for monozygotic twins, spouses to monozygotic twins, dizygotic twins, and spouses to dizygotic twins. Each of these four groups had a cluster size of $n = 2$. The correlations between individuals in these groups were calculated by using R-side random effects with an unstructured variance-covariance matrix. The model for continuous outcomes assumed normal distribution of residuals with an identity link function between the predictor term and the criterion. Dichotomous outcomes were assumed to be binary distributed with a logit link function. The parameters were estimated based on the residual log pseudo-likelihood (RSPL), which is equivalent to restricted maximum likelihood (31). All statistical analysis was performed by using the *Statistical Analysis System* (SAS), Version 9.1.3 (32), and generalized linear mixed effects models were implemented by using the PROC GLIMMIX procedure.

Acknowledgments

This project was supported by National Institute of Mental Health Grant R01MH 54610, Bank of Sweden Tercentenary Foundation Grant J2004-0036:1, and a postdoctoral fellowship sponsored by the Brain Foundation, Sweden (to L.W.).

Edited by Solomon H. Snyder, Johns Hopkins University School of Medicine, Baltimore, MD, and approved July 14, 2008 (received for review March 28, 2008)

Author contributions: H.W., L.W., S.H., J.M.N., D.R., J.M.G., E.L.S., N.L.P., E.E., and P.L. designed research; W.I. contributed new reagents/analytic tools; H.W. analyzed data; and H.W. and L.W. wrote the paper.

Authors declare: The authors declare no conflict of interest.

This article is a PNAS Direct Submission.

Freely available online through the PNAS open access option.

This article contains supporting information online at www.pnas.org/cgi/content/full/ 0803081105/DCSupplemental.

References

1. Dunbar RI, Shultz S (2007) Evolution in the social brain. *Science* 317:1344–1347.
2. Young LJ, Wang Z (2004) The neurobiology of pair bonding. *Nat Neurosci* 7:1048–1054.
3. Cho MM, DeVries AC, Williams JR, Carter CS (1999) The effects of oxytocin and vasopressin on partner preferences in male and female prairie voles (Microtus ochrogaster). *Behav Neurosci* 113:1071–1079.
4. Insel TR, Wang ZX, Ferris CF (1994) Patterns of brain vasopressin receptor distribution associated with social organization in microtine rodents. *J Neurosci* 14:5381–5392.
5. Ophir AG, Wolff JO, Phelps SM (2008) Variation in neural V1aR predicts sexual fidelity and space use among male prairie voles in semi-natural settings. *Proc Natl Acad Sci USA* 105:1249–1254.
6. Lim MM, *et al.* (2004) Enhanced partner preference in a promiscuous species by manipulating the expression of a single gene. *Nature* 429:754–757.
7. Young LJ, *et al.* (1999) Increased affiliative response to vasopressin in mice expressing the V1a receptor from a monogamous vole. *Nature* 400:766–768.
8. Hammock E A, Young LJ (2002) Variation in the vasopressin V1a receptor promoter and expression: Implications for inter- and intraspecific variation in social behaviour. *Eur J Neurosci* 16:399–402.
9. Thibonnier M, *et al.* (1996) Structure, sequence, expression, and chromosomal localization of the human V1a vasopressin receptor gene. *Genomics* 31:327–334.
10. Thibonnier M, *et al.* (2000) Study of V(1)-vascular vasopressin receptor gene microsatellite polymorphisms in human essential hypertension. *J Mol Cell Cardiol* 32:557–564.
11. Kim SJ, *et al.* (2002) Transmission disequilibrium testing of arginine vasopressin receptor 1A (AVPR1A) polymorphisms in autism. *Mol Psychiatry* 7:503–507.
12. Wassink TH, *et al.* (2004) Examination of AVPR1a as an autism susceptibility gene. *Mol Psychiatry* 9:968–972.
13. Yirmiya N, *et al.* (2006) Association between the arginine vasopressin 1a receptor (AVPR1a) gene and autism in a family-based study: Mediation by socialization skills. *Mol Psychiatry* 11:488–494.
14. Prichard ZM, Mackinnon AJ, Jorm AF, Easteal S (2007) AVPR1A and OXTR polymorphisms are associated with sexual and reproductive behavioral phenotypes in humans. Mutation in brief no. *981 Online Hum Mutat* 28:1150.
15. Knafo A, *et al.* (2007) Individual differences in allocation of funds in the dictator game associated with length of the arginine vasopressin 1a receptor RS3

promoter region and correlation between RS3 length and hippocampal mRNA. *Genes Brain Behav* 7:266–275.

16. Neiderhiser JM, *et al.* (2007) Father-adolescent relationships and the role of genotype-environment correlation. *J Fam Psychol* 21:560–571.
17. Meyer-Lindenberg A, *et al.* (2008) Genetic variants in AVPR1A linked to autism predict amygdala activation and personality traits in healthy humans. *Mol Psychiatry,* epub ahead of print.
18. Holmes TH, Rahe RH (1967) The Social Readjustment Rating Scale. *J Psychosomatic Res* 11:213–218.
19. Spanier GB (1976) Measuring Dyadic Adjustment: New scales for Assessing the Quality of Marriage and Similar Dyads. *J Marr Fam* 38:15–28.
20. Winslow JT, *et al.* (1993) A role for central vasopressin in pair bonding in monogamous prairie voles. *Nature* 365:545–548.
21. Fuentes A (2002) Patterns and Trends in Primate Pair Bonds. *Internat J Primatol* 23:1573–8604.
22. Krebs JR, Davies NB (1997) *Behavioral Ecology* (Blackwell, London).
23. Fuentes A (2000) Hylobatid communities: Changing views on pair bonding and social organization in hominoids. *Am J Phys Anthropol* 43:33–60.
24. Hinde RA (1983) *Primate Social Relationships: An Integrated Approach* (Blackwell, Oxford).
25. Rasmussen DR (1981) Pair-bond strength and stability and reproductive success. *Psycholog Rev* 88:274–290.
26. Simpson JA (1990) Influence of attachment styles on romantic relationships. *J Person Soc Psychol* 59:971–980.
27. Booth A, Johnson D, Edwards JN (1983) Measuring Marital Instability. *J Marr Fam* 45:387–394.
28. Falconer DS, Mackay TF (1996) *Introduction to Quantitative Genetics.* (Longman, Harlow).
29. Spotts EL, *et al.* (2004) Genetic and environmental influences on marital relationships. *J Fam Psychol* 18:107–119.
30. Jockin V, McGue M, Lykken DT (1996) Personality and divorce: A genetic analysis. *J Pers Soc Psychol* 71:288–299.
31. SAS Institute, Inc. (2006) The GLIMMIX Procedure (Sas Institute, Cary, NC). Available from http://support.sas.com/rnd/app/da/glimmix.html. Accessed January 7, 2008.
32. SAS Institute Inc. (2007) SAS/STAT Software (Version 9.1.3) (SAS Institute, Cary, NC).

SECTION 15

LANGUAGE

Introduction to Chapter 18

All human languages share a suite of layered and coordinated features that place them among the most complex elements of our phenotypes. Was our language facility designed by natural selection, or is it the result of some other process?

In this chapter, Steven Pinker defends the view that language represents a suite of evolved adaptations. Remember that an adaptation is a trait that exists because of a history of selection: It has been shaped to accomplish a particular fitness-relevant function. But how can we know whether language—or any trait—is an adaptation? There are several ways of addressing this question, two of which are exemplified in Pinker's chapter. First, we could ask whether the trait shows a good fit to the hypothesized function; do its various features match what would be needed to accomplish that function. This kind of match could be called *design specificity*. Second, we could look for evidence that the trait has been favored by selection. Pinker uses three separate approaches for estimating the role of natural selection in spreading genes for language, and I will explain each of these below. (You learned a third way—cross-species comparison—in Chapter 5. Can you see why Pinker does not make much use of this method is considering the evolution of language?) Let's examine the underpinnings of the methods Pinker uses.

One way to understand how evolutionists answer the adaptation question is to think about how you might examine a mysterious artifact—an unknown tool or device of human design. Like natural selection, people design artifacts for specific functions. A laptop makes a miserable can-opener, and vice versa. You already know what laptops and can-openers look like, but here is an example that I trust is new to you. I bought one of these in 1966 and used it for its intended purpose. What do you think that purpose was? Try to formulate some guesses before you turn the page.

Figure G. A Curta. What is its function?

The Curta, made in Liechtenstein, was the last of the pre-electronic, hand-held calculators. It can do addition, subtraction, multiplication, division and even (with some effort) square roots. Perhaps you guessed this function by noticing the registers, dials, sliding buttons, and cranks. If you had seen the inside of the Curta, you would have been even more likely to guess its function, because it's the individual components and, especially, the way they mesh together that lets any device—or adaptation—accomplish its function. The more times you disassembled and reassembled a Curta, sliding its buttons and turning its cranks, the more obvious its function would become. This is what we mean by design specificity.

A Curta *could* be a paperweight or a peppermill. But those hypotheses would not match the type and organization of its features. If a Curta were a paperweight, it would be hard to explain why it has so many finely machined internal components that make it no better at fighting stray breezes than a solid lump of metal would be. And if it were a peppermill, it would be puzzling why it lacks a reservoir for peppercorns and suitable grinding blades, but has seemingly irrelevant parts like counters, buttons and dials. Neither proposal—peppermill or paperweight—fits the Curta's detailed organization as well as the hypothesis that it is a calculator.

Figure H. A partially disassembled Curta.

Of course, selection also refines designs to accomplish specific ends, and we can use the same kinds of scrutiny to test hypotheses about the evolved function of phenotypic traits. Pinker makes exactly this kind of argument about language. Its features strongly suggest that language is *not* a paperweight, peppermill, pogo stick, pineapple corer, piñata or anything other than a highly organized acoustical system for the transmission of complex ideas. In the first several pages of the chapter, Pinker does the equivalent of taking apart the Curta of language, showing you how its various components fit and function together to accomplish that communicative function.

In case Pinker's argument seems absurdly obvious, you should know that some relatively well known biologists and psychologists have argued against it (one could, of course, be well known for being wrong). The various kinds of objections to Pinker's view boil down to one main theme: Language is an incidental byproduct of something that *is* an adaptation, and language simply got dragged along. Let's be careful; this kind of argument is not absurd. Some traits of organisms certainly *are* byproducts of something else. The white color of bone is an uncontroversial example of a byproduct. Let's work through that example to make sure we understand what a byproduct is.

An internal skeleton should be both as light and as strong as possible. Selection has hit on the solution of building skeletons out of calcium, which is both present in an array of potential foods and able to form strong-for-their-weight structures. Our question is, did selection favor calcium as the building block of bone because it built white bones, or because it built light but strong bones? It is not at all clear how whiteness might make a better skeleton, but it is obvious how a high strength/weight ratio might. So why is bone white? Because calcium is white. Thus, the whiteness of bone is a byproduct of selection for a bone-building material that is both light and strong.

So, returning to the topic of Chapter 18, could language be a byproduct of selection for something else? It could, but what would that other thing be? I'll let Professor Pinker have the pleasure of debunking those byproduct proposals. He argues that language is highly organized, complex and well suited to the purpose of communicating ideas. Something simple like a color could be a byproduct, but something so multi-layered and integrated and obviously functional (what do you do with language, after all?) seems very unlikely to have gotten dragged into existence by selection for something else.

Pinker offers a second category of argument that language is an adaptation. He argues that genetic evidence suggests a history of selection for language-related alleles. The evidence takes several forms. The first concerns specific language deficits that seem to have a genetic basis, because of how they are distributed within families or the pattern of their occurrence in twins. For example, if monozygotic (identical) twins are more likely to match on a trait—either both having it or both lacking it—than are dizygotic (fraternal) twins, this implies that the trait has a genetic basis. A number of narrow language disabilities fit this pattern. And in at least one case, the specific gene that is apparently responsible (FOXP2, on Chromosome 7) has been identified.

Now, if there are two alleles at a locus and one of them disrupts normal language development, and if language is a fitness-enhancing adaptation, what would you predict about the relative frequency of the two alleles? That the one that disrupts language should be very rare, of course, because selection will be working against it. That prediction is generally confirmed; Alleles that derail language are extremely rare.

The last kind of genetic evidence is subtle but worth understanding, in part because it exemplifies a class of argument that evolutionists are using more and more. This evidence involves a comparison between the effects of genetic drift and the effects of selection. Genetic drift, discussed in Chapter 1, is just random change in gene frequency. Under the influence of drift, an allele increases or decreases in frequency simply by chance. Here is a physical analogy I find useful.

Imagine a piece of driftwood floating on a large lake. Imagine also that there is no systematic current in the water of the lake or any consistent direction to the wind. Given these unsystematic forces, the driftwood is not especially likely to reach one shore or the other; it will just drift in one direction for a while and then in another. Now, let's think about its position on the lake—its distance from the shore—as a graphic representation of the frequency of two alternative alleles, *a* and *b*. When it is in the center of the lake, equidistant from both east and west shores, allele *a* and allele *b* are equally common in the population. If the wood drifts closer to the east shore and farther from the west, then allele *a* is more common, say 60%, and allele *b* is less common, say 40%. If it drifts the other direction, toward the west shore, then allele *b* is more common and allele *a* is less common. If, after drifting back and forth for along time, it actually reached, say, the east shoreline, then allele *a* would be 100% and allele *b* would be completely lost.

Of course, the essence of drift is that the drifting object is just as likely to reach the west shoreline—with allele *a* being lost—as it is to reach the east shoreline, where allele *b* is lost. Moreover, either beaching is likely to take a long time precisely because nothing is propelling motion in either direction. If it reaches a shoreline, that is because a series of chance drifting events moved it sufficiently far in one direction. Now, contrast drift with selection. In the case of drift, there is no consistent current or wind. But in the case of selection there is; that is the key difference. Selection for or against any particular allele (because of its positive or negative effects on fitness) will move it consistently towards one shore or the other—where it will be lost (0%) or become the only allele at that locus (100%). Because selection is systematic and unrelenting—the wind may blow, generation after generation, in the same direction—it typically changes gene frequencies quickly. This contrasts with the slow rate of change when gene frequency merely drifts up and down at random. OK, now we have our prediction: When selection has acted on a locus, allele frequencies change much more rapidly than if mere genetic drift has been at work.

If you have been persuaded by the power of selection to craft adaptations, you may wonder why drift might ever occur. Why wouldn't selection govern the fate of every allele, causing an allele to spread if it increases fitness and to be weeded out if it decreases reproductive prospects? One important reason could be that the allele in question has *no* effect on fitness; in other words, it is *selectively neutral.* An allele might be selectively neutral if it occurred in a non-coding region of the DNA—a region that never sends a messenger RNA message. Thus, the rates of evolutionary change in such non-coding regions give an indication of the rates of genetic change under the influence of drift. And these rates of genetic change can be estimated by comparing the same non-coding regions among species with known divergence times. How many allele substitutions per million years do we find in such non-coding regions?

Once we know how fast random drift can change allele frequencies, we can compare that to the rates of genetic change in language-related alleles. As Pinker summarizes, when we make that comparison, it seems that selection has indeed been at work in pushing up the frequency of the alleles that support our linguistic ability.

Chapter 18 Glossary

creole: A *lingua franca* that has both a rich vocabulary and a rich grammar; creoles usually develop from pidgins over one or more generations.

duality of patterning: Refers to the fact that two separate tiers of rules govern language: a set of (phonological) rules for combining meaningless sounds into meaningful words, overlaid by a different set of (grammatical) rules for combining words to convey ideas (the relationships among the words).

Dysarthria: A speech impairment (in the lips, tongue, vocal chords, etc,) as opposed to a language impairment (in the mental machinery for learning and using language).

evolutionary game theory: A branch of applied mathematics that looks for a "strategy" (trait) that is immune to invasion; in other words, a trait that is better than all its alternatives, and would therefore be perpetuated over evolutionary time.

lingua franca: A "bridge" language used for communication by people who have different first languages. Pidgins and creoles are examples.

pidgin: A *lingua franca* that has a limited vocabulary and an impoverished grammatical system.

polygenic: Shaped by genes at more than one locus (see Chapter one).

polyglot: Speaking multiple languages; the members of polyglot communities may have difficulty communicating because many interacting pairs may have no language in common.

voiced/unvoiced: Two kinds of "consonants;" the vocal chords vibrate when a voiced consonant (for example, /b/, /d/, or /g/) is being produced, but they do not vibrate when an unvoiced consonant is being produced (for example, /p/, /t/, or /k/). Put your hand on your throat to verify the difference.

Chapter 18
Language as an Adaptation to the Cognitive Niche* (2003)

Steven Pinker

Introduction

This chapter outlines the theory (first explicitly defended by Pinker and Bloom 1990), that the human language faculty is a complex biological adaptation that evolved by natural selection for communication in a knowledge-using, socially interdependent lifestyle. This claim might seem to be anyone's first guess about the evolutionary status of language, and the default prediction from a Darwinian perspective on human psychological abilities. But the theory has proved to be controversial, as shown by the commentaries in Pinker and Bloom (1990) and the numerous debates on language evolution since then (Fitch 2002; Hurford et al. 1998).

In the chapter I will discuss the design of the language faculty, the theory that language is an adaptation, alternatives to the theory, an examination of what language might be an adaptation for, and how the theory is being tested by new kinds of analyses and evidence.

The Design of Human Language

The starting point in an analysis of the evolution of language must be an analysis of language itself (for other overviews, see Bickerton 1990; Jackendoff 2002; Miller 1991). The most remarkable aspect of language is its *expressive power*: its ability to convey an unlimited

* Supported by NIH grant HD-18381. I thank Morten Christiansen and the members of his seminar on the evolution of language for helpful comments on an earlier draft.

number of ideas from one person to another via a structured stream of sound. Language can communicate anything from soap opera plots to theories of the origin of the universe, from lectures to threats to promises to questions. Accordingly, the most significant aspects of the language faculty are those that make such information transfer possible (Pinker 1994; 1999). The first cut in dissecting the language faculty is to separate the two principles behind this remarkable talent.

Words

The first principle underlies the mental lexicon, a finite memorized list of words. As Ferdinand de Saussure pointed out, a word is an arbitrary sign: a connection between a signal and a concept shared by the members of the community. The word *duck* does not look like a duck, walk like a duck, or quack like a duck, but I can use it to convey the idea of a duck because we all have learned the same connection between the sound and the meaning. I can therefore bring the idea to mind in a listener simply by making that noise. If instead I had to shape the signal to evoke the thought using some perceptible connection between its form and its content, every word would require the inefficient contortions of the game of charades.

The symbols underlying words are bidirectional. Generally, if I can use a word I can understand it when someone else uses it, and vice versa. When children learn words, their tongues are not moulded into the right shape by parents, and they do not need to be rewarded for successive approximations to the target sound for every word they hear. Instead, children have an ability, upon hearing somebody else use a word, to know that they in turn can use it to that person or to a third party and expect to be understood.

Grammar

Of course, we do not just learn individual words; we combine them into larger words, phrases, and sentences. This involves the second trick behind language, grammar. The principle behind grammar was articulated by Wilhelm von Humboldt as 'the infinite use of finite media.' Inside every language user's head is a finite algorithm with the ability to generate an infinite number of potential sentences, each of which corresponds to a distinct thought. For example, our knowledge of English incorporates rules that say 'A sentence may be composed of a noun phrase (subject) and a verb phrase (object)' and 'A verb phrase may be composed of a verb, a noun phrase (object), and a sentence (complement)'. That pair of rules is *recursive*: a phrase is defined as a sequence of phrases, and one or more of those daughter phrases can be of the same kind as the mother phrase. This creates a loop that can generate sentences of any size, such as *I wonder whether she knows that I know that she knows that he thinks she is interested in him.* By means of generating an infinite number of sentences, we can convey an infinite number of distinct thoughts, since every sentence has a different meaning (most linguists believe that true synonymy is rare or nonexistent).

Grammar can express an astonishing range of thoughts because our knowledge of grammar is couched in abstract categories such as 'noun' and 'verb' rather than concrete concepts such as 'man' and 'dog' or 'eater' and 'eaten' (Pinker 1994; 1999). This gives us an ability to talk about new kinds of ideas. We can talk about a dog biting a man, or, as in the journalist's definition of 'news', a man biting a dog. We can talk about aliens landing in Roswell, or the universe beginning with a big bang, or Michael Jackson marrying Elvis's daughter. The abstractness of grammatical categories puts no restriction on the content of sentences; the recursive, combinatorial nature of grammar puts no limits on their complexity or number.

A grammar comprises many rules, which fall into subsystems. The most prominent is *syntax*, the component that combines words into phrases and sentences. One of the tools of syntax is linear order, which allows us to distinguish, say, *Man bites dog* from *Dog bites man*. Linear order is the most conspicuous property of syntax, but it is a relatively superficial one. Far more important is *constituency*. A sentence has a hierarchical structure, which allows us to convey complex propositions consisting of ideas embedded inside ideas. A simple demonstration comes from an ambiguous sentence such as *On tonight's program Dr Ruth will discuss sex with Dick Cavett*. It is composed of a single string of words in a particular order but with two different meanings, which depend on their constituent bracketings: [discuss] [*sex*] [*with Dick Cavett*] versus [*discuss*] [*sex with Dick Cavett*]. Of course, most sentences in context are not blatantly ambiguous, but ambiguity illustrates the essential place of constituency in interpreting meaning from sentences. As with other symbolic systems that encode logical information, such as arithmetic, logic, and computer programming, it is essential to get the parentheses right, and that's what phrase structure in grammar does.

Syntax also involves *predicate–argument* structure, the component of language that encodes the relationship among a set of participants (Pinker 1989). To understand a sentence one cannot merely pay attention to the order of words, or even the way they are grouped; one has to look up information associated with the predicate (usually the verb) which specifies how its arguments are placed in the sentence. For example, in the sentences *The man feared the dog* and *The man frightened the dog*, the word *man* is the subject in both cases, but its semantic role differs: in the first sentence the man experiences the fear; in the second he causes it. In understanding a sentence, one has to look up information stored with the mental dictionary entry of the verb and see whether it says (for instance) 'my subject is the one experiencing the fear' or 'my subject is the one causing the fear'.

A fourth trick of syntax is known as *transformations, movement*, or *binding traces*. Once one has specified a hierarchical tree structure into which the words of a sentence are plugged, a further set of operations can alter it in precise ways. For example, the sentence *Dog is bitten by man* contains the verb *bite*, which ordinarily requires a direct object. But here the object is missing from its customary location; it has been "moved" to the front of the sentence. This gives us a way of shifting the emphasis and quantification of a given set of participants in an event or state. The sentences *Man bites dog* and *Dog is bitten by man* both express the same information about who did what to whom, but one of them is a comment about the man and the other is a comment about the dog. Similarly, sentences in which a phrase is replaced by a *wh*-word and moved to the front of a sentence, such as *Who did the dog bite?*, allow the speaker to seek the identity of one of the participants in a specified event or relationship. Transformations thus provide a layer of meaning beyond who did what to whom; that layer emphasizes or seeks information about one of the participants, while keeping constant the actual event being talked about.

Syntax, for all that complexity, is only one component of grammar. All languages have a second combinatorial system, *morphology*, in which simple words or parts of words (such as prefixes and suffixes) are assembled to produce complex words. The noun *duck*, for example, comes in two forms—*duck* and *ducks*—and the verb *quack* in four—*quack, quacks, quacked*, and *quacking*. In languages other than English morphology can play a much greater role. In Latin, for example, case suffixes on nouns convey information about who did what to whom, allowing one to scramble the left-to-right order of the words for emphasis or style. For example, *Canis hominem mordet* and *Hominem canis mordet* (different orders, same cases) have the same non-newsworthy meaning, and *Homo canem mordet* and *Canem homo mordet* have the same newsworthy meaning.

Language also embraces a third combinatorial system called *phonology*, which governs the sound pattern of a language. In no language do people form words by associating them directly with articulatory gestures like a movement of the tongue or lips. Instead, an inventory of gestures is combined into sequences, each defining a word. The combinations are governed by phonological rules and constraints that work in similar ways in all languages but whose specific content people have to acquire. English speakers, for example, sense that *bluck* is not a word but could be one, whereas *nguck* is not a word and could not be one (though it could be a word in other languages). All languages define templates for how words may be built out of hierarchically nested units such as feet, syllables, vowels and consonants, and features (articulatory gestures). Interestingly, whereas syntax and morphology are semantically compositional—one can predict the meaning of the whole by the meanings of the elements and the way they are combined—this is not true of phonology One cannot predict the meaning of *duck* from the meaning of /d/, the meaning of /Λ/, and the meaning of /k/. Phonology is a combinatorial system that allows us to have large vocabularies (e.g. 100,000 words is not atypical for an English speaker) without having to pair each word with a distinct noise. The presence of these two kinds of discrete combinatorial systems in language is sometimes called duality of patterning.

Phonology also contains a set of adjustment rules which, after the words are defined and combined into phrases, smooth out the sequence of articulatory gestures to make them easier to pronounce and comprehend. For instance, one set of rules in English causes us to pronounce the past-tense morpheme *-ed* in three different ways, depending on whether it is attached to *jogged*, *walked*, or *patted*. The adjustment for *walked* keeps the consonants at the end of a word either all voiced or all unvoiced, and the adjustment for *patted* inserts a vowel to separate two *d*-like sounds. These adjustments often function to make articulation easier or speech clearer in a way that is consistent across the language, but they are not merely products of a desire to be lazy or clean. These two goals are at cross purposes, and the rules of phonology impose shared conventions on the speakers of a language as to exactly when one is allowed to be lazy in which way.

Interfaces of Language with Other Parts of the Mind

Grammar is only one component of language, and it has to interface with at least four other systems of the mind: perception, articulation, conceptual knowledge (which provides the meanings of words and their relationships), and social knowledge (how language can be used and interpreted in a social context). While these systems also serve non-linguistic functions, and may have been carried over from earlier primate designs, at least some aspects of them may have evolved specifically to mesh with language. A likely example is the vocal tract: Darwin pointed to the fact that in humans every mouthful of food has to pass over the trachea, with some chance of getting lodged in it and causing death by choking. The human vocal tract has a low larynx compared to those of most other mammals, an arrangement that compromises a number of physiological functions but allows us to articulate a large range of vowel sounds. Lieberman (1984) has plausibly argued that physiological costs such as the risk of death by choking were outweighed in human evolution by the benefit of rapid, expressive communication.

Is Language an Adaptation?

In the biologist's sense of the word, an 'adaptation' is a trait whose genetic basis was shaped by natural selection (as opposed to the everyday sense of a trait that is useful to the individual). What are the alternatives to the theory that language is an adaptation? And what are the reasons for believing it might be one?

Is Language a Distinct Part of the Human Phenotype?

One alternative is that language is not an adaptation itself, but a manifestation of more general cognitive abilities, such as 'general intelligence', 'a symbolic capacity', 'cultural learning', 'mimesis', or 'hierarchically organized behaviour' (see e.g. Bates et al. 1991; Deacon 1997; Tomasello 1999). If so, these more general cognitive capacities would be the adaptation.

These alternatives are difficult to evaluate, because no one has spelled out a mechanistic theory of 'general intelligence' or 'cultural learning' that is capable of acquiring human language. Intelligence, learning, symbol comprehension, and so on do not happen by magic but need particular mechanisms, and it is likely that different mechanisms are needed in different domains such as vision, motor control, understanding the physical and social worlds, and so on (Pinker 1997). The ability to acquire and use the cultural symbols called 'language' may require learning mechanisms adapted to that job. Attempts to model the acquisition of language using general-purpose algorithms such as those in traditional artificial intelligence or connectionist neural networks have failed to duplicate the complexity of human language (Pinker 1979; Pinker 1999; Pinker and Prince 1988).

Though it is hard to know exactly what is meant by terms like 'cultural learning' or 'general intelligence', one can see whether mastery of language in the human species resembles abilities that are unambiguously culturally acquired, like agricultural techniques, chess skill, knowledge of government, and mathematical expertise, or whether it looks more like a part of the standard human phenotype, like fear, humor, or sexual desire. Some very general properties of the natural history of language suggests that the latter is more accurate (see Jackendoff 2002; Lightfoot and Anderson 2002; Pinker 1994).

First, language is universal across societies and across neurological normal people within a society, unlike far simpler skills like farming techniques or chess. There may be technologically primitive peoples, but there are no primitive languages: the anthropologists who first documented the languages of technologically primitive societies a century ago were repeatedly astonished by their complexity and abstractness (Voegelin and Voegelin 1977). And despite stereotypes to the contrary, the language of uneducated, working-class, and rural speakers has been found to be systematic and rule-governed, though the rules may belong to dialects that differ from the standard one (Labov 1969; McWhorter 2002).

Second, languages conform to a universal design. A language is not just any conceivable code that maps efficiently from sound to meaning. The design specifications listed in the preceding section—and, indeed, far more subtle and complex properties of grammar—can be found in all human languages (Baker 2001; Comrie 1981; Greenberg et al. 1978; Hockett 1960).

A third kind of evidence is the ontogenetic development of language. Children the world over pass through a universal series of stages in acquiring a language (Brown 1973; Ingram 1989; Pinker 1994). That sequence culminates in mastery of the local tongue, despite the fact that learning a language requires solving the daunting problem of taking in a finite sample of sentences (speech from parents) and inducing a grammar capable of generating the infinite language from which they were drawn (Pinker 1979; 1984). Moreover, children's speech patterns, including their errors, are highly systematic, and can often be shown to conform to linguistic universals for which there was no direct evidence in parents' speech (Crain 1992; Gordon 1985; Kim et al. 1994).

A fourth kind of evidence also comes from the study of language acquisition. If children are thrown together without a pre-existing language that can be 'culturally transmitted' to them, they will develop one of their own. One example, studied by Bickerton, comes from the polyglot slave and servant plantations in which the only lingua franca among adults was a pidgin, a makeshift communicative system with little in the way of grammar. The children in those plantations did not passively have the pidgin culturally transmitted to them, but quickly developed creole languages, which differ substantially from the pidgins and which have all the basic features of established human languages (Bickerton 1981). Another example comes from deaf communities, where complex sign languages emerge quickly and spontaneously. A recent study in Nicaragua has tracked the emergence of a complex sign language in little more than a decade, and has shown that the most fluent and creative users of the language were the children (Senghas and Coppola 2001).

A fifth kind of evidence is that language and general intelligence, to the extent we can make sense of that term, seem to be doubly dissociable in neurological and genetic disorders. In aphasias and in the genetically caused developmental syndrome called Specific Language Impairment, intelligent people can have extreme difficulties speaking and understanding (Leonard 1998; Siegal et al. 2001; van der Lely and Christian 1998). Conversely, in a number of retardation syndromes, such as Williams syndrome and the sequelae of hydrocephalus, substantially retarded children may speak fluently and grammatically and do well on tests of grammatical comprehension and judgement (Clahsen and Almazen 1998; Curtiss 1989; Rossen et al. 1996). Few of these dissociations are absolute, with language or non-linguistic cognition completely spared or completely impaired. But the fact that the two kinds of abilities can dissociate quantitatively and along multiple dimensions shows that they are not manifestations of a single underlying ability.

Did Language Evolve by Means Other Than Natural Selection?

A different alternative to the hypothesis that language is an adaptation is the possibility that it evolved by mechanisms other than natural selection, a hypothesis associated with Stephen Jay Gould and Noam Chomsky (Chomsky 1988; Gould 1997; see Piatelli-Palmarini 1989 and Pinker and Bloom 1990 for discussion). On this view, language may have evolved all at once as the product of a macromutation. Or the genes promoting language may have become fixed by random genetic drift or by genetic hitchhiking (i.e. genes that were near other genes that were the real target of selection). Or it may have arisen as a by-product of some other evolutionary development such as a large brain, perhaps because of physical constraints on how neurons can be packed into the skull.

It is hard to evaluate this theory (though, as we shall see, not impossible), because there have been no specific proposals fleshing out the theory (e.g. specifying the physical constraint that makes language a neurobiological necessity). So what is the appeal of the non-selectionist theories?

One is a general misconception, spread by Gould, that natural selection has become an obsolete or minor concept in evolutionary biology, and that explanations in terms of by-products (what he called 'spandrels') or physical constraints are to be preferred in principle (e.g. Piatelli-Palmarini 1989). This is a misconception because natural selection remains the only evolutionary force capable of generating complex adaptive design, in which a feature of an organism (such as the eye or heart) has a non-random organization that enables it to attain an improbable goal that fosters survival and reproduction (Dawkins 1986; Williams 1966). Moreover, natural selection is a rigorous concept which can be modelled mathematically or in computer simulations, measured in natural environments, and detected by statistical analyses of organisms' genomes (Kreitman 2000; Maynard Smith 1988; Przeworski et al. 2000; Weiner 1994).

A second appeal of non-selectionist theories comes from a scepticism that language could have provided enough reproductive benefits to have been selected for. According to one objection, popular among linguists, language has arbitrary features that do not obviously contribute to communication. However, *all* communication systems have arbitrary features (such as the particular sequences of dots and dashes making up Morse code), because arbitrary ways of linking messages to signals are useful as long as they are shared by sender and recipient. Moreover, since a feature that eases the task of the speaker (by omitting information or reducing the complexity of the signal) will complicate the task of the listener (by making the message more ambiguous or vulnerable to noise), a shared code must legislate arbitrary conventions that do not consistently favour any single desideratum (Pinker and Bloom 1990).

Another argument for non-selectionist theories is that grammar is more complicated than it needs to be to fulfil the communicative needs of a hunter–gatherer lifestyle. As one sceptic put it, 'How does recursion help in the hunt for mastodons?' But as Bloom and I pointed out, complex grammar is anything but a useless luxury: 'It makes a big difference whether a far-off region is reached by taking the trail that is in front of the large tree or the trail that the large tree is in front of. It makes a difference whether that region has animals that you can eat or animals that can eat you.' Since selection can proceed even with small reproductive advantages (say, one per cent), the evolution of complex grammar presents no paradox.

A third misconception is that if language is absent from chimpanzees, it must have evolved by a single macromutation. This is seen as an argument for a macromutational theory by those who believe that human language is qualitatively distinct from the communicative abilities of chimpanzees, and as an argument that human language cannot be qualitatively distinct from the communicative abilities of chimpanzees by those who believe that macromutations are improbable. But both arguments are based on a misunderstanding of how evolution works. Chimpanzees and bonobos are our closest living relatives, but that does not mean that we evolved from them. Rather, humans evolved from an extinct common ancestor that lived six to eight million years ago. There were many other (now-extinct) species in the lineage from the common ancestor to modern humans (australopithecines, *habilis*, *ergaster*, archaic *sapiens*, etc.) and, more important, many individuals making up the lineages that we group into species for convenience. Language could well have evolved gradually *after* the chimp/human split, in the 200,000–300,000 generations that make up the lineage leading to modern humans. Language, that is, could be an autapomorphy: a trait that evolved in one lineage but not its sister lineages.

The final appeal of the non-selectionist hypothesis is that language could only have been useful once it was completely in place: a language is useless if you are the only one to have evolved the ability to speak it. But this objection could be raised about the evolution of any communicative system, and we know that communication has evolved many times in the animal kingdom. The solution is that comprehension does not have to be in perfect synchrony with production. In the case of language, it is often possible to decode parts of an utterance in a language one has not completely mastered. When some individuals are making important distinctions that can be decoded by listeners only with cognitive effort, a pressure could thereby develop for the evolution of neural mechanisms that would make this decoding process become increasingly automatic and effortlessly learned (Pinker and Bloom 1990). The process whereby environmentally induced responses set up selection pressures for such responses to become innate, triggering conventional Darwinian evolution that superficially mimics a Lamarckian sequence, is known as the Baldwin Effect (Hinton and Nowlan 1987).

Opposing these spurious arguments for the non-selectionist hypothesis is a strong prima facie reason to favour the selectionist one: the standard argument in evolutionary biology that only natural selection can explain the evolution of complex adaptive design (Dawkins 1986; Williams 1966). The information-processing circuitry necessary to produce, comprehend, and learn language requires considerable organization. Randomly organized neural networks, or randomly selected subroutines from an artificial intelligence library, do not give rise to a system that can learn and use a human language. As we saw, language is not just a set of symbolic labels for concepts, not just the use of linear order, not just the use of hierarchical structure, and not just a blurting out of a sequence of sounds. It is an integrated system containing a lexicon, several components of grammar, and interfaces to input–output systems, possibly with language-specific modifications of their own. And this complexity is not just there for show, but makes possible a remarkable ability: language's vast expressive power, rapid acquisition by children, and efficient use by adults.

As with other complex organs that accomplish improbable feats, the necessary circuitry for language is unlikely to have evolved by a process that is insensitive to the functionality of the end product, such as a single mutation, genetic drift, or arbitrary physical constraints. Natural selection is the most plausible explanation of the evolution of language, because it is the only physical process in which how well something works can explain how it came into existence.

What Did Language Evolve For?

If language is an adaptation, what is it an adaptation for? Note that this is different from the question of what language is typically *used* for, especially what it is used for at present. It is a question about the 'engineering design' of language and the extent to which it informs us about the selective pressures that shaped it.

What is the machinery of language trying to accomplish? The system appears to have been put together to encode propositional information—who did what to whom, what is true of what, when, where and why—into a signal that can be conveyed from one person to another. It is not hard to see why it might have been adaptive for a species with the rest of our characteristics to evolve such an ability. The structures of grammar are well suited to conveying information about technology, such as which two things can be put together to produce a third thing; about the local environment, such as where things are; about the social environment, such as who did what to whom, when where and why; and about one's own intentions, such as *If you do this, I will do that*, allowing people to convey the promises and threats that undergird relations of exchange and dominance.

The Cognitive Niche

Gathering and exchanging information is, in turn, integral to the larger niche that modern *Homo sapiens* has filled, which John Tooby and Irven DeVore (1987) have called 'the cognitive niche' (it may also be called the 'informavore' niche, following a coinage by George Miller). Tooby and DeVore developed a unified explanation of the many human traits that are unusual in the rest of the living world. They include our extensive manufacture of and dependence on complex tools, our wide range of habitats and diets, our extended childhoods and long lives, our hypersociality, our complex patterns of mating and sexuality, and our division into groups or cultures with distinctive patterns of behaviour. Tooby and DeVore proposed that the human lifestyle is a consequence of a specialization for overcoming the evolutionary fixed defences of plants and animals (poisons, coverings, stealth, speed, and so on) by cause-and-effect reasoning. Such reasoning enables humans to invent and use new technologies (such as weapons, traps, coordinated driving of game, and ways of detoxifying plants) that exploit other living things before they can develop defensive countermeasures in evolutionary time. This cause-and-effect reasoning depends on intuitive theories about various domains of the world, such as objects, forces, paths, places, manners, states, substances, hidden biochemical essences, and other people's beliefs and desires.

The information captured in these intuitive theories is reminiscent of the information that the machinery of grammar is designed to convert into strings of sounds. It cannot be a coincidence that humans are special in their ability to outsmart other animals and plants by cause-and-effect reasoning, and that language is a way of converting information about cause-and-effect and action into perceptible signals.

A distinctive and important feature of information is that it can be duplicated without loss. If I give you a fish, I do not have the fish, as we know from sayings like *You can't have your cake and eat it.* But if I tell you how to fish, it is not the case that I now lack the knowledge how to fish. Information is what economists call a non-rival good, a concept recently made famous by debates about intellectual property (such as musical recordings that can be shared without cost on the internet).

Tooby and DeVore have pointed out that a species that has evolved to rely on information should thus also evolve a means to *exchange* that information. Language multiplies the benefit of knowledge, because a bit of know-how is useful not only for its practical benefits to oneself but as a trade good with others. Using language, I can exchange knowledge with somebody else at a low cost to myself and hope to get something in return. It can also lower the original acquisition cost—I can learn about how to catch a rabbit from someone else's trial and error, without having to go through it myself.

A possible objection to this theory is that organisms are competitors, so that sharing information is costly because of the advantages it gives to one's competitors. If I teach someone to fish, I may still know how to fish, but they may now overfish the local lake, leaving no fish for me. But this is just the standard problem of the evolution of any form of cooperation or altruism, and the solution in the case of language is the same. By sharing information with our kin, we help copies of our genes inside those kin, including genes that make language come naturally. As for non-kin, if we inform only those people who are likely to return the favour, both of us can gain the benefits of trade. It seems clear that we do use our faculties of social cognition to ration our conversation to those with whom we have established a non-exploitative relationship; hence the expression 'to be on speaking terms'.

Language, therefore, meshes neatly with the other features of the cognitive niche. The zoologically unusual features of *Homo sapiens* can be explained parsimoniously by the idea that humans have evolved an ability to encode information about the causal structure of the world and to share it among themselves. Our hypersociality comes about because information is a particularly good commodity of exchange that makes it worth people's while to hang out together. Our long childhood and extensive biparental investment are the ingredients of an apprenticeship: before we go out in the world, we spend a lot of time learning what the people around us have figured out. And because of the greater pay-off for investment in children, fathers, and not just mothers, have an incentive to invest in their children. This leads to changes in sexuality and to social arrangements (such as marriage and families) that connect men to their children and to the mothers of those children.

Humans depend on culture, and culture can be seen in part as a pool of local expertise. Many traditions are endemic to a people in an area because know-how and social conventions have spread via a local network of information sharing. Humans have evolved to have a long lifespan (one end of the evolutionarily ubiquitous trade-off between longevity and fecundity) because once you have had an expensive education you might as well make the most out of it by having a long period in which the expertise can be put to use. Finally, the reason that humans can inhabit such a wide range of habitats is that our minds are not adapted to a narrow, specialized domain of knowledge, such as how to catch a rabbit. Our knowledge is more abstract, such as how living things work and how objects collide with and stick to each other. That mindset for construing the world can be applied to many kinds of environment rather than confining us to a single ecosystem.

On this view, then, three key features of the distinctively human lifestyle—know-how, sociality, and language—co-evolved, each constituting a selection pressure for the others.

Alternatives to the Cognitive Niche Theory

Several alternative hypotheses acknowledge that language is an adaptation but disagree on what it is an adaptation for. One possibility, inspired by an influential theory of the evolution of communication by Dawkins and Krebs (Dawkins 1982), is that language evolved not to inform others but to manipulate and deceive them. The problem with this theory is that, unlike signals with the physiological power to manipulate another organism directly, such as loud noises or chemicals, the signals of language are impotent unless the recipient actively applies complicated computations to decode them. It is impossible to use language to manipulate someone who does not understand the language, so hominids in the presence of the first linguistic manipulators would have done best by refusing to allow their nascent language systems to evolve further, and language evolution would have been over before it began.

Another possibility is that language evolved to allow us to think rather than to communicate. According to one argument, it is impossible to think at human levels of complexity without a representational medium for propositions, and language is that medium (Bickerton 1990). According to another argument, we spend more time talking to ourselves than talking to other people, so if language has any function at all, it must be thought rather than communication (Chomsky 2002). These theories have two problems. One is that they assume the strongest possible form of the Whorfian hypothesis—that thought depends entirely on language—which is unlikely for a number of reasons (see Pinker 1994; 2002; Siegal et al. 2001; Weiskrantz 1988). The other is that if language evolved to represent information internally, much of the apparatus of grammar, which converts logical relationships into perceptible signals, would be superfluous. Language would not need rules for defining word orders, case markers, phonological strings, adjustment rules, and so on, because the brain could more efficiently code the information to itself silently, using networks of variables and pointers.

Considerations of language design rule out other putative selectional pressures. Language is unlikely to have evolved as a direct substitute for grooming (Dunbar 1998), or as a courtship device to advertise the fitness of our brains (Miller 2000), because such pressures would not have led to an ability to code complex abstract propositions into signals. A fixed set of greetings would suffice for the former; meaningless displays of virtuosity, as in scat singing, would suffice for the latter.

New Tests of the Theory That Language Is an Adaptation

Contrary to the common accusation that evolutionary hypotheses, especially ones about language, are post hoc 'just so' stories, the hypothesis that language is an evolutionary adaptation can be made rigorous and put to empirical test. I will conclude by reviewing two new areas of research on the evolution of language that have blossomed since my 1990 paper with Bloom and which are beginning to support its major predictions.

Language and Evolutionary Game Theory

Good theories of adaptation can be distinguished from bad ones (Williams 1966). The bad ones try to explain one bit of our psychology (say, humor or music) by appealing to some other, equally mysterious bit (laughing makes you feel better; people like to make music with other people). The good ones use some *independently established* finding of engineering or mathematics to show that some mechanism can efficiently attain some goal in some environment. These engineering benchmarks can serve as predictions for how Darwinian organisms ought to work: the more uncannily the engineering specifications match the facts of the organism, the more confidently one infers that the organism was selected to carry out that function.

Evolutionary game theory has allowed biologists to predict how organisms ought to interact with other organisms co-evolving their own strategies (Maynard Smith 1982). Language, like sex, aggression, and cooperation, is a game it takes two to play, and game theory can provide the external criteria for utility enjoyed by the rest of evolutionary biology. Modellers assume only that the transmission of information between partners provides them with an advantage (say, by exchanging information or coordinating their behaviour), and that the advantage translates into more offspring, with similar communicative skills. The question then is how a stable communication system might evolve from repeated pairwise interactions and, crucially, whether such systems have the major design features of human language.

The first such attempt was a set of simulations by Hurford (1989) showing that one of the defining properties of human language, the arbitrary, bidirectional sign, will drive out other schemes over evolutionary time (Hurford 1989). More recently, Nowak and his collaborators have now done the same for two of the other central design features of language (Nowak and Krakauer 1999; Nowak et al. 1999*a*; Nowak 2000).

Nowak and his colleagues pointed out that in all communication systems, errors in signalling or perception are inevitable, especially when signals are physically similar. Imagine organisms that use a different sound (say, a vowel) for every concept they wish to communicate. As they communicate more concepts, they will need additional sounds, which will be physically closer and hence harder to discriminate. At some point adding new signals just makes the whole repertoire more confusable and fails to increase its net communicative power. Nowak and colleagues showed that this limitation can be overcome by capping the number of signals and stringing them together into sequences, one sequence per concept. The sequences are what we call words, and as I mentioned earlier, the combination of meaningless vowels and consonants into meaningful words by rules of phonology is a universal property of language, half of the trait called 'duality of patterning'. Nowak and his colleagues have shown how its evolution is likely among communicators with a large number of messages to convey, a precondition that plausibly characterizes occupants of the cognitive niche.

Nowak and his colleagues have recently motivated another hallmark of language. Imagine a language in which each message was conveyed by a single word. For any word to survive in a community, it must be used frequently enough to be heard and remembered by all the learners. As new words are added to the vocabularies of speakers, old words must be used less often, and they are liable to fade, leaving the language no more expressive than before. Nowak et al. point out that this limitation can be overcome by communicators who use compositional syntax: rather than pairing each word with an entire event, they pair each word with a *component* of an event (a participant, an action, a relationship), and string the words together in an order that reflects their roles (e.g. *Dog bites man*). Such communicators need not memorize a word for every event, reducing the word-learning burden and allowing them to talk about events that lack words. Syntax and semantics, the other half of the duality of patterning, will evolve.

Nowak et al. note that syntax has a cost: the requirement to attend to the order of words. Its benefits exceed the costs only when the number of events worth communicating exceeds a threshold. This 'syntax threshold' is most likely to be crossed when the environment, as conceptualized by the communicators, has a combinatorial structure: for example, when any of a number of actors (dogs, cats, men, women, children) can engage in any of a number of actions (walking, running, sleeping, biting). In such a world, the number of words that have to be learned by a syntactic communicator equals the sum of the number of actors, actions, places, and so on, whereas the number that must be learned by a nonsyntactic communicator equals their *product*, a potentially unlearnable number. Nowak et al. thus proved the theoretical soundness of the conjecture of Pinker and Bloom (1990) that syntax is invaluable to an analytical mind in a combinatorial world.

Language and Molecular Evolution

Mathematical models and computer simulations can show that the advantages claimed for some features of language really can evolve by known mechanisms of natural selection. These models cannot, of course, show that language *in fact* evolved according to the proposed scenario. But recent advances in molecular and population genetics may provide ways of testing whether selection in fact occurred.

Evolution is a change in gene frequencies, and the first prediction of the theory that language is an evolutionary adaptation is that there should be genes that have as one of their distinctive effects the development of normal human language abilities. Such a gene would be identifiable as an allelic alternative to a gene that leads to an impairment in language. Since pleiotropy is ubiquitous, one need not expect that such a gene would affect *only* language; but its effects on language should not be consequences of some more general deficit such as a hearing disorder, dysarthria, or retardation.

Clinical psycholinguists have long known of the collection of syndromes called Specific Language Impairment (SLI), in which a child fails to develop language on schedule and struggles with it throughout life (Bishop et al. 1995; Leonard 1998; van der Lely et al. 1998). By definition SLI is not a consequence of autism, deafness, retardation, or other non-linguistic problems, though it may co-occur with them. In one form of the syndrome, sometimes called 'Grammatical SLI', the children are normal in intelligence, auditory perception, and the use of language in a social context, but their speech is filled with grammatical errors and they are selectively deficient in detecting ungrammaticality and in discriminating meaning based on a sentence's grammar (van der Lely et al. 1998; van der Lely and Stollwerck 1996). Though it was once thought that SLI comes from a deficit in processing rapidly changing sounds, that theory has been disproven (Bishop et al. 1999; Bishop et al. 2001; van der Lely et al. 1998).

SLI runs in families and is more concordant in monozygotic than in dizygotic twins, suggesting it has a heritable component (Bishop et al. 1995; Stromswold 2001; van der Lely and Stollwerck 1996). But the inheritance patterns are usually complex, and until recently little could be said about its genetic basis. In 1990 investigators described a large multi-generational family, the KEs, in which half the members suffered from a disorder of speech and language, distributed within the family in the manner of an autosomal dominant gene (Hurst et al. 1990). Extensive testing by psycholinguists showed a complex phenotype (Bishop 2002). The affected family members on average have lower intelligence test scores (perhaps because verbal coding helps performance in a variety of tasks), but their language impairment cannot be a simple consequence of low intelligence, because some of the affected members score in the normal range, and some score higher than their unaffected relatives (Bishop 2002; Lai et al. 2001). And though the affected members have problems in speech articulation (especially as children) and in fine movements of the mouth and tongue (such as sticking out their tongue or blowing on command), their language disorder cannot be reduced to a motor problem, because they also have trouble with identifying phonemes, understanding sentences, judging grammaticality, and other language skills (Bishop 2002).

In 2001, geneticists identified a gene on Chromosome 7, FOXP2, that is perfectly associated with the syndrome within the KE family and in an unrelated individual (Lai et al. 2001). They also argued on a number of grounds that the normal allele plays a causal role in the development of the brain circuitry underlying language and speech, rather than merely disrupting that circuitry when mutated.

A second crucial prediction of the language-as-adaptation theory is that there should be *many* genes for language. If human language can be installed by a single gene, there would be no need to invoke natural selection, because it is not staggeringly improbable that a single gene could have reached fixation by genetic drift or hitchhiking. But if a large set of co-evolved genes is necessary, probability considerations would militate against such explanations. The more genes are required for normal language, the lower the odds that our species could have accumulated them all by chance.

It seems increasingly likely that in fact many genes are required. In no known case of SLI is language wiped out completely, as would happen if language was controlled by a single gene which occasionally is found in mutated form. Moreover, SLI is an umbrella term for many distinct syndromes (Leonard 1998; Stromswold 2001; SLI Consortium 2002). Grammatical SLI, for example, is distinct from the syndrome affecting the KE family, which in turn is distinct from other cases of SLI known to clinicians (van der Lely and Christian 1998). In yet another syndrome, language delay, children are late in developing language but soon catch up, and can grow up without problems (Sowell 1997). Language delay is highly heritable (Stromswold 2001), and its statistical distribution in the population suggests that it is a distinct genetic syndrome rather than one end of a continuum of developmental timetables (Dale et al. 1998). There are yet other heritable disorders involving language (Stromswold 2001), such as stuttering and dyslexia (a problem in learning to read which may often be a consequence of more general problems with language). Both have been associated with specific sets of chromosomal regions (Stromswold 2001).

With recent advances in genomics, the polygenic nature of language is likely to become more firmly established. In 2002, an 'SLI Consortium' discovered two novel loci (distinct from FOXP2) that are highly associated with SLI but not associated with low non-linguistic intelligence (SLI Consortium 2002). Moreover, the two loci were associated with different aspects of language impairment, one with the ability to repeat non-words, the other with expressive language, further underscoring the genetic complexity of language.

The most important prediction of the adaptation theory is that language should show evidence of a history of selection. The general complaint that evolutionary hypotheses are untestable has been decisively refuted by the recent explosion of quantitative techniques that can detect a history of selection in patterns of statistical variation among genes (Kreitman 2000; Przeworski et al. 2000). The tests depend on the existence of neutral evolution: random substitutions of nucleotides in non-coding regions of the genome, or substitutions in coding regions that lead to synonymous codons. These changes have no effect on the organisms phenotype, and hence are invisible to natural selection. The genetic noise caused by neutral evolution can thus serve as a baseline or null hypothesis against which the effects of selection (which by definition reduces variability in the phenotype) can be measured.

For example, if a gene has undergone more nucleotide replacements that alter its protein product than replacements that do not, the gene must have been subject to selection based on the function of the protein, rather than having accumulated mutations at random, which should have left equal numbers of synonymous and amino-acid-replacing changes. Alternatively, one can compare the variability of a gene among the members of a given species with the variability of that gene across species; a gene that has been subjected to selection should vary more between species than within species. Still other techniques compare the variability of a given gene to estimates of the variability expected by chance, or check whether a marker for an allele is found in a region of the chromosome that shows reduced variation in the population because of a selective sweep. About a dozen such techniques have been devised so far. The calculations are complicated by the fact that recombination rate differences, migrations, population expansions, and population subdivisions can also cause deviations from the expectations of neutral evolution, and therefore can be confused with signs of selection. But techniques to deal with these problems have been developed as well.

It is now obvious how one can test the language-as-adaptation hypothesis (or indeed, any hypothesis about a psychological adaptation). If a gene associated with a trait has been identified, one can measure its variation in the population and apply the tests for selection. The day that I wrote this paragraph, the first of such tests has been reported in *Nature* (Enard et al. 2002). A team of geneticists examined the FOXP2 protein (the cause of the KE family's speech and language disorder) in the mouse, several primate species, and several human populations. They found that the protein is highly conserved among mammals: the chimpanzee, gorilla, and monkey versions of the protein are identical to each other and differ in only one amino acid from the mouse version and two from the human version. But two of the three differences between humans and mice occurred in the human lineage after its separation from the common ancestor with the chimpanzee. And though the variations in the gene sequence among all the non-human animals produce few if any functional differences, at least one of the changes in the human lineage significantly altered the function of the protein. Moreover, the changes that occurred in the human lineage have become fixed in the species: the team found essentially no variation among forty-four chromosomes originating in all the major continents, or in an additional 182 chromosomes of European descent. The statistical tests showed that these distributions are extremely unlikely to have occurred under a scenario of neutral evolution, and therefore that the FOXP2 gene has been a target of selection in human evolution. The authors further showed that the selection probably occurred during the last 200,000 years, the period in which anatomically modern humans evolved, and that the gene was selected for directly, rather than hitchhiking on an adjacent selected gene. Alternative explanations that rely on demographic factors were tested and at least tentatively rejected.

This stunning discovery does not *prove* that language is an adaptation, because it is possible that FOXP2 was selected only for its effects on orofacial movements, and that its effects on speech and language came along for the ride. But this is implausible given the obvious social and communicative advantages that language brings, and the fact that the deficient language in SLI is known to saddle the sufferers with educational and social problems (Beitchman et al. 1994; Snowling et al. 2001).

The studies I reviewed in this section are, I believe, just a beginning. I predict that evolutionary game theory will assess the selective rationale for an increasing number of universal properties of human language, and that new genes for language disorders and individual variation in language will be discovered and submitted to tests for a history of selection in the human lineage. In this way, the theory that language is an adaptation, motivated originally by the design features and natural history of language, will become increasingly rigorous and testable.

Further Reading

For general introductions to the structure and function of language, see Baker (2001); Bickerton (1990); Jackendoff (1994; 2002); Lightfoot and Anderson (2002); Miller (1991); Pinker (1994).

Good overviews of natural selection and adaptation include Dawkins (1986); Dawkins (1996); Maynard Smith (1986; 1989); Ridley (1986); Weiner (1994); Williams (1966). The debate over whether language is a product of natural selection may be found in the target article, commentaries, and reply in Pinker and Bloom (1990).

Specific Language Impairment is explained in Leonard (1998); van der Lely et al. (1998). An overview of the genetics of language can be found in Stromswold (2001). Evolutionary game theory is explained by its founder in Maynard Smith (1982). Methods for detecting natural selection in molecular genetic data are reviewed in Aquadro (1999); Kreitman (2000); Przeworski et al. (2000).

SECTION 16

MENOPAUSE

Introduction to Chapter 19

Menopause is almost exclusively limited to human females. We expect selection to favor anything that boosts reproductive success; why then would it favor a reproductive shutdown such as menopause? Is menopause an adaptation or a byproduct?

Menopause—the relatively abrupt and complete cessation of reproductive capacity when other bodily systems are still working well—is an evolutionary curiosity. I hope that, by this point in the course, it will strike you that way as well. From a Darwinian perspective, why bother to be alive if you cannot make any more babies? Bodily systems do wear out (this too requires explanation, but it is beyond the scope of this chapter and this course). But the menopause question is not so simple, because it involves the wearing out of only one physiological system, in one sex, of one species. This, in short, is the menopause question: Why do women's reproductive systems wear out before their other bodily systems; why do they wear out before men's reproductive systems; and why do other female mammals not show this same pattern, with early failure of reproduction?

Everybody over the age of 16 knows about menopause. And almost no one thinks it is odd, because it is "normal" for our species. I used to be a science fiction addict when I was young. Now I find that genre less intriguing because the authors seem to lack real creativity; they find it hard to imagine a truly alien world because, of course, they have human experiences and human minds. What would your life be like if you were a chimpanzee or a naked mole rat? I find this kind of radical perspective shift one of the most enjoyable aspects of human evolutionary biology. My point is that, if it were not a common feature of human experience, menopause would strike us as anything but "normal." Human males do not have it. The vast majority of other species do not have it. And it afflicts only the ovaries; not the lungs, liver, heart or brain. If we were Martian biologists, we would surely notice how odd menopause is.

Maybe an inspection of Figure 1 will help you put on your Martian glasses. Do you see that female fertility falls of a cliff while everything else is going along just fine? And remember, what is the function of all adaptations? Right: reproduction. I trust the magnitude of the puzzle is now coming into focus. How does a precipitous decline in fertility serve reproduction? Now you are ready to contemplate J. C. Peccei's question: Did selection design human females to stop reproducing? Could selection ever favor such a thing, or is it merely a byproduct? (Peccei uses the word "epiphenomenon" to refer to traits that are not themselves adaptations, but instead are incidental consequences of other processes. We called such traits "byproducts" in the previous chapter, and I will continue to use that word for continuity. You can treat "byproduct" and "epiphenomenon" as equivalent terms.) I will give one clear example of each kind of explanation for menopause—one adaptive explanation and one byproduct explanation—and then I will let you evaluate the range of answers offered by Peccei.

An adaptive explanation could be based on something you already know about humans: They are born very immature and take a long time to grow up. Let's invent a hypothetical hominin. Because of the combination of bipedality and a large brain, its offspring get a hind start in life, being born in a relatively fetal state. Because of this, and because it relies on complex extractive foraging, it takes a long time to master its ecology and become fully independent of its parent(s). Let's say this maturation process takes 10 years, and that offspring whose mothers die during their 10-year dependency period die soon after their mothers because they can not yet support themselves. Now assume some typical mortality curve for the species, such that the average female was likely to be dead by age 50. OK; when should she give birth to her last offspring? Age 40, right? No later. If our hypothetical hominin gave birth at age 45, everything she spent on that last offspring—in utero and in the first 5 years of its life—would be wasted, because such offspring would die at age 5 when their mothers died at age 50. This female would have been better off, evolutionarily speaking, if she had used those reproductive resources earlier in her life.

My claim is not that all moms die at 50; only that there is some statistical distribution of death in any population and that, based on that distribution, we can identify an *average* age at which females die. There is also a distribution of dependency periods—some offspring might need 11 years and some might be OK with only 9—but again, there is some *average* amount of parental care and education that is needed for an offspring to succeed. Given these two things, a female ought to stop having babies an average period of dependence before the average age at death. This is an adaptive theory of menopause. It says that menopause helps moms to better schedule their reproductive effort over their lifetimes. Clearly, it predicts female menopause in any species with an extended obligatory period of dependence on the mother. If you think humans have been subject to strong selection for paternal care, then you might ask why men do not exhibit menopause.

My job here is not to try to evaluate whether this explanation is correct. That is the subject of the chapter. I only need to be sure that you understand the difference between an adaptive explanation and a byproduct explanation.

OK, now let's try to construct a byproduct explanation of menopause. This explanation is going to begin by assuming that the average lifespan has increased significantly in the recent past. (Testing whether the assumptions of a model are true is an important part of testing the model; Peccei does that.) This explanation also assumes that eggs are costly (e.g., compared to sperm) and that selection would optimize the number of eggs a female would have. If a female only lived 40 years, selection would not endow her with enough eggs to last 100 years, because most of them would be wasted and their component energy and materials could have been spent on something else. Deleting excess eggs is just like deleting eyes where there is no light. On this byproduct view, females have menopause because their egg number evolved in a world where they lived shorter lives. Selection has not yet caught up with the fact that they could now use more eggs.

These two explanations—the adaptive one and the byproduct one—have some things in common. For example, each depends on its own particular assumptions about female mortality patterns. And they both might predict that females run out of eggs as they enter menopause. But the adaptive explanation suggests that a mutant female who had more eggs and continued to ovulate and conceive would have lower fitness. In contrast, the byproduct explanation would predict that such a female should have elevated fitness. Make sure you understand why they make different predictions.

Let's backtrack and reexamine the role of egg number. Why might each theory predict that menopausal females are running out of eggs? In the adaptive theory, egg number has been adjusted to make sure that mothers do not produce offspring that are unlikely to survive. In the byproduct theory, egg number is adjusted to a time when females did not live as long as they do now and has not yet caught up with current female lifespans. In either theory, egg number is part of the plumbing—part of the mechanism, part of the "how" explanation. It is not part of the evolutionary "why" explanation.

Chapter 19 Glossary

antagonistic pleiotrophy: A nice concept. Pleiotrophy refers to the fact that genes can have multiple effects on the phenotype. For example, a gene could make both your arms and your legs longer. Antagonistic pleiotrophy refers to the case where some of a gene's effects on fitness are positive (good) while some are negative (bad). Why would such a gene be favored? Think about it: A gene will be favored as long as the sum of its fitness effects is positive—if the good effects add up to more than the bad effects.

atresia/follicular atresia: Atresia has a general meaning in biology, but with respect to egg cells, it refers to a process of degeneration that prevents immature egg cells from reaching the stage where they are released (ovulated).

catarrhine legacy: Catarrhines are old world monkeys and apes (see Chapter 5). Catarrhine legacy refers to traits that are primitive (see Chapter 4) for this group.

epiphenomenon: Byproduct.

fecundability: The ability to become pregnant and carry an offspring.

fetal loss: Spontaneous abortion; probably a result of natural selection in the womb.

heritability: A ratio that measures how much of the variation in a trait is due to the fact that individuals have different genes affecting the trait. Age at menopause is moderately (40% to 60%) heritable. This means that roughly half of the differences between women in their age of menopause are caused by the fact they have different genes affecting this trait. If a trait has this much heritability, selection can shape it. In other words, if selection favored a later menopause, it would increase the frequency of the genes that cause a later menopause and decrease the frequency of genes that cause an earlier menopause. See Chapter 1 for more on heritability.

oocyte: Immature egg cell.

proximate explanations: "How" explanations, as opposed to evolutionary or "why" explanations.

secular trend: Any relatively steady change over time. For example, there has been a downward secular trend in age at sexual maturation for women over the last century. There has been no corresponding secular trend in age at menopause.

semelgametogenesis: Producing all your gametes (sex cells—eggs and sperm) at one time. Female mammals exhibit semelgametogenesis, producing all their eggs before they are born; male mammals do not and continue to produce gametes—though at decreasing rates—throughout life.

senescence: The decline in survival probability with age. An organism that did not senesce would not live forever, but its chances of dying would not increase as it got older. This term could also be used to refer to the decline in function of a single organ or system with age. In these terms, menopause represents a senescence of the female reproductive system that comes before senescence in any of her other bodily systems.

sibling competition: Consuming the parental resources (food, time, attention) that a sibling could benefit from. It has to be resolved for each population whether (and how) such competition affects the eventual reproductive success of sons and daughters. If resources are limited, it could be the case that mothers who have three offspring end with more grandchildren than mothers who have four offspring, because dividing parental resources into three slices gives each child enough to survive and reproduce, but dividing them into four slices does not.

Chapter 19
Menopause: Adaptation or Epiphenomenon? (2001)

Jocelyn Scott Peccei

Menopause is a nonfacultative and irreversible cessation of fertility that occurs in all female conspecifics well before the senescence of other somatic systems and the end of the average adult life span (Fig. 1).[1–3] So defined, menopause occurs only in humans and one species of toothed whales.[1–4] According to evolutionary theories of senescence, there should be no selection for postreproductive individuals.[5] Thus, evolutionary biologists and anthropologists have long been interested in why human females have menopause. Many have suggested that menopause is a hominine adaptation, the result of selection for a postreproductive life span that permitted increased maternal investment in existing offspring.[3,6–9] Others are persuaded that premature reproductive senescence is an epiphenomenon, either the result of a physiological trade-off favoring efficient reproduction early in the fertile part of life or simply the by-product of increases in life span or life expectancies.[10–17] Menopause poses two separate questions: why it originated and what is maintaining it?

Evolutionary biologists consider all complex design features of organisms to be ultimately the result of natural selection. As such, menopause can always be considered an adaptation. At the same time, it is also recognized that an adaptation is always morphologically,

Key Words: menopause, life-history evolution, female reproductive strategies, grandmother hypotheses, follicular atresia

---

Jocelyn Scott Peccei is a Research Associate at the Department of Anthropology, University of California Los Angeles, Los Angeles, CA 90095-1553, USA. E-mail: jpeccei@ucla.edu

physiologically, and developmentally constrained by an organism's phylogenetic heritage.[18] The question of origin is whether menopause is primarily an adaptation, in the sense that selection directly favored a postreproductive life span in human females, or whether it is an epiphenomenon of selection for efficient early reproduction or physiological constraints preventing prolongation of fertility in the presence of increases in human longevity. The distinction between adaptations, fitness trade-offs, and true phylogenetic constraints is the level of explanation. Appeals to the role of constraints without explanation of why these constraints themselves are not subject to evolutionary change constitute proximate explanations. Although it is useful for heuristic purposes to think in terms of three distinct alternatives—adaptation, trade-off, or constraint—the explanations overlap and interact. For instance, a trade-off is part adaptation and part constraint. In addition, the question of menopause cannot be isolated from the question of human longevity. In all three cases, the bottom line is that selection favors early reproduction relative to life span. In this sense, reproductive senescence is always premature. In this paper I critically review the evidence for the adaptation, physiological trade-off and by-product of increased longevity explanations for the origin of menopause.

The Adaptation Explanation

In the strictly adaptationist view of menopause, maternal investment is the key factor. Human females have menopause because their hominid ancestors who ceased reproducing before the end of their lives gained a fitness advantage over their still-fertile sisters in that they they could direct their remaining reproductive effort more profitably toward enhancing the reproductive success of existing progeny.[3,5–9,52–54] The fitness trade-off between greater investment in offspring already born versus producing more offspring, amounting to a quality versus quantity trade-off, very likely culminated during a time of rapid encephalization in the hominine line, which brought with it increases in infant altriciality and the prolongation of juvenile dependence.[8,9,52–54] With prolonged helplessness and nutritional dependence of offspring, each successive offspring imposed a greater cost on the mother,[6] in terms of the depletion of her physical reserves and the resources available for her to invest in existing offspring. With her own survival in question and the future of her existing offspring at stake, producing late babies with low survival probability was likely to lead to reproductive failure. In this scenario, menopause results from selection for reproductive cessation and is about stopping early.

There are two not necessarily mutually exclusive, adaptation hypotheses. The grandmother hypothesis is about inclusive fitness; the benefit comes from increasing the fertility of adult daughters and nieces, and the survival of their offspring. The principal proponents of this hypothesis are Hawkes, Blurton Jones, and O'Connell,[7,22,55] but many other researchers have examined it.[1,3,56–60] The mother hypothesis is about increasing the survival and fertility of one's own offspring.[5,6,8,9,61,62] The grandmother hypothesis of Hawkes and colleagues[7,22] and has recently evolved from an explanation for menopause into an explanation for the exceptionally long postreproductive life span of human females.[22,55] In the old grandmother hypothesis, menopause is an adaptation facilitating grandmothering. In the new grandmother hypothesis, grandmothering is the adaptation facilitating increases in longevity; menopause is a by-product. Although the grandmother hypotheses have received more attention than the mother hypothesis, I have argued that both versions of the former are more problematic than the mother hypothesis.[62]

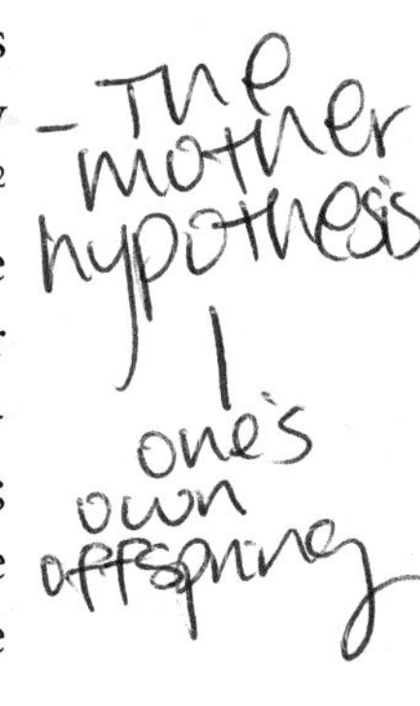

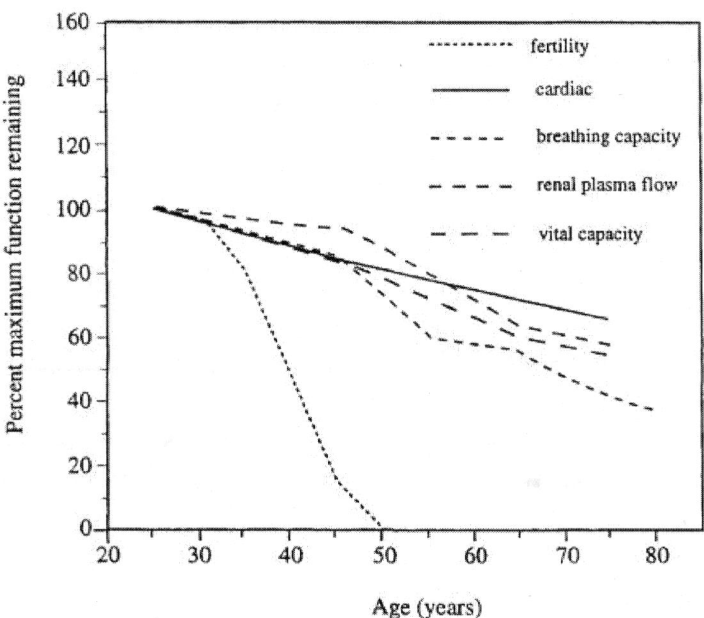

Figure 1. Comparative senescence of physiological functions in human females (redrawn from Hill and Hurtado[3]).

If menopause originated as an adaptation for postreproductive maternal investment, whether mothering or grandmothering, conditions had to exist that favored this adaptation. Box 2 lists the important predictions for which the evidence supports menopause as an adaptation, followed by the adaptation predictions that are not supported.

Reasons for Increased Maternal Investment

If menopause is an adaptation, we ought to find reasons in the course of human evolution for intensification in the quantity-quality trade-off between prolonged fertility and increased maternal investment. Two reasons can be advanced for substantial increases in maternal investment in the environment of evolutionary adaptedness: new ecological pressures due to changes in climate and diet and secondary altriciality of hominid infants due to cranial expansion and pelvic constraints.

Ecological pressures

Cooling and drying trends during the Plio-Pleistocene resulted in patchiness and seasonality in vegetation, necessitating dietary changes for survival.[21,63–65] For the hominine line, this dietary shift is believed to have led to expansion of home ranges, exploitation of a variety of habitats, and increasing foraging flexibility, including greater reliance on meat.[20,64–70] These changes required increased investment in offspring.

Secondary altriciality

In addition, there were periods of encephalization in the hominine line.[71–73] Whereas initially the limitation on increasing adult brain size was imposed by maternal metabolic output during gestation, there came a point when changes in pelvic dimensions facilitating more efficient bipedal locomotion put a stop to further rapid prenatal brain growth.[71] The resulting compromise was that the further rapid brain growth needed to attain greater adult brain size had to continue postpartum.[52,71,72] With much organizational development in addition to growth still to take place postnatally, *Homo* infants were born in a state of secondary altriciality, requiring intensified investment in infants and prolonged care of juveniles. Exactly when these life-history changes occurred is still debated. Many researchers believe major anatomical and behavioral changes began with *H. erectus* around 1.6 mya[72,75–78] (but see Ruff, Trinkhaus, and Holliday[79]). Recent studies agree that maximum life span has exceeded 50 years since early *H. erectus*,[74,80] which could indicate that menopause is 1.8 mya. However, early *H. erectus* (*H. ergaster*) is not generally associated with delayed maturity.[74,81,82] (but see Clegg and Aiello[77]). The first appearance of delayed maturity is estimated at 1.5 mya.[82] It seems reasonable that changes in rates of development kept pace with, but followed, increases in both adult brain size and secondary altriciality during human evolution.[76] It also would be logical to assume that the transformation from australopithecine to human-like life histories was completed by the time anatomically modern *H. sapiens* appeared on the scene. Thus, menopause could have arisen any time between 1.6 and 0.15 mya.

Menopause Unique to Human Females

If a protracted period of postreproductive maternal investment is the response to a unique set of socioecological, anatomical, and physiological pressures, and is also of critical importance to the way we evolved from our hominoid ancestors, we would expect menopause to be unique to humans or at least rare in other species.

Nonhuman primates

Some decline in age-specific fertility in later life is not uncommon among nonhuman primates.[83] Indeed, all iteroparous organisms can be expected to exhibit declining fertility as a function of general senescence.[84] However, in contrast to human females, nonhuman primates and even longer-lived species such as elephants, whales, and tortoises retain their capacity to reproduce until very old age. East African female elephants with a maximum life span of about 60 years still retain 50% of their reproductive capacity at age 55 years, an age which only 5% of the population ever reaches.[85–87] Female tortoises remain fertile far longer than 60 years,[53] and baleen whales are still reproductive in their nineties.[88] The exception to this general animal pattern are short-finned pilot whales (Globicephala macrorynchus). In this species, females experience menopause between the ages of 30 and 40 years and have a mean survival of ≥ 14 years after menopause.[4]

Box 1. Background on Menopause

We know that menopause has been around for at least 3,000 years from a Biblical reference to Sarah in the book of Genesis (18:11),[19] which says, "it ceased to be with Sarah after the manner of women," from which we can infer not only that Sarah herself had stopped menstruating, but that the authors were quite familiar with the phenomenon. Although many researchers have speculated that menopause is a very old trait,[20–22] we do not know whether menopause has been around since the hominoid-hominid split, *Homo erectus*, anatomically modern *H. sapiens*, or simply since maximum life spans exceeded 50 years. The life span predicted from body and brain size in early *Homo* suggests that a female postreproductive life span predates *H. sapiens*.[23]

Although there is a strong central tendency in the age of menopause in developed countries, with medians clustering around 50 years, there is considerable variation in the age of menopause both within and between populations.[16] In a sample of American women, the age of menopause ranged from 40 to 59 years.[24] Any age within this range is considered normal. Across populations, medians range from 43 years in Central Africa to 51.4 years among Caucasian Americans.[16] With heritability estimates of 40% to 60% heritability in the age of menopause,[25–27] there is plenty of genetic variation to increase or decrease the mean age of menopause if such changes brought increased fitness. Yet research suggests that there has been no secular trend of any kind in the age of menopause over the last 150 years.[28–31] More importantly, Greek and Roman writings suggest that there probably has been little or no secular movement for the last 2,500 years. Aristotle (fourth century B.C.) and Pliny (first century A.D.) give 50 years as the maximum age of menopause.[32] Texts from the Middle Ages give 50 years as the average age, with a range of 35 to 60 years.[33,34]

Physiologically, menopause is the cessation of menses due to the depletion of oocytes.[35] Human females produce all the oocytes they will ever have by the fifth month of gestation. Semelgametogenesis, the character of producing all of one's gametes at one time, is a trait common to female birds and mammals.[11] In humans the maximum of approximately 7 million oocytes is reduced to 2 million by birth, 400,000 at puberty, and 1,000 at menopause.[36] Oocytes, which are surrounded by follicles in the ovaries, are lost mostly through a programmed process of cell death induced by hormone withdrawal, known as atresia.[37] Atresia is the sole cause of follicular death before puberty and remains the predominant cause thereafter, because the number of follicles lost to ovulation is relatively small.[38] About 400 oocytes are ovulated over the menstruating lifespan.[11]

Oocytes remain inactive in their follicles in an arrested phase of meiosis from the fifth month of gestation until they either succumb to atresia or become part of an ovulatory cohort.[39] Normally, only one oocyte in a cohort is singled out to complete meiosis; the rest provide hormonal support for the development of the primary follicle or oocyte, after which they too become atretic.[39] As the follicle pool shrinks, it becomes more and more difficult to recruit a large enough cohort of follicles to produce ovulation.[39] In addition, as human females age, the "chosen" oocytes become increasingly susceptible to malfunction during completion of the meiotic process, producing chromosomally abnormal ova.[39]

Physiological sources of variation in the age of menopause include the original number of oocytes and the rates of atresia.[35] At present, histological investigation of ovaries removed from females of all ages, including embryos, suggests that human females experience at least three different rates of atresia, from birth to puberty, from puberty to about age 40, and from age 40 to menopause.[37,40] The change in rate of atresia of greatest interest is the acceleration that occurs around age 40, because it is believed to be functionally related to menopause.[36,41] Without this apparent acceleration, which is thought to begin when some threshold number of oocytes remain (for example, 25,000), women would have enough oocytes to last 70 years.[42] It is unclear why the rate of atresia increases. However, it is likely that individual variation in the age at which the acceleration occurs is a major determinant of variation in the age of menopause.[38] Not surprisingly, given the high heritability in the age at which menopause occurs, women with a family history of clinically premature (< 40 years) ovarian failure have earlier menopause.[43–45]

Several studies have examined the contribution of various environmental and life-history factors to variation in the age of menopause.[24,29,46–51] As with menarche, nutritional status has been a prime environmental suspect. However, the large-scale multivariate studies that have attempted to control for confounding variables such as socioeconomic status, ethnicity, marital status and parity have failed to show a nutritional effect.[16] Other suspected risk factors are body weight, weight loss, alcohol consumption, and stress. The only well-established environmental risk factor is long-term cigarette smoking, which lowers the median age of menopause by approximately 1.5 years.[29]

Box 2. Adaptation Predictions

Predictions Supported

1. Reasons for reproductive senescence in the environment of evolutionary adaptedness: altriciality of hominid infants and ecological pressures.
2. Protracted postreproductive life span unique to human females.
3. Fitness costs to prolonged fertility: reduced offspring survival.

Predictions Not Supported

4. Fitness costs to prolonged fertility: premature maternal death and sibling competition.
5. Fitness benefits of reproductive cessation.
6. Trade-off between fertility and longevity.
7. Nutritional contribution of females greater than males.
8. No negative health consequences of menopause.

In both field and captive studies, researchers have reported menopause like physiological phenomena in monkeys and apes.[2,83,89–92] However, on close scrutiny of these reports, it is clear that the reproductive changes observed in nonhuman primates represent something different from human menopause, at least from a comparative life-history perspective.[1,2] The reproductive changes reported are idiosyncratic and generally far from species-wide, while age at reproductive cessation is extremely variable and postreproductive life spans are relatively short.[1,2] In field studies, the majority of the oldest individuals in all species investigated show no signs of ovarian failure.[1] In studies of captive primate species in breeding institutions, where extrinsic sources of mortality are minimal, on average about 67% of old females continued to reproduce all their lives, and in all species postreproductive life spans were still relatively short compared to those of humans.[83]

Perhaps the best way to illustrate how different the human female fertility pattern is from that of other primates is to compare the maximum age of reproduction and mean life expectancy at maturity of women and our closest relatives, *Pan troglodytes*. Hill and

Hurtado's[87] comparative life-history diagram for Ache women, former foragers from Eastern Paraguay, and common chimpanzees shows that the maximum reproductive life span ends at age 42 years for Ache women and age 34 for chimpanzee females (Fig. 2). But whereas the average Ache woman who reaches maturity lives to age 60, the average reproductive-age chimpanzee female does not live past 27 years. In other words, half of all chimpanzee mothers never outlive their reproductive capacity; half of all reproductive-age Ache women live at least 18 years after reproductive cessation.

There is evidence that life spans exceeding reproductive capacity are part of our catarrhine legacy,[23] and it is clear that, given the right environment, female nonhuman primates will outlive their reproductive capacity. This means that in many species there is plenty of variation and raw material for selection to work on if a postreproductive life span were to become advantageous. It also implies that variation in the length of reproductive life span is an ancestral condition, indicating that selection for a postreproductive life span in hominid females would have been possible. Interestingly, in Caro and coworkers'[83] study, chimpanzees had the highest percentage of females terminating reproduction before death, with 60%.

Human males

Although human males usually exhibit a decline in fertility, in most cases this is a function of advanced overall senescence, ill health, or socio-cultural and economic factors.[1,93] This is not premature reproductive senescence. Most human males are physiologically capable of siring offspring until very old age, and it is in their interest to do so. For males and females, the estimated hazard rates of reproductive cessation due to biological causes are very different. For males the hazard rate of reproductive cessation due impotence rises very gradually after age 50 years, reaching only 0.3 at age 80. For females the hazard rate of reproductive cessation due to menopause rises sharply from less than 0.1 to almost 1.0 between the ages of 40 and 50.[16]

Fitness Costs of Prolonged Fertility

If menopause is an adaptation, we should find fitness costs of prolonged fertility in the form of reduced offspring survival and fertility. Here I will address three issues: reduced infant survival with late pregnancies in modern industrialized societies; the fitness cost of premature maternal death in one foraging population; and the fertility cost to offspring from sibling competition. Evidence supports only the first, although clearly more data from traditional societies are needed.

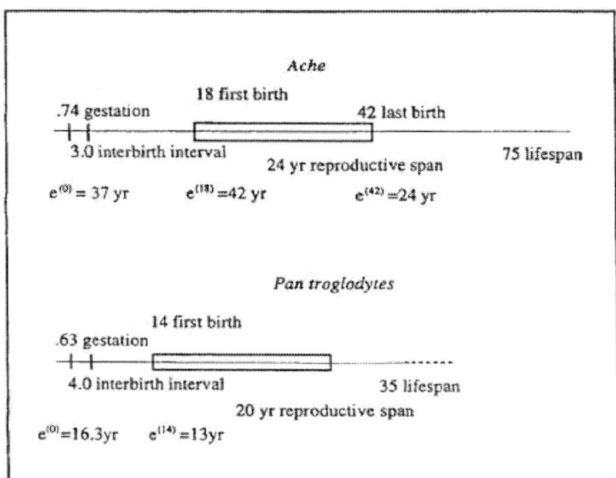

Figure 2. Comparative reproductive life histories of Ache women and female chimpanzees (redrawn from Hill and Hurtado[87]).

Elevated risk to baby associated with late pregnancies

If older mothers themselves are not at high risk of dying in childbirth, late pregnancy is still generally considered to carry high risk for fetuses and neonates, at least in Western societies for which we have data.[94-99] The risks include increased probability of fetal loss, stillbirth, and birth defects. Controlling for frequency of intercourse, older women experience increasing difficulty in becoming and staying pregnant.[16] Fetal wastage is the major contributor to fertility decline up to age 45 years.[16] The overall rate of fetal loss for women over 40 is 0.5. Maternal age is also predictive of an increasing incidence of most birth defects.[96] Indeed, 85% of the abortuses of women over age 40 have some detectable chromosomal abnormality, with Down syndrome representing the most dramatic example of this trend.[16] By age 43, the risk of carrying a baby with Down syndrome baby is one in ten.[100]

Fitness cost of premature maternal death

It used to be that the birth of each child jeopardized a mother's previous children because of her risk of dying in childbirth, a risk that increased with age.[16] In affluent Western societies of today, even though that risk is still seven times higher for women over the age of 40 than it is for 20-year-olds, the risk of dying in childbirth at any age is small.[16] Data from one traditional society—the Ache when they still lived exclusively from hunting and gathering—suggest that for hunter-gatherer women the risk of dying in childbirth is also small (about 1 in 150.)[87] Moreover, older women may not be at considerably greater risk.[87] If there was an increase in age-specific risk, it would have been minimal, since the annual mortality rate for 20-year-old and 50-year-old women was not much different (1% and 2%, respectively).[87] Thus, even though among the Ache a mother's death led to the certain death of her children under the age of one year and a five-fold increase in age-specific mortality for her children over that age, reduced offspring survival due to premature maternal death was not a major source of infant mortality. According to Hill and Hurtado,[87] "the assumption that older women should cease reproduction because they may die soon and their children will not survive maternal loss is notably incorrect" (p. 433).

Fertility costs to offspring from sibling competition

Regarding fitness costs to high and, by inference, prolonged maternal fertility in the form of reduced offspring fertility, data from the Ache suggest that fertility costs from sibling competition may be gender-dependent and variable. For example, during the forest period, there was a negative association between Ache daughters' fertility and number of siblings—that is, between daughters' fertility and mothers'.[87] The association between daughters' fertility and number of brothers was strongly negative. In contrast, there was a positive and much greater correlation between sons' fertility and number of siblings.

Fitness Benefits Associated with Reproductive Cessation

As a corollary to the fitness costs of prolonged reproduction, we expect to find fitness benefits associated with cessation of reproduction before death if menopause is an adaptation. To discover these benefits, researchers have traditionally relied on studies of the work performed by postreproductive women in extant foraging and horticultural populations. Evidence of these benefits is mixed.

In some traditional societies, including the Hadza,[7] the !Kung,[101] the Ye'kwana[57,102] (horticulturalists in Venezuela), and the residents of the Micronesian atoll, Ifaluk,[56] evidence supports the proposition that by providing material goods and services postreproductive women enable their daughters to raise more offspring, thereby contributing to their own inclusive fitness. Among the Hadza, the time women allocate to food acquisition continues to increase with age beyond menopause.[7,22] Older women spend significantly more time foraging than do females in any other age category. Variation in children's weight is correlated with grandmothers' foraging time. Although the hypothesis has not been formally tested, the implication is that relatively higher weight in grandchildren translates into a fitness advantage for the children and an inclusive fitness advantage for their hardworking grandmothers. However, hardworking grandmothers, like Hadza women aged 45 to 60, who bring in approximately 1,000 more calories on a daily basis than the average person consumes, appear to be exceptional.[60] Ache and Hiwi women never produce surplus calories.[60] In addition, even Hadza grandmothers provide less than 6% of the average daily protein intake.[60] Still, food sharing does not constitute the sole contribution of postmenopausal women to daughters' reproductive success in traditional societies. Grandmothers are frequent providers of child care and shelter and help with food processing and firewood collecting. Older females also acquire authority and are eligible for special status.[103] This newly acquired authority involves the ability to influence important decisions affecting younger kin, as well as the right to extract labor from younger family members. Accordingly, the work of older women tends to be administrative, involving the delegation and assignment of subsistence tasks to younger women. Nonetheless, Hill and Hurtado's[3,87] mathematical analysis, which was designed to test the hypothesis that reproductive cessation offers fitness-enhancing opportunities, suggests that the fertility of Ache sons and daughters and the survival of grandchildren were not significantly increased by the presence of postmenopausal mothers or grandmothers. I appreciate the difficulties of detecting such effects. To begin with, both the costs and the benefits are probably difficult to establish in extant populations because menopause already exists. In addition, if women differ in access to resources, those with abundant resources may continue bearing healthy fertile daughters late in life, so that the phenotypic relationship we observe between mother's and daughters' fertility is positive, even if in less optimal conditions late fertility is associated with reduced fitness. [104]

Trade-Off Between Decreased Fertility and Increased Longevity

Here again, the evidence is mixed. According to life-history theory, increased longevity should come at the cost of reduced fertility.[105] Although there are many reasons why studies working with variation among individuals might fail to show such a trade-off,[18,104] when considered in historical perspective there does appear to be a trade-off between fertility and human longevity.[106] A recent study of an historical dataset containing life-history records gathered from the British aristocracy between the eighth and nineteenth centuries, reveals that for women who reached 60 years, longevity was negatively correlated with number of progeny and positively correlated with age at first childbirth.[106] In addition, for women, maternal and paternal heritability of longevity were about 40% and 20%, respectively. According to Westendorp and Kirkwood,[106] these findings are "compatible with the hypothesis that human life history has a heritable component that involves a trade-off between fertility and longevity" (p. 746).

In extant foraging societies, the extreme degree and duration of offspring dependence probably presents a fitness challenge for women even today. Yet a trade-off between maternal fertility and subsequent survival has not been identified. Data from the Ache do not suggest a trade-off, even controlling for access to resources.[87] This trade-off may be undetectable in the Ache because the relevant data come from a period of population growth and abundance when life-history trade-offs may have been relaxed, or because help from close kin with few or no dependents permitted relatives to enjoy high fertility without negative consequences.[87]

Female Investment in Offspring Greater than Male Investment

If the postreproductive life span of human females is an adaptation permitting increased maternal investment, we might expect female investment in the nutrition of their progeny to be more important than male investment, at least after menopause. This does not appear to be the case. In hunter-gatherer societies for which there are quantitative data, Kaplan and colleagues[60] show that juveniles and reproductive-age women do not meet their own energy requirements. Comparison of maternal effort among baboons and Ache foragers supports the notion that, despite the heavier burden of multiple dependents, human females work less hard during their reproductive years, whereas baboon mothers work harder.[107] However, it appears to be men, not post-reproductive women, who provide the necessary nutritional supplement.[60] Even the famous hardworking Hadza grandmothers of Tanzania provide far fewer calories and protein through foraging than do Hadza male hunters of all ages. With new evidence of meat consumption during the Plio-Pleistocene[65,70] and new evidence of males' nutritional contribution in extant foraging societies, it is difficult to dismiss the importance of male investment in human reproduction. In general, women, young or old, do not appear to contribute more than males do to the nutrition of weaned offspring. Moreover, it is uncommon for post-reproductive women to produce a nutritional surplus.[60] Male hunter-gatherers, in contrast, appear to subsidize the energetics of reproduction throughout their adult lives.[60] Thus, the evidence does not support menopause as an adaptation favoring post-reproductive maternal investment, at least as far as nutrition is concerned.

Negative Health Consequences of Menopause

Kenneth Hill[108] has suggested that "the female reproductive period is broadly protective of health" (p. 113) whereas, in affluent Western countries in particular, reproductive senescence is associated with increases in cardiovascular disorders, osteoporosis, and cognitive impairment. [46,107–117] The notion of menopause as an unhealthy state may not seem consistent with menopause as an adaptation. However, all adaptations have costs and benefits, and the evidence regarding negative health consequences of menopause is mixed. As Leidy[11] emphasizes, chronic conditions commonly associated with estrogen withdrawal need to be considered cross-culturally and historically. Menopause may not be the most important risk factor for heart disease or osteoporotic fractures.[114] Indeed, considering the incidence of osteoporosis in historical and cross-cultural perspectives indicates that diet and exercise levels are important variables determining the rate at which bone is lost.[118]

Discussion

On balance, the evidence for selection for a postreproductive life span to increase maternal investment in existing offspring is inconclusive. I find little support for the notion that women, postreproductive or otherwise, are the major providers of the nutritional resources subsidizing human reproduction. However, the nutritional contribution of males versus females is probably the wrong comparison. First, food sharing is not the only contribution open to postreproductive females. Second, in sexually reproducing species males and females have an equal need for surviving offspring. What differs within and between species is how males and females allocate resources to somatic effort and reproductive effort, and how reproductive effort is divided between mating effort and parental effort.[119] When males contribute more than women do to the nutrition of their offspring, it is because women must allocate their energetic resources to other reproduction-related requirements. The diversity of human mating systems reflects the fact that male and female reproductive strategies differ within our species as a result of varying socioenvironmental conditions. Yet in all societies, historically and cross-culturally, women undergo menopause if they live long enough. If premature reproductive senescence is the result of certain conditions in the environment of evolutionary adaptedness, the universality of menopause implies that those conditions must still be present today. Menopause, or the postreproductive life span, must be the response to some unvarying constellation of pressures; my vote is for prolonged offspring dependence and overlapping child care.

Rapid encephalization required a change in female reproductive strategy. The challenge to females resulting from encephalization included the risk of the birth process itself,[120] the high metabolic costs of gestation and lactation,[16,52,121] offspring altriciality, and increased and prolonged dependence of juveniles.[6,64,122] It was not feasible to solve the problem of prolonged offspring dependence by increasing interbirth intervals. The period of dependence was too long: A mother faced a high probability of not surviving long enough to have a second child if she waited for the first to become fully independent before giving birth again. In the face of limited adult life expectancies,[123,124,125] the fitness-enhancing strategy was to shorten interbirth intervals and adapt to overlapping child care.

Besides optimizing birth spacing, overlapping child care also had some potential advantages. First, a mother with multiple dependents can reduce her total lifetime reproductive cost because certain tasks, such as protection against predators and conspecifics, provision of shelter, and food preparation, can benefit more than one dependent without the expenditure of much extra time and energy. Second, older siblings can help with provisioning and child care and, in the process, learn parenting skills. Still, even with male provisioning and some economies of scale associated with overlapping child care, early Homo females probably suffered chronic and increasing energy deficits during their reproductive years due to overlapping child care.[126–133]

In a previous analysis of the adaptation hypotheses, I emphasize how difficult it is to show that premature reproductive senescence is the result of selection for increased maternal investment.[62] However, if menopause is an adaptation, I believe that mothering, not grandmothering, is more likely to be the reason. Although studies on grandmother investment are numerous, this approach is probably flawed, mainly because these women already have undergone menopause. They are not choosing between having another baby and helping daughters; their only option is helping. To me the mother hypothesis is more compelling, given Hamilton's[134] rule, low life expectancies in the environment of evolutionary adaptedness,[80,123,124] the likelihood of male philopatry,[133,135,136] as well as the expediency of overlapping child care and the logical inference that when fertility ceases a woman is still likely to have a last-born to care for.

The Epiphenomenon Explanations

I come to the two explanations that cast menopause as an epiphenomenon: the physiological trade-off favoring efficient early reproduction and the by-product of increased longevity hypotheses. There is less to say about these, for until recently most evolutionary biologists and anthropologists have dismissed them as proximate explanations that fail to justify the post-reproductive life span in human females. The underlying assumption of both these explanations is that evolution is constrained by phylogenetic history, developmental limitations, and genetic correlations.[18] In both cases, response to selection is limited by the "technology" of an organism, which forces design trade-offs and negatively correlated, or antagonistic, responses. For example, a gardener might wish to breed peapods containing more and larger peas, only to discover that she cannot have both, either because oversized pods are too heavy to ripen on the vine (design trade-off) or because the size and number of peas are controlled by negatively correlated genes (antagonistic pleiotropy). Negative genetic correlations can result in intertemporal physiological trade-offs as well. Such is thought to be the case with reproductive senescence in human females: Pleiotropic genes are favored because they have positive effects at younger ages, even though they have negative effects later in life.[10–12,137] According to evolutionary theories of senescence, such time-delayed antagonistic pleiotropy can exist because selection against fitness-reducing traits weakens with age.[5]

The Physiological Trade Off

Given semelgametogenesis, the reason for a physiological trade-off favoring efficient early reproduction is that human female reproductive physiology should be designed to maximize reproductive output early in life before the dwindling supply of oocytes jeopardizes hormonal support for ovulation[12,38,137] and to terminate fertility before the negative consequences of "old eggs" predominate.[10] Selection might favor a longer reproductive life span in human females, but selection for efficient early fertility, which results in decreased fertility and eventual sterility in later life, provides greater lifetime reproductive success. Selection for efficient early fertility is not about starting reproduction early. In fact, the hypothesis is silent regarding when reproduction begins; what is at issue is the intensity of reproduction early in the fertile life span. In this scenario, as in the adaptation theory, reproductive senescence is about stopping early.

The physiological trade-off explanation and the adaptation explanation are not necessarily mutually exclusive. Besides the fact that selection for efficient early fertility can be considered an adaptation in its own right—for example, to accommodate overlapping child care—antagonistic pleiotropy or a design trade-off could be the proximate mechanism creating a postreproductive life span if that were favored. The difference between the adaptation and physiological trade-off hypotheses is that in the latter menopause per se is not what you are seeking to explain. What needs explaining is why age-specific fertility begins decreasing decades before menopause. Menopause is simply the last event in the process of declining fertility. Whether menopause is the result of selection for efficient early reproduction or selection for a postreproductive life span is exceedingly difficult to tease apart. Indeed, if overlapping child care is the truly unique reproductive character in human females, both the adaptation and physiological trade-off explanations are applicable. At any rate, these two explanations share some of the same predictions: long postreproductive life spans should be unique to human females; prolonged fertility should have fitness costs in the form of reduced offspring survival and fertility; and fitness benefits should be associated with reproductive cessation. Earlier, we saw that a long postreproductive life span is unique to human females, but that the costs of prolonged fertility and the benefits of reproductive cessation are more difficult to establish. There are also two predictions that are specific to the physiological tradeoff favoring early fertility.

Historical and Cross-Populational Evidence of Early Fertility

In support of the physiological tradeoff explanation, we find historical and cross-population evidence of selection for early fertility in human populations. In extant and historical natural-fertility populations, total fertility rates vary enormously, as do nutritional status and mortality rates.[16,87,138,139] Despite these differences, the pattern of age-specific marital fertility remains remarkably consistent across time and geographical boundaries, peaking around age 25, then decreasing monotonically with the cessation of fertility, generally preceding menopause by several years (Fig. 3).[140] This supports the importance of a biological explanation for reproductive cessation before menopause and for menopause itself.

Additional indication that the causes of the premenopausal cessation of fertility are physiological comes from analysis of age-specific apparent fecundabilities, or monthly probabilities of a recognized conception. Based on data from Taiwanese and Hutterite women and a statistical model, Wood and Weinstein[141] showed that apparent fecundability begins to decline around age 25 years. Declining coital rates are responsible for most of the yearly decrease in apparent fecundability up to age 35.[140,141] After age 35, biological causes take on major importance, eventually totally predominating.[16] The model suggests that the biological portion of the decline stems from the increasing risk of early fetal loss.[140]

Further validation of the physiological trade-off explanation comes from Wood and colleagues.[12,142] According to these investigators, the menstruating life spans of women of all ages are characterized by periods of ovarian inactivity in which regular cycling and, presumably, ovulation, do not occur because the production of ovarian steroids is insufficient to maintain negative feedback on lutenizing hormone and follicle-stimulating hormone, which is essential for ovulation. The pattern of these "inactive phases," which increase in frequency and duration as menopause is approached, is predictable from the age pattern of follicular depletion, suggesting that the characteristics of the follicular-depletion system determine the distribution of inactive phases and the probability of ovulatory cycles.[12,142] Wood, O'Connor, and Holman[12] hypothesize that menopause evolved by antagonistic pleiotropy because of selection acting on the follicular depletion system to maintain regular ovarian cycles at young adult ages.

Fertility in Other Mammals

The fact that biological factors involving a design trade-off and antagonistic pleiotropy (or both) appear to be responsible for the early reproductive peak in human females is still insufficient to explain menopause. One must also show that fertility functions of humans are different from those of other mammals. One must show that human females are unique both in terms of their early fertility peak and long postreproductive life span. Fertility patterns for nonprovisioned or semi-provisioned species such as Barbary macaques,[143] olive baboons,[144] lions,[144] and East African elephants[145] do, in fact, look very different from the human pattern.[146] Instead of resembling a left-skewed triangle with fertility starting to decrease when females are in their mid-twenties, the age-specific fertility functions of macaques[143] and elephants,[145] are box-like, with fertility remaining relatively constant over a relatively long period, then terminating abruptly only a few years before maximum age

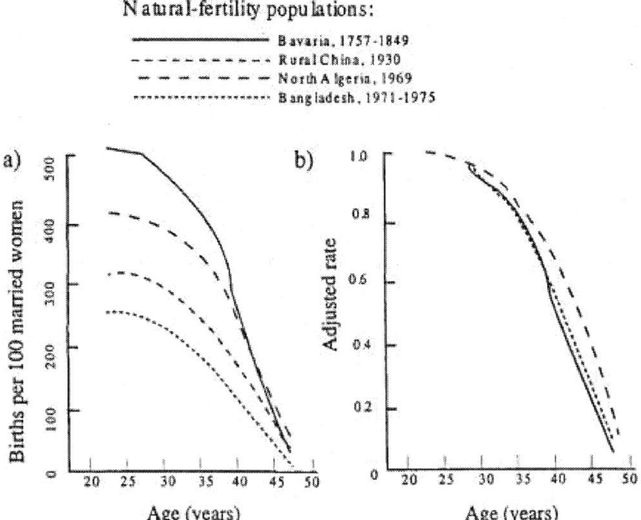

Figure 3. a) Comparison of age-specific marital fertility rates in natural fertility populations and b) age-specific marital fertility rates corrected for differences in total fertility rates. Raw rates at each age are divided by the rate at age 20 to 24 years. (Redrawn from Wood[16]).

at death (Fig. 4). For Mahale chimpanzees,[71] there is no correlation between females' age at last birth and length of interbirth interval [$r = 0.09 + -8.66$, $N = 19$], suggesting that noncaptive chimpanzees also have a box-like fertility pattern.[91] Many similar examples can probably be adduced. In addition, though some female nonhuman primates living in captivity show age-specific fertility patterns similar to those of humans, only among chimpanzees do more than than 50% of females have a postreproductive life span.[83] The finding that chimpanzees have menopause and a post reproductive lifespan if they live long enough is consistent with the similarity between the follicular depletion patterns and mechanisms in humans and chimpanzees.[12]

Across mammals, females' supply of follicles at puberty scales allometrically with species body size and life span.[15] To allow for the fact that the number of follicles at puberty rises more steeply with body weight than with life span, and to insure a lifetime supply, ovulation rates vary inversely with size.[15] At maturity, human females have the number of follicles predicted by body weight, and there is no evidence for a relatively high rate of follicular attrition.[15] In fact, there is some evidence that longer-lived species use follicles more conservatively.[15] Still, in other species senescence and death usually precede depletion of oocytes, whereas the postreproductive life span of human females is long and universal.[147]

The questions, then, are why does human fertility start to decrease when women are in their mid-twenties and terminate when they are around age 40, and why do human females outlive their supply of eggs? Leidy[148] hypothesizes that "the process of follicular atresia evolved as integral to the process of sexual reproduction and that the entire hominid somatic lifespan was more amenable to change than was the process of atresia" (p. 149). In my view, selection for efficient early reproduction is an adaptation, accommodating prolonged offspring dependence and the expedience of overlapping child care. Indeed, I consider the physiological trade-off favoring early fertility to be the most powerful explanation of all. In addition, although the proponents of selection for early fertility do not address the value of the postreproductive life span, a postreproductive period, albeit a modest one at first, would have afforded a fitness advantage if it increased offspring survival. That brings us back to the adaptation hypothesis.

Artifact of Longer Life Spans or Life Expectancies

I come to the explanation of menopause as a by-product of long life span or increase in life expectancies. The elucidation here is that, given the phylogenetic, physiological, and developmental constraints of semelgametogenesis, menopause is simply the result of human life spans and life expectancies increasing beyond the female's supply of eggs or ability to sustain ovulatory cycles.[13–17]

The physiological trade-off and artifact explanations are not mutually exclusive for two reasons. First, design trade-offs and antagonistic pleiotropy would be the proximate mechanisms preventing increases in reproductive life span. Second, increases in life span and life expectancies may be partly the result of selection for early fertility if reproductive effort released by the cessation of fertility is directed toward increased somatic repair or if the cessation of childbirth increases life expectancies for mothers and offspring. The artifact and adaptation explanations are not mutually exclusive either. If the dissynchrony between reproductive and somatic senescence arose in human females because selection for a postreproductive life span was greater than selection for longer fertility, menopause would be more adaptation than artifact.

As an explanation for the origin of menopause, we can dismiss the hypothesis that a postmenopausal life span is the result of a recent increase in life expectancies due to improved sanitation and medical care. Some females have lived past menopause for at least 3,000 years, and during most of this time living conditions for most women were certainly not very good. This leaves us to explain why life span exceeded reproductive capacity.

Females of other long-lived species do not have menopause—recall elephants, tortoises, and most whales, which live to be 60, 80, and 90 years old, respectively. According to

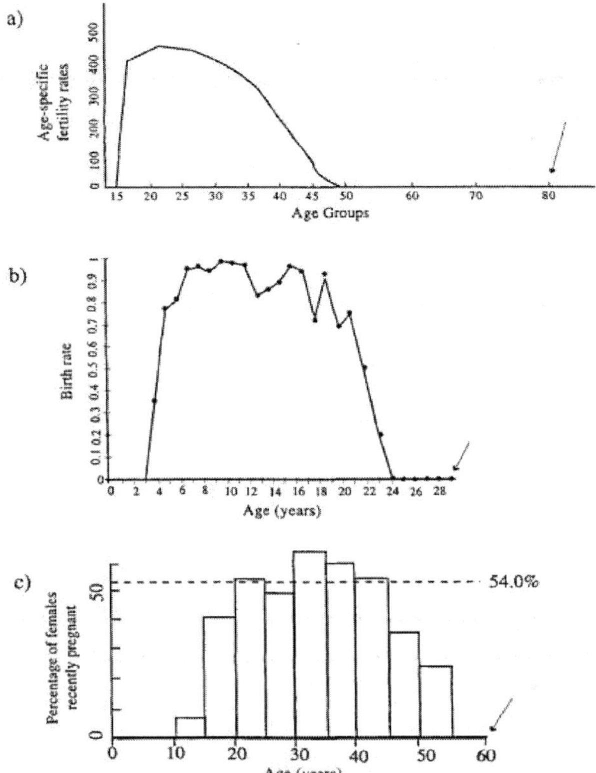

Figure 4. Age-specific fertility functions: a) Hutterite women, b) semi-free-ranging Barbary macaques, and c) East African elephants. Arrows indicate maximum age at death (redrawn from Robinson[146]; Paul, Keuster, and Podzuweit[143]; and Laws, Parker, and Johnstone[144]).

Diamond[53] there "is nothing evolutionarily inevitable about menopause from the perspective of mammals in general. Other species maintain fertility and viable oocytes longer than humans" (p. 116). Human females use up their supply of oocytes approximately half-way through the maximum life span.[2] In contrast, follicular depletion before the end of life is rare in other female mammals.[147] Females in other mammalian species rarely have postreproductive life spans; when they do, these are relatively short.[2]

According to evolutionary theories of senescence, there should be no selection for postreproductive individuals. Reproductive senescence is equivalent to death.[5] But no one is truly postreproductive. As Williams[5] put it, no one is truly postreproductive until the last child is self-sufficient. Diamond[53] goes further, stating that people are never truly postreproductive if they can influence the fitness of biological relatives. The notion that there can be no selection against mutations causing damaging effects in old people because they are postreproductive overlooks this fact. Especially in pre-literate foraging societies, Diamond[53] notes, older folk are valued for their ability to share their vast store of knowledge, in particular their knowledge of matters concerning survival. Accordingly, older individuals, including postreproductive females, could have been valued even before the origin of spoken language, when communication still relied on vocalizations, signs, and facial expressions. This makes it possible that menopause is a very old trait indeed. As for how humans evolved longer life spans, Diamond[49] suggests that perhaps we live longer because we evolved better repair mechanisms as we gained more control of our environment.

If human females have the number of follicles predicted for a mammal of our body weight at maturity, and if there is no evidence for a relatively high rate of follicular attrition, despite the acceleration in atresia,[15] why do we run out of oocytes prematurely? According to Gosden and Telfer,[15] the odd thing about human females is that, based on body weight, allometry predicts a life span of only 30 years. These researchers believe this constitutes "a prima facie case for arguing that menopause has arisen adventitiously during evolution" due to increases in life span (p. 174). In contrast, Judge and Carey[23] predict a human life span of 72 years based on body and brain mass of a catarrhine comparison group. Observing that this estimate exceeds average longevity in hunter-gatherers and the age of menopause by at least 20 years, Judge and Carey suggest "that a lifespan exceeding that of the female reproductive system is part of the phylogenetic legacy rather than a modern development related to uniquely human cultural innovations" (p. B205).

In the patriarch hypothesis Marlowe[17] posits that menopause is the by-product of selection for extension of maximum life span in males. The life span of females co-evolved with that of males, whereas commensurate increases in female reproductive life span were constrained by the depletion of viable oocytes. Without justifying the postreproductive life span, the artifact explanation is insufficient. However, menopause could be a result of life span outlasting female reproductive capacity if postreproductive females had indirect reproductive value.

Heritability in the Age of Menopause

Additional insight into the investigation of menopause and the adaptation-versus-epiphenomenon debate is provided by estimates of heritability in the age of menopause because heritability provides information about the history of selection on a trait.[141–151] Indeed, heritability estimates are particularly useful in this case because researchers have had to resort to a good deal of speculation about the origin of menopause, while empirical work on the maintenance of the trait is hindered by the fact that menopause is universal in our species. From a heritability estimate, we learn about the maintenance of menopause from the stability of the mean age of menopause over the relatively recent past—say, the last

2,000 years. We learn about the long-term maintenance of the trait from the amount of additive genetic variance (V_A).[152]

As discussed earlier, the evidence, though not conclusive, suggests that the age of menopause has remained relatively stable for a few thousand years throughout the world, despite tremendous socioeconomic and demographic change. With no upward secular trend in the mean age of menopause and heritablities as large as 40% to 60%,[25–27] there are three possible explanations. The first is that age of menopause has experienced upward movement that we have not detected. Lack of evidence for a secular trend is not definitive. The second is that age of menopause is selectively neutral. The third is that age of menopause is under some degree of stabilizing selection.

High heritability and no discernible upward movement in the mean age of menopause in the presence of improving socioeconomic conditions suggests a cost to prolonged fertility now, in modern industrialized and traditional agricultural societies, which supports the third option. By implication, this cost has existed since the domestication of plants and animals about 10,000 years ago. Finding a cost to prolonging female reproductive life span now is significant because it changes the terms of the menopause debate. Previous investigation has focused on the socioecology of hunter-gatherers in an attempt to understand the selection pressures of the environment of evolutionary adaptedness. The fact that there is presently a cost, as many have suspected, means that there is nothing peculiar to the foraging way of life that makes premature reproductive senescence adaptive. This is not unexpected, given the preponderance of evidence suggesting that reproductive patterns in human females are remarkably consistent across populations and time, regardless of mode of subsistence.

The next question is whether stabilizing selection on the age of menopause is weak or strong. Strong stabilizing selection is usually associated with low heritabilities, because strong selection is generally expected to reduce additive genetic variation.[149,150,153,154;cf.151,155] (Under certain circumstances, however, high heritability can remain in the presence of strong stabilizing selection.[151,156–159]) This implies that a broad range of intermediate ages of menopause is favored, and that menstruating life span is not correlated with lifetime reproductive success.[149] In this case, menstruating life span would have a flat fitness profile, perhaps with selection only against very early or very late menopause. Over much of its range, age of menopause could be considered a neutral trait. Weak stabilizing selection on the age of menopause could be the result of selection for some other trait that affects the age of menopause, such as selection for early fertility or a postreproductive life span. The nearly universal age at last birth of approximately 40 years, regardless of median age of menopause, is consistent with this notion. To me this represents further support for the hypothesis that menopause is an epiphenomenon of selection for efficient early reproduction. In this scenario, menopause is both the result of selection for intensive reproduction early in the fertile period to accommodate prolonged dependence of offspring through overlapping child care and an adaptation for more effective maternal investment, including a modest postreproductive life span. The long post-reproductive life spans now enjoyed by human females resulted from much later increases in life expectancies.

Conclusions

Undoubtedly all three explanations—adaptation, trade-off, and artifact—played some role in the origin of menopause. Indeed, selection for a postreproductive life span in human females was probably the result of a dynamic interplay among the need for prolonged offspring care, physiological trade-offs favoring early fertility, and increasing lifespans and life expectancies. Supporting the adaptation explanation is the fact that a protracted postreproductive life span is unique to human females. Given this, it is reasonable to hypothesize that ecological pressures and increasing secondary altriciality of hominid infants provided compelling reasons for selection for intensified and protracted maternal investment in the environment of evolutionary adaptedness.

In support of the physiological trade-off explanation, there is strong evidence of selection for "front-loaded" fertility. Cross-populational and historical fertility patterns are remarkably consistent in showing that age-specific fecundability and fertility peaks when human females are in their mid-twenties and terminate around age 40, well before menopause and irrespective of the cross-populational variation in the age of menopause. This pattern is different from that of other mammalian females. Evidence of the continuing importance of efficient early fertility is provided by recent heritability estimates of 40% to 60% for the age of menopause and the apparent lack of upward secular trends. In the presence of so much additive genetic variation, lack of increase in the age of menopause suggests that there is a cost to prolonging fertility now. This in turn suggests that the cost of prolonged fertility is not exclusive to socioeconomic conditions of the environment of evolutionary adaptedness or to any particular mode of subsistence. The reason for premature reproductive senescence still exists. Also in favor of selection for early fertility is the fact that loss of oocytes accelerates when women are in their late thirties. In addition, selection for early fertility via antagonistic pleiotropy is also consistent with the greater cross-populational variation in median age of menopause than in mean age at last birth, suggesting greater selection on the end of fertility than the end of menstruation.

I find no support for the notion that menopause is the result of recent increases in life expectancies, given that it probably existed at least 3,000 years ago, long before the occurrence of significant increases in life expectancies. The fact that human females have enough oocytes to last 70 years also does not support the hypothesis that menopause is purely the result of increases in life span. Nevertheless, in the presence of selection for efficient early reproduction, increases in life span or life expectancies would have resulted in a postreproductive life span for human females. On the other hand, the prolonged postreproductive lifespan now enjoyed by virtually all human females who reach reproductive age is very likely the result of relatively recent increases in life expectancies.

If premature cessation of fertility and increased maternal investment resulted in selection for longer life span in females, my hunch is that it was primarily the result of mothering: Women were better off investing in the survival and fertility of their own subadult offspring than in grandchildren or nondescendant relatives. Given the contribution of males to the energetics of human reproduction, longer-lived males would also have enjoyed a fitness advantage. There is no need to invoke a correlated response. On the basis of the preceding, I argue that selection for efficient early reproduction was and still is a fitness-enhancing adaptation accommodating prolonged offspring dependence by facilitating overlapping child care. Thus, ultimately, premature reproductive senescence can also be viewed as an adaptation for prolonged maternal investment.

Obviously, the origin of menopause will never be explained by physiology alone, but because it is reasonable to assume that female reproductive physiology has remained basically the same since the origin of *Homo*, we may want to focus on the currently recognized physiological mechanisms governing declining fertility and menopause for what they can tell us about the environment of evolutionary adaptedness and the ultimate reasons for menopause. I believe the most important clue lies in the fact that human females have enough oocytes to last 70 years if the rate of atresia were to remain constant throughout adult life.

Acknowledgments

I thank R. Boyd and R.D. Peccei for reading and critiquing drafts of this paper. I also thank E.A. Smith for extensive and very helpful editorial suggestions and two anonymous reviewers for useful comments on an earlier draft. Thanks as well to L.E. Leidy, H. Kaplan, K. Hill, J.B. Lancaster, and A.M. Hurtado for generously sharing their work with me. I am indebted to J.K.H. Lu, T. Plummer, and D. Read for guidance during the heritability study, to A. Voda for permitting me access to the Tremin Trust database, and to the American Federation of Aging Research for financial support.

References

1. Pavelka MSM, Fedigan LM. 1991. Menopause: a comparative life-history perspective. Yearbook Phys Anthropol 34:13–38.
2. Pavelka MSM, Fedigan LM. 1999. Reproductive termination in female Japanese monkeys: a comparative life history perspective. Am J Phys Anthropol 109:455–464.
3. Hill K, Hurtado AM. 1991. The evolution of premature reproductive senescence and menopause in human females: an evaluation of the "grandmother hypothesis." Hum Nat 2:313–350.
4. Marsh H, Kasuya T. 1984. Changes in the ovaries of the short-finned pilot whale, *Globicephala macrorhychus*, with age and reproductive activity. In: Perrin WF, Brownell RL, DeMaster DP, editors. Reproduction in whales, dolphins and porpoises. Cambridge, MA: Rep Int Whaling Comm. p 311–335.
5. Williams GC. 1957. Pleiotropy, natural selection, and the evolution of senescence. Evolution 11:398–411.
6. Lancaster JB, Lancaster CS. 1983. Parental investment: the hominid adaptation. In: Ortner D, editor. How humans adapt: a biocultural odyssey. Washington, DC: Smithsonian Institution Press. p 33–66.
7. Hawkes K, O'Connell JF, Blurton Jones NG. 1989. Hardworking Hadza grandmothers. In: Standen V, Foley RA, editors. Comparative socioecology. Oxford: Blackwell Scientific. p 341–366.
8. Peccei JS. 1995. A hypothesis for the origin and evolution of menopause. Maturitas 21:83– 89.
9. Peccei JS. 1995. The origin and evolution of menopause: the altriciality-lifespan hypothesis. Ethol Sociobiol 16:425–449.
10. O'Rourke MT, Ellison PT. 1993. Menopause and ovarian senescence in human females. Am J Phys Anthropol 16(suppl.):154.
11. Leidy LE. 1999. Menopause in evolutionary perspective. In: Trevathan W, McKenna J, Smith EO, editors. Evolutionary medicine. New York: Oxford University Press. p 407–427.
12. Wood JW, O'Connor KA, Holman DJ. 1999. Biodemographic models of menopause. Hum Biol Assoc Abstracts 182:133.
13. Washburn SL. 1981. Longevity in primates. In: March J, McGaugh J, editors. Aging, biology and behavior. New York: Academic Press. p 11– 29.
14. Weiss KM. 1981. Evolutionary perspectives on human aging. In: Amoss PT, Harrell S, editors. Other ways of growing old. Stanford, CA: Stanford University Press. p 25–28.

15. Gosden RG, Telfer E. 1987. Number of follicles and oocytes in mammalian ovaries and their allometric relationships. J Zool Lond 211:169–175.
16. Wood JW. 1994. Dynamics of human reproduction: biology, biometry, demography. New York: Aldine De Gruyter.
17. Marlowe F. 2000. The patriarch hypothesis: an alternative explanation of menopause. Hum Nat 11:27–42.
18. Stearns SC. 1992. The evolution of life histories. New York: Oxford University Press.
19. Holy Bible, King James Version. 1908. p 14. Cobb CA: First Glance Books.
20. Hill K. 1982. Hunting and human evolution. J Hum Evol 11:521–544.
21. Foley RA. 1987. Another unique species. New York: Longman Scientific and Technical.
22. Hawkes K, O'Connell JF, Blurton Jones NG, Alvarez H, Charnov EL. 1998. Grandmothering, menopause, and the evolution of human life histories. Proc Natl Acad Sci 95:1336–1339.
23. Judge D, Carey J. 2000. Postreproductive life predicted by primate patterns. J Gerontol 55A: B201–209.
24. Treloar AE. 1974. Menarche, menopause, and intervening fecundability. Hum Biol 46:89– 107.
25. Peccei JS. 1998. Heritability in the age of menopause and the genetic correlation between the ages of menarche and menopause. Dissertation, University of California Los Angeles.
26. Peccei JS. 1999. First estimates of heritability in the age of menopause. Curr Anthropol 40:553–558.
27. Snieder H, MacGregor AJ, Spector TD. 1998. Genes control the cessation of a woman's reproductive life: a twin study of hysterectomy and age at menopause. J Clin Endocrinol Metab 83:1875–1880.
28. Gray RH. 1976. The menopause: epidemiological and demographic considerations. In: Beard RJ, editor. The menopause: a guide to current research and practice. Lancaster, UK: MTP Press. p 25–40.
29. McKinlay SM, Bifano NL, McKinlay JB. 1985. Smoking and age at menopause in women. Ann Internal Med 103:350–356.
30. Flint M. 1978. Is there a secular trend in age of menopause? Maturitas 1:133–139.
31. Flint M. 1997. Secular trends in menopause age. J Psychosom Obstet Gynecol 18:65–72.
32. Amundsen DW, Diers CJ. 1970. The age of menopause in classical Greece and Rome. Hum Biol 42:79–86.

33. Post JB. 1971. Ages at menarche and menopause: some mediaeval authorities. Popul Stud 25:83–87.
34. Amundsen DW, Diers CJ. 1973. The age of menopause in medieval Europe. Hum Biol 45: 605–612.
35. Leidy LE. 1994. Biological aspects of menopause: across the lifespan. Ann Rev Anthropol 23:231–253.
36. Faddy MJ, Gosden RG. 1996. A model conforming the decline in follicle numbers to the age of menopause in women. Hum Reprod 11:1484–1486.
37. Gosden RG, Spears N. 1997. Programmed cell death in the reproductive system. Br Med Bull 52:644–661.
38. Gosden RG, Faddy MJ. 1998. Biological bases of premature ovarian failure. Reprod Fertil Dev 10:73–78.
39. Gosden RG. 1985. Biology of menopause: The causes and consequences of ovarian ageing. London: Academic Press.
40. Leidy LE, Godfrey LR, Sutherland MR. 1998. Is follicular atresia biphasic? Fertil Steril 79:851–859.
41. Richardson SJ, Senikas V, Nelson JF. 1987. Follicular depletion during the menopausal transition: evidence for accelerated loss and ultimate exhaustion. J Clin Endocrinol Metab 65:1231–1237.
42. Faddy MJ, Gosden RG, Gougeon A, Richardson SJ, Nelson JF. 1992. Accelerated disappearance of ovarian follicles in mid-life: implications for forecasting menopause. Hum Reprod 7:1342–1346.
43. Mattison DR, Evans MI, Schwimmer W, White B. 1984. Familial premature ovarian failure. J Hum Genet 36:1341–1348.
44. Cramer DW, Xu H, Harlow BL. 1995. Does "incessant" ovulation increase risk for early menopause? Am J Obstet Gynecol 172:568–573.
45. Cramer DW, Xu H. 1996. Predicting age at menopause. Maturitas 23:319–326.
46. Stanford JL, Haartge P, Brinton LA, Hoover RN, Brookmeyer R. 1987. Factors influencing the age at natural menopause. Int J Res Scholarship Clin Epidemiol Chronic Illness 40:995–1002.
47. Brambilla DJ, McKinlay SM. 1989. A prospective study of factors affecting age at menopause. J Clin Epidemiol 42:1031–1039.
48. Whelan EA, Sandler DP, McConnaughey DR, Weinberg CR. 1990. Menstrual and reproductive characteristics and age at natural menopause. Am J Epidemiol 131:625–632.
49. Parazzini F, Negri E, LaVecchia C. 1992. Reproductive and general lifestyle determinants of age at menopause. Maturitas 15:141–149.

50. Torgerson DJ, Avenell A, Russell IT, Reid DM. 1994. Factors associated with onset of menopause in women aged 45–49. Maturitas 9:83–92.
51. van Noord PAH, Dubas JS, Dorland M, Boersma H, teVelde E. 1997. Age at natural menopause in a population-based screening cohort: the role of menarche, fecundity and lifestyle factors. Fertil Steril 68:95–102.
52. Trevathan WR. 1987. Human birth: an evolutionary perspective. New York: Aldine de Gruyter.
53. Diamond J. 1997. Making more by making less: The evolution of female menopause. Why is sex fun? New York: Basic Books. pp 103–125.
54. Turke PW. 1997. Did menopause evolve to discourage infanticide and encourage continued investment by agnates? Evol Hum Behav 18:3– 13.
55. Hawkes K, O'Connell JF, Blurton Jones NG. 1997. Hadza women's time allocation, offspring provisioning, and the evolution of long post-menopausal life spans. Curr Anthropol 38:551– 577.
56. Turke PW. 1988. Helpers at the nest: child-care networks of Ifaluk. In: Betzig L, Borgerhoff Mulder M, Turke P, editors. Human reproductive behavior. Cambridge: Cambridge University Press. p 173–188.
57. Hames RB. 1988. The allocation of parental care among the Ye'kwana. In: Betzig L, Borgerhoff Mulder M, Turke P, editors. Human reproductive behavior. Cambridge: Cambridge University Press. p 237–251.
58. Hill K, Kaplan H. 1988. Tradeoffs in male and female reproductive strategies among the Ache: parts 1 and 2. In: Betzig L, Borgerhoff Mulder M, Turke P, editors. Human reproductive behavior. Cambridge: Cambridge University Press. p 277–305.
59. Rogers AR. 1993. Why menopause? Evol Ecol 7:406–420.
60. Kaplan H, Hill K, Lancaster J, Hurtado AM. 2000. A theory of human life history evolution: brains, learning and longevity. Evol Anthropol 9:156–185.
61. Lancaster JB, King BJ. 1985. An evolutionary perspective on menopause. In: Brown JK, Kerns V, editors. In her prime. South Hadley, MA: Bergin & Garvey. p 13–20.
62. Peccei JS. 2001. The grandmother hypotheses: old and new. Am J Hum Biol, in press.
63. Vrba ES. 1985. Ecological and adaptive changes associated with early hominid evolution. In: Delson E, editor. Ancestors: the hard evidence. New York: Alan R. Liss. p 63–71.
64. Foley RA, Lee PC. 1991. Ecology and energetics of encephalization in hominid evolution. Philos Trans R Soc Lond Series B 334:223–232.

65. deHeinselin J, Clark D, White T, Hart W, Renne P, WoldeGabriel G, Beyene Y, Vrba E. 1999. Environment and behavior of 2.5-million-year-old Bouri Hominids. Science 284:625–629.
66. Isaac GL. 1978. Foodsharing and human evolution: archaeological evidence from the Plio–Pleistocene of East Africa. J Anthropol Res 34: 311–325.
67. Kingston JD, Marino BD, Hill A. 1994. Isotopic evidence for Neogene hominid paleoenvironments in the Kenya Rift Valley. Science 264: 955–959.
68. Plummer TW, Bishop LC. 1994. Hominid paleoecology at Olduvai Gorge Tanzania as indicated by antelope remains. J Hum Evol 27:477– 475.
69. Sikes NE. 1994. Early hominid habitat preferences in East Africa: paleosol carbon isotopic evidence. J Hum Evol 27:25–45.
70. Asfaw B, White T, Lovejoy O, Latimer B, Simpton S, Suwa G. 1999. *Australopithecus garhi*: a new species of early hominid from Ethiopia. Science 284:629–635.
71. Martin RD. 1983. Human brain evolution in an ecological context. 52nd James Arthur lecture on the evolution of the human brain. New York: Am Mus Nat Hist.
72. McHenry HM. 1994. Behavioral ecological implications of early hominid body size. J Hum Evol 27:77–87.
73. Wood B, Collard M. 1999. The human genus. Science 284:65–71.
74. Bogin B, Smith BH. 1996. Evolution of the human life cycle. Am J Hum Biol 8:703–716.
75. Leonard WR, Robertson ML. 1992. Nutritional requirements and human evolution: a bioenergetics model. Am J Hum Biol 4:179–195.
76. Smith BH, Tompkins RL. 1995. Toward a life history of the Hominidae. Ann Rev Anthropol 24:257–279.
77. Clegg M, Aiello LC. 1999. A comparison of the Nariokotome *Homo erectus* with juveniles from a modern human population. Am J Phys Anthropol 110:81–93.
78. O'Connell JF, Hawkes K, Blurton Jones NG. 1999. Grandmothering and the evolution of *Homo erectus*. J Hum Evol 36:461–485.
79. Ruff CB, Trinkhaus E, Holliday TW. 1997. Body mass and encephalization in Pleistocene *Homo*. Nature 387:173–176.
80. Hammer MLA, Foley RA. 1996. Longevity and life history in hominid evolution. Hum Evol 11:61–66.
81. Smith BH. 1991. Dental development and the evolution of life history in Hominidae. Am J Phys Anthropol 86:157–174.
82. Smith BH. 1993. The physiological age of KNM-WT 15000. In: Walker A, Leakey R, editors. The Nariokotome *Homo erectus* skeleton. Cambridge: Harvard University Press. p 195–220.

83. Caro TM, Sellen DW, Parish A, Frank R, Brown DM, Voland E, Borgerhoff Mulder M. 1995. Termination of reproduction in nonhuman and human primate females. Int J Primatolol 16:205–220.
84. Wilson EO. 1975. The relevant principles of population biology: sociobiology. Cambridge: The Belknap Press. p 32–47.
85. Laws RM. 1969. The Tsavo research project. J Reprod Fertil Suppl 6:495–531.
86. Croze H, Hillmman AKK, Lang EM. 1981. Elephants and their habitats: how do they tolerate each other. In: Fowler CW, Smith TD, editors. Dynamics of large mammal populations. New York: John Wiley & Sons. p 297–316.
87. Hill K, Hurtado AM. 1996. Ache life history: the ecology and demography of a foraging people. New York: Aldine de Gruyter.
88. Mizroch SA. 1981. Analyses of some biological parameters of the Antarctic fin whale (*Balaenoptera physalus*). Rep Int Whaling Commission 31:425–434.
89. Graham C, Kling R, Steiner R. 1979. Reproductive senescence in female nonhuman primates. In: Bowden D, editor. Aging in nonhuman primates. New York: Van Nostrand Reinhold. p 183–202.
90. Hrdy SB. 1981. "Nepotists" and "altruists": the behavior of old females among macaques and langur monkeys. In: Amoss PT, Harrell S, editors. Other ways of growing old. Stanford, CA: Stanford University Press. p 59–76.
91. Nishida T, Takasaki H, Takahata Y. 1990. Demography and reproductive profiles. In: Nishida T, editor. The chimpanzees of the Mahale Mountains: sexual and life history strategies. Tokyo: Tokyo University Press. p 63–97.
92. Sommer V, Srivastava A, Borries C. 1992. Cycles, sexuality, and conception in free-ranging langurs (*Presbytis entellus*). Am J Primatol 28:1–27.
93. Harman SM, Talbert GB. 1985. Reproductive aging. In: Finch CE, Schneider EL, editors. The biology of aging. New York: Van Nostrand Reinhold. p 475–510.
94. Naeye RL. 1983. Maternal age, obstetric complications, and the outcome of pregnancy. Obstet Gynecol 61:210–216.
95. Spellacy WN, Miller SJ, Winegar A. 1986. Pregnancy after 40 years of age. Obstet Gynecol 68:452–454.
96. Gaulden ME. 1992. Maternal age effect: the enigma of Down syndrome and other trisomic conditions. Mutat Res 296:69–88.
97. Fretts RC, Schmittdiel J, McLean FH, Usher RH, Goldman MB. 1995. Increased maternal age and the risk of fetal death. New Eng J Med 333: 953–957.
98. Kirz DS, Dorchester W, Freeman RK. 1985. Advanced maternal age: the mature gravida. Am J Obstet Gynecol 152:502–511.

99. Berkowitz GS, Skovron ML, Lapinski RH, Berkowitz RL. 1990. Delayed childbearing and the outcome of pregnancy. New Eng J Med 322: 659–664.
100. Finch CE. 1994. The evolution of ovarian oocyte decline with aging and possible relationships to Down syndrome and Alzheimers disease. Exp Gerontol 29(3/4):299–304.
101. Biesele M, Howell N. 1981. "The old people give you life": Aging among !Kung hunter-gatherers. In: Amoss PT, Harrell S, editors. Other ways of growing old. Stanford, CA: Stanford University Press. p 77–98.
102. Hames R. 1992. Time allocation. In: Smith EA, Winterhalder B, editors. Evolutionary ecology and human behavior. New York: Aldine de Gruyter. p 203–235.
103. Brown JK. 1985. Introduction. In: Brown JK, Kerns V, editors. In her prime. South Hadley, MA: Bergin & Garvey Publishers. p 1–11.
104. Winterhalder B, Smith EA. 2000. Analyzing adaptive strategies: human behavioral ecology at twenty-five. Evol Anthropol 9:51–72.
105. Charnov EL. 1993. Life history invariants: some explorations of symmetry in evolutionary ecology. Oxford: Oxford University Press.
106. Westendorp RGJ, Kirkwood TBL. 1998. Human longevity at the cost of reproductive success. Nature 396:743–746.
107. Lancaster J, Kaplan H, Hill K, Hurtado AM. 2000. The evolution of life history, intelligence and diet among chimps and human foragers. In: Thompson N, Tonneau F, editors. Perspectives in ethology, vol 14. New York: Plenum Press. p 47–72.
108. Hill K. 1996. The demography of menopause. Maturitas 23:113–127.
109. Paganini-Hill A, Henderson VW. 1994. Estrogen deficiency and risk of Alzheimer's disease in women. Am J Epidemiol 140:256–261.
110. Henderson VW. 1997. Estrogen, cognition, and a woman's risk of Alzheimer's disease. Am J Med 103 Part A:11S–18S.
111. Avioli LV. 1994. Impact of the menopause on skeletal metabolism and osteoporotic syndromes. Exp Gerontol 29:391–415.
112. Van Der Graaf Y, De Kleijn MJJ, Van Der Schouw YT. 1997. Menopause and cardiovascular disease. J Psychosom Obstet Gynecol 18:113–120.
113. Kuller LH, Meilahn EN, Cauley JA, Gutai JP, Matthews. 1994. Epidemiologic studies of menopause: changes in risk factors and disease. Exp Gerontol 29:495–509.
114. Khaw KT. 1992. Epidemiology of the menopause. Br Med Bull 48:249–261.
115. Byington RP, Furberg CD, Riley W, Applegate W, Herd A, Herrington D, Hunninghake D, Lowery M. 1999. Effect of estrogen and progestin on progression of carotid atherosclerosis in postmenopausal women with documented heart disease: HERS B-mode substudy. J Am Coll Cardiol 33(Suppl A):265.

116. Brace M, McCauley E. 1997. Oestrogens and psychological well-being. Ann Med 29:283– 290.
117. Colditz GA, Willett WC, Stampfer MJ, Posner B, Speizer FC, Hennekens CH. 1987. Menopause and the risk of coronary heart disease in women. New Eng J Med 316:1105–1110.
118. Lees B, Molleson T, Anrett TR, Stevenson JC. 1993. Differences in proximal femur bone density over two centuries. Lancet 341:673– 675.
119. Trivers RL. 1972. Parental investment and sexual selection. In: Campbell B, editor. Sexual selection and the descent of man. Chicago: Aldine de Gruyter. p 136–179.
120. Lovejoy CO. 1988. The evolution of human walking. Sci Am Nov 118–125.
121. Oftedal TO. 1984. Milk composition, milk yield and energy output at peak lactation: a comparative review. Symp Zool Soc Lond 51:33–85.
122. Stanley SM. 1992. An ecological theory for the origin of *Homo*. Paleobiology 18:237–257.
123. Gage TB, McCullough JM, Weitz CA, Dutt JS, Abelson A. 1989. Demographic studies and human population biology. In: Little MA, Haas JD, editors. Human population biology: a trans-disciplinary science. New York: Oxford University Press. p 45–65.
124. Gage TB. 1988. Mathematical hazard models of mortality: an alternative to model life tables. Am J Phys Anthropol 76:429–441.
125. Konigberg LW, Frankenberg SR. 1992. Estimation of age structure in anthropological demography. Am J Phys Anthropol 89:235–256.
126. Jelliffe DB, Maddocks I. 1964. Ecologic malnutrition in the New Guinea highlands. Clin Pediatr 3:432–438.
127. Merchant K, Martorell R. 1988. Frequent reproductive cycling: does it lead to nutritional depletion of mothers? Prog Food Nutr Sci 12:339–369.
128. Merchant K, Martorell R, Haas JD. 1990. Consequences for maternal nutrition of reproductive stress across consecutive pregnancies. Am J Clin Nutr 52:616–620.
129. Merchant K, Martorell R, Haas JD. 1990. Maternal and fetal responses to the stresses of lactation concurrent with pregnancy and of short recuperative intervals. Am J Clin Nutr 52:280– 288.
130. Johnson PL, Wood JW, Weinstein M. 1990. Female fecundity in highland Papua New Guinea. Soc Biol 37:26–43.
131. Wood JW. 1990. Fertility in anthropological populations. Ann Rev Anthropol 19:211–242.
132. Tracer DP. 1991. Fertility-related changes in maternal body composition among the Au of Papua New Guinea. Am J Phys Anthropol 85: 393–405.

133. Miller JE, Huss-Ashmore R. 1989. Do reproductive patterns affect maternal nutritional status? An analysis of maternal depletion in Lesotho. Am J Hum Biol 1:409–419.
134. Hamilton WD. 1964. The genetical evolution of social behaviour I, II. J Theor Biol 7:1–52.
135. Foley RA, Lee PC. 1989. Finite social space, evolutionary pathways, and reconstructing hominid behavior. Science 243:901–906.
136. Wrangham RW. 1987. Evolution of social structure. In: Smuts B, Cheney DL, Seyfarth RM, Wrangham RW, Struhsaker TT, editors. Primate societies. Chicago: Chicago University Press. p 282–298.
137. Gosden RG, Faddy MJ. 1994. Ovarian aging, follicular depletion, and steroidogenesis. Exp Gerontol 29:265–274.
138. Frisch RE. 1978. Population, food intake, and fertility. Science 199:22–30.
139. Bongaarts J. 1980. Does malnutrition affect fecundity? A summary of evidence. Science 208: 564–569.
140. Wood JW. 1989. Fecundity and natural fertility in humans. In: Milligan SR, editor. Oxford reviews of reproductive biology, vol II. Oxford: Oxford University Press. p 61–102.
141. Wood JW, Weinstein M. 1988. A model of age-specific fecundability. Popul Stud 42:85– 113.
142. O'Connor KA, Holman DJ, Wood JW. 1998. Declining fecundity and ovarian ageing in natural fertility populations. Maturitas 30: 127–136.
143. Paul A, Kuester J, Podzuweit D. 1993. Reproductive senescence and terminal investment in female Barbary macaques (*Macaca sylvanus*) at Salem. Int J Primatol 14:105–124.
144. Packer C, Tatar M, Collins A. 1998. Reproductive cessation in female mammals. Nature 392:807–811.
145. Laws RM, Parker ISC, Johnstone RCB. 1975. Reproduction. elephants and their habitats. Oxford: Clarendon Press. p 204–227.
146. Robinson WC. 1986. Another look at the Hutterites and natural fertility. Soc Biol 33:65– 76.
147. Finch CE, Gosden RG. 1986. Animal models for the human menopause. In: Mastroianni L Jr, Paulsen CA, editors. Aging, reproduction and the climacteric. London: Plenum Press. p 3–34.
148. Leidy LE. 1998. Accessory eggs, follicular atresia, and the evolution of menopause. Am J Phys Anthropol Abstracts Suppl 26:148–149.

149. Falconer DS. 1989. Introduction to quantitative genetics, 3rd ed. New York: Longman Scientific.
150. Roff DA. 1997. Evolutionary quantitative genetics. New York: Chapman Hall.
151. Houle D. 1992. Comparing the evolvability and variability of quantitative traits. Genetics 130:195–204.
152. Houle D. 1991. Genetic covariance of fitness correlates: what genetic correlations are made of and why it matters. Evolution 45:630–648.
153. Gustafsson L. 1986. Lifetime reproductive success and heritability: empirical support for Fisher's fundamental theorem. Am Nat 128:761–764.
154. Mousseau TA, Roff DA. 1986. Natural selection and the heritability of fitness components. Heredity 59:181–197.
155. Pomiankowski A, Møller AP. 1995. A resolution of the lek paradox. Proc R Soc Lond B 206: 21–29.
156. Felsenstein J. 1976. The theoretical population genetics of variable selection and migration. Ann Rev Genet 10:253–280.
157. Lande R. 1976. The maintenance of genetic variability by mutation in a polygenic character with linked loci. Genet Res Cambridge 26:221–235.
158. Rose MR. 1982. Antagonistic pleiotropy, dominance, and genetic variation. Heredity 48: 63–78.
159. Wright S. 1969. The theory of gene frequencies, vol. 2. London: The University of Chicago Press.

SECTION 17

HOMOSEXUALITY

Introduction to Chapter 20

Homosexuality is an even a bigger evolutionary puzzle than menopause. The puzzle is not yet solved, but we can certainly sketch out the range of possible explanations and examine the evidence for clues as to which explanation might be correct. At present, there is no single idea that explains all instances of homosexuality.

This topic might be imagined to have political content. Precisely because of that possible reaction, I want to make clear at the outset that I have included homosexuality in this reader primarily because it is so difficult to explain in Darwinian terms: From the perspective of evolutionary theory, it is a challenging case. Students have consistently asked me, "If selection works as you say it does, why does homosexuality exist?" I have taken that scientific question seriously, without regard to any possible political implications. I trust you will take a similarly open-minded approach.

Professor Camperio-Ciani and his co-authors have focused exclusively on male homosexuality. I suspect that is because there have been many more studies of it than of female homosexuality. That research "bias," if it is one, is motivated by the strong statistical association between male homosexuality and HIV-AIDS, thus making male homosexuality a candidate for medically motivated research dollars. In any case, to best support your understanding of the chapter, I will mostly confine my introductory remarks to male homosexuality.

There is debate about the incidence of homosexuality in our species, but the more credible studies suggest that roughly 2% of men and 1% of women identify themselves as primarily homosexual; some studies would double those percentages, but that would be the upper limit of the scientifically based estimates. (Note that we are not talking about the percentage of men or women who have had homosexual experiences or feelings; here we are focusing on those who prefer to mate exclusively with a same-sex partner.) The key point is that figures like 2% are very far above the mutation rate. For reference, mutation rates are on the order of 0.0001%. In other words, homosexuality is not caused by a suite of new mutations every generation. To the extent that genes influence sexual orientation, those genes have apparently spread, because they now occur at frequencies that cannot be explained by mutation alone.

Let's list possible explanations for the persistence of homosexuality. In other words, why didn't selection eliminate any genes that tend to steer sexual orientation towards homosexuality?

1. Homosexuality is not influenced by genes; instead it is the result of environmental effects, such as conditions during gestation or early social interactions. That would solve the puzzle. If there were no genes for homosexuality, selection could not remove them. But, on the available evidence, the underlined clause of Explanation 1 seems to be incorrect. The evidence concerns heritability. As we just reviewed in the previous chapter, heritability assesses how much of the variation in a trait is caused by individuals having different genes affecting the trait. In this case, the trait is sexual orientation and the variation consists of homosexual, bisexual and heterosexual. Studies comparing the level of similarity in sexual orientation among pairs of identical twins, pairs of fraternal twins and pairs of ordinary brothers consistently find that identical twins match on sexual orientation more than the other two kinds of siblings. In other words, if you have a twin who is homosexual, you yourself are more likely to be homosexual if that twin is an identical twin than if that twin is a fraternal twin. This higher *concordance* in identical twins is the definitive evidence that genetic differences are, to some degree, involved in causing the sexual orientation differences. I said "to some degree." Heritability measures that degree quantitatively, based on *how much* higher the sexual orientation concordance is among identical twins. There have been several studies, and the range of heritability estimates from those studies clusters around 0.5. (Studies of female homosexuality find similar heritabilities, but the same genes are almost certainly *not* involved because male homosexuality and female homosexuality do not run in the same families.) Concluding that the heritability of sexual orientation is 0.5 does not mean that environmental influences are irrelevant. Quite the opposite: If genetic differences explain half (0.5) of the variation in sexual orientation, it follows that environmental differences must explain the other half. We will explore this idea more when we discuss Explanation 5.

2. Homosexuality does not reduce reproductive success, so there would actually be no selection against it. This is a non-starter. The data show that, on average, homosexual men have many fewer children than heterosexual men. You are probably not surprised by this finding, but scientists can not rely on hunches; they have to collect and analyze the relevant data.

3. Homosexuality does not reduce inclusive fitness because homosexual men systematically support the reproduction of relatives. This kin-selection (see Chapter 6) explanation also fails because it does not match the facts. Studies show that homosexual men do not invest more resources in their nieces, nephews, brothers and sisters than do heterosexual men.

Where are we so far? The twin studies say there is a gene (or genes) that predispose individuals to develop a homosexual orientation. Let's be clear. A "gene that predisposes individuals to develop a homosexual orientation" is, statistically speaking, "a gene for homosexuality," so we are going to use that simpler, if slightly less nuanced phrase. The essential point is that there are genes for homosexuality, but that homosexuals tend not to pass them on (due to their low personal fitness), and they do not altruistically help their relatives pass these genes on either. Thus, our original puzzle still remains: Why do these genes for homosexuality still exist? What other clues do we have?

In 1993, Dr. Dean Hamer and his collaborators published a bold new claim. They thought they had found at least one gene for homosexuality. They said it was on the X-chromosome (the chromosome that women have two of but men have only one of), and they specified its locus address: Xq28 (the 28th position in the q region of the X-chromosome). It is only fair to say that there has been some controversy about whether Hamer and his coauthors were right, because there have been both failures and successes at replicating this finding. But their claim is important because it is precisely what motivated the authors of Chapter 20 to plan and carry out their study. Scientists often work this way. In effect they say, "If Hamer is right, we should find this pattern in the world; let's test Hamer's idea by finding out if that pattern exists or not." That is what Camperio-Ciani and his team did. The logic that supports their study is subtle and fascinating. Stick with me as I lay out Explanation 4.

4. The genes for homosexuality persist because they are sexually antagonistic, reducing fitness in one sex but increasing it in the other. In general, the notion of a sexually antagonistic gene is not radical. Think of it this way: Selection is the ultimate statistician. If, *averaged over all the bodies* a gene is sitting in, it raises fitness, then the gene will spread. This is definitionally and automatically true. Some of those bodies are older and some are younger; some are male and some are female. No matter. It could be that, on average, a particular gene—for example a homosexuality gene—reduces male fitness but increases female fitness by a larger amount. The positive and negative effects are not evenly dispersed over the whole population; they are clustered by sex, but so what? The average effect is positive, so the gene spreads. Are you skeptical?

Here is a noncontroversial example: nipples. Why do male mammals have them? They are nonfunctional in the sense that they do not nourish offspring, so they provide no obvious fitness benefits. Plus, they have a minus side; there are costs to producing and maintaining nipples—for example, males can get breast cancer. So why don't males have featureless chests? Because the genes that produce nipples provide huge fitness benefits for females, benefits that far outweigh the relatively small fitness costs they produce in males.

But Xq28 has yet another, special card to play. Ordinarily, any sexually antagonistic gene must produce a benefit in sex A that is larger than the cost it produces in sex B. Why do I say "ordinarily" instead of "always"? Because a gene on the X-chromosome (like Xq28) would *not* have to jump such a high hurdle. An X-chromosome gene has to produce a female benefit that is only *half* as large as the cost it inflicts on males. Why? Simply because, at each and every moment in evolutionary time, there are twice as many copies of any X-chromosome gene in female bodies as there are in male bodies. In other words, females would be twice as effective at transmitting an X-chromosome gene as males would be, so a smaller female fitness benefit translates, through them, to a higher rate of gene transmission.

Let's study this possibility just a bit more. During evolution, mutation creates new alleles and selection evaluates them. There are no rules or limits about what kinds of mutations can occur. Perhaps, in the billion or so years that sexual reproduction has existed, mutations for same-sex attraction have arisen multiple times in multiple species. Usually such genes would have been eliminated by selection because they lowered fitness. Somewhat less often, mutation produced a gene that caused homosexuality in one sex but provided a fitness benefit in the non-homosexual sex. How likely are those benefits to outweigh the fitness costs of homosexuality? Do you see that the answer to this question depends on what chromosome the gene is on? A mutation on an autosome would have to provide a female benefit as large as the male cost; but a mutation on the X-chromosome would have to provide a female benefit only half as large as the male cost. Thus, it was simply more likely that an X-chromosome homosexuality gene could meet the requirement of a net fitness benefit than it was that an autosomal homosexuality gene could.

If you are still with me, this is your next question: OK, but is that what happened in the case of Xq28? Specifically, how could we figure out if an Xq28-like factor predisposes male bodies to be homosexual but has nevertheless persisted in human populations because, when it occurs in female bodies, it elevates fitness? Answering this question is the central theme of Chapter 20.

Before we review the details of the study, I want to clear up one small issue that can be confusing. Sometimes students have trouble imagining that a gene for homosexuality could increase the fitness of either sex. The assumption that is causing the problem is the notion that the gene makes both sexes homosexual. That assumption is not at all required and is probably not even correct. Xq28, at least, clearly does not make both sexes homosexual; we know this from the family studies. Here is another way to think about how an Xq28-like gene might work. If you don't think of it as "a gene for homosexuality" but instead think of it as "a gene for liking to have sex with men," then you can see that such a gene could have opposite effects on male and female fitness. I am not claiming to know exactly how it works—nobody yet knows. I simply want to suggest how a "homosexuality gene" might express itself differently in men and women. OK, now let's see what Professor Camperio-Ciani and his coworkers discovered in their northern Italian population.

The study began by recruiting both homosexual and heterosexual participants, about 100 of each. But it is actually the relatives of these participants who provide the essential data for testing the hypothesis that Xq28 (or some other X-chromosome allele) *both predisposes male homosexuality and is sexually antagonistic.* To explore this hypothesis, we need to know which relatives of the homosexual and heterosexual participants are themselves homosexual, and we also need to know how many children each relative had. Thus, relatives of the participants were censused regarding their sexual orientation and their fertility (number of offspring). Next—and this step is critical—the relatives were grouped by how likely they were to have the same X-chromosome as the participant. All men, both homosexual and heterosexual men, have certain relatives with whom they are likely to share their X-chromosome and other relatives with whom it is very unlikely that they would share an X-chromosome. (This sharing pattern is very predictable from basic genetic principles, and I will explain it soon.)

This approach allows the authors of Chapter 20 to test two key predictions of the sexually antagonistic Xq28 hypothesis. The first prediction involves the homosexual participants' male relatives, and the second involves their female relatives. First, if a gene on the X-chromosome is causing a man to be homosexual, then homosexuality should be more common among those relatives who have the same X-chromosome he does, but not among those relatives who do not share his X-chromosome. This natural contrast between the two types of relatives lets us see whether something on the X-chromosome seems to be making a difference in sexual orientation. Likewise, the second prediction relies on this same kind of contrast, but it focuses on the homosexual participants' female relatives. If the hypothesized X-chromosome allele is sexually antagonistic, female relatives who have the same X-chromosome as a homosexual participant should have elevated fitness (more children). In contrast, women who have a homosexual relative but do not share his X-chromosome, should not have elevated fitness. These two predictions are both tested in Chapter 20. But to appreciate the tests, you will now need to understand which kinds of relatives are likely to share an X-chromosome and which kinds are not. Let's take a look at Figure J.

Which men are most likely to share an X-chromosome with a participant? Certainly not his father; his father contributed a Y, not an X. Every participant got his X-chromosome from his mother but, of course, his mother is not a man. The men who are most likely to

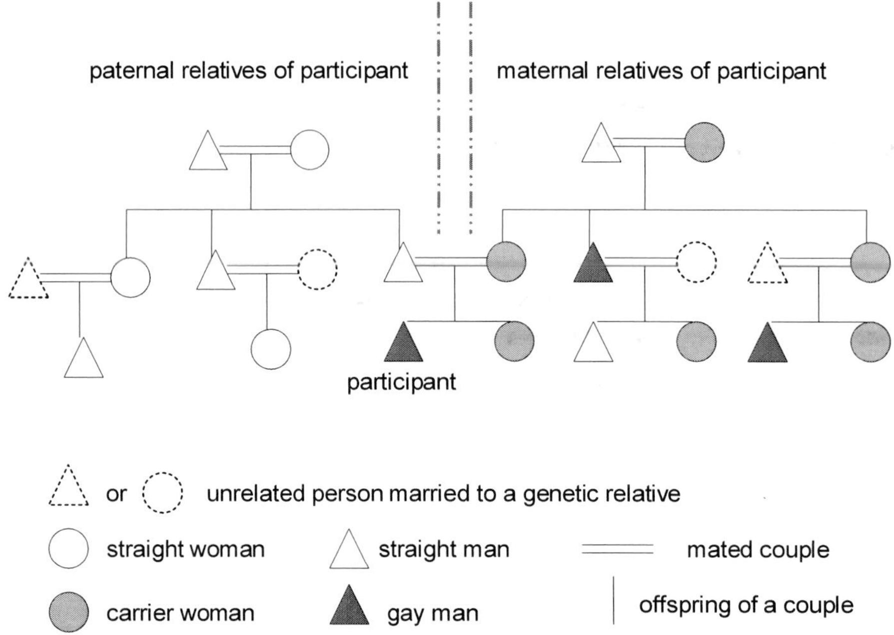

Figure J. The pattern of X-chromosome sharing among relatives. The diagram shows a homosexual male participant; his mother, father and sister; one brother and one sister of each of his parents (the participant's aunts and uncles); the mates (shown dashed because they are not genetic relatives of the participant and therefore irrelevant) of these aunts and uncles; some of the aunts' and uncles' offspring (cousins of the participant), and the participant's mother's and father's parents. A man's X-chromosome comes from his maternal line. Why? Men have unmatched sex chromosomes, X and Y, and produce roughly equal numbers of X-bearing and Y-bearing sperm. Females have two X's, so all their eggs are X-bearing. When a mother's egg unites with a Y-bearing sperm, a son is conceived; when her egg unites with an X-bearing sperm, a daughter is conceived. This means that a male absolutely got his X-chromosome from his mother; if he had gotten an X from his father, he would be a female. These facts alone determine the pattern of X-chromosome sharing.

have the same X-chromosome as a participant are his mother's brother (who most likely inherited it from the participant's mother's mother), and his mother's sister's son (his maternal cousin, who would have inherited it from the participant's mother's sister.) None of the men that a participant is related to through his father (his paternal relatives) could have his same X-chromosome because, remember, his X-chromosome did not come from his father's lineage. Similar thinking will show that the female relatives likely to share a participant's X-chromosome are, again, his maternal relatives.

What can we do with these genetic facts? The Xq28 hypothesis predicts that the male relatives of homosexuals who share their X-chromosome (their maternal relatives) should be more likely to be homosexual than the relatives who do not share their X-chromosome (their paternal relatives). But, because heterosexuals presumably lack the X-chromosome gene for homosexuality, sharing an X-chromosome with them should not elevate the chance of being homosexual. Put another way, the maternal relatives of heterosexuals should be no more likely to be homosexual than their paternal relatives. There is an equally important second prediction. According to the sexually antagonistic hypothesis, the female maternal relatives of homosexuals (those who share their X-chromosome) should have higher fitness than their paternal relatives, *and* higher fitness than either maternal or paternal relatives of heterosexuals. I will leave it to you to determine whether these predictions were supported in this northern Italian population.

At this point, do I dare to add another hypothesis? Well, I must, because I respect your intelligence, and we haven't paid any attention to the environmental side.

5. Certain family compositions predispose male homosexuality; in particular, men with multiple older brothers are more likely to be homosexual. Previous research by Ray Blanchard and others supports this idea. Note that, however we might imagine this result, it must be an environmental rather than a genetic effect. Having more or fewer older brothers will not affect your genotype. The "brother effect" might operate after birth, growing up with those older brothers or, as Blanchard argues, it might operate in the womb. The data strongly suggest that it is a brother effect and not a sibling effect; having more older brothers increases a boy's chances of becoming homosexual, while having more older sisters does not. Two facts strongly suggest a uterine effect rather than a socialization effect. First, having more older step-brothers (or half-brothers related only through the father) does not increase the likelihood that a boy will grow up to be homosexual. On the other hand, even older brothers who do not grow up in the same household do. This older-brother effect is substantial. One older brother increases a boy's chance of being homosexual by about 33%, but be careful how you interpret this. We need to remember that roughly 2% of men are homosexual. So, an increase of 33% will cause an increase in the likelihood of being homosexual from 2.0% to 2.6%. Each additional older brother would produce a similar increase, so three older brothers would essentially double the chance of being homosexual (from 2% to 4%). Just as older sisters do not seem to affect a boy's sexual orientation, neither older sisters nor brothers affect a girl's.

How might this kind of uterine effect operate? In other words, what process could allow the sex of your mother's previous fetuses to affect your sexual orientation? Here is the mechanism that Blanchard suggested: Because a male fetus has a Y-chromosome, he will produce proteins (from genes coded on his Y) that are foreign to his mother's body. She in turn will produce antibodies (immunological defenses) against these proteins. And the amount of these anti-Y antibodies she produces will probably increase with each son she carries. These maternally produced antibodies might then interfere with the Y-derived proteins of subsequent sons during their fetal development. This maternal interference could affect the development of the male-typical traits that the fetus's Y-derived proteins are trying to produce. Whether it is caused by maternal antibody interference is not yet clear, but a brain region involved in the regulation of male-typical sexual behavior differs between homosexual and heterosexual men, with homosexuals' brains resembling those of heterosexual women. Thus, while we cannot say exactly how the older-brother effect operates, Camperio-Ciani and his term did observe it: Their homosexual participants had a preponderance of older brothers, but their heterosexual participants did not.

To summarize, two different biological factors could be shaping male homosexuality in the northern Italian population described in Chapter 20. A particular allele, apparently located on the X-chromosome, might increase the likelihood of being homosexual, and this allele may persist in the population because it is sexually antagonistic. (Your job, remember, is to figure out if either of those effects are operating.) In addition to these X-chromosome effects, men with more older brothers are more likely to be homosexual than men with fewer older brothers.

When all those biological factors are considered, however, 80% of the variation still remains unexplained; so there are additional factors shaping male sexual orientation beyond X-chromosome genes and the number of older brothers. As mentioned above, previous heritability studies indicate that about 50% of the variation in sexual orientation is due to genetic differences. Since this study fell well short of 50%, there are apparently other genes elsewhere in the genome (*not* on the X-chromosome) that also affect sexual orientation. Likewise, additional, as yet unidentified environmental factors must also play a role in shaping sexual orientation.

Chapter 20 Glossary

carrier/non-homosexual carrier: A person who has a gene that predisposes homosexuality but who does not express the gene in that way and thus is heterosexual.

familiarity of homosexuality: (This must be a British usage; the journal that originally published Chapter 20 is British.) What the authors mean by this phrase is the way homosexuality is distributed in families—which relatives of a homosexual are likely to be homosexual. Studies that look for such patterns are called pedigree studies.

H-Y antigen: (Originally *anti*body *gen*erator) any molecule (e.g., protein) resulting from genes on the human Y-chromosome that stimulates the production of antibodies.

H-Y antibodies: Molecules produced by a mother to protect her against the foreign Y-chromosome proteins produced by her gestating sons.

Kinsey scale: (Named for the famous sex researcher who devised it) a simple tool used to assess sexual orientation. Participants are asked to report, separately, their attraction, behavior, fantasy, etc. on a 7-point scale where "0" means "always the opposite sex" and "6" means "always my own sex," with 1 to 5 representing various gradations in between.

partial penetrance: The situation when an allele is neither fully dominant nor fully recessive; when an allele is partially expressed.

pleiotropic: The situation when an allele affects more than one phenotypic trait.

sexually antagonistic gene: A gene that increases fitness in one sex and decreases it in another. Except for genes on the Y-chromosome, all genes occur in both sexes. They are favored by selection if their average effect on fitness is positive, regardless of how the pluses and minuses that sum to that positive effect are spread across males and females.

X-linked genetic factor: An allele on the X-chromosome.

Xq28: A small region of the X-chromosome claimed to carry alleles that affect sexual orientation.

Chapter 20
Evidence for Maternally Inherited Factors Favouring Male Homosexuality and Promoting Female Fecundity (2001)

Andrea Camperio-Ciani[1], Francesca Corna[1], and Claudio Capiluppi[2]*

The Darwinian paradox of male homosexuality in humans is examined, i.e. if male homosexuality has a genetic component and homosexuals reproduce less than heterosexuals, then why is this trait maintained in the population? In a sample of 98 homosexual and 100 heterosexual men and their relatives (a total of over 4600 individuals), we found that female maternal relatives of homosexuals have higher fecundity than female maternal relatives of heterosexuals and that this difference is not found in female paternal relatives. The study confirms previous reports, in particular that homosexuals have more maternal than paternal male homosexual relatives, that homosexual males are more often later-born than first-born and that they have more older brothers than older sisters. We discuss the findings and their implications for current research on male homosexuality.

Keywords: fecundity; male homosexuality; pedigree analysis; reproductive success

[1] Department of General Psychology, Università di Padova, via Venezia 8, 35100 Padova, Italy
[2] Department of Statistics, Università di Padova, via San Francesco 33, 35100 Padova, Italy
[*] Author for correspondence (andrea.camperio@unipd.it).

1. Introduction

The determinants of homosexuality are often the topic of heated discussion, partly because of alleged moral implications, but also because of a genuine difficulty in explaining how genetic factors that lower male fecundity survive natural selection (Moran 1972; Bell & Weinberg 1978). Data are often the missing element in such discussions. Here, we provide novel empirical data on the fecundities of the families of homosexuals and heterosexuals, together with findings regarding possible determinants of human male homosexuality. We also show that the data contradict a number of hypotheses about the genetic basis of homosexuality. It should be noted that, in this argument, all researchers do not assume that homosexuals never reproduce but that they reduce, on average, their direct fitness.

At present, two lines of evidence point to genetic factors being partially associated with human male homosexuality. The first line comes from studies of the familiarity of homosexuality. Family studies of brothers and twins report that homosexuality is more common in brothers of homosexual subjects (Bailey & Zucker 1995). Hamer and co-workers (Hamer *et al.* 1993; Hamer & Copeland 1995), using pedigree analysis, have shown an elevated homosexuality rate in the maternal line of homosexuals. This finding has been taken to suggest the existence of X-linked genetic factors favouring male homosexuality. DNA linkage analyses, performed on homosexual brothers, have localized a candidate factor on the Xq28, a distal region of the short arm of the X-chromosome (Hamer *et al.* 1993; Hamer & Copeland 1995). These findings, however, have been difficult to replicate (Bailey *et al.* 1999; Rice *et al.* 1999).

The second, independent, line of evidence comes from studies of sexual differentiation of the brain during foetal life, which found that, in men, homosexual orientation correlates with late birth order and an excess of older brothers (Blanchard & Klassen 1996; Blanchard 1997). Blanchard (1997) hypothesized that late birth order and sibling sex ratio reflected the progressive immunization of some mothers to H-Y antigen, presented by the male foetus. After a number of pregnancies with male foetuses, the increasing effect of this maternal immunity reaction, according to the hypothesis, should reduce the sexual differentiation of the brain in succeeding male foetuses (Blanchard 1997). Blanchard *et al.* (1997) suggest that each additional older brother increases the odds of homosexuality in the next male born by *ca.* 33%.

The primary aim of our work was to replicate the above findings. Note that the two lines of evidence are not mutually exclusive. Therefore, we investigated both hypotheses concomitantly, using a family-tree analysis to compare families of homosexual and heterosexual males.

We also sought to analyse the possible persistence of genetic factors favouring homosexuality, which contradicts the expectation that natural selection would eliminate such factors. This Darwinian paradox has been the topic of several studies, but is still unresolved. Wilson (1975), attempting to solve the paradox, suggested a possible role for homosexuals as helpers in their families, increasing the fitnesses of their relatives and, thus, balancing their reduced direct fitness. However, both Muscarella (2000) and Bobrow & Bailey (2001) in recent empirical studies, showed that homosexuals do not act as helpers and do not give more financial or emotional resources to siblings than do heterosexual men. Other studies by Ř. Trivers (personnal communication), Rice (1998) and Miller (2000) have suggested the partial penetrance of a candidate homosexual genetic factor and hypothesized that pleiotropic or sexually antagonistic effects, acting on personality, increase fecundity in non-homosexual carriers, thereby balancing the reduction in homosexual fecundity (Miller 2000). No supportive evidence or empirical data, however, has yet been shown.

Table 1. Estimated distribution of male homosexuals in the families of study subjects.

	maternal line		paternal line	
	N	homosexuals	N	homosexuals
male relatives of homosexual subjects	396	22[a]	593	12
male relatives of heterosexual subjects	370	0[b]	604	8

[a] Homosexual male relatives of homosexual subjects: expected (based on the paternal line) (12/593 x 396) = 8.01; observed = 22; $X^2 = 8.92$; d.f. = *1*; $p < 0.005$.

[b] Homosexual male relatives of heterosexual subjects: expected (based on the paternal line) (8/604 x 370) = 4.9; observed = 0; $X^2 = 3.45$; d.f. = 1; not significant.

2. Methods

We asked 98 homosexual and 100 heterosexual men, living in northern Italy, to fill in an anonymous questionnaire, in a private setting, following written instructions. Subjects reported their own sexual orientation and provided demographic information and sexual-orientation data on their siblings, first cousins, parents, aunts, uncles and grandparents.

Homosexual subjects were sampled using the targeted sampling methodology of Watters & Biernacki (1989) for accessing 'hidden' populations. Subjects were recruited from three associations for homosexual men and two discotheques. For comparison, the heterosexual control group was sampled from two after-work clubs and two discotheques, located in the same geographical region, controlling further for age of subjects. Sampling occurred at different times to ensure that subjects with different habits were represented. The tendency to over-sample larger families, which could have two or more homosexual siblings, was controlled by asking the composition of the family and the estimates were corrected by weighting the units with the inverse of their probability of selection. More generally, estimates referring to populations of units different from the survey units (i.e. the population of the grandmothers of the interviewed subjects) were corrected, when necessary, by weighting the units with the inverse of their probability of selection in the sample.

Accessing a 'hidden' population is difficult because no sampling frame exists and public acknowledgement of membership could be potentially prejudicial to the subjects; therefore, standard probabilistic sampling methods produce low response rates and unreliable responses (Heckathorn 1997).

Targeted sampling is a widely employed method for accessing hidden populations, in preference to snowball sampling (Goodman 1961) and other examples of chain-referral. All these procedures introduce well-documented biases (Spreen & Marius 1992), which we were aware of. We considered that these biases would have limited relevancy in this study, and our procedures were unlikely to be associated with such biases, owing to the fact that we accessed only demographic variables (such as number of siblings, uncles, etc.). Moreover, the control sample was selected, using the same methodology, to reproduce the same possible biases and to guarantee the internal validity of the comparisons.

The questionnaire was designed to yield the following information: size of the aforementioned relative classes, birth order and sex of siblings, and sexual orientation of all male relatives. The questionnaires showed that the two subject groups did not differ in age (mean homosexuals, 33.22 years; mean heterosexuals, 33.06 years; two-tailed Mann-Whitney tests p=0.903), education (p= 0.655) or professional status (p= 0.989). The information provided was considered trustworthy owing to the anonymity of the questionnaire, its simplicity (e.g. recalling numbers of brothers and first cousins) and the lack of emotionally laden questions. Sexual orientation was self-reported, and confirmed by answers to five questions from the seven-point Kinsey scale on sexual self-identification, fantasy, attraction, imagination and personal behaviour (Kinsey *et al.* 1948).

Subject age was self-reported; level of education was in accordance with the Italian scholastic system; profession was separated into eight categories, devised by us. Six subjects reported information on parents and siblings only.

The homosexual frequency on the maternal line of homosexual subjects was compared with the expected frequency on the corresponding paternal line (the observed rate of homosexuality in paternal line multiplied by the number of relatives in the material line). This was preferred to a comparison with the relative frequency for the whole population, the estimate of which, in Italy, is provisional and unreliable (Barbaglio & Colombo 2001); in fact, population estimates are based only on those individuals that have declared their sexual orientation in ersus forms. Furthermore, the whole country population rate is not adequate for comparison with the rate of geographically restricted area.

3. Results

According to subjects' reports, homosexuals have more homosexual relatives on the maternal than on the paternal pedigree line; families of heterosexuals do not share this feature (table 1).

In table 1, it should be noted that the higher total number (N) in the paternal line than in the maternal line naturally emerges from the following. (i) The presence of one more kin class in the paternal line (sons of paternal uncles); while in the maternal line the corresponding kin class (sons of maternal uncles) could not be included because the members of this kin class do not share the X chromosome with our subjects. (ii) The fact that the number of fathers classified in the paternal line is higher than the number of brothers classified in the maternal line, as expected in a population with low general fecundity, such as the studied population from northern Italy. We also included fathers in the analysis, as they could, in principle, be homosexual; homosexuals are reproductive and can transmit genetic factors (Moran 1972; Bell & Weinberg 1978).

It should also be noted that we did not compare homosexuals' and heterosexuals' estimates, since homosexuals may have reported a higher frequency of homosexuality among

Table 2. Reported fecundities of subjects' relatives from the maternal and paternal lines (*p*-Value calculated using the Mann-Whitney test; n.s., not significant.)

		homosexuals			heterosexuals			
relative class	likelihood of sharing X chromosome	*N*	mean fecundity	s.d.	*N*	mean fecundity	s.d.	*p*
mothers	1	98	2.69	1.30	100	2.32	1.05	0.02
first-borns' mothers	1	32	1.94	0.88	52	1.77	0.61	n.s.
maternal aunts	0.75	95	1.98	0.98	121	1.51	0.97	0.001
maternal uncles	0.25	114	1.75	0.91	117	1.73	0.94	n.s.
maternal grandparents	0.5	91	3.55	2.57	100	3.39	1.85	n.s.
sons and daughters of maternal grandparents[a]	0.25–1	307	2.17	0.85	338	1.83	0.72	0.001
paternal aunts	0	111	1.75	1.07	129	1.94	1.13	n.s.
paternal uncles	0	134	1.75	0.95	135	1.67	0.94	n.s.
paternal grandparents	0	88	4.03	2.72	99	3.81	2.43	n.s.
sons and daughters of paternal grandparents (excluding father)[b]	0	239	1.77	0.85	264	1.80	0.89	n.s.

[a]Cumulative fecundity of mothers, maternal aunts and maternal uncles.

[b]Cumulative fecundity of paternal aunts and paternal uncles.

their relatives (Bailey *et al.* 1999). It is unknown whether homosexuals over-estimate, heterosexuals underestimate, or both biases occur.

Regarding the relationship between birth order and sexual orientation, we found: (i) a birth-order distribution of homosexuals that was significantly different (less first borns, more second, third and fourth borns) from that of heterosexuals, both in our sample ($X^2 = 9.89$, d.f. = 3, $p < 0.05$) and in the whole population of northern Italy ($X^2 = 11.03$, d.f. = 3,$p < 0.02$), as reported in census data from the Italian Bureau of Statistics (ISTAT 1951 1981); (ii) an excess of males among older siblings in homosexuals (observed: 69 brothers, 45 sisters; expected: 57 brothers, 57 sisters; $X^2 = 5.06$, d.f. = 1, $p < 0.05$).

We then estimated the importances of the excess of homosexuals in the maternal line and the excess of older brothers and other possible biological factors. A multiple linear regression and a logistic regression are carried out, using a stepwise selection method, to identify biological factors that might explain the observed variability in sexual orientation, measured on the seven-point Kinsey scale (Kinsey *et al.* 1948) and then dichotomized. Both models selected the same factors; therefore, only outcomes from linear regression are reported. The first predictor, selected by the stepwise method, was 'number of homosexual relatives in maternal line', accounting for 14% of the variance in sexual orientation (beta = −0.489, R^2=0.14 (p< 0.001), partial $R^2 = 0.12$). The second predictor selected, 'number of previous male brothers', explains 6.7% of the residual variance (beta = −0.141, $R^2 = 0.067$ ($p = 0.001$), partial $R^2 = 0.078$). Predictors not selected were: number of homosexual relatives in the paternal line, birth order, total number of brothers and age. The above model explains a limited 20% of the sexual-orientation variance ($R^2 = 0.207$, corrected $R^2 = 0.195$).

The most intriguing result derives from the pedigree analysis of fecundity. Table 2 shows that maternal relatives of homosexuals have higher fecundity than maternal relatives of heterosexuals; this difference does not appear in the paternal line.

Especially noteworthy are the differences between the groups formed by maternal aunts and mothers of homosexuals and heterosexuals. A potential confounding variable is that, owing to male birth-order effects, homosexuals may belong, on average, to slightly larger families than heterosexuals. Excluding mothers of non-first-born homosexuals from the analysis is a conservative way of controlling for this effect (conservative because birth order is only tenuously associated with homosexuality; see above).

Fecundities of grandparents of homosexuals and heterosexuals are not significantly different, whereas the difference in the fecundities of sons and daughters of maternal grandparents is highly significant (table 2).

4. Discussion

The results confirm the existence of previously proposed biological predictors that partly explain male homosexuality: (i) the prevalence of homosexuals in the maternal line, suggesting possible genetic factors in the X-chromosome (Hamer *et al.* 1993); and (ii) the number of older brothers of homosexuals, suggesting a possible maternal immunization effect (Blanchard & Klassen 1996; Blanchard 1997). Stepwise regression analysis shows that both variables have a limited effect, explaining *ca.* 20% of the variance in sexual orientation; the maternal effect, however, is weighted relatively greater (14%) than the number of older brothers (6.7%). The fact that birth order and total number of brothers did not enter the regression means that these variables are already explained by the number of older brothers.

Another result is that females in the maternal lines of homosexuals are significantly more fecund than those in the maternal lines of heterosexuals. No significant differences are found, however, when comparing paternal relatives of homosexuals and heterosexuals. It should be noted that higher fecundity in mothers of homosexuals is predicted by the immunization hypothesis of Blanchard (1997). In fact, multiple male births are necessary for immunization to happen, and this occurs only in highly fecund mothers in our society. It could be argued that aunts might present higher fecundity owing to familiarity effects. Familiarity effects do not, however, explain why higher fecundity should be present only in the maternal line and not in aunts of the paternal line. Furthermore, higher fecundity, while not significant (possibly owing to the small sample size), is also found in mothers whose first son is homosexual, where the immunization hypothesis could not apply and higher fecundity should not be expected.

The observed differences in fecundity are compatible, at present, with either physiological or behavioural causes (e.g. lower abortion rate or increased ability to find mates, respectively), or both. The results in tables 1 and 2 suggest that genetic factors, transmitted in the maternal line, both increase the probability of being homosexual in males and increase fecundity in females. Grandparents do not show significant differences in fecundity. Note that if the grandmother is the carrier of the factors (likelihood of 0.5), she should show a higher fecundity, but if the grandfather is the carrier (likelihood of 0.5), we do not expect him to show higher fecundity. Therefore, a significant difference between the fecundities of grandparents of homosexuals and heterosexuals is not expected.

We have already mentioned that the hypothesis of genetic factors favouring homosexuality contradicts the expectation that natural selection would eliminate such factors, creating a paradox. Our data resolve this paradox by showing that there might be, hitherto unsuspected, reproductive advantages associated with male homosexuality. Existing genetic models of homosexuality are unable, however, to accommodate our results. A simple one-locus genetic model may predict the persistence of homosexuality, if homosexuals are assumed to be homozygous for an allele that is beneficial to heterozygotes (MacIntyre & Estep 1993; McKnight 1997; Werner 1998).

Such a model, however, does not explain the differences between paternal and maternal pedigree lines, nor does it explain the preferential maternal inheritance of homosexuality. Instead, both features can be found in one-locus models of genes residing on sex chromosomes (Rice 1998). Specifically, the assumption of an X-linked allele beneficial to female fecundity, but detrimental to male fecundity, would fit the pattern in our data. The existence of X-linked genetic factors associated with male homosexuality has been suggested previously from DNA-linkage analysis of homosexual brothers (Hamer *et al.* 1993; Hamer & Copeland 1995; for dissenting views, see Risch *et al.* 1993; Rice *et al.* 1999). The model, however, faces another difficulty. Based on our data, the X-linked allele should substantially enhance female fecundity, while being, at most, slightly detrimental to overall male fecundity (note that, in table 2, the fecundity of maternal uncles of homosexuals is not depressed, despite the fact that five of these individuals were childless homosexuals or bisexuals). The model would, thus, predict that the allele is very common (Rice 1998), whereas homosexuality is uncommon (Kinsey *et al.* 1948; Whitam *et al.* 1993; Hamer & Copeland 1995; Barbaglio & Colombo 2001).

The problem is not solved by assuming that the allele leads only rarely to homosexuality, since, in this case, the allele should also be prevalent in heterosexuals' families and, thus, could not explain differences in fecundity. Finally, it has been hypothesized (Miller 2000) that homosexuality may result from the accumulation, in a single individual, of many alleles, each of which is, by itself, beneficial, but whose cumulative effect is to favour homosexuality. This may account for persisting rare homosexuality, but not for differences between paternal and maternal family lines or the preferential maternal inheritance of homosexuality. This model, however, may be combined with the previous one to obtain a polygenic model where one or more alleles are X-linked. Such a model may, in principle, reproduce our findings, but a full analysis of this possibility is beyond the scope of the present paper.

Finally, we emphasize that over 79% of the variance in male sexual orientation in our sample remains unaccounted for by the factors of an excess of maternal homosexual kin and number of older brothers. This is consistent with theoretical and empirical studies, which show that individual experiences are a powerful determinant of human sexual behaviour and self-identity (Churchill 1967; Enquist *et al.* 2002; for other species, see D'Udine & Alleva 1983; Hogan & Bolhius 1994). Indeed, it is still possible that the higher incidence of homosexuality in the maternal line results from culturally, rather than genetically, inherited traits. In many societies, such as in northern Italy, mothers spend a lot of time with children of both sexes, especially during the early years, which are critical for the development of sexual identity and orientation (Bailey & Zucker 1995; Smith *et al.* 1998). This suggests that the mother and the mother's family could be the preferential source of some of a child's behaviour and attitudes (Cavalli-Sforza & Feldman 1981; Cavalli-Sforza *et al.* 1982), including traits relevant to the child's future sexual preferences and behaviour. One may also speculate about co-evolution between genes and culture (Cavalli-Sforza & Feldman 1981; Boyd & Richerson 1985; Laland *et al.* 1995). For instance, a genetic mutation with the characteristics described above may not be advantageous when fecundity is high and limited only by the availability of resources, as in most traditional societies, but may spread more readily if fecundity is low and resources plentiful, as found in industrialized societies, such as Italy.

In conclusion, it is clear that our findings, if confirmed by further research, are only one piece in a much larger puzzle on the nature of human sexuality.

We acknowledge the fundamental contribution of Giorgia Camperio Ciani to the theoretical issues in this study. We thank Robert Trivers, Jeffery Kurland and two anonymous referees for helpful suggestions and discussion on the arguments presented, and Stefano Ghirlanda for discussing the predictions of proposed genetic models of male homosexuality. This research was funded from our own pockets.

References

Bailey, J. M. & Zucker, K. J. 1995 Childhood sex typed behavior and sexual orientation: a conceptual analysis and quantitative review. *Dev. Psychol.* 31, 43–56.

Bailey, J. M., Pillard, R. C., Dawood, K., Miller, M. B., Farrer, L. A., Tivedi, S. & Murphy, R. L. 1999 A family history study of male sexual orientation using three independent samples. *Behav. Genet.* 29, 79–86.

Barbaglio, M. & Colombo, A. 2001 *Omosessuali moderni. Gay e lesbiche in Italia.* Bologna: Il Mulino.

Bell, A. P. & Weinberg, M. 1978 *Homosexualities: a study of diversity among men and women.* New York: Simon & Schuster.

Blanchard, R. 1997 Birth order and sibling sex ratio in homosexual versus heterosexual males and females. *A. Rev. Sex Res.* 8, 27–67.

Blanchard, R. & Klassen, P. 1996 H-Y antigen and homosexuality in men. *J. Theor. Biol.* 185, 373–378.

Bobrow, D. & Bailey, M. J. 2001 Is male homosexuality maintained via kin selection. *Evol. Hum. Behav.* **22**, 361–368.

Boyd, R. & Richerson, P. J. 1985 *Culture and the evolutionary process.* University of Chicago Press.

Cavalli-Sforza, L. L. & Feldman, M. 1981 *Cultural transmission and evolution.* Princeton University Press.

Cavalli-Sforza, L. L., Feldman, M. W., Chen, K. H. & Dornbusch, S. M. 1982 Theory and observation in cultural transmission. *Science* **218**, 19–27.

Churchill, W. 1967 *Homosexual behavior among males: a cross-cultural and cross-species investigation.* Englewood Cliffs, NJ: Prentice-Hall.

D'Udine, B. & Alleva, G. E. 1983 Early experience and sexual preferences in rodents. In *Mate choice* (ed. P. Bateson), pp. 311–327. Cambridge University Press.

Enquist, M., Ghirlanda, S., Wachtmeister, C.-A. & Lundqvist, D. 2002 An ethological theory of attractiveness. In *Advances in visual cognition. I. Facial attractiveness* (ed. G. Rhodes & L. A. Zebrowitz), pp. 127–151. Westport, CT: Ablex Press.

Goodman, L. A. 1961 Snowball sampling. *Ann. Math. Stat.* 32, 148–170.

Hamer, D. H. & Copeland, P. 1995 *The science of desire.* New York: Simon & Schuster.

Hamer, D. H., Hu, S., Magnuson, V. L., Hu, N. & Pattattucci, A. M. 1993 A linkage between DNA markers on the X chromosome and male sexual orientation. *Science* **261**, 321–327.

Heckathorn, D. D. 1997 Respondent-driven sampling: a new approach to the study of hidden populations. *Soc. Probl.* **44**, 174–199.

Hogan, J. A. & Bolhius, J. J. 1994 *Causal mechanisms of behavioural development.* Cambridge University Press.

ISTAT, 1951–1981 *Annali ISTAT: mortalità, natalità, fecondità, comportamenti riproduttivi.* Rome: Istituto Nazionale di Statistica.

Kinsey, A. C., Martin, C. E. & Pomeroy, W. B. 1948 *Sexual behavior in the human male.* Philadelphia: W. B. Saunders.

Laland, K. N., Kumm, J. & Feldman, M. W. 1995 Geneculture co-evolutionary theory: a test case. *Curr. Anthropol.* **36**, 131–156.

MacIntyre, F. & Estep, K. W. 1993 Sperm competition and the persistence of genes for male homosexuality. *Biosystems* **31**, 223–233.

McKnight, J. 1997 *Straight science: homosexuality, evolution and adaptation.* New York: Routledge.

Miller, E. M. 2000 Homosexuality, birth order and evolution: toward an equilibrium reproductive economics of homosexuality. *Arch. Sex. Behav.* **29**, 1–34.

Moran, P. A. P. 1972 Familial effects in schizophrenia and homosexuality. *Aust. N. Z. J. Psychiatry* **6**, 116–119.

Muscarella, F. 2000 The evolution of homoerotic behavior in humans. *J. Homosex.* **40**, 51–77.

Rice, G., Anderson, C., Risch, N. & Ebers, G. 1999 Male homosexuality: absence of linkage to microsatellite markers at Xq28. *Science* **284,** 665–667.

Rice, W. 1998 Sex chromosomes and the evolution of sexual dimorphism. *Evolution* **38**, 735–742.

Risch, N., Squires-Wheeler, E. & Keats, B. J. B. 1993 Male sexual orientation and genetic evidence. *Science* **262**, 2063–2065.

Smith, P. K., Cowie, H. & Blades, M. 1998 *Understanding children's development.* Oxford: Blackwell.

Spreen, M. & Marius, H. 1992 Rare populations, hidden populations and link-tracing designs: what and why? *Bull. Methodol. Sociol.* **6**, 34–58.

Watters, J. K. & Biernacki, P. 1989 Targeted sampling options for the study of hidden populations. *Soc. Probl.* **36**, 416–430.

Werner, D. 1998 Sobre a evolição cultural na homosexualidade masculina. In *Masculino, feminino, plural* (ed. J. M. Pedro & M. P. Grossi), pp. 99–129. Florianópolis, Brazil: Mulheres.

Whitam, F. L., Diamond, M. & Martin, J. 1993 Homosexual orientation in twins: a report on 61 pairs and three triplet sets. *Arch. Sex. Behav.* **22**, 187–206.

Wilson, E. O. 1975 *Sociobiology: the new synthesis.* Cambridge, MA: Harvard University Press.

SECTION 18

DOMESTICATION

Introduction to Chapter 21

For millions of years, hunting and gathering of wild foods was the only mode of subsistence our ancestors knew. The human body is thus adapted to live on that diet. We are reaping a harvest of health problems because of the various ways in which our modern diet differs from the ancestral one.

Seven thousand years may sound like a long time. But, compared to the seven million years since our lineage diverged from the one that leads to chimpanzees, seven thousand years is just an evolutionary eye blink. I mention seven thousand years because it is roughly the length of time that humans have been practicing agriculture—farming crops and tending domesticated animals. We were not fully dependent on agriculture seven thousand years ago; there was a slow ramping-up period. And the process started a bit later in some parts of the world than in others. But, before that time, all humans got all of their food from wild plants and animals. Thus, our ancestors were pre-agricultural hunters and gatherers for 99.9% of the time our lineage has existed.

That does not mean there has been no evolution in the last seven thousand years. There has demonstrably been some. For example, most mammals cannot digest milk as adults. The gene that codes for *lactase*—the enzyme that breaks down lact*ose* (milk sugar)—turns off after they have been weaned by their mothers. Lactose became available to adult humans after the domestication of milk-producing animals. As you might expect, this constituted a selection pressure for adults to continue producing lactase. In fact, there is a clear statistical relationship showing an evolutionary response: The longer any given human population has kept dairy animals, the larger the percentage of adults who produce lactase. In other words, mutations that prevented a shutting down of the lactase locus spread where milk was available as a food for adults. But this is not a very big or very fancy evolutionary change: just the continued production of an enzyme that selection had already designed for milk digestion. Also note that even this minor innovation has not spread across the entire species: Many people are still lactose-intolerant, being unable to extend their lactase production past infancy. More elaborate adaptations to our new agricultural diet will probably take considerably longer than a few thousand years.

In fact, we still bear the stamp of many selection pressures that predominated during our species' long hunter-gatherer period. Our dietary preferences are good examples. Hunter-gatherers must harvest (find, process, detoxify, run down, kill, butcher etc.) every calorie they consume. Getting this food was not free; in other words, to avoid starvation, they had to consume more calories than they expended in getting it. Hence, we prefer foods that are calorically dense (that is, foods that have a lot of calories per unit weight). Sugars and fats are calorically dense. Need I say more? These are tastes we love. When humans domesticated plants, they used artificial selection to increase the sugar content of numerous plant species, and they did the same to elevate fat levels in their domesticated animals. Wild animals of the type hunter-gatherers would have eaten have body fat levels between 2% and 4%, whereas domestic cattle or swine can have body fat levels over 25%. When you pay more for "USDA Prime" meat, you are paying for more fat. Salt is another example. It provides essential electrolytes, and insufficient salt intake can result in death. If they do not live in a seaside habitat, hunter-gatherers would generally find that salt was quite scarce. Hunter-gatherers travel long distances to collect it—sometimes eating soil to satisfy their needs. And salt is one of the first items hunter-gatherers trade for when they come into contact with agricultural peoples.

The bottom line is that we have strong taste preferences for the nutrients that were both essential and scarce during our hunter-gatherer past. Sometimes those ancestral taste preferences cause problems for us, precisely because fat, sugar and salt are no longer scarce. In fact, in many parts of the world they are cheap and abundant. Thus, recent overconsumption of fat and sugar is correlated with heart (cardiovascular) disease and diabetes, and overconsumption of salt is correlated with high blood pressure (hypertension) which can cause fatal or brain-damaging strokes. To put it simply, we are suffering from too much of what was, for our ancestors, a good thing.

That part of the story is relatively well known, and you may have read about it elsewhere. But O'Keefe and Cordain are emphasizing another way our diets differ from those of our ancestors. They are concerned about what we are getting too much of; but they are also paying attention to the things we are missing. You may be surprised to learn that one of the most critical missing nutrients is a kind of fat. How could that be? We drizzle cheese on our french fries. We deep fry everything. The simple fact is that there are many different kinds of fat. Some of them are greatly oversupplied in our contemporary diet, but one essential type is seriously undersupplied.

Let's begin by laying out the various kinds of fats (technically, chemists call them fatty acids). You surely know some of them: Saturated fats, monounsaturated fats, polyunsaturated fats, and trans-fats are all names you will have seen on standard nutrition labels. All of these fatty acids share the same basic molecular composition. They are medium to long chains consisting mostly of carbon and hydrogen atoms. Most of their carbon atoms are bonded to two hydrogen atoms (except the first carbon which is bonded to three). When a carbon is bonded to two (or three) hydrogen atoms, the bond is "saturated." When a carbon is bonded to only one hydrogen atom, it forms a special double bond with its neighboring carbon atom (to make up for the missing hydrogen), and the resulting bond is said to be "unsaturated."

OK, now things are simple. If all the bonds in a fatty acid molecule are saturated bonds (with two or three hydrogens on each carbon), you have a saturated fat. If just one of the bonds is unsaturated (having one rather than two or three hydrogens), you are looking at a *mono*unsaturated fat. If more than one of the bonds is unsaturated (you guessed it), you have a *poly*unsaturated fat. How many bonds could be unsaturated? In the longest and most polyunsaturated fatty acid (the one that is most missing from our modern diets), there are six unsaturated bonds.

Unsaturated bonds make a fatty acid molecule floppy and flexible, as opposed to stiff and rigid. Thus, saturated fats are quite stiff, which you can see with your eyes because they tend to be solid at room temperature. Monounsaturated fats are somewhat more flexible, for example, liquid at room temperature but solid in your refrigerator. Polyunsaturated fats are still more flexible—liquid even in the refrigerator—and they become progressively more flexible the more unsaturated bonds they have. The one with six unsaturated bonds is liquid in the freezer.

Polyunsaturated fatty acids come in three major types, depending on where in the chain the first unsaturated bond occurs. They are called omega-3, omega-6 and omega-9 fatty acids, denoting fatty acids whose first unsaturated bond occurs at the 3rd, 6th or 9th carbon, respectively. ("Omega" is sometimes written as the corresponding Greek letter, ω.) Despite such seemingly small molecular differences, these various omega fats do very different jobs in the body; they cannot substitute for one another, and even significantly compete with each other.

There is one more import dimension along which fatty acids differ. In principle, any monounsaturated or polyunsaturated fatty acid could be a trans-fat or a cis-fat. Trans- (and its opposite, cis-) refer to the geometric orientation of the two carbon atoms participating in an unsaturated bond: whether they lie on the same or opposite sides of the bond. (Note that this orientation issue is irrelevant to saturated fat because they have no unsaturated bonds.) As a result of this orientation difference, trans-fats are more rigid and stable and tend to be solid at body temperature. These differences in turn make them less prone to spoilage but at the same time interfere with one of their essential roles in the body, which I will explain below. You already know that the flexibility of a mono- or polyunsaturated fatty acid depends on how many double bonds it has. What I am saying now is that unsaturated cis-bonds are more flexible than unsaturated trans-bonds. So, there are two factors that jointly determine the flexibility of a fatty acid. The more unsaturated bonds it has, the more flexible it will be, and the more of those unsaturated bonds are cis-bonds, the more flexible it will be. For the record, trans-fats are rare in nature; most naturally occurring mono- and polyunsaturated fats are cis-fats. Food producers have developed techniques for turning cis-bonds into trans-bonds because it improves the shelf life of their products. What it does for your life is more dubious.

Fatty acids perform several important functions in the body. One well known function is energy storage. Many kinds of fat can be made from sugar. And that is precisely what the body does when it has more sugar than it needs at the moment; it converts that excess sugar to fat. Then, the fat can be burned at some future date when calories are in short supply. This energy-storage function was critical for our hunter-gatherer ancestors because their natural food supply had inevitable ups and downs. Our bodies are, of course, still anticipating that next bad season. Do you see the consequence of that? This, of course, is a topic on the "too much" side of our modern diet; let's return to the more surprising "too little" side.

Another very important role of fatty acids is to facilitate processes at cell membranes. Each kind of cell has an enclosing membrane made mostly out of fat, and much of the cell's biological activity depends on what happens in and across that membrane. The "queen" of the membrane fats is that very long, polyunsaturated fatty acid with 6 unsaturated bonds that we briefly mentioned above. Its name is DHA (docosahexaenoic acid). This omega-3 fatty acid can not be made from sugar and is generally far too valuable to be burned for calories. It is super-floppy and flexible and it makes everything that happens in membranes happen more quickly and efficiently. Shortly, I will make painfully obvious why this is a big deal.

There are a variety of omega-3 fatty acids (ones with their first unsaturated bond at the 3rd carbon). Of these, DHA is the longest and has more unsaturated bonds than any of the others, making it, as I have said, the best membrane fat. Our bodies can make DHA from the shorter omega-3 fats. But—and this is a big but—there are two problems with our contemporary diet: 1) *all* of the omega-3's, both the shorter and the longer ones, are seriously undersupplied, and 2) the omega-6's interfere with the process of converting shorter omega-3's into the longer membrane-critical DHA. And, guess what: The omega-6's are wildly *over*supplied in our present diet. The current US diet has more than 15 times as much omega-6 as omega-3.

The reason for this omega-6/omega-3 imbalance is simple. Omega-6 fats are concentrated in plant seeds. You think you don't eat many seeds? Think again. Most of what Americans eat comes from two seeds: corn and soybeans. We eat plenty of corn and soybean oil directly because they are standard frying agents, and they are also components of salad dressings, mayonnaise, etc. But, just as importantly, corn and soybeans are what cattle, swine and poultry are raised on, so all the meat, chicken, milk, cheese, and eggs is also loaded with omega-6. Fish—as long as it is not breaded and fried with corn or soybean oil—is a good source of omega-3; unless it is farmed! Guess what farmed fish are fed.

O'Keefe and Cordain are very interested in the effects of this omega imbalance on heart health. Heart disease was virtually unknown as recently as 1910. But, in less than a century, it became one of the two leading causes of death (each year it is a close contest between heart disease and all cancers combined). The rise in heart disease (and a variety of other health problems such as obesity) closely parallels the narrowing of our diet to corn and soybeans. O'Keefe and Cordain's concern is well placed, and much evidence suggests they are right.

Something that O'Keefe and Cordain mostly neglect is the equally important role of omega-3's, especially DHA, in brain health. At any given moment, half of all the DHA in your body is in your brain. Remembering that your brain is only about 2% of your total body weight makes it clear that the brain is a DHA hog. The reason is that brain cells—neurons—are very long and skinny and hence have proportionately large membranes. And it is very rapid transactions across those membranes that let neurons do their job of carrying information. Omega-3-starved brains do not work very well. Could this be the reason that the US is now last among developed nations in math and science achievement?

This final chapter is, in more ways than one, food for thought. I hope you enjoy it.

Chapter 21 Glossary

atherosclerosis: Thickening of the blood vessel walls due to a build up of fatty materials; these build ups are called plaques. Remember the phrase "solid at body temperature."

cardiovascular disease: Diseases of the hearth or blood vessels; atherosclerosis is the most common type.

diabetes: Disorder resulting from abnormally high levels of blood sugar. The kind of diabetes affected by diet is called "Type 2 diabetes" and is a consequence of high insulin resistance in which the body responds poorly to the blood-sugar-reducing effects of the hormone insulin.

metabolic syndrome: A combination of medical disorders that increase the risk of both cardiovascular disease and diabetes.

HDL/LDL: So called "good" and "bad" cholesterol. HDL reduces and LDL promotes atherosclerotic plaques.

Chapter 21
Cardiovascular Disease Resulting from a Diet and Lifestyle at Odds with Our Paleolithic Genome: How to Become a 21st-Century Hunter-Gatherer

James H. O'Keefe, Jr. MD, and Loren Cordain, PhD

Our genetic make-up, shaped through millions of years of evolution, determines our nutritional and activity needs. Although the human genome has remained primarily unchanged since the agricultural revolution 10,000 years ago, our diet and lifestyle have become progressively more divergent from those of our ancient ancestors. Accumulating evidence suggests that this mismatch between our modern diet and lifestyle and our Paleolithic genome is playing a substantial role in the ongoing epidemics of obesity, hypertension, diabetes, and atherosclerotic cardiovascular disease. Until 500 generations ago, all humans consumed only wild and unprocessed food foraged and hunted from their environment. These circumstances provided a diet high in lean protein, polyunsaturated fats (especially omega-3 [ω-3] fatty acids), monounsaturated fats, fiber, vitamins, minerals, antioxidants, and other beneficial phytochemicals. Historical and anthropological studies show hunter-gatherers generally to be healthy, fit, and largely free of the degenerative cardiovascular diseases common in modern societies. This review outlines the essence of our hunter-gatherer genetic legacy and suggests practical steps to realign our modern milieu with our ancient genome in an effort to improve cardiovascular health.

HDL = high-density lipoprotein; LDL = low-density lipoprotein

Humans evolved during the Paleolithic period, from approximately 2.6 million years ago to 10,000 years ago. Although the human genome has remained largely unchanged (DNA evidence documents relatively little change in the genome during the past 10,000 years),[1] our diet and lifestyle have become progressively more divergent from those of our ancient ancestors. These maladaptive changes began approximately 10,000 years ago with the advent of the agricultural revolution and have been accelerating in recent decades. Socially, we are a people of the 21st century, but genetically we remain citizens of the Paleolithic era.

Today most of us dwell in mechanized urban settings, leading largely sedentary lives and eating a highly processed synthetic diet. As a result, two thirds of Americans are overweight or obese.[2] The lifetime incidence of hypertension is an astounding 90%,[3] and the metabolic syndrome is present in up to 40% of middle-aged American adults.[4] Cardiovascular disease remains the number 1 cause of death, accounting for 41% of all fatalities, and the prevalence of heart disease in the United States is projected to double during the next 50 years.[5] Despite remarkable pharmacological and technological advances, the pandemic of cardiovascular disease continues. At least for today, the genes we are born with are those that we will live and die with. Thus, the most practical solution for reducing the incidence of chronic degenerative diseases such as atherosclerosis is to realign our current maladaptive diet and lifestyle to simulate the milieu for which we are genetically designed.

Living organisms thrive best in the milieu and on the diet to which they were evolutionarily adapted; this is a fundamental axiom of biology. All of the food consumed daily by our ancient ancestors had to be foraged or hunted from wild plants and animals in their natural world. In many respects, that Paleolithic world is gone forever, but insights gained from a wide array of disciplines are providing a clear picture of the ideal diet and lifestyle for humans. The hunter-gatherer mode of life became extinct in its purely non-westernized form in the 20th century.[6] At the beginning of the 21st century, we are the first generation to have the genetic and scientific understanding to allow us to reconstruct the essence of this lifestyle and the means to afford it.

Historical and archaeological evidence shows hunter-gatherers generally to be lean, fit, and largely free from signs and symptoms of chronic diseases.[7] When hunter-gatherer societies transitioned to an agricultural grain-based diet, their general health deteriorated.[8,9] Average adult height was substantially shorter for both men and women who consumed cereals and starches compared with their hunter-gatherer ancestors who consumed lean meats, fruits, and vegetables.[10] Furthermore, studies of bones and teeth reveal that populations who changed to a grain-based diet had shorter life spans, higher childhood mortality, and a higher incidence of osteoporosis, rickets, and various other

Table 1. Comparison of Diets

	Hunter-gatherer	Low-carbohydrate (Atkins diet)	Traditional low-fat (Ornish diet)	Traditional Mediterranean
Protein (%)	High (19–35)	Moderate (18–23)	Low (<15)	Moderate (16–23)
Carbohydrates (%)	Moderate (22–40)	Low (4–26)	High (80)	Moderate (50)
Total fat (%)	Moderate (28–47)	High (51–78)	Low (<10)	Moderate (30)
Saturated fat	Moderate	High	Low	Low
Monounsaturated fat	High	Moderate	Low	High
Polyunsaturated fat	Moderate	Moderate	Low	Moderate
Omega-3 fat	High	Low	Low	High
Total fiber	High	Low	High	High
Fruits and vegetables	High	Low	High	High
Nuts and seeds	Moderate	Low	Low	Moderate
Salt	Low	High	Low	Moderate
Refined sugars	Low	Low	Low	Low
Glycemic load	Low	Low	High	Low

mineral- and vitamin-deficiency diseases.[8,9] When former hunter-gatherers adopt Western lifestyles, obesity, type 2 diabetes, atherosclerosis, and other diseases of civilization become commonplace.[11,12]

This review outlines the essence of the hunter-gatherer lifestyle and diet and suggests practical steps to realign our modern milieu with our ancient genome in an effort to improve cardiovascular health, vigor, and longevity.

The Ideal Human Diet

Perhaps no scientific topic has generated more controversy and confusion in recent times than the question of the ideal human diet. Medical experts espouse divergent views of human nutrition with evangelical zeal, each citing scientific data to validate their respective contradictory conclusions. This confusing dialogue is epitomized by the Atkins[13] vs Ornish[14] debate. The Atkins diet includes high protein, high saturated fat, and avoidance of nearly all carbohydrates. In contrast, the Ornish diet consists of 80% carbohydrates and minimized consumption of all animal protein fats. Proponents of both diets insist theirs is the answer to the American epidemics of obesity and cardiovascular disease; however, the advice for these diets is mutually exclusive and diametrically opposed.

In truth, the ideal diet is neither of these extremes nor what many medical professionals now promote. In a recently published large review of approximately 150 studies on the link between diet and cardiovascular health,[15] the authors concluded that 3 major dietary approaches have emerged as the most effective in preventing cardiovascular events: (1) replacing saturated and *trans*-fats with monounsaturated and polyunsaturated fats; (2) increasing consumption of omega-3 (ω-3) fats from either fish or plant sources such as nuts; and (3) eating a diet high in various fruits, vegetables, nuts, and whole grains and avoiding foods with a high glycemic load (a large amount of quickly digestible carbohydrates). Despite common misperceptions, this report found no strong evidence for a link between risk of cardiovascular disease and intake of meat, cholesterol, or total fat.

These broad characteristics are consistent with the diet that Paleolithic humans evolved eating. This is the diet that our hunter-gatherer ancestors thrived on until the advent of the agricultural revolution. Through the millennia, our genome and physiology became adapted to this diet. Of course, this diet varied by paleontological period, geographic location, season, and culture, but many characteristics remained consistent until recent times (Table 1).

Real Food, not Synthetic Food

Our remote ancestors consumed only natural and unprocessed food foraged and hunted from their environment. This subsistence strategy provided a diet of lean protein that was high in fiber, vitamins, minerals, antioxidants, and other beneficial phytochemicals[16] (Table 2). The typical Paleolithic diet compared with the average modern American diet contained 2 to 3 times more fiber, 1.5 to 2.0 times more polyunsaturated and monounsaturated fats, 4 times more ω-3 fats, but 60% to 70% less saturated fat. Protein intake was 2 to 3 times higher, and potassium intake was 3 to 4 times higher; however, sodium intake was 4 to 5 times lower.[17] Finally, the Paleolithic diet contained no refined grains and sugars (except for seasonally available honey). Clearly, the ongoing epidemic of cardiovascular diseases is at least in part due to these striking discrepancies between the diet we are designed to eat and what we eat today.

In growing season, abundant fruits, berries, and vegetables were consumed. The one variable on which nearly all nutritional experts can agree is the need for increased intake of fruits and vegetables in our modern diet. We do not fully understand all the health-promoting components of unprocessed whole-plant foods; thus, the only way to ensure the benefits is to consume these foods regularly in their natural and unprocessed state. Most experts recommend an intake of 5 servings of fruits and vegetables per day; studies indicate that only 16% of adults are meeting this goal.[18] However, approximately 8 or more daily servings of fresh fruits and vegetables (avoiding potatoes and bananas, because of their high glycemic loads) are necessary to replicate the dietary composition that we evolved eating[17] and to lower the risk of coronary heart disease.[19]

Large randomized controlled trials recently have shown antioxidant supplements to be ineffective in improving cardiovascular outcomes.[20,21] In contrast, many epidemiological studies have shown cardiovascular protection from diets that contain foods naturally high in antioxidants, such as vitamins A, C, and E.[19,22] The hunter-gatherer diet is high in beneficial phytochemicals and antioxidants, thus rendering multivitamin and mineral supplements superfluous.[17]

Caloric Intake

Throughout most of human history, food consumption (energy intake) was obligatorily linked to food acquisition (energy output). Accordingly, our ancient ancestors expended more energy finding and obtaining food calories than do typical sedentary, westernized citizens for whom there is virtually no connection between energy intake and energy expenditure.

Our cravings for calorie-dense foods, such as fats, sweets, and starches, are legacies of our Paleolithic ancestors, who sought these foods because they conferred positive survival value in an environment in which these food types were scarce. These cravings betray us in our modern world, where calorie-dense foods are abundant and inexpensive, and most people die of caloric excess manifested as obesity, the metabolic syndrome, hypertension, and cardiovascular disease. Compounding the issue is the fact that our genome became adapted to an environment in which caloric intake was often sporadic and sometimes inadequate. This promoted efficient energy use and storage, commonly referred to as the *thrifty gene hypothesis.* Although this genetic adaptation (which results in storage of excess calories as intra-abdominal fat) provides a survival advantage in an environment of scarcity, it becomes a liability in the setting of long-term excessive caloric intake.

Although the key to weight loss is simply the daily consumption of fewer calories than are expended, it is easier to moderate caloric intake in a diet that has adequate quantities of protein and fat because of superior satiety compared with a high-carbohydrate, low-fat diet.[15,23,24] This strategy in part accounts for the success of the Atkins diet in inducing weight loss,[25] but its high levels of saturated fat, low levels of antioxidants, and net metabolic acidosis, which may promote osteoporosis and atherosclerosis, make this a suboptimal eating style.[26,27] A growing consensus indicates that a diet containing moderate amounts of beneficial fat and protein in addition to carbohydrates consisting exclusively of low-glycemic-load foods (nonstarchy vegetables and fruits) in conjunction with daily exercise is the most effective way to achieve and maintain ideal body weight and prevent cardiovascular disease.[15,23,24,26] This approach was the eating pattern and lifestyle of prehistoric humans.

Table 2. Fundamentals of the Hunter-Gatherer Diet and Lifestyle

Eat whole, natural, fresh foods; avoid highly processed and high-glycemic-load foods
Consume a diet high in fruits, vegetables, nuts, and berries and low in refined grains and sugars. Nutrient-dense, low-glycemic-load fruits and vegetables such as berries, plums, citrus, apples, cantaloupe, spinach, tomatoes, broccoli, cauliflower, and avocados are best
Increase consumption of omega-3 fatty acids from fish, fish oil, and plant sources
Avoid trans-fats entirely, and limit intake of saturated fats. This means eliminating fried foods, hard margarine, commercial baked goods, and most packaged and processed snack foods. Substitute monounsaturated and polyunsaturated fats for saturated fats
Increase consumption of lean protein, such as skinless poultry, fish, and game meats and lean cuts of red meat. Cuts with the words round or loin in the name usually are lean. Avoid high-fat dairy and fatty, salty processed meats such as bacon, sausage, and deli meats
Incorporate olive oil and/or non-trans-fatty acid canola oil into the diet Drink water
Participate in daily exercise from various activities (incorporating aerobic and strength training and stretching exercises). Outdoor activities are ideal

ω-3 Fats

The polyunsaturated fats are classified as ω-6 (generally proinflammatory) and ω-3 (anti-inflammatory with several other inherent cardioprotective effects). ω-3 Fats were abundant in the diet of our Paleolithic ancestors.[28] In the natural world, the broad base of the food chain is composed of ubiquitous algae in the sea and of grasses and leaves on land. The small amount of fat in algae, grasses, and leaves is rich in ω-3 fatty acids, which become more concentrated in larger animals up through both the land and marine food chains, especially in fish and larger grazing animals. Today, meat from domesticated animals is low in ω-3 fats because these animals are generally grain-fed or corn-fed rather than grass-fed.[29] This and other issues have resulted in much lower intake of ω-3 fats today compared with our remote ancestors.[28,29]

The correction of this ω-3 deficiency in the modern diet is a key step to improving the cardiovascular risk in our population.[30] Two randomized trials, the Lyon Diet Heart Study,[31] which involved 600 postinfarction patients, and the Indo-Mediterranean Diet Heart Study[32] (Figure 1), which involved 1000 coronary heart disease patients, evaluated a standard low-fat American Heart Association diet vs a traditional Mediterranean diet (similar in composition to our ancestral hunter-gatherer diet; Table 1). The patients on the Mediterranean diet rich in ω-3 and monounsaturated fats, fruits, vegetables, legumes, and nuts experienced 50% to 70% reductions in risk of cardiovascular events during long-term follow-up.

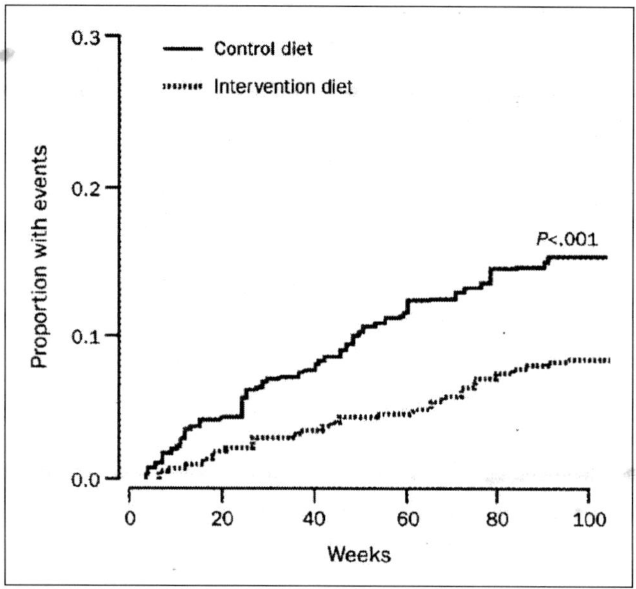

Figure 1. The Indo-Mediterranean Diet Heart Study[32] showed a reduction of cardiac deaths and myocardial infarctions in patients on the intervention diet (a traditional Mediterranean diet high in omega-3 fats, fruits, and vegetables and low in saturated fat) compared with a standard American Heart Association (control) diet.

The Gruppo Italiano per lo Studio della Sopravvivenza nell'Infarto Miocardico Prevenzione study[33] randomized more than 11,000 myocardial infarction survivors to 1 g/d of an 85% ω-3 supplement or control. The ω-3 group experienced a 45% reduction in sudden cardiac death and a 20% decrease in all-cause mortality during a 3½-year period[33] (Figure 2). Prospective studies indicate that increased intake of fat in the form of ω-3 fatty acids from either plant sources (a-linolenic) or fish oils (eicosahexa-noic acid and docasa-hexanoic acid) will reduce cardiovascular risk up to 32% to 50%.[29–34] Recently, for the first time, the American Heart Association recommended that a nutrient, ω-3 fatty acids, be consumed as a supplement if the diet contained an insufficient amount of this fat.[35]

Monounsaturated Fats

Monounsaturated fats made up approximately half of the total fat in the diets of most hunter-gatherers.[36] Monounsaturated fats reduce cardiovascular risk, especially when substituted for easily digestible starches and sugars.[37] Nuts are a valuable source of monounsaturated fats and have been shown to be cardioprotective in at least 6 epidemiological studies.[15,22,38]

Our hunter-gatherer ancestors relied on nuts as an easily accessible source of calorie-dense, highly nutritious food that was often available in non-summer months. The calories in nuts typically are 80% from fat, but most of this is in the form of healthy monounsaturated and polyunsaturated fatty acids (including some ω-3 fat). Epidemiological studies show that frequent nut consumption (5 or more times per week) is associated with up to a 50% reduction in risk of myocardial infarction compared with the risk of people who rarely or never eat nuts.[38] Other studies show that nut consumption reduces the risk of developing type 2 diabetes,[39] lowers the atherogenic low-density lipoprotein (LDL) cholesterol level without lowering the high-density lipoprotein (HDL) level,[40] and provides plant-based protein and other potentially cardioprotective nutrients such as vitamin E, folate, magnesium, copper, zinc, and selenium. Because of their high levels of fiber, protein, and fat, nuts also provide better and longer-lasting satiety compared with high-glycemic-load snack foods typically consumed today. Oleic acid is the major monounsaturated fat in our diets and is found in meats, nuts, avocados, dark chocolate, and olive oil. Although some of these foods were not part of the ancient ancestral diet, they can improve the cardiovascular risk profile when substituted for sugar, starches, *trans*-fats, and saturated fats that are prevalent in the modern diet. Studies suggest that replacing saturated fat with monounsaturated fat would result in a 30% reduction in risk, or 3 times the risk reduction achieved by replacing saturated fat with carbohydrates.[37]

Vegetarian vs "Breaditarian"

All evidence points to the fact that hunter-gatherers were omnivorous.[41] Strictly vegetarian diets are difficult to follow and are not necessarily associated with better health. A study of 2 groups of Bantu villagers in Tanzania compared 618 people who lived on a lakeshore and consumed large amounts of fish to 645 people who lived in the nearby hills and were vegetarians.[42] The lifestyles, gene pools, and diets (except for the fish) were similar in the 2 groups. The fish-consuming group had lower blood pressure levels; lower triglyceride, cholesterol, and leptin levels; and higher plasma ω-3 fat levels than the vegetarian group.[42,43]

Many current vegetarians would be more appropriately labeled "breaditarians." Modern vegetarian diets often rely heavily on processed carbohydrates such as white rice, potatoes, and white flour and sugars. The *South Asian paradox* refers to the relatively high prevalence of coronary heart disease despite low levels of LDL cholesterol and low prevalence of obesity in urban vegetarians from India who consume a diet high in refined carbohydrates.[32] In westernized societies, sugar intake has increased substantially during the past 2 centuries (Figure 3[44]). A recent study showed that a high-glycemic-load diet is the most important dietary predictor of HDL level (as an inverse relationship).[45] A high-glycemic-load diet predisposes a person to the metabolic syndrome and cardiovascular disease and is one of the most atherogenic features of our modern eating pattern.[45–48]

Can Meat Be Cardioprotective?

Comprehensive studies of diverse hunter-gatherer populations show that these people typically derived 45% to 60% of their calories from animal food.[36,41] Only 14% of hunter-gatherer societies obtained more than 50% of their calories from plant sources.[36,41] Paleolithic humans often lived in temperate climates and were confronted with winters during which most plant-based food was unavailable. Early humans adapted to these conditions by eating meat, organs, marrow, and fat from animals during the winter months. Paradoxically, these meat-based hunter-gatherer diets were nonatherogenic.[36,41] Although increased meat consumption in Western diets has been associated with increased cardiovascular risk, the hunter-gatherer societies were relatively free of the signs and symptoms of cardiovascular disease.[7]

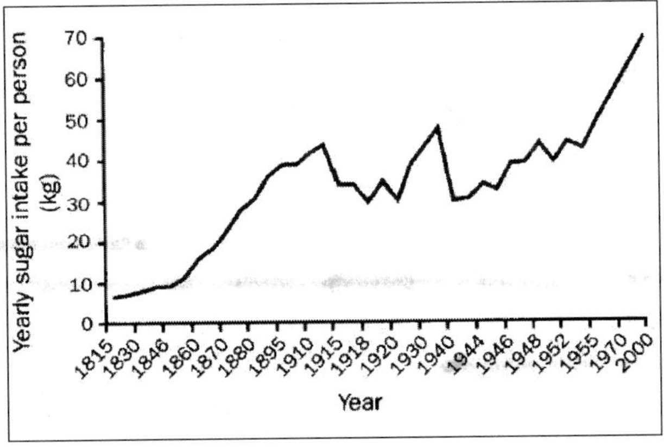

Figure 3. Average per capita consumption of sugar in England (1815–1970) and in the United States (1970–2000).[44]

The flesh of wild game is typically about 2% to 4% fat by weight and contains relatively high levels of monounsaturated and ω-3 fats compared with fatty grain-produced domestic meats, which can contain 20% to 25% fat by weight, much of it in the form of saturated fat.[27] Wild game meat is not widely accessible today, and many people do not prefer the "game" taste, which is at least in part conferred by a higher ω-3 content and by aromatic oils from plant foods consumed by the herbivore. The modern-day alternative is to choose animal protein sources that are low in saturated fat, such as skinless poultry, fish, eggs (especially high–ω-3 varieties), and lean cuts of red meat with visible fat trimmed.

It is not the amount of meat eaten but rather the composition of the meat and cooking methods that determine the health effects of this food. Accumulating scientific evidence indicates that meat consumption is not a risk for cardiovascular disease, but instead, the risk is secondary to high levels of saturated fat typically found in the meat of most modern domesticated animals.[44,49] Diets high in lean protein can improve lipid profiles and overall health, especially if care is taken to trim any visible fat from the meats and to allow the fat to drain when cooking.[50–55] Lean animal protein eaten at regular intervals (with each meal) improves satiety levels,[56–58] increases dietary thermogenesis,[56,59,60] improves insulin sensitivity,[55,61,62] and thereby facilitates weight loss[51,63,64] while providing many essential nutrients.[65] However, cooking red meats at high temperatures produces charring and high levels of heterocyclic amines, which have been implicated in the risk of gastrointestinal and prostate cancers.[66] Highly salted and preserved meats may also contain carcinogens. Lean, fresh meat cooked appropriately is a healthy and beneficial component of a varied diet, especially in conjunction with a high intake of vegetables and fruits.[65]

Trans-Fatty Acids

Trans-fatty acids are found in small quantities in the fat tissues of all ruminant animals. However, in recent decades, intake of *trans*-fatty acids has increased markedly because of their ubiquitous presence in commercially prepared foods. *Trans*-fatty acids are synthesized when hydrogen is applied to edible oils under high pressure and temperature in the presence of a catalyst. Hydrogenation of the edible oils is typically done in the prepared food industry to prolong shelf-life in commercial baked goods such as cookies, crackers, donuts, croissants, and processed snack foods. *Trans*-fatty acids are also found in shortenings, most margarines, and deep-fried foods, and recently in many brands of commercially available canola oils.[67] *Trans*-fats lower HDL levels, increase LDL levels, and increase risk of both cardiovascular disease and cancer.[24–37]

Studies indicate that replacing *trans*-fatty acids (typically 2% of total daily calories in the American diet) with the same amount of natural unsaturated fatty acids would result in a large (50%) decrease in risk of coronary heart disease.[37]

Beverages

Our Paleolithic ancestors drank water almost exclusively. Recent data suggest that generous water intake, 5 or more glasses daily, is associated with a lower risk of coronary heart disease.[68] This may be simply a function of the fact that water, when consumed frequently, displaces calorie-dense beverages such as sugared sodas from the diet. Or it may be that water provides adequate hydration and reduces blood viscosity better than other commonly ingested drinks. In any event, water is the beverage we are adapted to drink, and evidence suggests that it should remain the principal fluid we drink.

Sugared sodas are the predominant beverage consumed in America today. These are calorie-dense, nutritionally barren drinks that have contributed to the rise in obesity and insulin resistance. Generally, fruit juices are also high in sugar, and thus it is preferable to eat the whole fruit, which provides fiber and a lower glycemic load.[19,47]

Tea (*Camellia sinensis*) has been brewed for thousands of years as a favorite drink in several parts of the world. This beverage has been shown to be high in natural antioxidant phytochemicals (polyphenolic compounds). Drinking tea has been shown to reverse endothelial vasomotor dysfunction in people with coronary artery disease,[69] which may in part explain the inverse relationship between tea consumption and cardiovascular disease seen in observational studies. In 2 recent epidemiological studies, tea consumption (>2–3 cups per day) was associated with approximately half the risk of myocardial infarction compared with non-tea consumption.[70,71] Thus, tea appears to be a natural beverage that may help prevent cardiovascular disease, although more randomized prospective data are needed.

Hunter-Gatherer Fitness

Our Paleolithic ancestors exerted themselves daily to secure their food, water, and protection.[72,73] Although modern technology has made physical exertion optional, it is still important to exercise as though our survival depended on it, and in a different way it still does. We are genetically adapted to live an extremely physically active lifestyle. A sedentary existence predisposes us to obesity, hypertension, the metabolic syndrome, diabetes, and most types of cardiovascular disease, whereas regular exercise decreases the risks of developing all these diseases. Even in times of caloric excess, hunter-gatherers avoided weight gain in part because they were extremely physically active. Studies of obesity consistently show that the best way to maintain weight loss (regardless of the type of diet used) is by daily physical exercise.[74]

Our remote ancestors participated in various physical activities daily. They walked and ran 5 to 10 miles daily as they foraged and hunted for their food sources.[72,73] They also lifted, carried, climbed, stretched, leaped, and did whatever else was necessary to secure their sustenance and protection. Days of heavy exertion were followed by recovery days. In modern terms, these people cross-trained with aerobic, resistance, and flexibility exercises. According to recent data on physical activity, fitness programs that use various exercises are the most effective in preventing cardiovascular diseases.[75]

Summary

The hunter-gatherer diet and lifestyle are the milieu for which we remain genetically adapted. Although it is neither practical nor even possible to replicate all prehistoric living conditions today, these general characteristics should serve as a template to design and test effective interventions to reduce the incidence of degenerative cardiovascular diseases.

We acknowledge Connie Smith for her assistance with the preparation of the submitted manuscript.

From the Mid America Heart Institute, Cardiovascular Consultants, Kansas City, Mo (J.H.O.); and Department of Health and Exercise Science, Colorado State University, Fort Collins (L.C.).

Individual reprints of this article are not available. Address correspondence to James H. O'Keefe, Jr, MD, Mid America Heart Institute, Cardiovascular Consultants, 4330 Wornall Rd, Suite 2000, Kansas City, MO 64111 (e-mail: jho-keefe@cc-pc.com).

References

1. Macaulay V. Richards M, Hickey E, et al. The emerging tree of West Eurasian mtDNAs: a synthesis of control-region sequences and RFLPs. *Am J Hum Genet.* 1999;64:232–249.
2. Flegal KM, Carroll MD, Ogden CL, Johnson CL. Prevalence and trends in obesity among US adults, 1999–2000. *JAMA*. 2002;288: 1723–1727.
3. Vasan RS, Beiser A, Seshadri S, et al. Residual lifetime risk for developing hypertension in middle-aged women and men: the Framingham Heart Study. *JAMA.* 2002;287:1003–1010.
4. Ford ES, Giles WH, Dietz WH. Prevalence of the metabolic syndrome among US adults: findings from the third National Health and Nutrition Examination Survey. *JAMA*. 2002;287:356–359.
5. Foot DK, Lewis RP, Pearson TA, Beller GA. Demographics and cardiology, 1950–2050. *J Am Coll Cardiol.* 2000;35(5, suppl B): 66B–80B.
6. Lee RB, Daly R, eds. *The Cambridge Encyclopedia of Hunters and Gatherers.* Cambridge, UK: Cambridge University Press; 1999.
7. Eaton SB, Konner M, Shostak M. Stone agers in the fast lane: chronic degenerative diseases in evolutionary perspective. *Am J Med.* 1988;84:739–749.
8. Cohen MN. The significance of long-term changes in human diet and food economy. In: Harris M, Ross EB, eds. *Food and Evolution: Toward a Theory of Human Food Habits.* Philadelphia, Pa: Temple University Press; 1987:261–283.
9. Cassidy CM. Nutrition and health in agriculturalists and hunter-gatherers: a case study of two prehistoric populations. In: Jerome NW, Kandel RF, Pelto GH, eds. *Nutritional Anthropology: Contemporary Approaches to Diet & Culture.* Pleasantville, NY: Redgrave Publishing Co; 1980:117–145.
10. Cohen MN. *Health and the Rise of Civilization.* New Haven, Conn: Yale University Press; 1989:118–119.
11. Daniel M, Rowley KG, McDermott R, Mylvaganam A, O'Dea K. Diabetes incidence in an Australian aboriginal population: an 8-year follow-up study. *Diabetes Care.* 1999;22:1993–1998.
12. Ebbesson SO, Schraer CD, Risica PM, et al. Diabetes and impaired glucose tolerance in three Alaskan Eskimo populations: the Alaska-Siberia Project. *Diabetes Care.* 1998;21:563–569.
13. Atkins RC. *Dr. Atkins' The New Diet Revolution.* New York, NY: Avon Books; 1998.
14. Ornish D. *Dr. Dean Ornish's Program for Reversing Heart Disease: The Only System Scientifically Proven to Reverse Heart Disease Without Drugs or Surgery.* New York, NY: Random House; 1990.

15. Hu FB, Willett WC. Optimal diets for prevention of coronary heart disease. *JAMA.* 2002;288:2569–2578.
16. Eaton SB, Eaton SB III, Konner MJ. Paleolithic nutrition revisited: a twelve-year retrospective on its nature and implications. *Eur J Clin Nutr.* 1997;51:201–216.
17. Cordain L. The nutritional characteristics of a contemporary diet based upon Paleolithic food groups. *J Am Neutraceut Assoc.* 2002;5:15–24.
18. DeBoer SW, Thomas RJ, Brekke MJ, et al. Dietary intake of fruits, vegetables, and fat in Olmsted County, Minnesota. *Mayo Clin Proc.* 2003;78:161–166.
19. Joshipura KJ, Hu FB, Mason JE, et al. The effect of fruit and vegetable intake on risk for coronary heart disease. *Ann Intern* Med. 2001;134:1106–1114.
20. Heart Protection Study Collaborative Group. MRC/BHF Heart Protection Study of antioxidant vitamin supplementation in 20,536 high-risk individuals: a randomised placebo-controlled trial. *Lancet.* 2002;360:23–33.
21. GISSI-Prevenzione Investigators (Gruppo Italiano per lo Studio della Sopravvivenza nell'Infarto miocardico). Dietary supplementation with n-3 polyunsaturated fatty acids and vitamin E after myocardial infarction: results of the GISSI-Prevenzione trial [published correction appears in *Lancet.* 2001;357:642]. *Lancet.* 1999; 354:447–455.
22. Curtis BM, O'Keefe JH Jr. Understanding the Mediterranean diet: could this be the new "gold standard" for heart disease prevention? *Postgrad Med.* 2002;112:38,41–45.
23. Willett WC, Stampfer MJ. Rebuilding the food pyramid. *Sci Am.* 2003;288:64–71.
24. Sacks FM, Katan M. Randomized clinical trials on the effects of dietary fat and carbohydrate on plasma lipoproteins and cardiovascular disease. *Am J Med.* 2002;113(suppl 9B):13S–24S.
25. Brehm BJ, Seeley RJ, Daniels SR, D'Alessio DA. A randomized trial comparing a very low carbohydrate diet and a calorie-restricted low fat diet on body weight and cardiovascular risk factors in healthy women. *J Clin Endocrinol Metab.* 2003;88:1617–1623.
26. Bravata DM, Sanders L, Huang J, et al. Efficacy and safety of low-carbohydrate diets: a systematic review. *JAMA.* 2003;289:1837–1850.
27. Reddy ST, Wang CY, Sakhaee K, Brinkley L, Pak CY. Effect of low-carbohydrate high-protein diets on acid-base balance, stone-forming propensity, and calcium metabolism. *Am J Kidney Dis.* 2002;40:265–274.
28. Eaton SB, Eaton SB III, Sinclair AJ, Cordain L, Mann NJ. Dietary intake of long-chain polyunsaturated fatty acids during the paleolithic. *World Rev Nutr Diet.* 1998;83:12–23.

29. Cordain L, Watkins BA, Florant GL, Kelher M, Rogers L, Li Y. Fatty acid analysis of wild ruminant tissues: evolutionary implications for reducing diet-related chronic disease. *Eur J Clin Nutr.* 2002;56:181–191.
30. O'Keefe JH Jr, Harris WS. From Inuit to implementation: omega-3 fatty acids come of age. *Mayo Clin Proc.* 2000;75:607–614.
31. de Lorgeril M, Salen P, Martin JL, Monjaud I, Delaye J, Mamelle N. Mediterranean diet, traditional risk factors, and the rate of cardiovascular complications after myocardial infarction: final report of the Lyon Diet Heart Study. *Circulation.* 1999;99:779–785.
32. Singh RB, Dubnov G, Niaz MA, et al. Effect of an Indo-Mediterranean diet on progression of coronary artery disease in high risk patients (Indo-Mediterranean Diet Heart Study): a randomized single-blind trial. *Lancet.* 2002;360:1455–1461.
33. Marchioli R, Barzi F, Bomba E, et al, GISSI-Prevenzione Investigators. Early protection against sudden death by n-3 polyunsaturated fatty acids after myocardial infarction: time-course analysis of the results of the Gruppo Italiano per lo Studio della Sopravvivenza nell'Infarto Miocardico (GISSI)-Prevenzione. *Circulation.* 2002;105:1897–1903.
34. Lemaitre RN, King IB, Mozaffarian D, Kuller LH, Tracy RP, Siscovick DS. N-3 Polyunsaturated fatty acids, fatal ischemic heart disease, and nonfatal myocardial infarction in older adults: the Cardiovascular Health Study. *Am J Clin Nutr.* 2003;77:319–325.
35. Kris-Etherton PM, Harris WS, Appel LJ, American Heart Association, Nutrition Committee. Fish consumption, fish oil, omega-3 fatty acids, and cardiovascular disease [published correction appears in *Circulation.* 2003;107:512]. *Circulation.* 2002;106:2747–2757.
36. Cordain L, Eaton SB, Miller JB, Mann N, Hill K. The paradoxical nature of hunter-gatherer diets: meat-based, yet non-atherogenic. *Eur J Clin Nutr.* 2002;56(suppl 1):S42–S52.
37. Ascherio A. Epidemiologic studies on dietary fats and coronary heart disease. *Am J Med.* 2002; 113(suppl 9B):9S–12S.
38. Albert CM, Gaziano JM, Willett WC, Manson JE. Nut consumption and decreased risk of sudden cardiac death in the Physicians' Health Study. *Arch Intern Med.* 2002;162:1382–1387.
39. Jiang R, Manson JE, Stampfer MJ, Liu S, Willett WC, Hu FB. Nut and peanut butter consumption and risk of type 2 diabetes in women. *JAMA.* 2002;288:2554–2560.

40. Lovejoy JC, Most MM, Lefevre M, Greenway FL, Rood JC. Effect of diets enriched in almonds on insulin action and serum lipids in adults with normal glucose tolerance or type 2 diabetes. *Am J Clin Nutr. 2O02J 6:*1000–1006.
41. Cordain L, Miller JB, Eaton SB, Mann N, Holt SH, Speth JD. Plant-animal subsistence ratios and macronutrient energy estimations in worldwide hunter-gatherer diets. *Am J Clin Nutr.* 2000,71:682–692.
42. Pauletto P, Puato M, Caroli MG, et al. Blood pressure and atherogenic lipoprotein profiles of fish-diet and vegetarian villagers in Tanzania: the Lugalawa study. *Lancet.* 1996;348:784–788.
43. Winnick M, Somers VK, Accurso V, et al. Fish-rich diet, leptin, and body mass. *Circulation.* 2002;106:289–291.
44. Cordain L, Eades MR, Eades MD. Hyperinsulinemic diseases of civilization: more than just Syndrome X. *Comp Biochem Physiol A Mol Integr Physiol.* 2003;136:95–112.
45. Ford ES, Liu S. Glycemic index and serum high-density lipoprotein cholesterol concentration among US adults. *Arch Intern Med.* 2001;161:572–576.
46. Leeds AR. Glycemic index and heart disease. *Am J Clin Nutr.* 2002;76:286S–289S.
47. Ludwig DS. The glycemic index: physiological mechanisms relating to obesity, diabetes, and cardiovascular disease. *JAMA.* 2002; 287:2414–2423.
48. Liu S, Willett WC. Dietary glycemic load and atherothrombotic risk. *Curr Atheroscler Rep.* 2002;4:454–461.
49. O'Dea K, Traianedes K, Chisholm K, Leyden H, Sinclair AJ. Cholesterol-lowering effect of a low-fat diet containing lean beef is reversed by the addition of beef fat. *Am J Clin Nutr.* 1990;52:491–494.
50. Wolfe BM, Piche LA. Replacement of carbohydrate by protein in a conventional-fat diet reduces cholesterol and triglyceride concentrations in healthy normolipidemic subjects. *Clin Invest Med.* 1999; 22:140–148.
51. Parker B, Noakes M, Luscombe N, Clifton P. Effect of a high-protein, high-monounsaturated fat weight loss diet on glycemic control and lipid levels in type 2 diabetes. *Diabetes Care.* 2002; 25:425–430.
52. Wolfe BM, Giovannetti PM. Short-term effects of substituting protein for carbohydrate in the diets of moderately hypercholesterolemic human subjects. *Metabolism.* 1991;40:338–343.
53. Layman DK, Boileau RA, Erickson DJ, et al. A reduced ratio of dietary carbohydrate to protein improves body composition and blood lipid profiles during weight loss in adult women. *J Nutr.* 2003;133:411–417.

54. O'Dea K, Traianedes K, Ireland P, et al. The effects of diet differing in fat, carbohydrate, and fiber on carbohydrate and lipid metabolism in type II diabetes. *J Am Diet Assoc.* 1989;89:1076–1086.
55. Torbay N, Baba NH, Sawaya S, et al. High protein vs high carbo hydrate hypoenergetic diet in treatment of obese normoinsulinemic and hyperinsulinemic subjects. *Nutr Res.* 2002;22:587–598.
56. Westerterp-Plantenga MS, Rolland V, Wilson SA, Westerterp KR. Satiety related to 24 h diet-induced thermogenesis during high protein/carbohydrate vs high fat diets measured in a respiration chamber. *Eur J Clin Nutr.* 1999;53:495–502.
57. Stubbs RJ. Macronutrient effects on appetite. *Int J Obes Relat Metab Disord.* 1995;19(suppl 5):S11–S19.
58. Long SJ, Jeffcoat AR, Millward DJ. Effect of habitual dietary-protein intake on appetite and satiety. *Appetite.* 2000;35:79–88.
59. Crovetti R, Porrini M, Santangelo A, Testolin G. The influence of thermic effect of food on satiety. *Eur J Clin Nutr.* 1998;52:482– 488.
60. Johnston CS, Day CS, Swan PD. Postprandial thermogenesis is increased 100% on a high-protein, low-fat diet versus a high-carbohydrate, low-fat diet in healthy, young women. *J Am Coll Nutr.* 2002;21:55–61.
61. Piatti PM, Monti F, Fermo I, et al. Hypocaloric high-protein diet improves glucose oxidation and spares lean body mass: comparison to hypocaloric high-carbohydrate diet. *Metabolism.* 1994;43:1481–1487.
62. Layman DK, Shiue H, Sather C, Erickson DJ, Baum J. Increased dietary protein modifies glucose and insulin homeostasis in adult women during weight loss. *J Nutr.* 2003;133:405–410.
63. Skov AR, Toubro S, Ronn B, Holm L, Astrup A. Randomized trial on protein vs carbohydrate in ad libitum fat reduced diet for the treatment of obesity. *Int J Obes Relat Metab Disord.* 1999;23:528–536.
64. Baba NH, Sawaya S, Torbay N, Habbal Z, Azar S, Hashim SA. High protein vs high carbohydrate hypoenergetic diet for the treatment of obese hyperinsulinemic subjects. *Int J Obes Relat Metab Disord.* 1999;23:1202–1206.
65. Red Meat and Health Expert Advisory Committee. *The Role of Red Meat in Healthy Australian Diets.* February 2001. Available at: http://www.dbctalkabouttaste.com.au/nushelth/meat4health.pdf. Accessibility verified November 21, 2003.
66. Rohrmann S, Linseisen J, Becker N, et al, European Prospective Investigation into Cancer and Nutrition (EPIC). Cooking of meat and fish in Europe—results from the European Prospective Investigation into Cancer and Nutrition (EPIC). *Eur J Clin Nutr.* 2002;56:1216–1230.

67. Vermunt SH, Beaufrere B, Riemersma RA, et al, TransLinE Investigators. Dietary *trans* α-linolenic acid from deodorised grapeseed oil and plasma lipids and lipoproteins in healthy men: the TransLinE Study. *Br J Nutr.* 2001;85:387–392.
68. Chan J, Knutsen SF, Blix GG, Lee JW, Fraser GE. Water, other fluids, and fatal coronary heart disease: the Adventist Health Study. *Am J Epidemiol.* 2002;155:827–833.
69. Duffy SJ, Keaney JF Jr, Holbrook M, et al. Short- and long-term black tea consumption reverses endothelial dysfunction in patients with coronary artery disease. *Circulation.* 2001;104:151–156.
70. Mukamal KJ, Maclure M, Muller JE, Sherwood JB, Mittleman MA. Tea consumption and mortality after acute myocardial infarction. *Circulation.* 2002;105:2476–2481.
71. Geleijnse JM, Launer LJ, Van der Kuip DA, Hofman A, Witteman JC. Inverse association of tea and flavonoid intakes with incident myocardial infarction: the Rotterdam Study. *Am J Clin Nutr.* 2002;75:880–886.
72. Cordain L, Gotshall RW, Eaton SB, Eaton SB III. Physical activity, energy expenditure and fitness: an evolutionary perspective. *Int J Sports Med.* 1998;19:328–335.
73. Cordain L, Gotshall RW, Eaton SB. Evolutionary aspects of exercise. *World Rev Nutr Diet.* 1997;81:49–60.
74. Wing RR. Physical activity in the treatment of the adulthood over weight and obesity: current evidence and research issues. *Med Sci Sports Exerc.* 1999;31(11, suppl):S547–S552.
75. Tanasescu M, Leitzmann MF, Rimm EB, Willett WC, Stampfer MJ, Hu FB. Exercise type and intensity in relation to coronary heart disease in men. *JAMA.* 2002;288:1994–2000.